CARSOLOGICA

EVOLUTION OF KARST: FROM PREKARST TO CESSATION

ZALOŽBA
ZRC

Carsologica

Evolution of Karst: From Prekarst to Cessation

Edited by
Franci Gabrovšek

Language review
Trevor R. Shaw
Graphic art and design
Milojka Žalik Huzjan

Published by
Inštitut za raziskoavnje krasa ZRC SAZU, Založba ZRC
Represented by
Tadej Slabe, Oto Luthar
Editor-in-Chef
Vojislav Likar

Printed by
Littera picta, d.o.o, Ljubljana, Slovenija

The publlcatlon was flnancialy supported by
Ministrstvo za šolstvo znanost in šport RS.

CIP - Kataložni zapis o publikaciji
Narodna in univerzitetna knjižnica, Ljubljana

551.44(082)

EVOLUTION of Karst : from prekarst to cessation / editor Franci Gabrovšek. - Postojna-Ljubljana : Inštitut za raziskovanje krasa, ZRC SAZU, Založba ZRC, 2002. - (Zbirka Carsologica)

ISBN 961-6358-63-4
1. Gabrovšek, Franci, 1968-
119732736

EVOLUTION OF KARST: FROM PREKARST TO CESSATION

Edited by Franci Gabrovšek

POSTOJNA - LJUBLJANA
2002

CONTENTS

KARST GEOMORPHOLOGY

SPELEOLOGY AND SPELEOGENESIS

KARST HIDROLOGY

PALEOKARST AND KARSTIFICATION IN VARIOUS SETTINGS

DATING AND GEOPHYSICAL METHODS

FOREWORD

Karst is the complex consequence of the simple fact that some rocks tend to dissolve in natural waters. Mankind has long been fascinated by it for many reasons, e.g. Its underground and surface beauties, the facts that we drink water from karst aquifers and pump oil from the karstified carbonate reservoirs etc.

Karst, as we know and observe, is a result of ongoing dynamic processes, which last from the creation of karstifiable rocks to their cessation. Therefore, understanding karst means understanding the stages and processes of its evolution.

Karstology is a dissected science. It is modern to call it multidisciplinary. The heterogeneity is an advantage if we make use of it. If not, it can be an obstacle.

In karstology both can be found. On the one hand there is a strong community ("family") which co-operates, socialises and meets regularly in the frame of karst conferences and on the other hand there are many important karst related papers of researchers from "far away" sciences who are not aware of this community.

The main goal of this book and the accompanying symposium was to bring together old and new people in the scene, to meet and to present and discuss many aspects of karst evolution.

To realise this we have invited several scientists who have contributed a lot during the last decades and to make a review of their work and the work of their colleagues. This makes up half of the book and covers many aspects such as the speleogenesis and morphogenesis in karst regions, karst hydrological systems from the evolutionary viewpoint, initial and final stages of karstification, response of life to the specific karst environments and dating of processes in karst.

The book would be incomplete without the papers which follow and present the actual research on all the topics listed above.

This book is not a bible. I am aware that some important aspects of karst evolution are missing and that we have missed some errors and typos. Nevertheless, I still think it is an important work thanks to all the contributing authors.

Franci Gabrovšek

Proceedings of the Symposium
Evolution of Karst: From Prekarst to Cessation
Postojna 17th to 21st September 2002

Honorable Sponsor
Dr. Lucija Čok, Minister of Education, Science and Sport of the Republic of Slovenia

Organising committee
Dr. Franci Gabrovšek
Bojan Otoničar
Dr. Metka Petrič
Mag. Tanja Pipan
Dr. Tadej Slabe

Honorary Board
Adac. Prof. Dr. Ivan Gams
Dr. Oto Luthar, Director of the Scientific Research Centre of SASA
Zofija Klemen Krek, Director of the Bureau of the National Commission for UNESCO
Josip Bajc, Mayor of the Municipality of Postojna

KEYNOTE LECTURES

Evolution of Karst: From Prekarst to Cessation, 13-30, Ljubljana-Postojna 2002

DISSOLUTION AND POROSITY DEVELOPMENT IN CARBONATES

V. PAUL WRIGHT

Abstract

Dissolution, porosity development and related diagenetic processes in carbonates take place across a wider range of diagenetic settings than had previously been appreciated. Dissolution in marine waters, triggered by undersaturation caused by microbial decay processes, is now thought responsible for both massive aragonite loss during very shallow burial. Similarly aragonite dissolution, metastable mineral stabilization and cementation are also now known to be capable of taking place at shallow to intermediate depths in marine pore waters. The importance of burial dissolution is becoming better appreciated, even for the creation of a range of karst-like features. Our understanding the effects of different burial-related processes on porosity-permeability relationships is also improving. With carbonate rocks (limestones and dolomites) holding about 45% of the world's hydrocarbons, let alone their significance as aquifers, an understanding of porosity development is both economically and scientifically desirable. Porosity systems in carbonates are very complex, a consequence of the complex architectures of carbonate grains, complex textural variations reflecting the interaction of depositional, biological and diagenetic processes, and the complex shapes and distributions of secondary pores. The result is that there is often a poor correlation between porosity and permeability in carbonate reservoirs. This is a major drawback for predicting reservoir properties in the subsurface because whereas porosity can be derived from the subsurface using well logs, it is more difficult to assess permeability. It is quite common to find permeability differences of two orders of magnitude, or occasionally even three, within a single short core interval. (Lucia, 1999) This results in many carbonate reservoirs being regarded as "homogeneously heterogeneous" and bulk values for permeability being assigned. The aim of this paper is to review the controls on porosity development, and to emphasize how the diagenetic potential of limestones for porosity development is strongly environmentally and time (stratigraphic age) controlled. In addition the little appreciated role of very early burial dissolution will be discussed as will also the role of deeper burial dissolution. The issue of dolomitisation will not be reviewed but the reader is referred to Warren (2000) for a recent synthesis.

DIAGENETIC POTENTIAL FOR POROSITY FORMATION

Porosity and permeability in carbonate sediments are controlled by the texture (matrix or grain-supported), granulometric properties (such as grain size and sorting), the mineralogical composition (diagenetic potential) and by other effects such as fracturing and non-fabric selective dissolution. The composition of a carbonate sediment influences its subsequent diagenesis and porosity development. A modern day carbonate sand will consist of aragonite, high Mg calcite (HMC) (>4 mole%Mg) and low Mg calcite (LMC) (<4 mole% <Mg). Aragonite and HMC are metastable in meteoric and in some marine

pore waters. As a result HMC is replaced by the more stable form LMC, without significant change in porosity, but aragonite is typically dissolved and the resulting pore may remain open or become filled by sediment, cement or even hydrocarbons. Less frequently aragonite is replaced by LMC via a delicate process called calcitisation which does not produce porosity (Tucker and Wright, 1990). The dissolution of aragonite releases carbonate for cementation, and the solubility contrast between aragonite and LMC means that aragonite can be dissolving in a pore that is simultaneously becoming occluded by LMC cement.

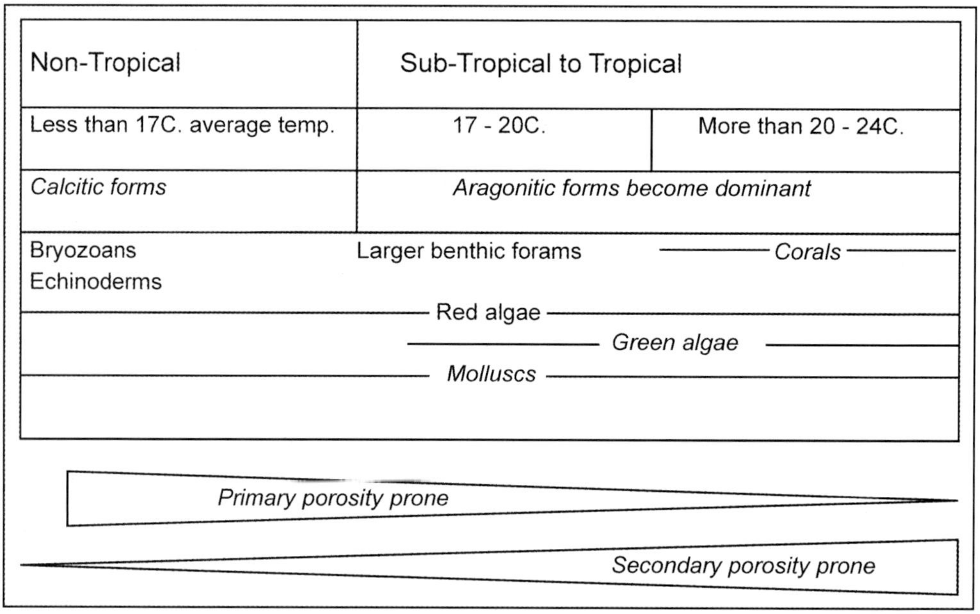

Fig.1. Sea surface temperatures, major shallow water carbonate producers and porosity potential.

Carbonate sediments contain two main components: biogenic and abiogenic carbonates The former, essentially the skeletal remains of calcareous animals and algae are the dominant component. The proportions of organisms producing aragonite or calcite (HMC and LMC) vary as a result of ecological factors both with depth and temperature (Fig. 1). Aragonite, for example, is favoured as the precipitate by organisms inhabiting warmer waters (Morse and MacKenzie, 1990). Carbonate sediments deposited in cooler waters typically contain less aragonite (but see below), and are thus less affected by dissolution and create less secondary porosity. An example is seen in the Tertiary limestones of southern Australia (James and Bone 1989) (Fig. 2). Cool water carbonates from the cool water Gambier Limestone were predominantly calcitic with bryozoans and echinoderm bioclasts. Mouldic porosity potential was low but intergranular and intragranular porosity are preserved, largely because there was little dissolution of aragonite to supply calcium carbonate for cementation. In the case of the Naracoorte Limestone, deposited in warmer waters, the greater content of aragonite resulted in mouldic porosity and increased cementation.

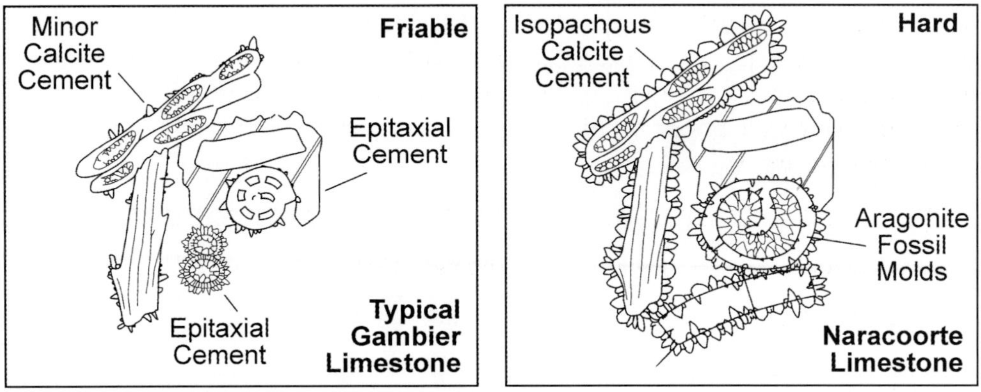

Fig. 2. Contrasting diagenesis and porosity types from two Tertiary limestones from southern Australia (modified from James & Bone, 1989). The originally calcite dominated Gambier Limestone had little aragonite that could have produced secondary, mouldic porosity or carbonate for cementation. The Naracoorte Limestone had aragonitic grains and hence produced mouldic porosity and more extensive cementation.

A compositional difference also exists in terms of depth, but indirectly. Deeper water carbonates, where sediment is mainly from planktic fallout of carbonate skeletal remains, are mainly LMC because the two main producers of planktic carbonate are the coccolithophorid algae and planktic foraminifera; both groups produce stable LMC.

Not only have there been spatial controls but the composition of biogenic particles has also changed through time (Fig. 3). For example, Palaeozoic shallow water carbonates, even those deposited in tropical waters, were composed mainly of LMC and HMC, composed of brachiopods, bryozoans, crinoids and tabulate and rugose corals. By contrast a Cretaceous shallow water limestone would have been dominated by green algae, scleractinian corals and molluscs, which were predominantly aragonitic.

The composition of abiogenic particles has also changed through geologic time, as has that of other carbonate materials such as precipitated muds and cements (Fig.4). These shifts in the nature of the abiogenic precipitates are regarded as reflecting changes in seawater chemistry through time (Sandberg, 1983; Hardie, 1996). The concensus view is that these changes in the mineralogy of the precipitates was caused by variations in the Mg/Ca and calcium ion concentrations, driven by changes in the rates of sea floor spreading (Hardie, 1996). Other workers have proposed tectonically induced changes in the partial pressure of carbon dioxide as the cause (MacKenzie and Piggott, 1981; see critique in Stanley and Hardie 1998). There may have been feed-back effects of these changes affecting biogenic carbonate contributors such as reefal organisms (Stanley and Hardie, 1998).

These changes resulted in the abiogenic precipitates, either forming grains such as

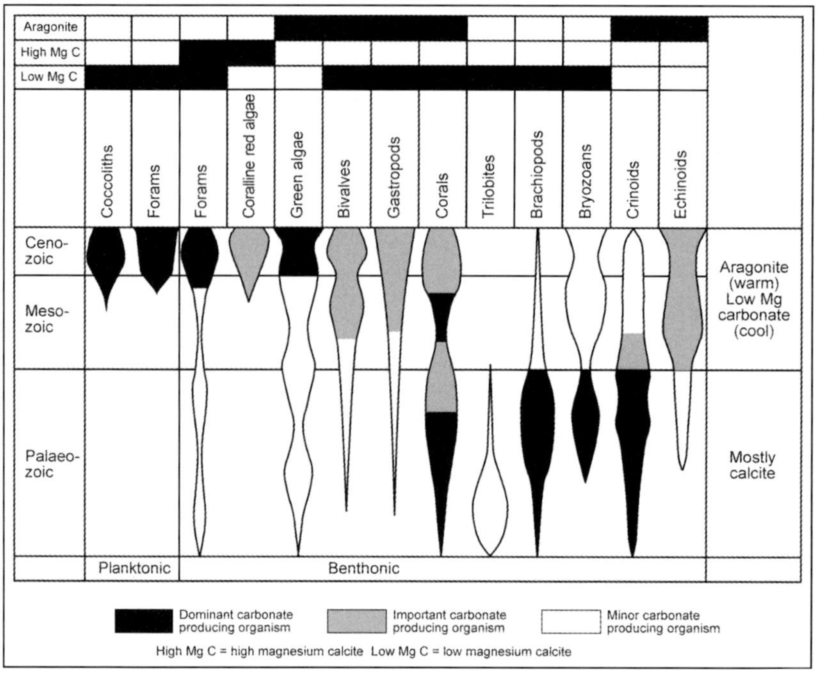

Fig. 3. Distribution of main groups of animals and plants that produce carbonate sediments, plotted through the Phanerozoic. Various sources, originally from Wilkinson, 1982.

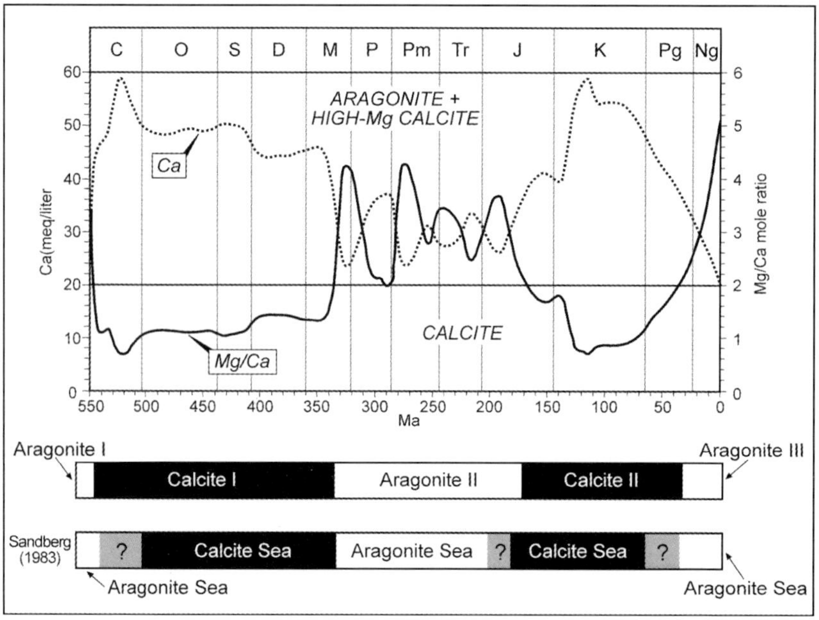

Fig. 4. Temporal distributions of non-skeletal carbonate precipitates, with periods when seawater should have produced calcite or aragonite-&-calcite. From Hardie, 1996, Stanley & Hardie, 1998.

ooids, or muds or cements, being either aragonitic or calcitic (mainly HMC) (Fig. 4). A modern day carbonate sediment from a tropical shoreline, as discussed above, is a mixture of the three main forms of calcium carbonate. Studies of such carbonates through Quaternary successions shows that progressive stabilisation takes place during subaerial exposure (Fig. 5), resulting in the loss of HMC (converted to LMC), followed by the loss of aragonite. The latter effect produces porosity. However, a lower to mid Palaeozoic limestone (or indeed a cool water one from any geological interval) would start with a different composition and undergo a very different stabilisation pathway (Fig. 5). Thus many Palaeozoic limestones had a diagenetic pathway more similar to modern cool water types (Dodd and Nelson, 1998).

Secondary porosity in these situations is largely produced through dissolution of aragonite grains (bioclasts and ooids). However, secondary porosity can also be produced during the stabilisation of the fine-grained (muddy) matrices. Moore (2001, p.272) has proposed that during intervals when the global ocean chemistry favoured calcite precipitation (calcite seas), chemically precipitated calcite micrite (effectively clay-sized carbonate crystals) would, on burial, resist chemical compaction (as in the case of pelagic limestone; see below). Moore (2001) suggests that aragonitic muds, being more susceptible to diagenesis quickly stabilize into an interlocking calcite mosaic, typically >4 microns in size, with low porosities and permeabilities. This is the case in some Palaeozoic and Neogene former aragonite-dominated muds (Munnecke et al., 1997), but Melim et al. (2001b) have shown that microporosity can form in former aragonitic muds from the subsurface of the Great Bahama Bank.. Many former calcitic (former HMC) ooids,do stabilise to produce microporosity This is a distinctive form of porosity, also known as chalky porosity, which is associated with shallow water limestones in which

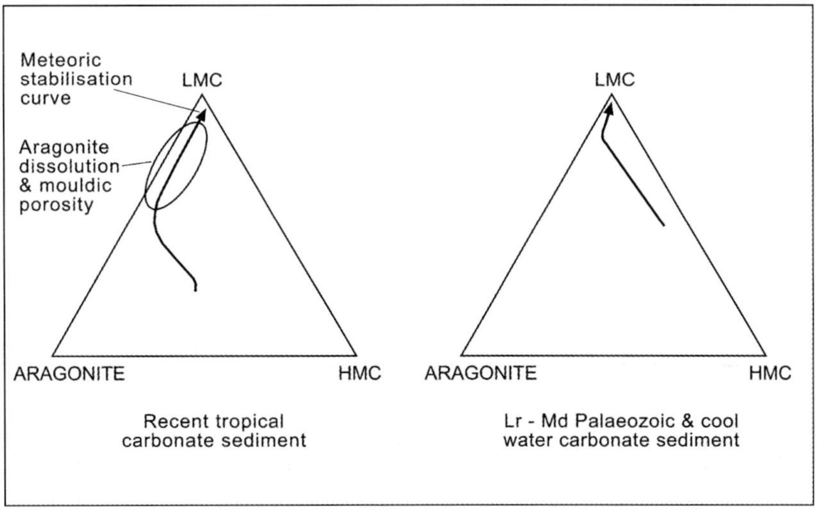

Fig. 5. Diagenetic pathways for stabilisation of metastable components for typical modern tropical carbonate sand (left) and lower to mid Palaeozoic tropical or typical cool water carbonate sand (right).

intercrystalline porosity, including solution enhanced porosity, dominates. Typical porosities are in the range 15-30%, with permeabilities of >1md, and with euhedral microrhombic crystals 4 microns in size (Moshier, 1989).

These issues over compositional controls are not merely of academic interest but impact upon our understanding of hydrocarbon reservoir properties. An example of this, which also serves to illustrate how local effects on seawater chemistry can also influence carbonate precipitation, is provided by the work of Heydari and Moore (1994). In this example, from the important Upper Jurassic Smackover Formation oolitic reservoirs of the southern USA, reservoir quality is spatially varied. In restricted settings the local hypersaline seawater produced aragonitic ooids (Fig. 6), that later produced mouldic porosity. However, in less restricted areas, bathed in normal Jurassic tropical seawater, calcitic ooids formed; these did not produce mouldic porosity. However, during later depositonal episodes when conditions were less restricted all the ooids formed as calcite. Understanding the spatial controls on precipitation provides a potential predictive tool.

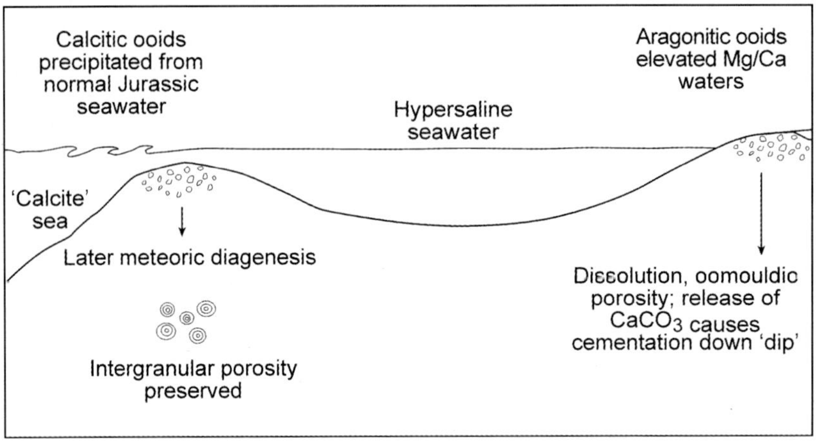

Fig. 6. Distribution of calcitic and aragonitic ooids during part of the deposition of the Upper Jurassic Smackover Limestone of Mississippi. Aragonitic ooids formed around the shores of hypersaline lagoons, whereas calcitic ones precipitated from seawater. Based on Heydari and Moore, 1994.

DISSOLUTION IN SEA WATER

Dissolution of carbonate in deeper waters has long been appreciated. This dissolution is a consequence of elevated partial pressures of CO_2, and temperature decreases with increasing water depth (Tucker and Wright, 1990) causing undersaturation for firstly aragonite, and at greater depths, for calcite. Aragonite ceases to accumulate at the ACD (aragonite compensation depth). Aragonite has been regarded as relatively stable in shallow, tropical waters, and during shallow burial in such settings. There is a growing awareness that the preservation of aragonite during early, shallow burial is a much more complex issue that had been previously thought. Walter and Burton (1990) and Walter et al. (1993) have demonstrated that dissolution, especially of aragonite, by acidity caused by microbially mediated reactions associated with the decay of organic matter, causes significant dissolution in even the shallow tropical platform interiors of the Florida Bay - Bahamas region.

Carbonate sedimentologists have been slow to respond to these studies, which suggest that as much as 50% of the carbonate entering the sediment column can be lost by early (effectively syn-depositional) dissolution. Aragonite dissolution may produce porosity but this does not seem to be readily preserved because the sediment is unconsolidated and any secondary pores either collapse, or are destroyed by bioturbation. Not only are these dissolution effects likely to reduce the accumulation rates, but will reduce the amount of aragonite available for later porosity formation.

Striking support for the importance of very early, shallow burial aragonite dissolution comes from the work of Cherns and Wright (2000), from Silurian shallow carbonate successions from Sweden. In this example the authors compared rare, silicified lagerstatten preserving what were life assemblages of molluscs, to the depleted faunas found in more typical, non-silicified horizons. The typical faunas were composed of classical

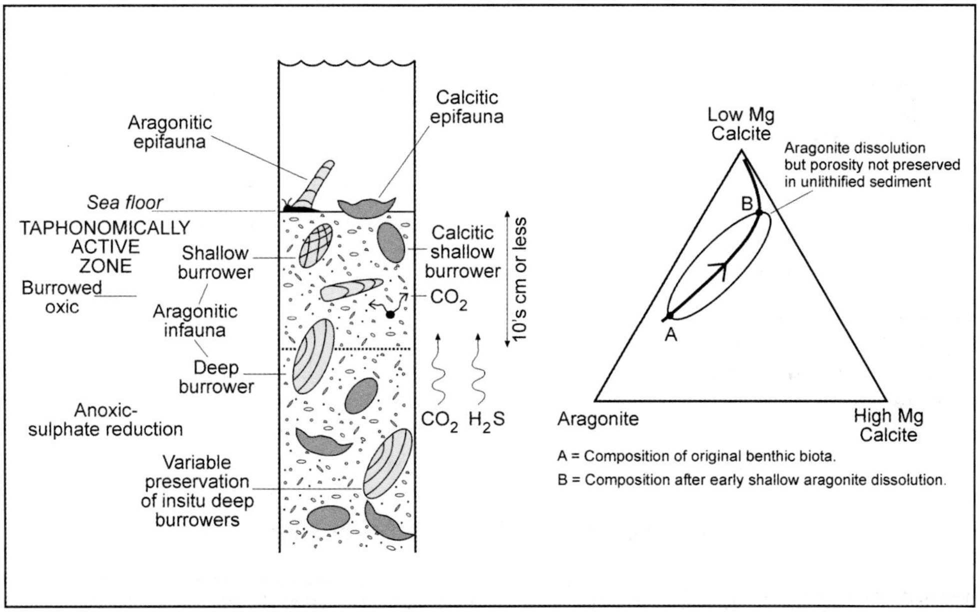

Fig. 7. Effects of early, very shallow burial aragonite dissolution on the faunas of early Jurassic offshore ramp deposits, South Wales. Aragonitic epifaunal and infaunal molluscs were dissolved, leaving only calcitic or bimineirallic forms and deep burrowing bivalves, that lived largely beneath the taphonomically active dissolution zone. The ternary diagram shows how the mineral composition of the sediments is shifted by this early dissolution towards a composition more typical of cool water limestones. The forms that could generate secondary porosity during later diagenesis have been removed during very shallow burial, reducing the reservoir potential of these sediments.

Silurian former HMC and LMC fossils, such as brachiopods and bryozoans. The silicified assemblage is dominated by former aragonitic bivalves and gastropods. Wright et al. (in press) extended the work to a Lower Jurassic succession in South Wales, which showed typical assemblages dominated by calcitic molluscs in non-silicified horizons but, where very early silicification had occurred, the assemblage was instead dominated by former aragonitic forms (Fig. 7). The model presented for both cases is that early, microbially mediated dissolution led to the selective removal of the aragonitic forms. The result of this early removal was that the sediments had lost all their aragonite before significant burial, greatly reducing their potential to produce secondary porosity (Fig. 7). No moulds were left in the unconsolidated sediments. These depleted sediments were in fact behaving as if they were cool water sediments, but this was purely an artifact of very early selective dissolution. Brachert and Dullo (2000) have also identified early dissolution as a process skewing the nature of fossil assemblages in Neogene periplatform carbonates from the north east Australian shelf.

In both the Silurian and Lower Jurassic examples the release of carbonate by dissolution of aragonite was interpreted as the source for extensive early diagenetic limestones in the same successions. It is likely that many other diagenetic limestones ("limestone-marl" rhythms) owe their origins to similar processes. These dissolution processes are important where organic matter can accumulate to levels where microbial activity causes extensive dissolution. Such settings are typically low energy with mud deposition. If cementation, triggered by locally elevated carbonate contents in pore waters as a result of aragonite dissolution is common, we should look for evidence in fine-grained carbonates. Indirect evidence for pervasive cementation in such carbonates may come from the work of Budd (2001). In studies of porosity and permeability changes with depth in Palaeogene limestones of Florida, Budd (2001) noted that the fine-grained limestones showed far less porosity loss with depth than was predicted. Matrix-rich limestones should undergo 50% compaction at depths of 150-200m (Goldhammer, 1997), yet in the case of the Florida carbonates the reduced levels of compaction and porosity loss must reflect pervasive early cementation.

POROSITY EVOLUTION IN SHALLOW WATER LIMESTONES

With the exception of highly localised loss of porosity by marine cementation to produce hardgrounds, beach rocks and in reefs, relatively little porosity loss takes place during early burial (but see Beach, 1993). However, by virtue of the fact that most limestone deposition takes place in very shallow waters (Tucker and Wright, 1990), these labile sediments are prone to the effects of undersaturated meteoric-derived groundwaters as a consequence of even small scale sea-level falls. This has been especially the case during periods when fluctuations in continental ice sheets triggered high frequency and high amplitude sea-level oscillations during the "ice-house" intervals of the mid Carboniferous to early Permian and late Pleistocene (Read and Horbury, 1993). Studies of carbonate sediments that have undergone early subaerial exposure typically display both cementation and stabilization of the metastable components (Tucker and Wright, 1990). This led some workers to invoke meteoric diagenesis as the prime mechanism for lithification and porosity occlusion for all limestones. Several studies have shown that carbonates stabilized under meteoric diagenetic conditions show as little as 15-20% porosity loss (Halley and Schmoker, 1983; Schmoker and Hester, 1986). Halley and Evans (1983), in a study of the Pleistocene Miami Oolite, showed that as the originally 100% aragonitic oolitic sands were progressively reduced to 30% aragonite, the average porosity remained the same at around 45% (Fig. 8). However, there was a change in the type and range of porosity values (Fig. 8), whereby primary porosity was reduced by cementation but secondary porosity, including vuggy porosity, increased.

To reduce porosity further, to the levels typically seen in non-reservoir carbonates, either compaction (mechanical and chemical) and/or cementation must take place. This is not to state that meteoric diagenesis cannot bring about more significant porosity loss. Multiple phases of meteoric diagenesis, whereby some other unit or units, perhaps updip, are acting as donors for carbonate, can achieve more extensive porosity loss. Subsequent loss during burial diagenesis has been documented for shallow water limestones (Halley and Schmoker, 1983; Scholle and Halley, 1985) (Fig. 9A). Such data sets supported the view that shallow burial processes, such as cementation related to near-surface meteoric processes, had little effect on the overall porosity evolution. The wide

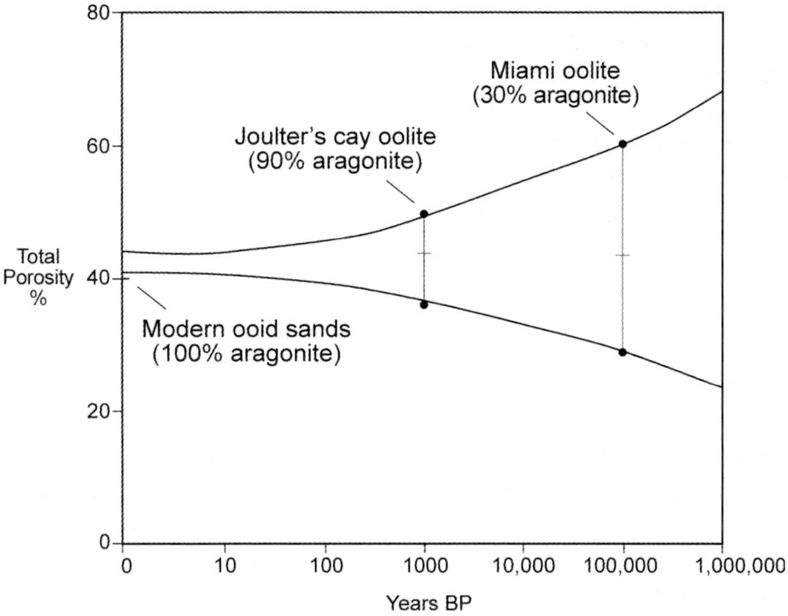

Fig. 8. Porosity changes during stabilization of oolitic sediments in Florida and the Bahamas (from Halley and Evans, 1983). A modern oolitic sand has a porosity of 45% and is 100% aragonite. During partial stabilization the average porosity remains fairly constant but the range increases, reflecting the development of vuggy porosity.

range of porosity values at any given depth (Fig. 9A) indicates that depth is not the only control on porosity loss.

Recently Budd (2001, 2002) has evaluated these trends using Palaeogene carbonates from Florida, and has focussed on changes in permeability (k) with depth (Fig. 9B & C), from core data taken to a depth of nearly 500m. In the succession studied cementation was minor and loss in k was primarily due to mechanical and chemical compaction. There is little change in k with depth in the matrix-rich wackestones (Fig. 9B), potentially suggesting early cementation may have been a factor (see above). There is a decrease in k with depth for grain-rich limestones (Fig. 9C), but with a wide range of values indicating the influence of depositional and textural effects. Furthermore, this depth-k decrease is greater than might be expected from known depth-porosity changes and is interpreted as due to the effects of compaction on pore throats and to increasing tortuosity of the pores network (Budd, 2002). The dolomites in the cores showed no depth-k relationship over the depth range studied.

Budd (2002) evaluated how cementation and compaction (mechanical and chemical comopaction or pressure solution) actually affected k decrease in the grainstones. The pore networks and k respond differently to these processes (Fig. 10A). Pressure

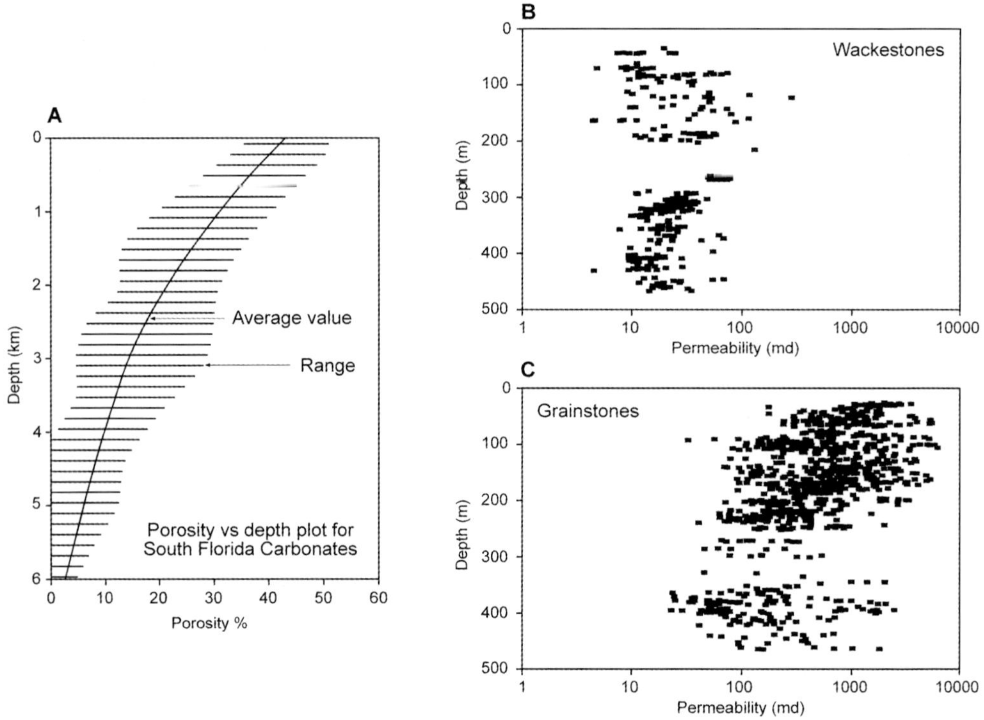

Fig. 9. A - Porosity-depth values from 15 wells in south Florida (from Scholle & Halley, 1985); B - and C are measured permeabilities with depth for wackestones (B) and grainstones (C)) from the middle Eocene limestones of west-central Florida, from Budd, 2002. Note the lack of a trend for the matrix-rich wackestones; see text.

solution was more effective in decreasing k than cementation, and mechanical compaction was least effective. Cementation was progressive (Fig.10A), reducing porosity but not preferentially affecting pore throats. However, pores changed from open voids to polyhedral pores to a mix of ployhedral and sheet-like pores between the cement crystals as the pores occluded.

However, plots for the units dominated by compaction are quite different (Fig. 10A). Mechanical compaction (repacking and ductile deformation), while reducing porosity, had less effect on k.. Budd (2002) argued that the pore system was not being radically changed in the range 5000-500md (Fig. 10A), but that loss in k was due to an increase in the length of the pore throats and tortuosity of flow pathways. Below 335m pressure solution became more important, although not producing stylolites, at the grain-to-grain level, causing pore throats to become blocked, resulting in an increase in the loss in k relative to porosity loss (Fig. 10A).

These conclusions were supported by capillary pressure analysis (Fig. 10B), which shows the progressive decrease during cementation in pore volumes accessed by large pore throats and in the abundance of pore volumes accessed by small pore throats. During compaction k decrease is associated with little change in the injection curves

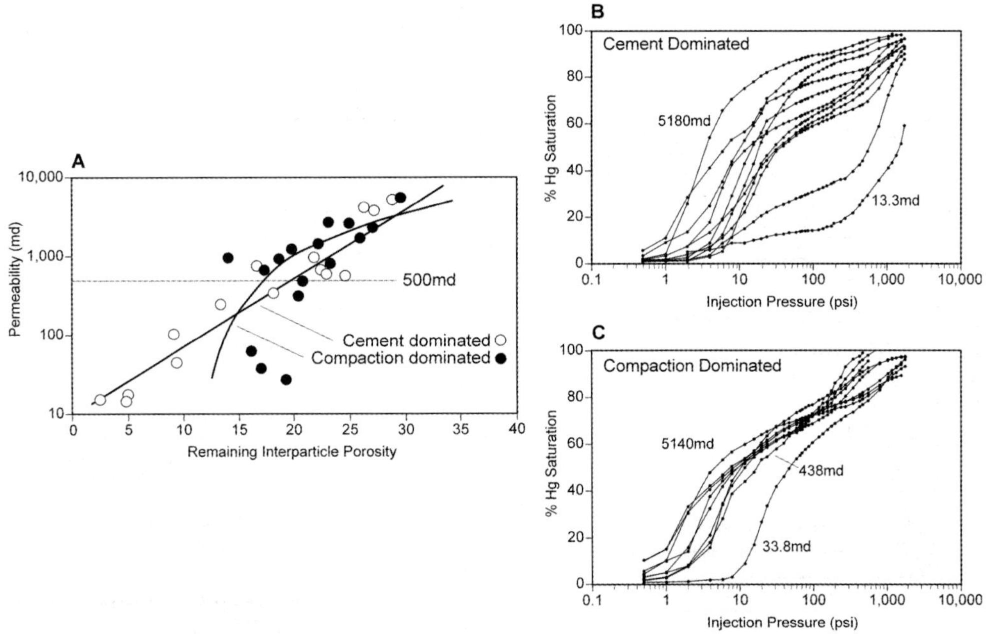

Fig. 10. A -Total remaining interparticle porosity against permeability for Eocene limestones from south-central Florida, showing that permeability decline caused by cementation was progressive, but that loss in permeability by compaction less progressive and declined more sharply when pressure solution began. B - capillary pressure tests for cement dominated limestones showing that the increase in cementation caused a change in pore volumes accessed by different pore throats. C - shows the tests for compaction dominated samples where the decrease in permeability caused, initially, only small decreases in the abundance of pore volumes accessed by larger pore throats. Modified from Budd, 2002.

(Fig. 10C), implying only relatively small decreases in the abundance of pore volumes accessed by the larger pores. It is only below 500md that a shift is seen towards pore volumes being accessed by smaller pores.

Heydari (2000), using the well documented Upper Jurassic Smackover oolitic limestones of the subsurface of the southern USA (see above), assessed compaction effects in material with 0% intergranular porosity. The oolitic limestones lack any pre-burial cements, and this allowed the roles of mechanical compaction and pressure solution to be assessed. It was noted (Heydari, 2000) that all the key processes (mechanical compaction, pressure solution and burial cementation) had similar effects on porosity change, with pressure solution slightly more effective than mechanical compaction, and cementation being the least effective. In this example the carbonate relaeased by pressure solution is approximately equivalent to the amount of cementation, implying a somewhat closed system.

In conclusion, allowing for the marked range of porosity values with depth (Fig. 9A), the general rule is that porosity is destroyed during burial by cementation and compaction, but that once pressure solution begins k decreases dramatically.

DISSOLUTION AND POROSITY DEVELOPMENT IN CARBONATES FORMED IN DEEPER SETTINGS

From the above we see that aragonite dissolution can be an important process in shallow water settings where the decay of organic matter provides the acidity. However, this process does not result in porosity formation, but does skew the fossil record and reduces the diagenetic potential for later porosity development. Shallow water carbonates are also prone to dissolution by the penetration of undersaturated meteoric waters during sea-level lowstands, but what about porosity development and dissolution in other settings? The general assumption has been that metastable carbonate sediments deposited below the effects of meteoric water penetration, but above the ACD are relatively stable in seawater. Such a diagenetic setting would have been even more widespread during the "Greenhouse" intervals in the past when high amplitude sea-level oscillations were rare (Read and Horbury, 1993). Recently, Melim et al. (2001a) have recorded aragonite dissolution, stabilization and cementation from metastable, deeper platform margin to lower slope limestones of Mio-Pliocene age (but above the ACD) from the Great Bahama Bank. Melim et al. (2001b) have discussed porosity development during such marine, shallow burial diagenesis, including the importance of mouldic pores and of pore type-k relationships. Brachert and Dullo (2000) have also recorded stabilization and aragonite dissolution taking place in periplatform carbonates to burial depths of 600m, in marine waters. Thus our previously held ideas on shallow marine burial processes require a major re-evaluation.

The diagenesis and porosity evolution of pelagic and shelf chalks is well documented. These are Cretaceous and younger fine-grained carbonates largely composed of the remains of LMC plankton (see above). Initial porosities in such oozes can reach 70%, reduced to 40% by 300m burial depth. Some chalks have 50% porosity at depths of 2.5-3km, where porosities should be in the range 10-15%. Some North Sea Cretaceous chalks have very high porosities of over 40% at burial depths of over 3km. Permeabilities are however low, 0.2-2md, with pore throats of 0.1-0.8um. (Oakman and Partington, 1998). The aragonitic grains were removed buring early burial and their remains can be seen "fossilised" as moulds in hardgrounds. The remaining material, dominantly LMC was relatively unreactive during later burial, but at depths of 1-2km pressure solution begins to reduce porosities. The development of over-pressure or the emplacement of hydrocarbons has acted in many cases to reduce the effects of diagenesis. Oakman and Partington (1998) provide a review.

POROSITY FORMATION DURING DEEPER BURIAL

As shown in Figure 9A, burial is associated with porosity loss, excluding the effects of burial dolomitization. However, porosity formation also takes place as a result of carbonate dissolution in the deeper subsurface (Mazzullo and Harris, 1992). Fluids in the deeper subsurface are highly varied in composition (Moore, 2001), and processes invoked to cause dissolution relate to the thermal degradation of hydrocarbons and the thermochemical reduction of sulphates. Corrosion processes related to the mixing of different fliuds is also a possibility (Morse et al., 1997).

Such solution effects are typically fine scale, more extensive dissolution and even cavity collapse and brecciation can occur (Morrow et al., 1986; Sass-Gustkiewicz et al., 1982). Whether this type of dissolution should be referred to as burial karstification (Dravis and Muir, 1993) is unclear.

Burial dissolution as a term is used here to describe porosity formation in mesogenetic settings, below the zone of penetration of undersaturated meteoric waters (including those related to uplift), typically after the onset of compaction and pressure solution.

It is widely believed that the main processes is the thermal degradation of organic matter to produce hydrocarbons, releasing CO_2, H_2S, methane and organic acids. In the presence of sulphate ions the methane further breaks down to produce solvents. These porosity forming processes can occur ahead of migrating hydrocarbons, thus potentially creating sites for their storage. Although the emplacement of hydrocarbons leads ususally to the cessation of diagenesis, further degradation of the hydrocarbons in the reservoir, at more elevated temperatures in excess of 150 C, leads to further production of CO_2, H_2S, methane and pyrobitumen. These former two products may further contribute to porosity development in the overlying gas cap, whereas the pyrobitumen acts to decrease porosity (Moore, 2001).

An additional process which can produce porosity is thermochemical sulphate reduction (TSR) (Machel, 2001), which takes place in the temperature range of 100-140 C (more rarely in the range 160-180 C) (Fig. 11). Biogenic sulphate reduction takes place at lower temperatures, <80 C. TSR takes place relatively rapidly, geologically speaking

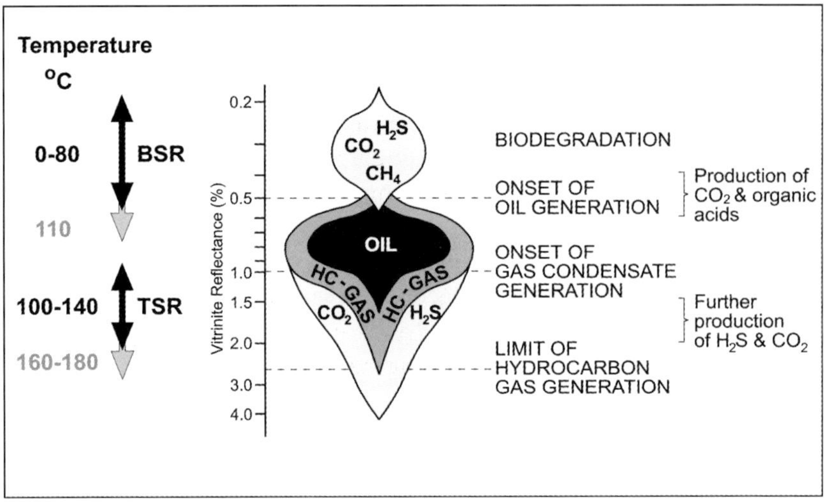

Fig. 11. Acidity produced by oil and gas generation and sulphate reduction. Modified from Machel, 2001.

and is associated with hydrocarbons, to produce sulphide and bicarbonate (which can contribute to cementation) and CO_2. The process is not regarded as a significant porosity producer, except at a local level. The porosity is created by the actual removal (in solution) of the sulphate, and is also triggered by associated metal sulphide precipitation, and by CO_2 and H_2S activity (Machel 2001).

Porosity generated by the acitivity of hydrogen sulphide released by whatever process in the deeper subsurface, can be created by two mechanisms (Hill 1995). Oxidation can take place to produce sulphuric acid, which reacts with the limestone to produce gypsum, which is then later dissolved. Alternatively the mixing of fluids with different H_2S contents can generate mixing corrosion. The latter process may be more important in deeper burial settings, whereas the former has been termed "sulphuric acid oil field karst" by Hill (1995).

Criteria for the recognition of deeper burial dissolution have been reviewed by Mazzullo and Harris (1992). Secondary porosity closely related to kaolinite cements, normally rare in limestones, may indicate the former activity of organic-rich pore fluids (Maliva et al., 1999). Hill (1995) has reviewed criteria for the identification of H_2S-related dissolution. One common feature of burial dissolution is a form of porosity inversion whereby deeper water nodular limestones have zones of increased porosity developed along pressure solution seams. These seams, defined by mm-scale irregular zones of insoluble residues, created by the pressure solution, are normally associated with areas of reduced porosity due to cementation of the carbonate released by pressure solution. These zones can create baffles or barriers to flow but the seams themselves become the sites for later dissolution or even dolomitization, which can also enhance porosity and permeability.

POROSITY PREDICTION

Attractive as a predictive tool the simple burial-porosity curves may appear (Fig. 9A), the variability prevents their actual use. The diagenesis and porosity development for any carbonate will ultimately depend on regional (basin-scale) factors such as depositional style, early diagenesis, burial history etc. The combination of these will be more or less unique to that basin.

Schmoker (1984) evaluated porosity loss against thermal maturity (Lopatin's time-temperature index of thermal maturity or TTI), for a range of data sets for carbonate successions (Fig. 12). He noted that there was a decrease in carbonate porosity with an increase in thermal maturation, reflecting burial diagenesis. Porosity and TTI were related by a power function where :-

porosity = a(TTI)b (b averages -0.372).

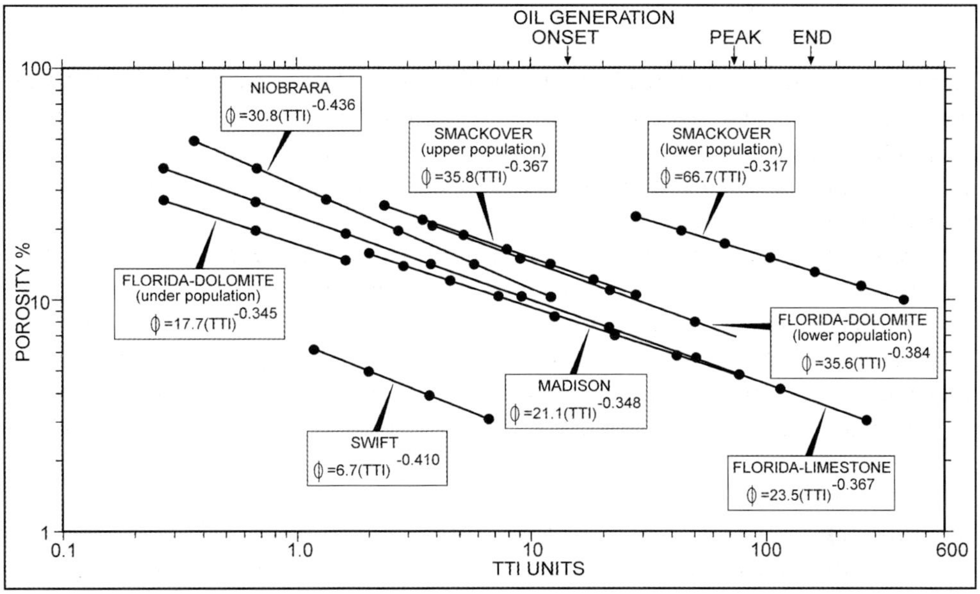

Fig. 12. Porosity versus Lopatin's time-temperature index of thermal maturity (TTI) for various carbonate successions. Modified from Schmoker, 1984.

The multiplying coefficient **a** incorporates the net effect of all the depositional and diagenetic parameters on porosity. The exponent **b** is an independent factor and Schmoker (1984) suggested it reflected the rate-limiting process of diffusive flow. The TTI is depth dependent and so porosity can be related to burial history and potentially calculated to track porosities at different time intervals..

CONCLUSIONS

In the past dissolution of carbonates was largely seen as a process taking place during the penetration of meteoric ground waters, particularly affecting metastable carbonates and causing stabilization and lithification. Marine waters, at depths above the ACD were not regarded as capable of causing significant dissolution of stabilization. Recent studies have questioned this view and very early, very shallow burial dissolution in shallow marine waters is known to cause significant loss of aragonite, and skewing of the fossil record. Furthermore, dissolution in slightly deeper water sediments, but above the ACD, and at intermediate burial depths also takes place to create porosity; stabilization and cementation also take place in marine burial fluids. Porosity is progressively lost during burial, and the effects of compaction and cementation on porosity and permeability are now becoming better understood. Burial does not always cause porosity loss and burial dissolution is now being increasingly recognised as an important process in the deeper subsurface, even in the generation of "burial karst".

REFERENCES

Beach, D.kK, 1993: Submarine cementation of subsurface Pliocene carbonates from the interior of Great Bahama Bank, - Journal of Sedimentary Petrology, 63, 1059-1069, Tulsa

Brachert, T.C. & Dullo, W-C., 2000: Shallow burial diagenesis of skeletal carbonates: selective loss of aragonite shell material (Miocene to Recent), Queensland Plateau and Queensland Trough, northeast Australia - implications for shallow cool-water carbonates, - Sedimentary Geology, 136, 169-187, Amsterdam

Budd, D.A., 2001: Permeability loss with depth in the Cenozoic carbonate platform of west central Florida, - Bulletin American Association of Petroleum Geologists, 85, 1253-1272, Tulsa

Budd, D.A., 2002: The relative roles of compaction and early cementation in the destruction of permeability in carbonate grainstones: a case study from the early Paleogene of west-central Florida, USA, - Journal of Sedimentary Research, 72, 116-128, Tulsa

Cherns, L., & Wright, V.P., 2000: Missing molluscs as evidence of large –scale early skeletal aragonite dissolution in a Silurian sea, - Geology, 28, 791-794

Dodd, J.R. & Nelson, C.S., 1998: Diagenetic comparisons between non-tropical Cenozoic limestones of New Zealand and tropical Mississippian limestones from Indiana, USA: Is the non-tropical model better than the tropical one?, - Sedimentary Geology, 121, 1-21, Amsterdam

Dravis, J.J., & Muir, I.D., 1993: Deep-burial brecciation in the Devonian Upper Elk Point Group, rainbow Basin, Alberta, western Canada. Society of Economic Paleontologists and Mineralogists Core Workshop, 18, 119-166

Goldhammer, R.K., 1997: Compaction and decompaction algorithms for sedimentary carbonates, - Journal of Sedimentary Research, A67, 26-35, Tulsa

Halley, R. B. & Evans, C.C., 1983: The Miami Limestone: a guide to selected outcrops and their imterpretation, - Miami Geological Society, 67pp, Miami

Halley, R.B. & Schmoker, J.W., 1983: High-porosity Cenozoic carbonate rocks of South Florida: progressive loss of porosity with depth, - Bulletin American Association of Petroleum Geologists, 67, 191-200, Tulsa

Hardie, L.A.,1996: Secular variation in seawater chemistry: an explanation for the coupled secular variation in the mineralogies of marine limestones and potash evaporites over the past 600m.y., - Geology, 24, 279-283

Heydari, E., 2000: Porosity loss, fluid flow and mass transfer in limestone reservoirs: application to the Upper Jurassic Smackover Formation, Mississippi, - Bulletin, American Association of Petroleum Geologists, 84, 100-118, Tulsa

Heydari, E. & Moore, C.H., 1994: Paleoceanographic and paleoclimatic controls on ooid mineralogy of the Smackover Formation, Mississippi salt basin: implications for Jurassic seawater composition, - Journal of Sedimentary Research, A64, 101-114, Tulsa

Hill, C.A., 1995: H_2S-related porosity and sulphuric acid oil field karst. Memoir, American Association of Petroleum Geologists, 63, 301-306, Tulsa

James, N.P. & Bone, Y., 1989: Petrogenesis of Cenozoic, temperate water calcarenites, South Australia: a model for meteoric/shallow water calcite sediments, - Journal of Sedimentary Petrology, 59, 191-203

Lucia, F.J., 1999: Carbonate reservoir Characterisation, 226pp, Springer, Berlin

Machel, H.G., 2001: Bacterial and thermochemical sulphate reduction in diagenetic settings - old and new insights,- Sedimentary Geology, 140, 143-175, Amsterdam

Mackenzie, F.T., & Piggott, J.D., 1981: Tectonic controls on Phanerozoic sedimentary rock cycling, - Journal of the Geological Society of London, 138, 183-196, London

Maliva, R.G., Dickson, J.A.D., & Fallick, A.E.,1999: Kaolin cements in limestones: potential indicators of organic-prone pore waters during diagenesis, - Journal of Sedimentary Research, 69, 158-163, Tulsa

Mazzullo, S.J., & Harris, P.M. 1992: Mesogenetic dissolution: its role in porosity development in carbonate reservoirs, - Bulletin American Association of Petroleum Geologists, 76, 607-620, Tulsa

Melim, L.A., Swart, P.K., & Maliva, R.G., 2001a: Meteoric and marine-burial diagenesis in the subsurface of Great Bahama Bank.- Society of Economic Paleontologists & Mineralogists, Special Publication, 70, 137-161, Tulsa

Melim, L.A., Anselmetti, F.S., & Eberli, G.P., 2001b: The importance of pore type on permeability of Neogene carbonates, Great Bahama Bank. – Society of Economic Paleontologists & Mineralogists, Special Publication 70, 217-238, Tulsa

Moore, C.H., 2001: Carbonate Reservoirs: Porosity Evolution and Diagenesis in a Sequence Stratigraphic Framework, 444pp. Elsevier, Amsterdam

Morrow, D.W., Cumming, G.L. & Koepnick, R.B., 1986: Manetoe facies – a gas bearing, megacrystalline, Devonian dolomite, Yukon and Northwest Territories, Canada, - Bulletin American Association of Petroleum Geologists, 70, 702-720, Tulsa

Morse, J.W. & Mackenzie, F.T., 1990: Geochemistry of Sedimentary Carbonates, 696pp, Elsevier, Amsterdam

Morse, J.W., Hanor, J.S., & He, S., 1997: The role of mixing and migration of basinal waters in carbonate mineral mass transport, - Society of Economic Paleontologists and Mineralogists Special Publication 57, 41-50, Tulsa

Moshier, S.O., 1989: Microporosity in micritic limestones: a review, - Sedimentary Geology, 63, 191-216, Amsterdam

Munnecke, A., Westphal, H., Reijmer, J.G. & Samtlebaen, C.,1997: Microspar development during early marine burial diagenesis: a comparison of Pliocene carbonates from the Bahamas with Silurian limestones from Gotland (Sweden), - Sedimentology, 44, 977-990, Oxford

Oakman, C.D., & Partington, M.A.. 1998: Cretaceous, In - Petroleum Geology of the North Sea (ed. By K.W. Glennie), p.294-349, Blackwell, Oxford

Read, J.F. & Horbury, A.D. 1993: Eustatic and tectonic controls on porosity evolution beneath sequence-bounding unconformities and parasequence disconformities on carbonate platforms, - American Association of Petroleum Geologists, Studies in Geology 36, 155-198, Tulsa

Sandberg, P.A., 1983: An oscillating trend in Phanerozoic non-skeletal carbonate mineralogy, - Nature, 305, 19-22, London

Sass-Gustkiewicz, M., Dzulynski, S., & Ridge, J.D., 1982: The emplacement of zinc-lead sulphide ores in the Upper Silesian district – a contribution to the understanding of Mississippi Valley-type deposits, - Economic Geology, 77, 392-412

Schmoker, J.W., 1984: Empirical relation between carbonate porosity and thermal maturity: an approach to regional porosity prediction, - Bulletin, American Association of Petroleum Geologists, 68, 1697-1703, Tulsa

Schmoker, J.W., & Hester, T.C., 1986: Porosity of the Miami Limestone (Late Pleistocene), lower Florida Keys, - Journal of Sedimentary Petrology, 56, 629-634, Tulsa

Scholle, P.A. & Halley, R.B., 1985: Burial diagenesis: out of sight, out of mind! Society of Economic Paleontologists and Mineralogists Special Publication 36, 309-334, Tulsa

Stanley, S.M., & Hardie, L.A., 1998: Secular oscillations in the carbonate mineralogy of reef-building and sediment-producing organisms driven by tectonically driven shifts in seawater chemistry. Palaeogeography, Palaeoclimatology, Palaeoecology, 144, 3-19, Amsterdam

Tucker, M.E., & Wright , V.P.,1990: Carbonate Sedimentology, 482pp, Blackwells, Oxford

Walter. L.M. & Burton, E.A., 1990: Dissolution of platform carbonate sediments in marine pore fluids, - American Journal of Science, 290, 601-603

Walter, L.M., Bischoff, S.A., Patterson, W.P., & Lyons, T.W., 1993: Dissolution and recrystallization in modern shelf carbonates: evidence from pore water and solid phase chemistry, - Royal Society of London Philosophical Transactions, series A, 344, 27-36, London

Warren, J. 2000: Dolomite: occurrence, evolution and economically important associations, - Earth-Science Reviews, 52, 1-81, Amsterdam

Wilkinson, B.H., 1982: Cyclic cratonic carbonates and Phanerozoic seas, - Journal of Geological Education, 30, 189-203

Wright, V.P., Cherns, L. & Hodges, P.(in press): Missing molluscs: groundtruthing taphonomic loss in the Mesozoic through early, large-scale aragonite dissolution, - Geology

---

Address:
Department of Earth Sciences
Cardiff University, Cardiff, CF10 3YE, Wales, UK, and BG Group
100 Thames Valley Park Drive, Reading, RG6 1PT
E-mail: wrightvp@cardiff.ac.uk

Evolution of Karst: From Prekarst to Cessation, 31-41, Ljubljana-Postojna 2002

FROM PRE-KARST TO CESSATION: THE COMPLICATING EFFECTS OF DIFFERING LITHOLOGY AND GEOLOGIC STRUCTURE ON KARST EVOLUTION

DEREK FORD

Abstract
Karst is created by groundwater circulating through caves and thus is profoundly affected by variations in bedrock lithology and structure. The Classical Karst is not a suitable model type area because its structures are too complex. Four more simple models are presented to frame pre-karst, karstification and karst cessation concepts of development in differing geologic structures, and illustrated with examples from Canada. Limestone purity, texture, dolomitization, frequency of penetrable bedding planes, and presence of sulphate or salt interbeds are particularly important lithologic controls. Geologic structure is important at all scales, from local jointing to plate tectonic deformation and translocation. In some geologic settings it is an easy matter to define a set of "pre-karst" conditions but in others it seems irrelevant if not impossible: the same is true of cessation of karstification.
Keywords. *Karst; pre-karst; limestone; dolomite; dolostone; carbonate purity; rock texture; penetrable bedding planes; jointing; fold,fault and complex structures.*

INTRODUCTION: PROCESS, LITHOLOGY AND STRUCTURE

The purpose of this symposium is to evaluate models of karstic evolution, from presumed initial conditions of no karst phenomena present - "pre-karst" - to the cessation of the karst process and of enlargement of the forms (surface or underground) created by it. It is well to remember here the dictum of the eminent American geomorphologist, W.M.Davis, that the landforms we study are "the product of structure, process and stage". He presented this argument in his essay on the Geographical Cycle of Erosion that was published in 1899. He will have written it somewhat earlier, however, because in that year he was travelling in Europe, in particular in Dalmatia, Bosnia and Herzegovina with the leading Austrian geomorphologist of the day, Albrecht Penck (Davis 1901). The two and their students were concerned to investigate the karst, recently brought to international prominence by Jovan Cvijic (1893). They had a pre-karst model to test - that karst landforms develop from prior fluvial landscapes - but did not entirely convince themselves of its validity. And I sometimes wonder whether Davis, as he traversed from the great limestone terrains onto dolostones and back again, wondered whether he should not telegraph his publisher to revise his dictum to become "the product of lithology, structure, process and stage"!

Today Davis' concepts of landform evolutionary stages of youth, maturity and old age have fallen out of favour (see e.g. Ford 1998) but the remainder of his dictum still rings true. Karst is differentiated from the other geomorphic systems by the predominant importance of bedrock dissolution processes. The principal consequence of this rock solubility is that waters are directed underground through caves rather than running off in surface channels that carve river valleys. The further, and inescapable, consequence of that relationship is that lithological and structural conditions within the rock exert a much more profound effect upon the evolution of the hydrodynamic systems, caves and landforms than is found in the fluvial, glacial or other geomorphic systems A first irony of karst morphological research thus is that the student is concerned with a much more limited range of the Earth's rock types than other geomorphologists study (with the exception of the specialist in volcanic landforms) but will have to make a greater effort to understand their influence. Lithologic and diagenetic features are profoundly important in the evolution of karstic porosity, as Professor Wright shows in this symposium.

A second irony, I submit, is that The Classical Karst where we are meeting, which with its neighbouring regions is the home of Western karst studies, is a very poor type area for the study of karst evolution! This is because its geological structure is much too complicated for general evolutionary modelling purposes. Plate tectonic compression with deformation and differential uplift has created staircase sequences of topographically closed basins rising from the Adriatic coast. Many basins host poljes that, because of their magnitude, dominate the karst morphology and hydrology. Nowhere else in the world is there such a pattern of large, complexly linked, poljes. Recently, the tectonic complexity has been emphasised by the suggestion that around Postojna the older cave systems themselves have been torn apart by strike-slip faulting (Sustersic 2000).

For comparison, a set of evolutionary model situations utilising much more simple geologic structures is shown in Figure 1. The pre-karst condition will here be defined as that existing before underground dissolutional channels have "broken through" to the springs, i.e. before there is efficient groundwater flow that is notably faster than that in non-karst aquifers - Professor Dreybrodt elaborates on this point in his contribution to this symposium. In Figure 1A the karst formation rests on and is covered by insoluble and impermeable rocks. There are pre-karst conditions beneath the cover. Karst is initiated where it is stripped back (Strip 1). The karst hydrologic system and its landforms cease to exist where they, in turn, are stripped from the impermeable substratum (Strip 2). This ideally simple model can be applied (in part at least) in the karst of N.W Yorkshire, England, or the Burren of Eire.

Figure 1B is a simplification of the structural situation in regions such as the Mammoth Cave area of Kentucky or the gypsum maze cave country of Ukraine. There are impermeable cover rocks remaining between the sinkpoints and the springs. There is thus no true pre-karst surviving because there is karsticgroundwater flow beneath the cover. The flow is to river valleys but it cannot be said that the karst is derived from the fluvial pattern in the sense that Davis and Penck understood it. Nor is there any true

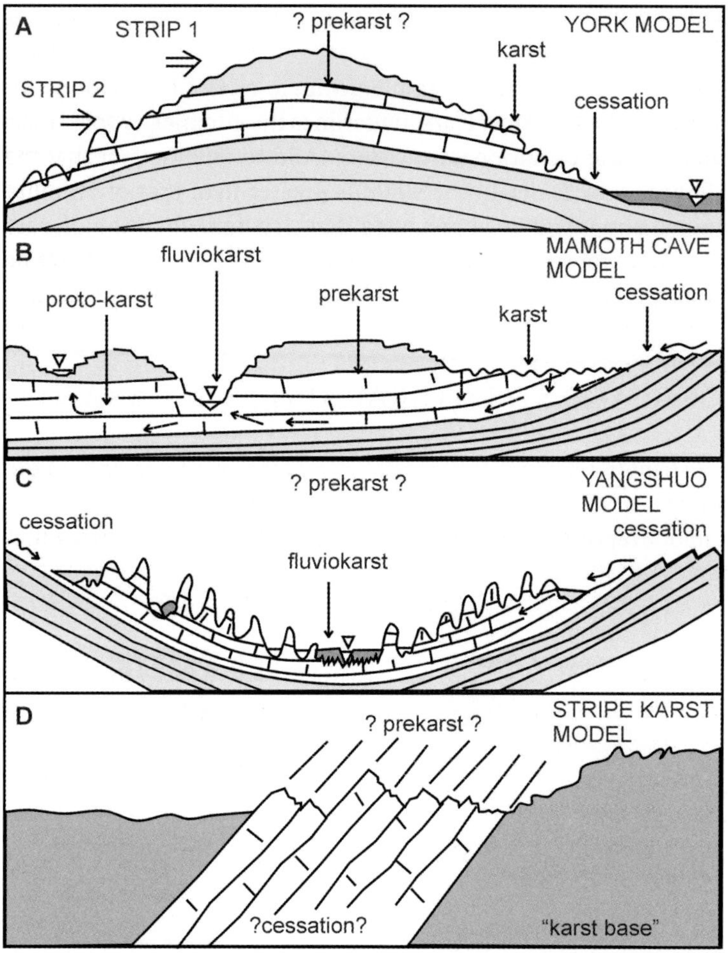

Fig. 1. Illustrating pre-karst, karst development, and cessation in some differing geologic structural settings. See discussion in the text for details.

cessation in the model as I have drawn it; karstic flow will continue to propagate down-dip and out of the diagram. In Figure 1C the structure becomes a little more complicated. Pre-karst conditions cannot be reconstructed with confidence because the cover strata are gone - or perhaps never existed. The impermeable substratum encloses the karst, rising above it on the flanks and supplying insoluble detritus that introduces the complications of aggradation and burial to karst evolution. Development is episodic and cessation may be long delayed in such situations; however, it is possible to envisage a time when all karst rock is gone. Figure 1D models stripe karst, common structural situations where the concept of "pre-karst" appears meaningless. The nature of "cessation" is also problematic. Karstic groundwater flow will probably be to the strike, to springs rising in valleys crossing the outcrop. At any given time we might arbitrarily designate a "karst base level" of dissolution somewhere below which lithostatic pressure restricts most flow. This will be below the elevation of the valleys, will roughly keep pace with the latter if they are being entrenched, or extend progressively below them where entrenchment ceases. There is the possibility that groundwater may flow down dip, however, passing through a syncline into another stripe.

The attempt in Figure 1 to explore more simple geologic model foundations for karst evolution than can exist in the Classical Karst underlines the complexity that structural settings will contribute to the evolutionary problem. Add to this the fact that the number of different carbonate rock facies in the world is greater than that of all other sedimentary facies combined and it will be appreciated that structure and lithology are always of great importance in karst studies. The remainder of this paper will illustrate these arguments with examples from the wide range of karstic settings found in Canada.

KARST LITHOLOGIC AND STRUCTURAL STYLES IN CANADA

Karst rocks are widely distributed around the central Precambrian Shield in Canada (Figure 2). In outcrop there are ~500 000 km² of limestone and marble, 600 000 km² of dolostone and 80 000 km² of evaporite rocks. Along the southern and western fringes of

Fig. 2. The outcrop of karst rocks and subcrop of the Prairie Salt in Canada. Numbered sites are principal areas of karst study, some being discussed in the text.

the Shield ("B" regions, Fig 2) these rocks occur as thin, little disturbed sedimentary veneers of Paleozoic age, dominated by shallow marine, lagoonal and reefal facies, and passing beneath younger sandstones, shales and clays downdip. To the east ("C") and north deposits are thicker, more varied, generally folded and faulted by Appalachian (Hercynian) or Innuitian tectonism. The Western Cordillera ("D") contain thick sequences of shallow marine, reefal and lagoonal facies, some marbles, and deeper marine rocks on the west coast. These mountain ranges were built by thrust faulting, plutonic emplacements and strike-slip translocations. They are generally young (Cretaceous-Tertiary in age) with some uplift and deformation continuing today. Canadian karst outcrops thus offer a very wide range of lithologies and structures for study, although there are no very young, diagenetically immature, strata.

Modern eco-climatic conditions on the karsts range from coastal rainforest to high alpine and polar deserts. Most of Canada experienced repeated glaciations during the Quaternary, and permafrost becomes continuous in the north: these controls have limited karst development when compared to e.g. the Classical Karst, but nevertheless it is widespread, as indicated by the numbered field study sites (B3, D11, etc) in Figure 2.

FEATURES OF THE LITHOLOGY

Mineral purity is a fundamental consideration. There is general agreement that karst is diminished where calcite or dolomite fall below 90% weight/volume in limestones or dolostones. This is true in Canada as elsewhere. For example, at the local scale in the Niagaran dolostones of Ontario (B3, Fig 2) a lower, clay-rich formation has developed postglacial epikarst in zones extending only 10 -20 m back of escarpments (i.e. the zones of highest hydraulic gradient): an upper, pure and Ca-rich, dolomite formation has zones extending more than 1000 m (Enyedy 1995). At the greater regional scale, extensive limestone outcrops throughout northern British Columbia (North of D4, Fig 2) also appear to lack karst because of abundant clay-rich facies.

Mention of the Niagaran rocks raises the general question of the role of dolomite in karst? Globally, primary dolomite is small in amount. Secondary dolomitisation (conversion of the $CaCO_3$ of limestone to $CaMg(CO_3)_2$) usually increases matrix porosity but always reduces aqueous solubility considerably because the reaction kinetics are of higher order. As a consequence many karst researchers have come to look upon dolostones as semi-karstic at best, functioning as aquitards underground and impoverishing or prohibiting dissolutional landform development at the surface. This is an emphasis in Cvijic' writings (1893, 1918) and was noted by Davis (1901), for example.

Canada offers a good test case because it has all kinds of dolomite, occuring as mere patches in limestones, as interbeds, or as entire separate formations (dolostones). It is found in all structural provinces, and outcrops over a greater aggregate area than does limestone. Further, recent glaciations have repeatedly scoured away much of the epikarst, setting the "evolution of karst" clock back towards pre-karst conditions each time. This presents many opportunities to compare early (postglacial age) karst development on limestone and dolostone around the country.

To generalise, the dolostones do not form good karst in our mountain regions. This is because these are high energy environments, where the steep gradients permit fluvial, mechanical and frost processes to compete very effectively at the surface, reducing development of groundwater intakes such as sinkholes. However, on the circum-Shield platform rocks (B regions of Fig 2), the relief is of low escarpments backed by long, gentle dip slopes. These are low energy environments for surface processes. Fluvial processes and frost do not compete as effectively there. Holokarst pavement develops on escarpment promontories, merging into fluviokarst on the dip slopes (e.g. Cowell and Ford 1980). There is little difference between its extent on limestone and dolostone, although it tends to be deeper on the former. The aggregate area of dolostone pavement in Canada far exceeds the area of the celebrated limestone pavements of the British Isles.

It is well established that grain size and homogeneity have profound effects on surficial karren and similar bedrock sculpture underground (e.g Fornos and Gines 1996, Slabe 1995). For example, rillenkarren tend to be limited to the finer-grained limestones in Canada as they are elsewhere, and the enigmatic trittkarren (Bogli 1961) appear to be restricted to porcellaneous beds. Rinnen and rundkarren, pits and pans dissect the clint blocks between dissolutional grikes (kluftkarren) on most types of limestone but, strikingly, there are only small pits or shallow pans on the dolostone clints - the lower solubility is clearly a constraint at this scale of development.

It is significant to note that these textural controls are less important in coastal phytokarst, where biogenic processes may become significant. The Great Northern Peninsula of Newfoundland (Fig 2, region C1; Malis 1997) provides something of a global limiting case because the shoreline is young, stabilizing after glacial isostatic rebound only a few thousand years ago, and the waters are cold, sea ice being locked to the shore for four months or longer each winter. Nevertheless, there is abundant phytokarst pitting on all limestones, even extremely heterogeneous fore-reef breccias. The forms are essentially the same as those of Galway Bay, Eire, (Williams 1970) but smaller due to the shorter formative period. There is no phytokarst on the dolomite salt water coast, however, only mechanical abrasion damage. Dense shoreline pitting is found on Niagaran dolostones in the freshwaters of Lake Huron and Georgian Bay (Fig 2, B3) but it is thought to be abiotic in origin and development (Vajoczki and Ford 2000). It appears that aquatic fauna and flora dislike dolomite!

In karst geomorphology the thickness of a limestone, etc. bed is defined as the separation between successive bedding (or parting) planes that water can penetrate under the prevailing conditions. It is widely held that thick to massive bedding (parting planes 30 - 100 cm or more apart) is best suited for karst (e.g Ford and Williams 1989). The circum-Shield platforms are again good places to investigate this contention because they have negligible fold or thrust deformation to complicate the picture. Anticosti Island in the Gulf of St Lawrence (Fig 2, B1) is 150 km in length, 20-50 km in width.

It is composed of regularly bedded, shallow platform carbonate formations totalling than 1400 m in thickness and rising to 350 m asl, a potentially great holokarst. However, a majority of formations are thin to medium bedded and can support only shallow epikarst that becomes shattered by frost and root wedging, and drains only to surface streams. The few thick-bedded units are holokarstic, and able to swallow streams flowing onto them from the thin units (Roberge and Ford 1983). The importance of bedding planes in thick to massive rocks is also a basic feature of the Four-State Mod-

3a

3b

Fig. 3. Examples of lithologic and structural contrasts in the undeformed circum-Shield carbonate karstlands of Canada. ***a)*** *A Silurian dolostone bioherm on the shore of Georgian Bay, Ontario, that has been gutted by dedolomitization and wave action to create a cave.* ***b)*** *A thick-bedded platform limestone of Silurian age on the south shore of Anticosti Island, Quebec, emphasising the master joint and secondary joint pattern created by stress from an underlying continental suture of Proterozoic age. The master joint set extends the full length and breadth of the island (150 x 50 km), and through 1400 m of carbonate strata.*

el of cave pattern genesis: Canada's longest cave, Castleguard, is an outstanding example (Ford et al. 2000).

Finally, reefs, bioherms, dunes and other mound deposits in which bedding planes are absent or only partial may create their own distinctive variants in karst landform and drainage pattern. They are abundant in the circum-Shield rocks of Canada. At Attawapiskat (Figure 2, B4) limestone reef knolls are resistant and rise above muskeg (peat bogs) that cover the surrounding, thin and weak, inter-reef beds: acid wetland drainage flows into the knolls, creating curvilinear sinkholes around them that look like moats around castles (Cowell 1983). Reefs are usually strong and upstanding on the platform dolostone surfaces of Ontario (B3) and Manitoba (B4) also; however, some are weakened by the process of dedolomitization and become preferentially excavated as caves instead, as shown in Figure 3A.

FEATURES OF GEOLOGIC STRUCTURE

Joint fractures, normal to the bedding planes or nearly so, are the basic structural elements present in all carbonate formations and most gypsum and anhydrite. On the stripped but little-deformed circum-Shield platforms their role in karst development tends to be limited to the epikarst zone where erosional unloading has sprung them open: at greater depths bedding planes are the principal routes for karst initiation and development (Klimchouk and Ford 2000). There are always exceptions, however. The Ordovician and Silurian limestones of Anticosti Island are deposited close to the Grenville Front, a Proterozoic plate tectonic suture. Movements on the Front have created one master strike joint set throughout all formations on the Island (Figure 3B), which dominates the development of the karst at the surface and underground.

Larger structures become more important controls of karst in the regions of strong deformation and mountain building, C and D. They are often inhibitors. For example, in the Rocky Mountains of Canada the eastern or 'Front" ranges are formed by resistant Paleozoic carbonate formations repeatedly thrust over weaker Mesozoic clastic rocks, creating series of cuestas that are now dissected by alpine glacial action. Where a thrust plate was thin - a single, upper Paleozoic carbonate formation or group in the overthrust - a single cuesta with steep scarp and backslopes was created that did not favour karstification because surface gradients were too high, inducing rapid fluvial runoff or intense glacial dissection. Thicker plates contained multiple carbonate formations separated by weaker contact units, forming multiple scarps with elevated vales on the backslopes that could intercept the runoff and promote underground drainage (Ford 1993). The effects are enhanced where major valleys are cut across these structures, setting up the conditions for strike-oriented underground drainage on regional scales.

In the western or 'Main" ranges of the Rockies and in the Franklin and Mackenzie Mountains north of them (Figure 2, D6-7, D8-9), structures become larger, more complex and varied, including fault blocks and uplifted plateaus, domal and inverted fold topography. They support a wide range of karst settings, similar to those reported in the Alps and other young mountain chains by Maire (1990). Canadian karst development tends to be more limited because of the greater intensity of glaciation, however, and the structural patterns never approach the complexity of those occuring in the Classical Karst.

Stripe karst structural settings predominate in the mountains further west in British Columbia and YukonTerritory because carbonate strata are comparatively rare and the deformation is intense. For example, Mount Tupper System (Fig 2, D5) is a cave in a ten metre marble stripe (bed) in micaschists that passes through a mountain and discharges its waters at express train speed in a spring just above the principal trans-Canada railway (Ford 1967). It is a karst that will achieve cessation when the mountain is eroded down to the rail line! In Vancouver Island and the Queen Charlotte Islands (Fig 2, D11, D12) the karst rocks are thick and pure micritic limestones that dip steeply and outcrop as benches on the flanks of stronger volcanic rocks rising above them. The setting is one of very high energy, with the limestones swallowing the abundant Pacific rainforest runoff pouring on to them from the volcanics (Ford 1993). This region has the greatest density of river caves and stream sinkhole formation in Canada as a consequence. It is difficult to imagine any pre-karst conditions once the modern geologic structure was established. The limestones sit above a subduction zone and dip far below sea level: it is equally difficult to imagine the cessation of karstification until the Pacific Plate has been consumed.

Geologic structures with complexity comparable to those of the Classical Karst, but of different style, occur in the Atlantic coast Hercynian region. In the south (Fig 2, C3-5) the karst rocks are chiefly gypsum and anhydrite, which are so much weaker and more soluble than carbonates that lithologic and structural controls are subordinate to the local circumstances of glacial erosion and deposition (Ford 1997). In western Newfoundland (Fig 2, C2) however, "thin-skinned" plate tectonism emplaced granitic rocks over highly deformed limestones, dolostones and clastic metasedimentary rocks that are exposed in windows. Rivers from the granites carved valleys through the carbonates, creating relief up to 300 m and high hydraulic gradients along their flanks. Patches of cockpit karst with affinities to the modern cockpit country in Jamaica, Puerto Rico or Belize and to flysch margin karst in Slovenia were able to develop, their grain and density determined by a combination of steep stratal dips and major fracturing. Repeated glaciations then remoulded the surface landforms and disrupted the aquifers (Karolyi and Ford 1983).

CONCLUSIONS

The evolution of karst at the surface and underground is a complex phenomenon. At one extreme it can be initiated within hours of primary deposition of the rock if there is dissolution on a sabkha or a carbonate dune. Towards the other extreme (and more commonly) it begins only after long burial and attainment of diagenetic maturity. The modern phase of karstification in a region may extend far back into the Tertiary or earlier and be preceded by paleokarst episodes. Lithology can exert profound effects on the style, extent and rate of karstification: limestone purity, texture, dolomitization, frequency of penetrable bedding planes, and presence of sulphate or salt interbeds are particularly important. Geologic structure is important at all scales from local jointing to plate tectonic deformations and translocations. In some geologic settings it is an easy matter to define a set of "pre-karst" conditions but in others it seems irrelevant if not impossible: the same is true of cessation of karstification.

REFERENCES

Bogli, A. 1961. Karrentische, ein Beitrag zur Karstmorphologie.*Zeitschrift fur Geomorphologie, 5;* 185-193.

Cowell, D.W. and Ford, D.C. 1980. Hydrochemistry of a dolomite terrain; the Bruce Peninsula, Ontario, *Canadian Journal of Earth Sciences* 17(4), 1980, 520-526.

Cowell, D.W. 1983. Karst hydrogeology within a subarctic peatland: Attawapiskat River, Hudson Bay Lowlands, Canada. *Journal of Hydrology, 61(1/3);* 169-177.

Cvijic, J. 1893 Das Karst phaenomen: Versuch einer morphologischen Monographie. *Geographisches Abhandlung Wien, 5(3);* 218-329.

Cvijic, J. 1918. Hydrographie souterraine et evolution morphologique du karst. *Travaux, Institute de Geographie Alpine, 6(4);* 375-426.

Davis, W.M. 1899. The Geographical Cycle. *Geographical Journal, 14;* 481-504.

Davis, W.M. 1901 An Excursion in Bosnia, Hercegovina and Dalmatia. *Geographical Society of Philadelphia, Bulletin, 3;* 21-50.

Enyedy, S.R. 1995. *The karst geomorphology of Manitoulin Island, Ontario.* MSc thesis, Mcmaster University. 312 p.

Ford, D.C. 1967. The sinking streams of Mt. Tupper - a remarkable karst in Glacier National Park, B.C., *Canadian Geographer, XI(1)*, 49-52.

Ford D.C. 1993. Karst in the Cold Environments. in French H.M. and Slaymaker, O., (Eds.) *Canada's Cold Environments.* McGill-Queen's University Press; 199-222.

Ford, D.C.1997. Principal features of evaporite karst in Canada. *Carbonates and Evaporites, 12(1)*, 15-23.

Ford, D.C. 1998 Perspectives on Karst Geomorphology in the 20th Century. In Kranjc, A. (ed) *Papers presented at the Classical Karst Symposium, 4th International Conference on Geomorphology, Acta Carsologica, XXVII/I,* pp 79-98.

Ford, D.C. Lauritzen, S.-E. and Worthington, S.R.H. 2000. Speleogenesis of Castleguard Cave, Rocky Mountains, Alberta, Canada. in Klimchouk A., Ford D.C., Palmer A.N. and Dreybrodt W. Klimchouk, A.B., Ford, D.C., Palmer, A.N. and Dreybrodt, W. (Eds.) *Speleogenesis; Evolution of Karst Aquifers.* Huntsville, Al. National Speleological Society Press. 332-337.

Ford, D.C. and Williams, P.W. 1989. *Karst Geomorphology and Hydrology.* Unwin-Hyman, London. 601 p.

Fornos, J.-J. and Gines, A. (eds.) *Karren Landforms.* Palma de Mallorca, Universitat de les Illes Balears. 450 p.

Karolyi, M.S., and Ford, D.C. The Goose Arm Karst, Newfoundland, *Journal of. Hydrology, 61(1/3),* pp. 181-186.

Klimchouk, A. and Ford, D.C. 2000. Types of Karst and Evolution of Hydrogeologic Settings. In Klimchouk, Ford, Palmer, A.N. and Dreybrodt, W. (Editors). *Speleogenesis: Evolution of Karst Aquifers.* Huntsville, Al. National Speleological Society of America. 45-53.

Maire, R. 1990. *La Haute Montagne Calcaire.* Karstologia Memoires, 3; 731 p.

Malis, C.E. 1997. *Coastal karren of the Great Northern Peninsula, Newfoundland.* MSc thesis, McMaster University. 309 p.

Roberge, J.S. and Ford, D.C. 1983. Karst of the Salmon River, Anticosti Island, Quebec. *Journal of Hydrology, 61(1/3),* 159-162.

Slabe, T. 1995. *Cave Rocky Relief and its Speleological Significance.* Lubljana, Znanstvenoraziskovalni Center SAZU. 128 p.

Sustersic, F. 2000. Speleogenesis in the Lubljanica River Drainage Basin, Slovenia. in Klimchouk, A., Ford, D.C., Palmer, A.N. and Dreybrodt,W. (Editors). *Speleogenesis: Evolution of Karst Aquifers.* Huntsville, Al. National Speleological Society of America. 397-406.

Vajoczki S. and Ford D.C. 2000. Underwater dissolutional pitting on dolostones, Lake Huron-Georgian Bay, Ontario. *Physical Geography, 21(5),* 418-432.

Williams, P.W. 1970. Limestone morphology in Ireland. in Stephens, N. and Glasscock R.E. (eds.) *Irish Geographical Studies.* Belfast, Queen's University Press. 105-124.

Address
School of Geography and Geology
McMaster University
Hamilton, ON L8S 4K1, Canada
E-mail: dford@mcmaster.ca

Evolution of Karst: From Prekarst to Cessation, 43-59, Ljubljana-Postojna 2002

SPELEOGENESIS IN CARBONATE ROCKS

ARTHUR N. PALMER

Abstract
This paper outlines the current views on cave origin in carbonate rocks, combining ideas from a variety of sources. A typical dissolution cave develops in several stages that grade smoothly from one to the next: (1) Initial openings are slowly enlarged by water that is nearly at solutional equilibrium with the local bedrock. (2) As the early routes enlarge, those with the greatest amount of flow grow fastest. (3) These favoured routes eventually become wide enough that groundwater is able to retain most of its solutional aggressiveness throughout the entire distance to the spring outlets. This breakthrough time usually requires times on the order of 10^4 to 10^5 years and ends the inception phase of speleogenesis. (4) Discharge along these selected routes increases rapidly, allowing them to enlarge into cave passages rather uniformly over their entire length. Maximum enlargement rates are roughly 0.001-0.1 cm/yr, depending on the local water chemistry and lithology. (5) The cave acquires a distinct passage pattern that depends on the nature of groundwater recharge, the geologic setting, and the erosional history of the region. Branchwork patterns dominate in most carbonate aquifers. Maze caves are produced by any of the following: steep hydraulic gradients (e.g. during floods), short flow paths, uniform recharge to many openings, and mixing of waters that contrast in chemistry. (6) Enlargement rate usually decreases as passages become air-filled, owing to loss of aggressiveness as carbon dioxide escapes through openings to the surface. (7) The cave typically evolves by diversion of water to new and lower routes as the fluvial base level drops. (8) The cave is eventually destroyed by roof collapse and by intersection of passages by surface erosion. At any given time, different parts of the same cave may be experiencing different stages in this sequence.
Keywords: *Speleogenesis, Karst, Carbonates*

INTRODUCTION

Caves are present in all rather pure carbonate rocks that are in geologic settings and climates that allow abundant groundwater recharge. For this reason, it is clear that cave origin requires no special chemical mechanism beyond the circulation of meteoric groundwater. Dissolution caves can form by other processes, but this is the common speleogenetic mode in most carbonate aquifers and is the main topic of this paper. Most of the concepts presented here are not new, but, where possible, alternate viewpoints are given in the hope of encouraging further discussion.

CAVE INCEPTION

Speleogenesis requires one basic thing: Groundwater must dissolve the bedrock rapidly enough to produce caves before the rock is removed by surface erosion. This requires the through-flow of large amounts of solutionally aggressive water along stable flow paths.

THE EARLIEST STAGES

At great depth beneath the surface there is very little groundwater flow because openings in the rock are narrow and few, and hydraulic gradients are feeble. But as uplift and erosion expose these rocks near the surface, increasing amounts of groundwater pass through them. Along any given flow path, the solutional enlargement rate is controlled by a simple mass balance. The mass removed from the walls of the growing conduits is equal to that which is carried away in solution. The increase in volume thus depends on how much water passes through the conduit, and how rapidly the water dissolves the rock. In other words, the two major controls are discharge and chemical kinetics.

Early in the development of a carbonate aquifer, all groundwater becomes nearly saturated with dissolved calcite and/or dolomite before it emerges at the surface. The total amount of rock removed along any flow path is nearly independent of chemical kinetics, because the water has enough time to equilibrate with the rock, regardless of dissolution rates. The saturation concentration depends on the minerals present, CO_2 concentration, type of system (open vs. closed), temperature, and interactions with other dissolved components. All these show considerable variation, both spatially and temporally, but it is unlikely that there will be major differences between neighboring flow paths within a given aquifer. In contrast, there are great variations in discharge from one flow path to another - and this is the main control over which of the early paths are able to grow into caves.

Most dissolution takes place at the upstream ends of the flow paths, where aggressive water first enters the carbonate rock. ("Upstream" and "downstream" in the following discussion refer to the up-gradient and down-gradient ends of the system, even where the flow is only laminar seepage.) With time and distance, there is an increase in saturation ratio of the dissolved minerals (actual concentration divided by saturation concentration, C/Cs). At first the dissolution rate decreases in a roughly linear manner. But as the saturation ratio rises above approximately 60-90% (the exact value depends on temperature and CO_2 content), the dissolution rate decreases much more rapidly. The result is that the final approach toward saturation is very slow (see Berner & Morse, 1974; Plummer & Wigley, 1976; Plummer et al., 1978; Dreybrodt, 1990; Palmer, 1991).

Dissolution is so rapid in the upstream sections that if the remainder of the dissolution followed the same trend, the water would lose virtually all its aggressiveness after only a short distance of flow. Dissolution would be so slow in the rest of the aquifer that cave development would be almost impossible (Palmer, 1984). Except in the most ideal situations (wide, short fractures with steep hydraulic gradients, e.g. along escarpments), enlargement of the initial openings to cave size would require many millions of years, during which the carbonate rock is likely to be entirely removed by erosion.

Interestingly, it would be unlikely for caves to form with *either* the rapid dissolution at low saturation ratios *or* the slow dissolution at high saturation ratios. Early slow dissolution along the entire flow path is essential for preparing the way for the rapid dissolution that follows. But the slow dissolution alone cannot enlarge the routes rapidly enough to form caves within a geologically feasible time. Rapid dissolution at low saturation ratios is necessary to achieve this. But, as shown above, the rapid dissolution by itself cannot form caves in most situations.

GEOLOGICAL ASPECTS OF CAVE INCEPTION

The initial width of fissures (e.g. fractures and partings) is perhaps the most uncertain of all field conditions that influence cave inception. By the time a cave is large enough for humans to enter, the evidence has long disappeared. Initial fissure width is a slippery concept, because the widths increase with time even without being dissolved, simply by release of stress as the overlying rocks are eroded away. Field evidence suggests that a minimum initial fissure width of about 0.01 mm is required for cave development (Böcker, 1969). However, this value depends on hydraulic gradient, flow distance, water chemistry, and length of time available, and so the threshold for initial fissure width is not a fixed value, but instead depends on the local setting.

To clarify how wide the initial fissures in limestone might be, it is helpful to gather data from relatively insoluble rocks that are approximately as brittle as limestone. Intrusive igneous rocks such as granite should give a close approximation. Water wells in these rocks have fairly small yields, especially at depths of more than 50 m below the surface (Freeze & Cherry, 1979, p. 158). But even with conservative estimates for hydraulic gradient and fissure frequency, the observed well yields require fissures that are roughly 0.1-0.5 mm wide. Surely only a few of the many fissures are this large, but they are important ones, which in soluble rock would grow into caves.

Inception horizons were originally defined by Lowe (1992) as beds or stratal interfaces that provide a chemical environment that favours cave development. The presence of pyrite along a geologic contact was cited as a typical example, whereby oxidation of the sulphide to sulphuric acid might give a substantial boost to cave development. One difficulty with this particular example is the deficiency of oxygen in most deep groundwater. Structural and hydraulic factors are also crucial in determining which initial openings are able to develop into caves.

The presence of interbedded sulphates within carbonate rocks provides a suitable environment for cave inception. Dissolution of the sulphates can boost porosity, although this process forces calcite to precipitate by the common-ion effect. Because of differences in molar volume, the precipitated calcite usually does not occupy all the porosity generated by dissolution of gypsum or anhydrite. This process is even more potent when limestone, dolomite, and gypsum interact within the same system. As calcite is forced to precipitate, the solubility of gypsum rises to almost 1.5 times more than that of gypsum alone, and the solubility of dolomite rises to several times its normal value. Because dolomite dissolves so slowly, the process is drawn out over long distances and times, potentially resulting in long, continuous paths of increased porosity that may pave the way for later cave development. The geochemical process has been validated by field measurements (e.g. Bischoff et al., 1994), but its impact on cave development is still unclear.

BREAKTHROUGH

Eventually the entire length of an incipient cave becomes large enough to allow water to pass all the way through while still retaining most of its aggressiveness. At this time there is a fairly sudden transition ("breakthrough") to rapid dissolution throughout the entire flow path. From then on, the entire route enlarges rapidly at a roughly uniform rate of about 0.001-0.01 cm/yr, depending on the water chemistry. This rate varies with the amount of turbulence, but only at low saturation ratios (Plummer & Wigley, 1976; White, 1984). At the high saturation ratios of most karst water the effect is minor. In mature caves, abrasion by coarse sediment load can increase local rates of cave development (Smith & Newson, 1974). These factors are insignificant compared to the truly great differences in growth rate that distinguish true cave passages with low saturation ratios from narrow flow paths whose water is nearly saturated with dissolved carbonates.

Figure 1 shows the mean enlargement rate in an ideal fissure as a function of discharge and flow length. The steep parts of the curves represent the slow dissolution rates governed by the mass balance, and the horizontal segments at the top represent the

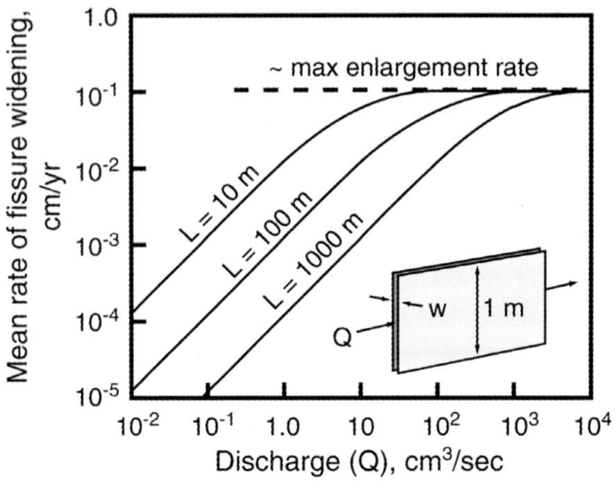

Fig. 1. Mean enlargement rate of a fissure in limestone, as a function of discharge (Q) and flow length (L). Q = discharge per metre of fissure height (long dimension of fissure cross section). Assumptions include closed conditions, T = 10° C, initial P_{CO_2} = 0.01 atm. (See Palmer, 1991.)

rapid dissolution controlled mainly by kinetics (Palmer, 1991). Because the enlargement rates are not uniform throughout the fissure, the rates shown in Figure 1 cannot be translated directly into the time required for an incipient cave to reach breakthrough. To do this, finite-difference modelling is necessary. The results are shown in Figure 2.

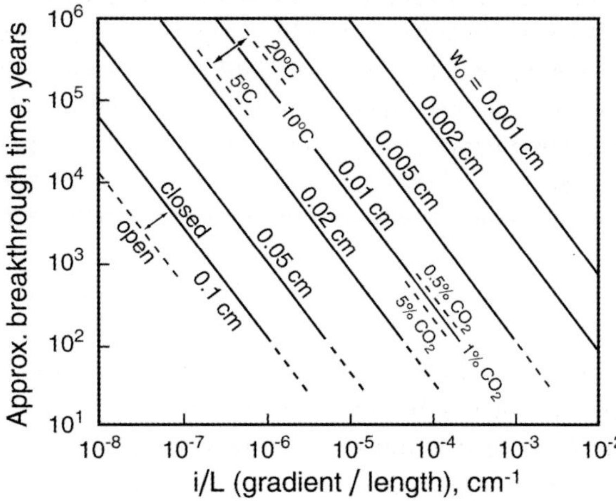

Fig. 2. Approximate breakthrough times for cave inception along fissures in limestone. The main part of the graph shows closed conditions at T = 10° C and initial P_{CO2} = 1%. Variation of breakthrough time with initial fissure width, temperature, and initial P_{CO2} are shown. The combined variable i/L represents the hydraulic gradient (Δh/L) divided by flow distance (L). Modified from Palmer (1991). See also Dreybrodt (1996).

The time required for chemical breakthrough can be considered the "gestation time" through which an incipient cave must pass in order to allow it to grow into a true cave. It is difficult to specify exactly when this time begins. In some ways, it involves the entire age of the carbonate aquifer, if one includes all the effects of early diagenesis, burial, and uplift in order to reach its present state (Klimchouk and Ford, 2000). But before cave growth can truly begin, there must be a substantial hydraulic gradient. Thus it is customary to start the clock when the carbonate rock is first exposed above base level, at the time when both recharge zones and discharge zones are well defined. Computer models can track the growth of idealized fissures of specified initial width, length, hydraulic gradient, and chemical attributes. These show that the breakthrough time is approximately proportional to $w^3 (i/L)^{-1.4} P^1$, where w = initial fissure width, i = mean hydraulic gradient, L = flow distance, and P = initial P_{CO2} (Palmer, 1988, 1991). Dreybrodt (1996) provided an analytical derivation arriving at nearly the same functional relationships. Laminar discharge through the fissure is proportional to $w^3\ i$, which is essentially the inverse of two of the most important variables that determine breakthrough time. Thus the paths that develop most rapidly into caves are those with high discharge and short flow distance. High P_{CO2} is also favourable, as long as CO_2 is not lost by degassing.

Temperature plays a complex role in determining how long it takes for breakthrough to occur. Higher temperatures speed the chemical reactions, but in long flow systems this can *increase* the breakthrough time by depleting most of the water's solutional capacity in the upstream parts, leaving less for the downstream parts. High temperature increases the flow velocity by reducing the viscosity of the water, but it also decreases the amount of limestone or dolomite that can be dissolved. The net result is an increase in breakthrough time with rising temperature. However, another complication is that in warmer climates the CO_2 production in the soil is greater, which shortens breakthrough times.

As shown in Figure 2, breakthrough time decreases as much as 5 times if the CO_2 consumed by carbonate dissolution is quickly replaced, for example when the water is in close contact with a CO_2 source such as soil. This is rare. In general, the early phase of growth takes place in an approximately closed system, where CO_2 is used up as dissolution proceeds. In caves with open atmospheres, CO_2 is likely to be lost by air exchange with the surface, which more than offsets the apparent advantage of the open system.

Figure 2 shows that initial fissures 0.01-0.1 cm wide would require no more than a few thousand or tens of thousands of years to reach the maximum enlargement rates, from the time aggressive groundwater first begins to flow through the limestone. For example, in a fissure 1 kilometre long, with an initial width of 0.02 cm, hydraulic gradient of 0.02 (20 m/km), P_{CO2} of 0.05 atm, temperature of 10° C, and closed to further uptake of CO_2, the maximum rate of enlargement is reached in about 30,000 years. These conditions are typical, perhaps even conservative. Lab work and computer modelling by Dreybrodt (1990, 1996) suggest even shorter breakthrough times that are probably more valid. Acids can also be generated within passages by oxidation of organic compounds in the water or iron sulphide in the bedrock, diminishing the breakthrough times. Water chemistry and flow vary with the seasons, but their effects average out over the years.

TIME REQUIRED FOR A CAVE TO REACH TRAVERSABLE SIZE

Beyond the breakthrough time, growth rate of a cave depends chiefly on the nature of its water input. In dense, rather pure limestone, the rate of wall retreat (S) can be estimated with the equation

$$S = 11.7\, k\, (1 - C/Cs)^n \text{ cm/yr}$$

where C/Cs is the saturation ratio, k is a reaction coefficient, and n is the reaction order (see Palmer, 1991 for units and further details). Values for k and n vary with P_{CO2}, and k also varies with temperature. For quick applications, some representative averages can be given. At $C/Cs < \tilde{}\,0.7$, k and n are approximately 0.015 and 1.7 respectively. At $C/Cs > \tilde{}\,0.7$, k and n are roughly 0.24 and 4 respectively. Because (1-C/Cs) is less than 1, the larger exponent gives a smaller value of S.

For example, water that collects on insoluble rock and then flows as a sinking stream directly into a limestone cave usually has a P_{CO2} of about 0.001-0.005 atm. This value is higher than that of the outside atmosphere (0.00036 atm) because even though the stream is open to the atmosphere, it acquires CO_2 from seepage that enters the stream through the soil. At ponors, most sinking streams have saturation ratios of about 0.1-0.5. Under these conditions, limestone surfaces in the cave will dissolve as fast as 0.15 cm/yr. Ideally, a water-filled cave can increase its diameter up to 2-3 m in 1000 years. (The diameter increases at twice the rate of wall retreat, *S*.) Measurements with dial micrometers, repeated over several years, have verified these rates in caves fed by sinking streams (High, 1970; Coward, 1975).

In contrast, many caves are fed by water that infiltrates through soil and reaches the caves only after having traveled for a considerable distance along the soil-limestone contact and through narrow fissures in the epikarst. This water has a high P_{CO2} (about 0.01-0.05 atm) but has a high saturation value, usually about 0.75-0.95 by the time it reaches the caves. The diameter of a water-filled passage grows no more than about 20 cm per 1000 years under those conditions.

ORGANIZATION OF CONDUITS

It has been shown that caves in a typical karst aquifer are able to form only along flow paths that increase their discharge with time. This can be achieved in either of two ways:

- By increasing the flow efficiency in a system with a fixed head difference. An example is leakage of water from a stream or other body of water that drains to a lower outlet. As the initial fissures widen, the discharge rises dramatically. The upstream head begins to decrease only when the conduit becomes large enough to transmit the entire stream flow. By that time breakthrough has already taken place.
- By increasing the catchment area that feeds an incipient cave passage. At first, water drains into the growing caves as widely dispersed seepage. Dolines form by subsidence into the rapidly growing voids at the soil/bedrock interface. As dolines increase their catchment area, their mean-annual discharge increases to the caves that they feed. Discharge to the caves increases in an irregular manner, much less rapidly than in routes fed by leaking streambeds, and hydraulic gradients decrease with time, even during the earliest periods of growth.

The difference between these two systems is important. Because the routes fed by surface streams can increase their flow much more rapidly, they are usually the first parts of a cave to form. Passages fed by depressions of limited catchment area require longer times to form, and they usually join the earlier passages as tributaries of a branchwork system. The first passages to form in a cave are usually short and direct, except where short paths are prohibited by the geologic setting. With time, these early passages serve as low-head targets for passages having more remote recharge sources (Ford & Ewers, 1978; Ford et al., 2000).

Less time is required for a cave to grow in small steps (i.e. where new, relatively short upstream passages link to earlier downstream ones) than for a single long passage to form. This is partly due to the non-linear relation between breakthrough time and flow distance. Although the growth of any single passage propagates in the downstream direction, the overall system grows in the upstream direction, away from the springs, by addition of new passages (Ewers, 1982; Ford et al., 2000).

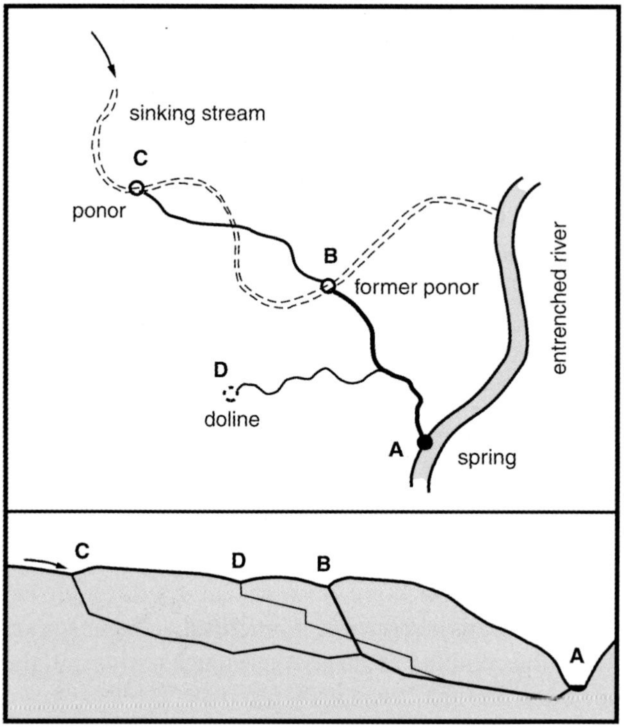

Fig. 3. Evolution of a typical branchwork cave by successive piracy of sinking streams and development of recharge sources through dolines. Segment B-A forms first because of the short path length and steep gradient. Segment C-B links up later, aided by steepening of the gradient as segment B-A develops. (C-B does not necessarily join B-A at point B.) The passage from doline D is last to form because of its limited catchment area. See Ford and Ewers (1978) and Ford et al. (2000) for descriptions of hardware models that illustrate this concept.

A typical sequence is shown in Figure 3. Assume, for simplicity, that passage segments B-A and C-B have identical lengths and gradients. The breakthrough time for a single passage from C to A would be $(L_{C\text{-}A} / L_{B\text{-}A})^{1.4}$ longer than the breakthrough time for either of the two segments - i.e. about 2.6 times longer. This is 30% longer than it would take for segments B-A and C-B to reach breakthrough separately, one after the other. Just as importantly, the gradient of C-B would normally be less than that of B-A until the head dropped in B-A (Ford et al, 2000). The tributary from doline (D) has a smaller catchment area and is slower to reach cave dimensions.

Since the flow of water through carbonate aquifers is controlled partly by the history of river entrenchment, the vertical arrangement of cave passages also reflects this control. The traditional view is that the largest passages are formed when base level is relatively static (Sweeting, 1950; Davies, 1960). At such times, rivers develop floodplains, and springs are held at fairly constant elevations for lengthy periods of time. Meanwhile the passages that feed the springs are able to grow large. In contrast, passages that form during rapid river entrenchment are usually small. The major passages form different levels, which in most cases decrease in age downward. Fluvial aggradation may cause some or all neighboring cave passages to fill with sediment over the vertical range of base-level rise.

This conceptual model has been well validated in Mammoth Cave, Kentucky (Palmer, 1989; Granger et al., 2001). However, in many caves there are several complications that disrupt this simple interpretation. Vadose passages may be perched on insoluble strata and grow to large size above base level. Most phreatic passages contain vertical loops that descend far below the local base level. Some phreatic caves follow favourable stratigraphic units such as zones of former sulphates. Even the ideal cave levels controlled by pauses in fluvial entrenchment are not perfectly "level". For this reason, many people prefer to call them *storeys* or *tiers*, and either of these terms is preferred in general applications. However, the term *cave level* is still appropriate where there is a clear relation to fluvial base level. But the critical elevation is not the average elevation of a phreatic passage, but instead where there is a clear transition from vadose to phreatic morphology (for example, a transition from canyon to tube). This transition is not clear in some passages.

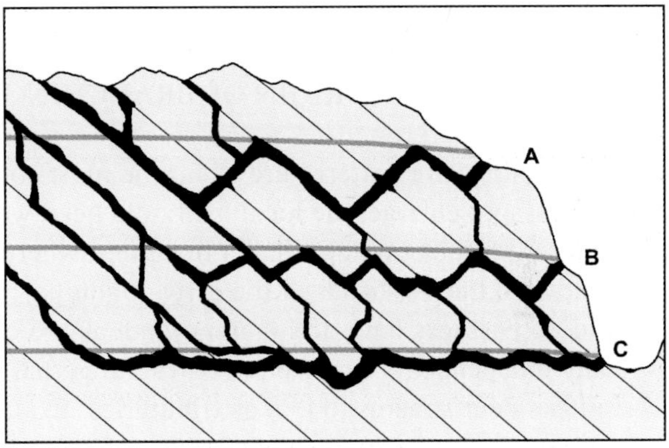

Fig. 4. Vertical layout of a typical cave, showing decreasing amplitude of phreatic loops with depth. This trend has been interpreted by Ford (1971) and Ford and Ewers (1978) to be the result of increasing fissure frequency with time. Successive positions of the water table are shown as gray lines. Some researchers consider these lines to represent the upper extent of epiphreatic flow (see text).

Figure 4 is an idealized profile through a multi-storeyed cave, as described by Ford (1971). Three main stages of cave development are shown, with decreasing loop amplitudes from the highest storey to the lowest. This is not a characteristic of all multi-storeyed caves, but it is a conceptual ideal. Ford (1971) ascribed the decrease in amplitude to increasing fissure frequency in the host rock with time. Fissures are sparse at first, and passages are constrained to only a few deeply descending loops. As erosional unloading and cave development persist, fissures become more numerous until eventually the passages are able to form more or less along the water table, with minimal phreatic looping. In some caves the greater amplitude of loops in upper passages is instead caused by floodwaters, which superpose ungraded, looping bypass routes around low-flow routes that have more uniform gradients (Palmer, 1972). In the same vein, on the basis of studies in the Alps, Audra (1994) and Häuselmann et al. (2001) ascribe an epiphreatic origin to looping passages.

The earliest passages in a cave system (usually fed by sinking streams) may not show a clear distinction between vadose and phreatic development, because their discharge fluctuates a great deal, and because the initial potentiometric surface is relatively high. As a result, most of these passages are subjected to a variety of flow conditions –

phreatic at first, and then vadose and epiphreatic at later times. Still, many of them show a fairly sharp transition from vadose canyons (with continuous downward trends) to phreatic tubes (with low gradients and usually irregular looping profiles). This transition is more sharply defined in secondary passages fed by karst depressions of limited catchment area, because the flow is more uniform with time and the water sources are usually well above the potentiometric surface.

Because of their gravitational flow, many vadose passages have a strong down-dip component, especially those in well-bedded rocks. Phreatic passages show no consistent relation to the dip, except where that is the only path to potential outlets, or where prominent fractures also extend in that direction. In well-bedded rocks, the intersection between the dipping beds and low-gradient water table encourage many phreatic passages to develop nearly along the strike of the beds. These relationships tend to be obscure where the geologic structure is complex.

ORIGIN OF BRANCHING SYSTEMS

Branching cave patterns are by far the most common for several reasons:

- As passages enlarge, the local hydraulic head within them decreases. Groundwater flows from surrounding smaller openings, where the potentiometric surface is higher, toward the low heads of the early conduits.
- Vadose passages have no inherent tendency to converge, because they are hydraulically independent. However, the structures that they follow often intersect, forcing independent streams to join as tributaries. Examples include intersecting fractures, and synclinal structures in bedding-plane partings.
- Water from broad recharge areas converges toward outlets of limited extent, generally stream valleys, which causes a natural tendency for conduits to converge simply by competition for space. After two streams have converged, there is little opportunity for them to diverge farther downstream. The exception is in the vicinity of the spring outlet, where local distributary systems may develop because of collapse, backflooding, and widening of fissures by erosional stress release.

MAZE DEVELOPMENT

Besides branchworks, most other caves are mazes in which all the passages form more or less simultaneously. A maze cave can form only if the growth rate is similar along many alternate flow paths. This can happen if all passages evolve simultaneously at the maximum rate shown in Figure 1. If the ratio of discharge to flow distance (Q/L) is large in many alternate flow routes, they will enlarge at roughly the same rate (Palmer, 1991). Specifically, this condition is achieved if $Q/rL > 0.001$ (cgs units), where r = mean conduit radius. In fissures, this condition is reached if $Q/bL > 0.001$, where b = long dimension of the fissure cross section, perpendicular to the narrow dimension *w*. Specific settings where this condition is met include:

A. High-discharge or high-gradient flow during floods. Water is forced into all fissures in adjacent carbonate rocks under steep gradients, causing them to enlarge at approximately the maximum possible rate (Palmer, 2001). This process is most active in the vicinity of constrictions in the main stream passages, which result from collapse, sediment chokes, or poorly soluble strata.
B. Short flow paths from where the water first enters the soluble rock. Because of the short flow distances, all fissures except for the narrowest enlarge simultaneously at similar rates. The epikarst is an example. Network mazes are also formed by recharge through a permeable but insoluble material such as quartz sandstone (Palmer, 1975, 2000).
C. Uniform recharge to all fissures, regardless of their width. This can be achieved by seepage through porous, insoluble materials, as in B above.
D. Sustained high gradients, for example beneath dams.
E. Mixing zones, where the groundwater aggressiveness is locally boosted by mixing of waters of contrasting CO_2 content or salinity, or by oxidation of sulphide-rich water. Over short flow distances, many alternate routes are enlarged. Mixing of waters of varied CO_2 content can decrease breakthrough times, but large differences in CO_2 concentration are necessary (Gabrovšek, 2000).

The differences in maze types depend partly on geologic structure. *Network mazes* consist of intersecting fissures, with a pattern resembling city streets. They require many

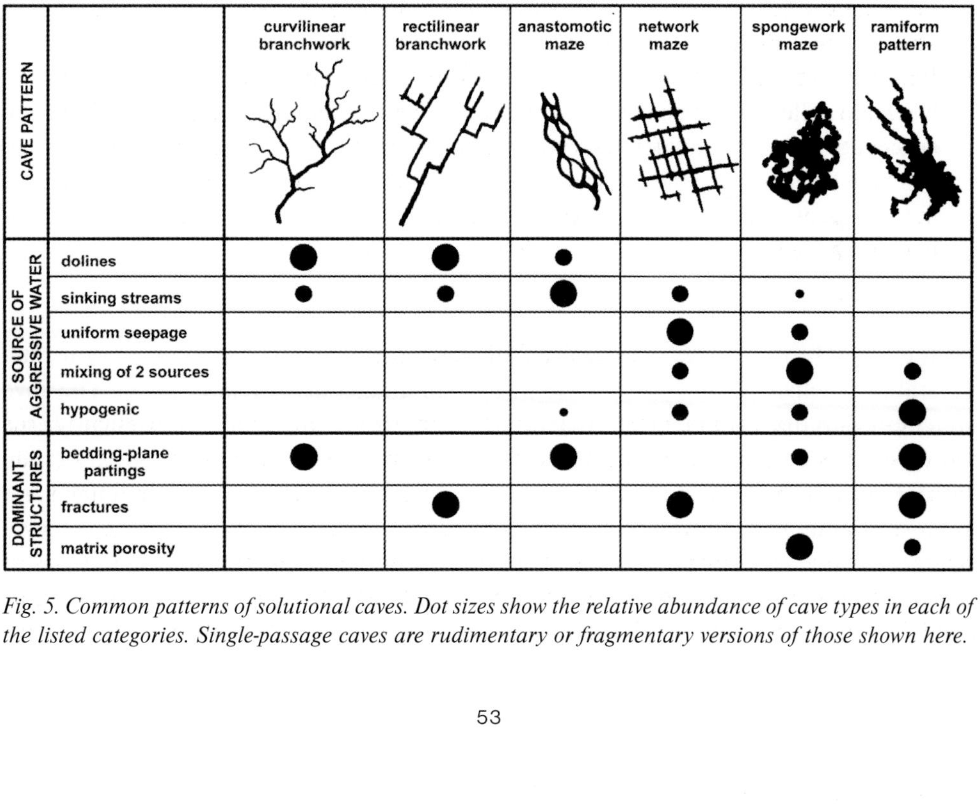

Fig. 5. Common patterns of solutional caves. Dot sizes show the relative abundance of cave types in each of the listed categories. Single-passage caves are rudimentary or fragmentary versions of those shown here.

intersecting fractures (joints or faults), which are typical of massive or thick-bedded rock. Most are formed by processes B, C, or E above. *Anastomotic mazes* have a braided pattern of intersecting tubes, usually arranged two-dimensionally along a single parting or fault. They are nearly all formed by process A above. *Spongework mazes* form where primary (matrix) porosity is dominant. In pattern they resemble the intersecting holes in a sponge. Most of them form by process E, and less commonly by process A. A two-dimensional variety can form along bedding-plane partings. *Ramiform mazes* consist of rooms with offshoots extending outward from them at various elevations. They usually include areas of network or spongework maze development and are formed mainly by process E. Many network and anastomotic mazes, and a few spongework mazes, are merely superimposed on a basic branchwork pattern and represent only part of the entire cave development.

Figure 5 provides a summary of typical cave patterns, showing their relation to source of aggressive water and to dominant structural characteristics.

SUPPORTING EVIDENCE FROM COMPUTER MODELS

Finite-difference computer models support and clarify some of these relationships. Conspicuously absent from the list of ways to form maze caves is slow groundwater flow through artesian aquifers. This origin seems logical, and many maze caves are indeed located in aquifers that are partly artesian. However, artesian conditions by themselves do not produce maze caves. Modelling by Palmer (1991) showed that different-sized branches of a loop are *least* likely to enlarge at the same rate in slow-moving water near saturation. Dreybrodt & Siemers (2000) supported this idea by showing that as breakthrough time increases, passages tend to become unitary and exhibit less complexity. Modelling by Clemens et al. (1997) verified the development of network mazes by uniform seepage through an insoluble caprock, as described in B above. The insoluble cap encourages maze development because it is permeable, rather than a confining unit.

CONDUIT GROWTH AND MODIFICATION

At the breakthrough time, when an incipient cave reaches its maximum growth rate, several other changes take place more or less simultaneously (White, 1977). The cave water changes from laminar to turbulent, which increases the solution rate slightly (see earlier discussion). The flow also becomes competent enough to transport detrital sediment. For example, it is able to carry away the soil that subsides into caves through karst depressions, allowing the depressions to grow more rapidly. The sediment load can also help to enlarge caves by mechanical abrasion, but, in places, sediment accumulates in thick beds that retard dissolution and erosion. Where sediment accumulates, upward dissolution by paragenesis is a possible consequence, especially in caves enlarged by periodic floodwaters. However, water within the sediment is often undersaturated and can still dissolve the underlying rock (Vaughan et al., 1998).

When a cave is able to transmit the entire flow from its recharge area, the average flow can increase no further. Instead the head within the passage decreases as the cross section continues to enlarge. Much of the upstream part of the cave becomes vadose, and streams may entrench canyons in the passage floors.

As caves acquire entrances that allow air exchange with the surface, many free-surface cave streams lose part of their aggressiveness. Inflowing water is fairly rich in soil-derived CO_2, and may acquire even more by oxidation of organic materials as it flows through the caves (Bray, 1972). Loss of CO_2 through entrances and other openings can drive the stream water to supersaturation with dissolved calcite or dolomite, so that many vadose cave streams are aggressive only during high flow. Some vadose stream channels even acquire a thin coating of calcite in sections of supercritical flow during dry seasons. These deposits are usually removed during the following wet season, but with only a small net amount of solutional entrenchment each year. Measurements in caves of New York State show that the overall entrenchment rate of active stream canyons of this type can be as slow as 10-20 mm per thousand years (Palmer, 1996), despite the continuous flow of water. During six months of continuous monitoring in the largest stream in Mammoth Cave, Meiman & Groves (1997) found that 70% of the passage enlargement took place during the highest 7% of flow.

Dating of cave sediments by $^{26}Al/^{10}Be$ isotope ratios in quartz-rich cave sediment is a powerful tool for interpreting rates of cave development. Usually this sediment is deposited by the most recent active stream flow and gives a minimum age for the passage. At Mammoth Cave, $^{26}Al/^{10}Be$ dating suggests that the development of each passage level required at least 10^5 years (Granger et al., 2001). This value is compatible with the range of probable times required for breakthrough (Figure 2) and for later enlargement to the present diameters of about 5-10 m in the major passages.

Headward erosion of resistant beds by cave streams can require a surprisingly long time. For example, sediment on ledges above an entrenched canyon in Mammoth Cave were dated at 1.13 million years, validated by samples at similar elevations elsewhere in the cave (Granger et al., 2001). The passage is floored by a metre-thick sequence of shaly and cherty limestone, which has been breached by a deep canyon that post-dates the sediment. Headward entrenchment has progressed only 360 m along the passage, and only about half of that has occurred upstream from the sampling site. The entrenching stream is still active today and is quite capable of transporting gravel. The rate of headward entrenchment appears to be less than half a metre per thousand years.

But under favourable conditions, diversion of passages from one level to another can take place rather rapidly. Post-glacial diversion of water in New York State caves has formed traversable passages up to a metre in diameter and 200 m long since the last glacial retreat about 13,000 years ago (Mylroie, 1977). In many vadose canyons throughout the world, examples can be seen where loops or cutoffs have developed along prominent bedding-plane partings exposed in the canyon floor (Figure 6). As a result, the floor of the upper level coincides with the ceiling of the lower level. The new passage must develop before the parting is bypassed by deepening of the original canyon. This implies that the breakthrough time for the diversion route is virtually nil, allowing the new narrow path to enlarge competitively with the old well-established one. Most such diversions are short.

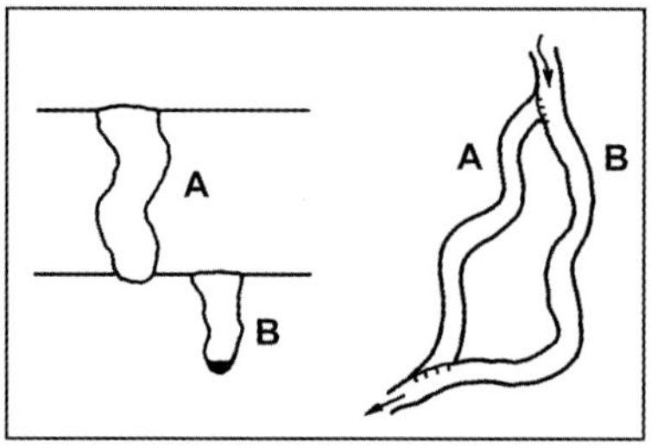

Fig. 6. Stream diversion in an entrenching vadose canyon. The lower loop illustrates nearly zero breakthrough time along the guiding bedding-plane parting, as shown by the minimal entrenchment of segment A below the parting. This is a common occurrence, especially in well-bedded carbonates, but it is not a general rule.

As the land surface becomes dissected by erosion, patterns of groundwater recharge change. The few large initial water sources may be divided into many smaller ones. Vadose water must travel increasingly greater distances to reach the water table, and extensive complexes of vadose canyons and shafts can form. The resulting pattern of active cave streams is much denser than that of the original surface drainage. Growing dolines eventually form a continuous karst surface. Eventually the only surface streams that retain their flow are the main entrenched rivers and the ephemeral upstream ends of sinking streams.

THE FINAL STAGE

As the land erodes, the surface intersects underlying cave passages, segmenting them and eventually destroying them entirely. Evidence for the cave may persist for a while as a canyon-like feature or a rubbly zone of collapsed blocks. This final episode in the life of a cave passage usually occupies tens of thousands or even hundreds of thousands of years. However, newer passages continue to develop where the soluble rock extends to lower elevations. In dipping carbonate rocks, new areas of rock are uncovered by erosion at about the same rate as they are eroded away in the up-dip areas. This process ends when the entire soluble rock in the cave region is eroded away.

REFERENCES

Audra, P., 1994: Karsts alpins; genčse des grands réseaux souterrains. Karstologia Mémoirs 5, 279 p.

Berner, R.A., & J.W. Morse, 1974: Dissolution kinetics of calcium carbonate in sea water; IV: Theory of calcite dissolution. American Journal of Science 274, 108-134.

Bischoff, J.L., R. Julia, W.C. Shanks, & R.J. Rosenbauer, 1994: Karstification without carbonic acid; bedrock dissolution by gypsum-driven dedolomitization. Geology 22/11, 995-998.

Böcker, T., 1969: Karstic water research in Hungary. International Association of Scientific Hydrology Bulletin 14, 4-12.

Bray, L.G., 1972: Preliminary oxidation studies on some cave waters from south Wales. Cave Research Group of Great Britain, Transactions 14, 59-66.

Clemens, T., D. Hückinghaus, M. Sauter, R. Liedl, & G. Teutsch, 1997: Simulation of the evolution of maze caves. 12th International Congress of Speleology, and 6th Conference on Limestone Hydrology and Fissured Media, La Chaux-de-Fonds, Switzerland, 2, 65-68.

Coward, J.M.H., 1975: Paleohydrology and streamflow simulation of three karst basins in southeastern West Virginia. Ph.D. dissertation, McMaster University, Hamilton, Ontario, Canada, 394 p.

Davies, W.E., 1960: Origin of caves in folded limestone. National Speleological Society Bulletin 22/1, 5-18.

Dreybrodt, W., 1990: The role of dissolution kinetics in the development of karst aquifers in limestone: a model simulation of karst evolution. Journal of Geology 98/5, 639-655.

Dreybrodt, W., 1996: Principles of early development of karst conduits under natural and man-made conditions revealed by mathematical analysis of numerical models. Water Resources Research 32, 2923-2935.

Dreybrodt, W., & J. Siemers, 2000: Cave evolution on two-dimensional networks of primary fractures in limestone. In A. Klimchouk, D.C. Ford, A.N. Palmer, and W. Dreybrodt (eds.), Speleogenesis – evolution of karst aquifers. Huntsville, Ala., National Speleological Society, 201-211.

Ewers, R.O., 1982: Cavern development in the dimensions of length and breadth. Ph.D. dissertation, McMaster University, Hamilton, Ontario, 398 p.

Ford, D.C., 1971: Geologic structure and a new explanation of limestone cavern genesis. Transactions of the Cave Research Group of Great Britain 13/2, 81-94.

Ford, D.C., & R.O. Ewers, 1978: The development of limestone cave systems in the dimensions of length and depth. Canadian Journal of Earth Sciences 15, 1783-1798.

Ford, D.C., S.-E. Lauritzen, & R.O. Ewers, 2000: Modeling of initiation and propagation of single conduits and networks. In A. Klimchouk, D.C. Ford, A.N. Palmer, & W. Dreybrodt (eds.), Speleogenesis – evolution of karst aquifers. Huntsville, Ala., National Speleological Society, 175-183.

Freeze, R.A., & J.A. Cherry, 1979: Groundwater. Englewood Cliffs, N.J., Prentice-Hall, 604 p.

Gabrovšek, F., 2000: Evolution of early karst aquifers: from simple principles to complex models. Postojna, Slovenia, Inštitut za razusjivanje krasa ZRC SAZU, 150 p.

Granger, D.E., D. Fabel, & A.N. Palmer, 2001: Pliocene-Pleistocene incision of the Green River, Kentucky, determined from radioactive decay of ^{26}Al and ^{10}Be in Mammoth Cave sediments. Geological Society of America Bulletin 113/7, 825-836.

Häuselmann, P., P.-Y. Jeannin, & M. Monbaron, 2001: Relation between alpine paleogeography and cave genesis: the case of the cave system of Sieben Hengste (Berne, Switzerland). In P. Häuselmann & M. Monbaron (eds.), Cave genesis in the Alpine belt. Proceedings of 1st Workshop for Alpine Speleogenesis, University of Fribourg, Fribourg, Switzerland, 115-123.

High, C.J., 1970: Aspects of the solutional erosion of limestone, with special consideration of lithological factors. Ph.D. dissertation, University of Bristol, Bristol, U.K., 228 p.

Klimchouk, A., & D.C. Ford, 2000: Types of karst and evolution of hydrogeologic setting. In A. Klimchouk, D.C. Ford, A.N. Palmer, & W. Dreybrodt (eds.), Speleogenesis – Evolution of karst aquifers. Huntsville, Ala., National Speleological Society, 45-53.

Lowe, D.J., 1992: The origin of limestone caverns: an inception horizon hypothesis. Ph.D. dissertation, Manchester Polytechnic University, U.K., 512 p.

Meiman, J., & C. Groves, 1997: Magnitude/frequency analysis of cave passage development in the Central Kentucky Karst. Proceedings of 6th Annual Mammoth Cave National Park Science Conference, 11-13.

Mylroie, J.E., 1977: Speleogenesis and karst geomorphology of the Helderberg Plateau, Schoharie County, New York. Ph.D. dissertation, Rensselaer Polytechnic Institute, Troy, N.Y., 336 p.

Palmer, A.N., 1972: Dynamics of a sinking stream system, Onesquethaw Cave, New York. National Speleological Society Bulletin 34/3, 89-110.

Palmer, A.N., 1975: The origin of maze caves. National Speleological Society Bulletin 37, 56-76.

Palmer, A.N., 1984: Recent trends in karst geomorphology. Journal of Geological Education 32, 247-253.

Palmer, A.N., 1988: Solutional enlargement of openings in the vicinity of hydraulic structures in karst regions. Dublin, Ohio, Proceedings of 2nd Conference on Environmental Problems in Karst Terranes, Association of Ground Water Scientists and Engineers, 3-13.

Palmer, A.N., 1989: Geomorphic history of the Mammoth Cave System. In W.B. White and E.L. White (eds.), Karst Hydrology: concepts from the Mammoth Cave area. New York, Van Nostrand Reinhold, p. 317-363.

Palmer, A.N., 1991: Origin and morphology of limestone caves. Geological Society of America Bulletin 103, 1-21.

Palmer, A.N., 1996: Rates of limestone dissolution and calcite precipitation in cave streams of east-central New York State [abstract]: Northeast Section, Geological Society of America 28/3, 89.

Palmer, A.N., 2000: Maze origin by diffuse recharge through overlying formations. In A. Klimchouk, D. Ford, A. Palmer, & W. Dreybrodt (eds.), Speleogenesis - evolution of karst aquifers. Huntsville, Ala., National Speleological Society, 387-390.

Palmer, A.N., 2001: Dynamics of cave development by allogenic water. Acta Carsologica 30/2, 13-32.

Plummer, L.N., & T.M.L. Wigley, 1976: The dissolution of calcite in CO_2-saturated solutions at 25° C and 1 atmosphere total pressure. Geochimica et Cosmochimica Acta 40, 191-202.

Plummer, L.N., T.M.L. Wigley, & D.L. Parkhurst, 1978: The kinetics of calcite dissolution in CO_2-water systems at 5° to 60° C and 0.0 to 1.0 atm CO_2. American Journal of Science 278, 179-216.

Smith, D.I., & M.D. Newson, 1974: The dynamics of solutional and mechanical erosion in limestone catchments on the Mendip Hills, Somerset. In K.J. Gregory & D.E. Walling (eds.), Fluvial processes in instrumented watersheds. Institute of British Geographers, Special Publication 6, 155-167.

Sweeting, M.M., 1950: Erosion cycles and limestone caverns in the Ingleborough District of Yorkshire. Geographical Journal 124, 63-78.

Vaughan, K., C. Groves, & J. Meiman, 1998: Carbonate chemistry of interstitial fluids within cave stream sediments [abstract]. Conference on Carbon Cycling in Karst, International Geological Correlation Program, Western Kentucky University, Bowling Green, Kentucky, 33-34.

White, W.B., 1977: Role of solution kinetics in the development of karst aquifers. In J.S. Tolson & F.L. Doyle (eds.), Karst hydrogeology. International Association of Hydrogeologists, 12th Memoirs, 503-517.

White, W.B., 1984: Rate processes: chemical kinetics and kast landform development. In R.G. LaFleur (ed.), Groundwater as a geomorphic agent. Boston, Allen and Unwin, 227-248.

Address
Department of Earth Sciences
State University of New York, Oneonta, NY 13820, USA
E-mail: Palmeran@snyoneva.cc.oneonta.edu

Evolution of Karst: From Prekarst to Cessation, 61-96, Ljubljana-Postojna 2002

EVOLUTION OF KARST IN EVAPORATES

ALEXANDER KLIMCHOUK

Abstract

Karst that develops in evaporites has many features in common with carbonate karst but it also has significant peculiarities imposed by specific features of evaporite geology and of dissolution chemistry and kinetics. Evaporites widely support different types of intrastratal karst but exposed types of karst (open and denuded) are less common than in carbonate rocks. Dissolution of gypsum and salt is commonly assumed to be diffusion controlled, i.e. the dissolution rates follow a linear first-order law. Dissolution rates in gypsum are generally much higher than that of calcite and no switch to a high-order kinetics occurs until solution is saturated (or it occurs very close to saturation, as some recent studies suggest). This causes important consequences in speleogenesis and evolution of karst in evaporites. The early conduit development is extremely sensitive to variations of boundary conditions such as fissure aperture widths and hydraulic gradient, so that the range of variations, within which speleogenetic initiation of conduits occurs either almost immediately or unfeasibly long, is very narrow. The two opposed consequences are that evaporite karst either readily commences in deep-seated intrastratal settings or evaporite deposits survive through geologically long times of burial having experienced almost no karstification. Evolution of geomorphic and hydrogeologic settings is therefore very important in the development of evaporite karst. Moreover, changes due to human activity may induce and dramatically intensify evaporite karst. Initiation of tight long lateral flow paths through evaporites is virtually impossible. In deep-seated (confined) settings conduit development can occur in gypsum where: 1) there is transverse circulation across the gypsum between the underlying and overlying aquifers in a multi-storey artesian system or, 2) there is lateral contact circulation along the bottom of the gypsum unit, with natural convection replacement of saturated water with aggressive water. Depending on structural and hydrogeologic conditions either maze caves or discrete conduits can form in deep-seated settings. In case of transverse speleogenesis, there is a specific hydrogeologic mechanism that suppresses speleogenetic competition in a fissure network and favours to development of maze patterns in gypsum. Deep-seated karstification of salt probably never occurs inside the rock but contact karstification along sides of along the bottom can be significant, commonly driven by natural convection. In open gypsum karsts conduit development is extremely competitive and it occurs only where fissures are wide enough, or hydraulic gradients are steep enough, to support undersaturated flow though fissures. Linear or crudely branching caves form, rapidly adjusting to the contemporary geomorphic setting and available recharge. Vertical pipes or pits form in the vadose zone where gapping tectonic fissures exist. No deep phreatic zone develops in open gypsum karsts. In denuded (former intrastratal) karsts the presence of inherited solution porosity and wide fissures allows further conduit development to widely occur in both vadose and phreatic zones. The direct field measurements of dissolution rates in gypsum show dramatic variations between different environments (flow components in an aquifer system), many of which are also characterised by high rate variations with respect to time. Overall karst denudation rates determined from mass balance differ much between types of karst according to characteristic hydrogeologic conditions and inheritance in

karstification. The highest karstification intensity is commonly found in subjacent karsts, which also presents most severe subsidence hazard, and the lowest intensity is in deeply drained entrenched karst. Exposed settings do not necessarily imply high overall denudation.
Keywords: *karst evolution, evaporite karst, gypsum karst and speleogenesis, artesian speleogenesis, karst denudation.*

INTRODUCTION

Interaction between groundwater flow and dissolution processes provides mechanisms that drive the development of karst. Karst develops where solutional enlargement of fissures, bedding planes or interconnected pores creates highly permeable conduits in rocks. Hence, the mechanisms of karst development are essentially speleogenetic. The nature of these mechanisms lies in mutual enhancement of flow rate and solutional conduit enlargement. Hydrogeologic and speleogenetic aspects are therefore invariably important in karst evolution, whereas geomorphologic aspects evolve in certain types of karst where the karst development manifests itself to the surface.

The overall evolution of karst is expressed through successive change of karst types, determined by the general geological/hydrogeological evolution, from deposition through burial to reemergence and subsequent denudation and exposure (Klimchouk & Ford 2000). Repeated burial may interrupt the cycle, with paleokarst formed in result, and subsequent uplifts may rejuvenate the development of karst.

Karst that develops in evaporites has many features in common with carbonate karst but it also has significant peculiarities imposed by specific features of evaporite geology and of dissolution chemistry and kinetics.

EVAPORITE KARST

Evaporite deposits form in seas, lagoons and internal-drainage lakes where more water leave the basin by evaporation than enters the basin as rainfall, surface and subsurface flow. Evaporite rocks are inorganic in origin and form by chemical precipitation in concentrating water solution. Common evaporite rocks include gypsum, anhydrite and halite, although other rarer salts can be of local karst significance. Carbonates such as calcite and dolomite can also be of evaporitic origin, although the term "evaporite karst" is normally employed to denote karst in the above mentioned more soluble salts, most commonly in gypsum and salt.

As evaporites are much more soluble than carbonates, they are less common in outcrops. This is one of the reasons why evaporite karst had been considered of limited significance and received relatively little appreciation in the past in the mainstream of karstology. However, it has been increasingly realised during recent decades that karst processes in evaporites such as gypsum and salt operate extensively when they occur below various types of cover beds within the upper few hundreds meters of sedimentary sequences, the settings widely distributed over continents.

Gypsum karst is the most important in terms of its global distribution and practical significance and it has received an adequate appreciation in the international karst literature during the recent decade (see the "Gypsum Karst of the World", Klimchouk et al. 1996 and Proceedings of a Symposium on "Evaporite Karst: Processes, Landforms, Examples, and Impacts", published as a special issue of Carbonates & Evaporites 12, 1997). Gypsum karst will be given a particular attention in this paper in the context of karst evolution.

GEOLOGICAL OCCURRENCE OF EVAPORITE ROCK

Evaporite rocks underlie about 25 % of continental surface (Ford & Williams 1989) although this fraction is greater in some large regions: 35-40 % for the territory of the contiguous United States (Johnson 1997) and for the former Soviet Union. In the latter region sulphate rocks alone underlie about 5 million km^2 (Gorbunova 1977). Major epochs of evaporite deposition occurred in the late Cambrian, the Permian, the Jurassic, and the Miocene. Lesser but still significant episodes took place in the Silurian, the Devonian, the Triassic and the Eocene. Ancient platform and basin-wide evaporite or combined evaporite/carbonate/siliciclastic sequences often reach thicknesses exceeding 1000 m and extend laterally across huge areas. Evaporite accumulation in the Quaternary was of incompatibly lesser scale. Penecontemporaneous evaporites are most often found in the arid and semiarid zones, in the circumtropical desert areas that lie between 15 and 45° north and south of equator. Modern evaporite accumulation locally occurs outside the major desert belts, in the strictly continental environment, in high mountain deserts, in the rain shadows of high mountain ranges and in polar and circumpolar regions.

A variety of depositional settings, in which evaporites can form ranges from deep water to subaerial and lacustrine, so the mode of occurrence of evaporites and association of lithofacies are quite diverse. The picture is further complicated by the fact that evaporites are most susceptible to recrystallization, dissolution and replacement among common rocks. Gypsum deposited at the shallow subsurface is converted to anhydrite with burial, and back to gypsum as the sulphate re-enters the meteoric realm and is washed in cooler and fresher fluids. In contrast to the common belief, the volume expansion during hydration of anhydrite does not always occur, however the topic is very controversial and poorly understood.

Sulphates and halides widely occur as rare to frequent interbeds in sequences containing carbonates and siliciclastic sediments but also as massive beds. Individual beds of gypsum with thicknesses 10-40 m are rather common although sequences of them may be as thick as 200-300 m. Massive salt units may reach more than 1000 m in thickness. When massive deposits of salt are buried by denser strata, it flows upward and approaches the surface as diapirs or dikes. Diapirs may rise from original salt bodies occurring beneath several thousands meters of cover strata, disrupting and deforming them.

Capability of gypsum of flow due to plasticity, and its negative effect upon groundwater circulation and speleogenesis in gypsum, was commonly overstated in the past. It seems that fluidity of gypsum may be substantial only where the rock mass is thick and fairly uniform. In contrast, numerous observations in gypsum caves, particularly in those occurring in intrastratal settings, prove that open fissures and cavities in gypsum beds can survive through lengthy periods of geologic time. Where gypsum beds are sandwiched between hard rocks such as limestones, dolomites or sandstones, or where intercalated beds of other lithologies occur within a thick gypsum sequence, reinforcement effect of the adjacent or intercalated beds prevents the plastic flow of gypsum and sealing of discontinuities.

EVAPORITE FORMATIONS OCCUR IN VARIOUS MODERN TECTONIC SETTINGS

In cratonic regions sulphate rocks lie horizontally or at gentle angles (1-5°) and extend over large areas ranging up to several tens of thousands of km^2. Intrastratal gypsum karst is by far the most dominant type in this setting. A block-fault structure is common but the vertical displacement between blocks is small. Gypsum beds are commonly well fissured, with fissure networks rather uniformly distributed in area, but in the vertical section fissures are often confined to certain, often multiple, horizons. Cratonic regions are characterized by a stable tectonic regime and rather slow groundwater circulation. Karst development in deep-seated settings may occur over prolonged time spans but it is

Fig. 1. Geomorphic features of different types of gypsum karst. ***1:*** *Extremely dense honeycomb-like surface karstification in the open (denuded?) karst at 2900 m in the Bajsuntau range, Central Asia, Uzbekistan.* ***2:*** *Open karst in Sicily, Italy. Surface and underground karst features are scarce and highly localized, not counting for solution microforms.* ***3:*** *Scarcely fractured gypsum surface with solution microforms, open karst in Sicily, Italy.* ***4:*** *Open karst of Sorbas, South Spain: Solution doline associated with a vertical shaft. Note a scarcely fractured surface of the gypsum massif.* ***5:*** *A patch of denuded gypsum within the entrenched karst zone in the Western Ukraine: dolines formed after vertical solution pipes and outlet cupolas of an artesian cave.* ***6:*** *Deeply drained entrenched karst in the Western Ukraine, the outcrop near the entrance to the Krystalna Cave 24 km long.* ***7:*** *Subjacent karst in the Western Ukraine, the Kryvsky gypsum quarry. A sump at the center is a focus of the drawdawn cone caused by groundwater withdrawal at the rates of 700-800 m^3/hour. Before quarrying, the water table had been positioned some 2 m below the gypsum top. The drop of the water table has opened the 92 km long maze of Zoloushka Cave.* ***8:*** *A collapse doline in an interfluve massif in the entrenched karst zone of the Western Ukraine, the entrance to the Ozerna Cave, 117 km long maze.* ***9:*** *Entrenched karst in the pre-Ural region, Russia. Gypsum outcrops by the Iren River near the 5.6 km long Kungurskaya Ice Cave.* ***10:*** *The surface of an interfluve massif in the entrenched karst of the pre-Ural, dotted with collapse dolines.*
Photo: *1 - by LaVenta Association; photos 2-7 - by A.Klimchouk; photos 9-10 - by V.Andrejchuk.*

intensified when uplifts bring sulphate beds into relatively shallow subsurface. Caves are numerous and varying in origin and morphology from extensive artesian mazes to linear stream tubes. Deep-seated cavities are frequently encountered by mines and boreholes.

In foredeeps the strata are usually gently folded or occur monoclinally with dips of up to 10-20°. Beds are often broken by faults and displaced, so that their lateral continuity is disrupted. Areas of outcrop and near-surface occurrence of gypsum are linear, elongated along the strike of the foredeep or local fold structures. Sulphates tend to plunge down-dip to considerable depths below non-karstifiable sequences toward the adjacent folded system. The karst that develops is limited in area but it is often quite intense. In deep-seated confined aquifers circulation and karstification are intensified where upward discharge is focused along tectonic faults that disrupt regional flow and the continuity of major aquifers. Large and deep collapse features are common in this structural setting.

In orogenic regions, stratiform sulphate formations are folded to varying extent, with beds commonly becoming vertical or even overturned. Areas where gypsum is at shallow occurrence or outcrop to the surface are rather small. Because of very thick sulphate sequences are not common and the overall strength of gypsum is lower than that of carbonates, and because of rapid dissolution on exposed gypsum surfaces, large gypsum massifs, comparable to carbonate massifs in extension, vertical magnitude and the thickness of vadose zone, cannot form in mountains. Patches of gypsum can be variably fractured, depending on local tectonic and geomorphic position and history. Some gypsum outcrops exhibit extremely high intensity of surface karstification, expressed as honeycomb or badland landscapes (e.g. in the North Caucasus and Central Asia, Fig 1A), whereas others are relatively massive and display scarce point-recharge forms such as dolines and blind valleys (e.g. in the Apennines, Sicily and south of Spain). Recrystallization and other processes that occur on exposed gypsum masses often seal fissures. Caves are usually numerous but rather small. They appear to form in adjustment with the contemporaneous geomorphic system and tend to be linear, directly connecting recharge and discharge points. Data about deep-seated karst in orogenic settings are scarce.

EQUILIBRIUM CHEMISTRY AND DISSOLUTION KINETICS

Chemical equilibrium and reaction kinetics for evaporite dissolution differ from that of calcite, imposing some important consequences for speleogenesis and evolution of karst.

Under normal conditions, the solubility of gypsum is roughly four orders of magnitude greater that the solubility of calcite, although when calcite dissolves in the presence of CO_2 this difference decreases to 10-30 times. The solubility of salt is 140 times greater than the solubility of gypsum. There are several chemical and physical factors, especially important in deep-seated settings, which can considerably enhance or renew gypsum solubility:

- Presence of other salts in groundwaters, which enhances the ionic strength of the solution (Shternina 1949)
- Anaerobic reduction of sulphates in the presence of organic matter (Kaveev 1963; Klimchouk 1994; Kolodij 1991, Palmer 1995, Turyshev 1965)

- Dedolomitization of intercalated dolomite layers (Bischoff et al. 1994; Palmer 1995; Raines & Dewers 1997; Stankevich 1970)
- Pressure applied to the rock (Manikhin 1966; Pechorkin 1986)

From the perspective of speleogenesis and karst evolution, the main difference of dissolution processes between carbonates and evaporates lies in kinetics. The process of dissolution in carbonate rocks is controlled mainly by the reaction at the rock surface. Experimental studies of dissolution rates for limestones (for summary see Palmer 1991 and Dreybrodt & Eisenlohr 2000) suggest that relatively high rates drop rapidly when a solution reaches about 70-90 % of saturation because kinetic reaction changes its order in this region. In contrast, dissolution of the common evaporates such as gypsum and salt is controlled mainly by diffusion across a boundary layer. Dissolution rates are generally much higher than that of calcite. It is well established that the dissolution reactions of gypsum and salt follow the first-order rate law and no switch to a high-order kinetics occurs until solution is nearly saturated. Although recently a switch to the high-order kinetics at the region of very high saturation (>95 %) was reported from experiments with samples of natural gypsum (Jeschke et al. 2001), the difference in dissolution kinetics between calcite and gypsum remains very substantial.

The ultimate importance of dissolution kinetics for speleogenesis in carbonates has been well appreciated (White 1977; Palmer 1981, 1984, 1991), and this laid a basis for the modern in-depth understanding of speleogenetic mechanisms. This understanding emerged during last few decades from mathematical modelling that coupled flow and dissolution processes, either for single conduits (Dreybrodt 1990, 1992, 1996; Groves & Howard 1994a; Palmer 1988, 1991, 1998) or for conduit network (Groves & Howard, 1994b; Howard & Groves 1995; Gabrovsek 2000; Gabrovsek & Dreybrodt 2000). Clemens et al. (1996) simulated conduit development in a karst aquifer using a model that couples diffuse flow in the fissure system to conduit flow in a pipe network. These studies established important regularities and mechanisms of early evolution of conduits and their patterns by revealing how enlargement rates in conduits relate to their aperture widths, discharge, flow distance and water chemistry. In case of gypsum, it was shown on the conceptual level that the specificity of the dissolution kinetics imposes some limitations and peculiar features on the early evolution of conduits (Klimchouk 1996a; 2000c). These peculiarities appear to be an extreme and hence more obvious illustration of the general regularities of speleogenesis inferred from conceptual and numerical modelling of early conduit growth in limestones. The study of speleogenesis in gypsum is therefore a useful playground for testing validity and limitations of general speleogenetic concepts. Recently, the conceptual models of speleogenesis in gypsum have been largely justified by mathematical modelling (Birk 2002).

THE PROBLEM OF RAPID DISSOLUTION KINETICS IN THE EARLY CONDUIT EVOLUTION

High dissolution rates and linear kinetics impose one of the major limitations on speleogenesis in gypsum, and even more so in salt. The problem was recognised for limestones too, and a solution was found in a kinetic switch from rapid (linear) dissolution to slow (non-linear) dissolution:

> *"The origin of a limestone cave hangs by a delicate thread. For it to reach traversable size in a feasible time, dissolution must be rapid; yet too high a rate is detrimental to its early development. In a narrow crack, rapid dissolution would cause near-saturation after only a few centimeters of flow, and enlargement downstream would be negligible. Only slow, uniform dissolution can initiate long passages. This paradox is reconciled by the abrupt slowing of dissolution while the water is still far from saturation. This transition... is expressed by the increase in reaction order (n)."* (Palmer 1991, 8).

It is this transition that makes it possible speleogenetic initiation and early development of narrow flow paths in limestones. In the light of the above, the initiation of flow paths in gypsum within reasonable geological times seems to be virtually impossible in many settings common for limestone caves. Unlike calcite, in case of gypsum dissolution no change of kinetic order occurs with an increase in concentration (or it occurs at the region too close to saturation to have pronounced speleogenetic significance). Hence slow but uniform enlargement throughout long flow paths in gypsum cannot occur to initiate them. This limitation is even more obvious in salt.

It is evident from the above consideration that caves in gypsum could form only where gradients are high enough, or initial widths of openings are large enough, and/or where flow distances are short enough to enable establishment of the breakthrough conditions (when solution remains undersaturated all the way through an initial flow path) within a feasible time.

Another peculiar feature of speleogenesis in evaporites is that, because of the diffusion control of dissolution rates, they are highly dependent on hydrodynamic conditions. Unlike in limestone, dissolution rates in gypsum and salt are proportional to flow velocity. Before the breakthrough event, disparity of dissolution rates between alternative flow paths in gypsum seems to be greater than in limestone. After breakthrough, enlargement rates increase much more dramatically in gypsum that in limestone, where the solutional growth rate is limited by the level of 100-1000 μm/a due to restrictions imposed by the reaction-controlled kinetics. These differences determine that speleogenetic competition between alternative flow paths is much stronger in gypsum that in limestone, and that a "runaway" development of the favourable paths is even more pronounced.

Maze caves, which origin and hydrologic function presented a specific interpretive problem with regard to speleogenesis in limestones (Palmer 1975), should be even more problematic in gypsum due to the above reasons. This statement is contrary to the popular view that gypsum is more favourable for maze caves to form. This view is erroneous, being based simply on a celebrity of the great gypsum mazes of the Western Ukraine. In both lithologies, specific hydrogeological mechanisms are operative in some settings to suppress speleogenetic competition and allow for the development of maze patterns.

UNCONFINED VERSUS CONFINED SETTINGS, LATERAL VERSUS TRANSVERSE SPELEOGENESIS

Confined (artesian) settings had been long viewed as unfavourable for speleogenesis because commonly implied lateral flow through a soluble unit can hardly support any considerable conduit development along inherently long flow paths. This is even more the problem in gypsum because of dissolution is controlled by diffusion and occurs at high rates. A new impetus to the artesian speleogenetic theory has been given by recognition of the importance of cross-formational hydraulic communication between aquifers in multi-storey artesian systems (Klimchouk 1997a; 2000a). Soluble units may initially serve as separating beds between "normal" aquifers but they change their hydrogeologic role to karstic aquifers in the course of speleogenetic evolution. Most of recharge to soluble beds comes from adjacent aquifers rather than from marginal recharge areas.

A concept of *transverse speleogenesis* has been suggested (Klimchouk 2000a) to describe conduit development in multi-storey artesian systems, particularly in a soluble bed sandwiched between aquifers, and to contrast this case to the development that occurs along the long dimension of fissures which are lateral relative to bedding, the common case in unconfined settings (in the phreatic zone or at the water table).

Transverse speleogenesis denotes conduit development driven by the vertical hydraulic gradient across a layered sequence so that flow is directed transversely relative to bedding and the long dimensions of intrastratal fissures (Fig. 2). In this concept, of primary importance are low Q/L ratios in flow paths (*sensu* Palmer, 1984; 1991) and the fact that laterally extensive resultant cave systems do not necessarily imply long conduits *sensu* flow paths.

The speleogenetic importance of the distinction between phreatic unconfined and confined settings has not been fully recognized in karst science until recently. Within unconfined phreatic conditions, the resistance of the path itself, particularly of its narrowest part, governs discharge through a developing flow path. Discharge increases with the growth of the conduit before and, more dramatically, after breakthrough until the amount of available recharge begins to limit the flow (Palmer 1984; 1991). Because of the positive feedback loop, enlargement rates increase accordingly. In confined conditions as described above the evolution of transverse conduits is different after breakthrough (Klimchouk, 2000a). The rapid conduit growth quickly diminishes the hydraulic head gradient between the aquifers. As the hydraulic resistance of the conduit becomes smaller than that of the aquifers, discharge through the conduit is controlled by the hydraulic conductivity of the aquifers and by the boundary conditions, but no longer by the diameter of the conduit. Unless and until the boundary conditions change, the flow rate and the enlargement rate in the conduit remain constant at some level. The positive feedback loop is no longer the determinant of conduit development. Moreover, alternative transverse proto-conduits do not languish their growth, as is would happen in unconfined settings after the breakthrough in the winner conduit. Because the vertical hydraulic head gradient between the aquifers is still maintained, although diminished, at some lateral distance apart from the successful conduit, alternative conduits continue to grow and eventually reach the breakthrough, either to the downgradient aquifer or laterally to the conduit that had been "broken through" earlier. This is a hydrogeologic mech-

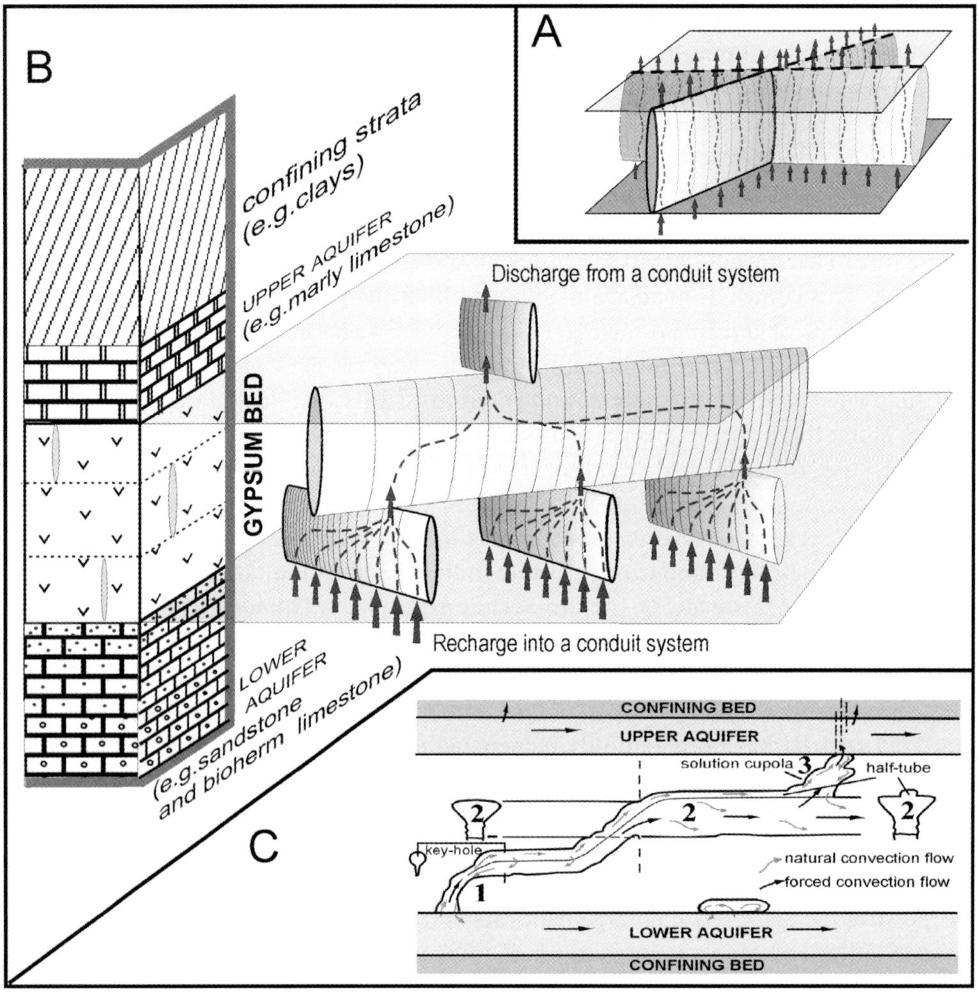

Fig. 2. Diagrams illustrating the concept of artesian transverse speleogenesis, fissure arrangement and cross-formation flow. A: a simple case of joints crossing a bed for the while thickness; B: Fissure networks in multiple levels, the case of the Western Ukraine; C: flow pattern and morphogenetic features in a mature transverse system in the Western Ukraine. Numbers indicate: 1 = feeding conduits, 2 = master passages, 3 = outlet cupolas (from Klimchouk, 2000b).

anism that suppresses the speleogenetic competition in a network and favours to development of maze patterns in confined settings (Klimchouk 2000a). Validity of the above interpretation of transverse speleogenesis has been recently proven for gypsum by numerical modelling (Birk 2002). The latter work provided important contribution to further understanding of transverse speleogenesis in gypsum.

The resultant effect of differences between confined and unconfined speleogenesis is well illustrated by comparison of morphometric parameters that characterise cave porosity. Analysis of samples of typical caves formed in the respective settings shows that average passage network density (the ratio of the cave length to the area of the cave field, km/km^2) for unconfined settings is 16.6 km/km^2 while this parameter for confined settings is 177.6 km/km^2. Average areal coverage (a fraction of the area of the cave field occupied by passages in a plan view) for unconfined speleogenesis is 6.16 % while it is 32.8 % for confined speleogenesis. Cave porosity (a fraction of the volume of a cave block, occupied by mapped cavities) for unconfined speleogenesis is 0.54 % but it is an order of magnitude greater for confined speleogenesis (5.4 %). In fact, these differences are even more pronounced for gypsum. The sample that illustrates unconfined speleogenesis consists of solely limestone caves whereas gypsum caves of this type tend to be much less dendritic. The sample that illustrates confined speleogenesis consists of both limestone and gypsum caves.

SPELEOGENETIC INITIATION OF CONDUITS IN GYPSUM IN THE CONTEXT OF GENERAL GEOLOGICAL EVOLUTION

Fast linear dissolution kinetics in evaporites causes much higher sensitivity of the early conduit development to variations of hydrogeologic and structural factors, as compared to speleogenesis in limestones. In the numerical modelling performed by Birk (2002), the sensitivity analysis of the breakthrough time in response to change of various parameters has shown that the most influential hydraulic parameter is the initial conduit diameter and (although to a lesser degree) the hydraulic gradient. Among chemical parameters, the mass transfer coefficient is shown to impose quite powerful control, whereas the undersaturation of inflow with respect to gypsum being of lesser importance.

The results of numerical modelling show that breakthrough conditions are attained either almost instantaneously or virtually never in a geologically reasonable timescale. For instance, under chosen set up of the model simulating artesian transverse speleogenesis in gypsum (Birk, 2002), the breakthrough occurs almost instantaneously if the initial conduit diameter is increased from 0.4 to 0.5 mm (by 20 %) but if the diameter is reduced to 0.34 mm (i.e. by 15 %) no breakthrough is observed within one million years. Doubling the factor of leakage through the confining layer, that increases the hydraulic gradient across the gypsum, reduces the breakthrough times by several orders of magnitude.

As compared to carbonate karst, in evaporites the range of variations in the most influential boundary conditions, within which the breakthrough time changes from "virtually never" to "almost immediately", is quite narrow. This has at least two opposed consequences for karst evolution:

1) Paradoxically, but it is the fast dissolution kinetics that favours preservation of evaporites in some settings in the course the geological evolution. Many evaporite deposits survive through geologically long time of burial having experienced almost no karstification. This happen if changing boundary conditions remain outside of the abovementioned narrow range that allow reasonably fast breakthrough. However, karstification will ultimately evolve with exposure, when at least some fissures become wide open due to unloading and stress release, although the specific of dissolution kinetics will cause highly selective development.

2) Changes in the boundary conditions that occur in the coarse of geomorphic and hydrogeologic evolution of confined systems may encompass the "critical" range. In this case conduit porosity in evaporites readily evolve under deep-seated settings. The evolutionary changes of settings are therefore particularly important for artesian speleogenesis in evaporites (Klimchouk, 2000a). Furthermore, the results of the numerical modelling of an artesian transverse speleogenesis suggest that gradual changes in the boundary conditions favour to the initiation of alternative conduits, i.e. to more pervasive karstification (Birk, 2002). Another important conclusion is that the degree of karstification is generally higher if breakthrough times are larger.

The most important, from the perspective of artesian speleogenesis, changes that affect the early conduit development, are 1) incision of rivers into the confining layer, resulting in the increase of the hydraulic gradient between aquifers in the multi-storey artesian system due to decrease of both the river head and thickness of the confining layer, and 2) increase of fissure aperture widths and the formation of new fissures in response to neotectonic movements and unloading. Both kinds of changes commonly occur during uplift and denudation, so it is quite likely that they induce breakthrough events in the deep-seated gypsum at some stage *en route* to the surface.

Human activity such as groundwater abstraction, dam construction and opencast mining that reduces thickness of the confining layer or completely breaches confinement, also results in the increase of hydraulic gradients, the changes that may bring the boundary conditions into the "critical" range and induce rapid breakthrough and consequent runaway development of conduits. Environmental problems due to human-induced karstification in evaporite karsts are commonly even more severe and "unexpected" than in limestone karst regions (Klimchouk & Andrejchuk 1996b).

GENETIC TYPES OF CAVES IN GYPSUM

In confined settings conduit development can occur at least in two hydrogeologic situations: 1) where there is transverse circulation through the gypsum unit between the underlying and overlying aquifers in a multi-story artesian system; or 2) where the gypsum is underlain by a major aquifer and there is lateral contact circulation along the bottom of the gypsum unit.

The former situation generates maze caves where uniformly distributed laterally extensive fissure networks exist in the gypsum. For maze patterns to evolve, it is important that there are systematic heterogeneities in the vertical conductivity across the gypsum, e.g. the effects of poor vertical connectivity between the superimposed multi-level networks (see Fig. 2A) or of the low conductivity of the upper aquifer (Birk 2002; Klimchouk 2000a). Figure 3A depicts schematically this case. In contrast, discrete conduits will form where structural conditions favour that some preferable flow paths effectively capture transverse flow between the aquifers. The extreme case is where the otherwise low-fissured gypsum is disrupted only by prominent tectonic fractures (Fig.3B).

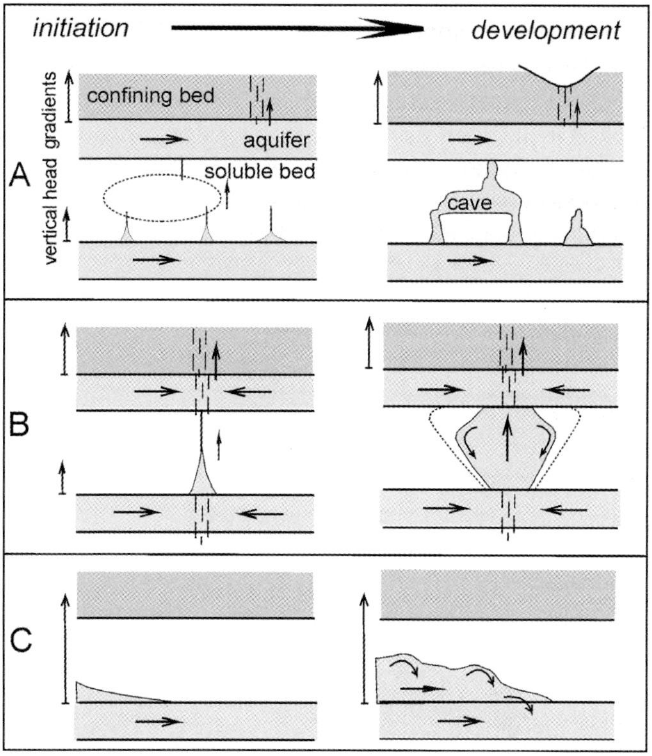

Fig. 3. Initiation and development of conduits and cavities under artesian conditions (from Klimchouk, 2000a): A = transverse speleogenesis along uniformly distributed common fissures, B = transverse speleogenesis along a single prominent fissure across an otherwise low-fissured bed, C = lateral contact speleogenesis in the case of a massive impermeable bed driven by natural convection.

In the second situation (Fig.3C) cavities may form where the gypsum is underlain by a major aquifer and there is lateral contact circulation along the bottom of the gypsum unit. Fissures or other irregularities at the lower contact of gypsum may induce cave development even if no transverse flow across the unit is allowed at all due to large thickness of massive gypsum or presence of the impervious underlying bed. Initial enlargement at the bottom then continues via natural convection mechanism, with replacement of saturated water by buoyant currents of less dense water and removal of solute load through the underlying aquifer (Kempe 1996).

In the saturated zone of unconfined aquifers speleogenetic initiation of initial tight flow paths in gypsum is very slow and it may not occur within reasonable geological time. Conduit development occurs only where fissures are wide enough, or hydraulic gradients are steep enough, to support undersaturated flow though fissures. Because of peculiarities of the dissolution kinetics, speleogenesis in gypsum in unconfined conditions is extremely competitive. Linear or crudely branching caves form, rapidly adjusting to the contemporary geomorphic setting and available recharge (Fig.4). In the unsaturated vadose zone, cave development concentrates along vertical percolation paths and free stream courses. As vadose percolation and free-flowing waters in gypsum quickly reach near-saturation, most of the dissolution occurs where water first enters the gypsum, or is focused along streambeds during high-flow events. No deep phreatic karstification develops in unconfined gypsum aquifers.

When high conductivity has developed in gypsum (or inherited) and water table establishes, rapid enlargement of existing conduits occurs at the water table, particularly if periodic backflooding takes place from the adjacent river. In more stable conditions, such as in the interiors of massifs, extensive horizontal notching may develop at the level of the water table, promoted by chemical stratification in the water.

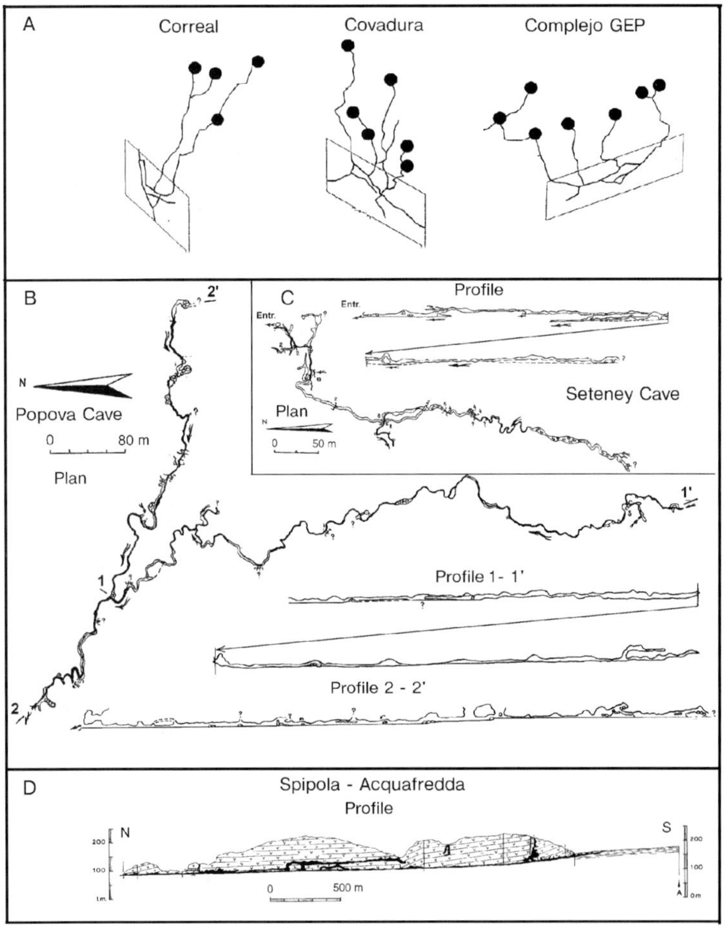

Fig. 4. Typical sketches, plans, and profiles of gypsum "through caves": A = in the open karst of Sorbas, Spain; feeding dolines are indicated by dots (from Calaforra 1998); B and C = in the open karst of the Ekeptze-Gadyk massif, North Caucasus, Russia (from Ostapenko 2001); D = the Spipola-Acquafredda system in the open karst of the Emilia Romagna, Italy (from Grimandi 1987).

In highly soluble aquifers such as gypsum and salts, gravitational separation of water due to density differences and natural convection circulation play an important role in speleogenesis (Frumkin 2000; Kempe 1972; Klimchouk 1997b). Dissolution due to natural convection is important in cave initiation and development under confined conditions where recharge to gypsum by low-density fresh water occurs from below. The mechanism of the initiation and development of cavities along the lower contact of gypsum has been mentioned above. In addition, in the transverse speleogenesis scheme directed (un-looped) buoyant currents operate in mature conduit system because less-dense water tends to occupy the uppermost available space (Fig.2B). This accounts for the formation of keyhole sections and ceiling half-tubes under artesian conditions. Under shallow phreatic conditions, characteristic tip-down triangular cross sections develop, with flat ceilings ("Laugdecke" in German), combined with inclined facets. Their formation is attributed to natural convection (Kempe, 1972).

Mechanisms and preferential styles of speleogenesis change in coarse of karst evolution. This is illustrated by Table 1, which attempts to relate genetic types of gypsum caves to the stages of the evolution of karst. The general evolution trend in the karst development is considered in the section below.

***Table 1**: Genetic classification of caves in gypsum, with relation to karst types and speleogenetic settings*

TYPE OF KARST	SPELEOGENETIC SETTINGS			CHARACTERISTICS OF SOLUTION CAVES
	Hydro-geological conditions **principal** *complementary*	Initial permeability (before speleo-genesis)	Flow pattern through gypsum and type of recharge	
Intrastratal deep-seated	**confined (artesian)**	Fairly homogeneous generally low	Ascending transverse flow across gypsum unit sandwiched between aquiferous beds, with possible lateral component; dispersed basal recharge	1. Rectilinear 2-D or 3-D (multi-storey) mazes
		Very hetero-geneous, generally low to negligible, locally high	Ascending transverse flow; localized basal recharge	2. Discrete voids, commonly large and isometric
			Lateral flow in the underlyingaq-uifer, natural convection "cells"in gypsum	-"-
Intrastratal subjacent	**confined, phreatic, water table,** *vadose*	Heterogeneous: low to high	Ascending flow with possible considerable lateral compo-nent; localized or dispersed basal recharge	Continuing develop-ment of types 1 and 2
			Descending flow with considerable lateral compo-nent; localized recharge from coverbeds and via superficial sink points; possible backflood-ing from nearby rivers	3. "Through caves": linear or crudely dendritic in plan, horizontal, inclined, or step-like in profile
Intrastratal entrenched				Lateral enlargement of inherited artesian cavesat the water table

TYPE OF KARST	SPELEOGENETIC SETTINGS			CHARACTERISTICS OF SOLUTION CAVES
	Hydro-geological conditions **principal** *complementary*	Initial permeability (before speleo-genesis)	Flow pattern through gypsum and type of recharge	
Intrastratal entrenched	*phreatic,* **water table, vadose**	Heterogeneous: low to high	Descending flow with possible considerable lateral component; localized recharge from coverbeds and via superficial sink points; possible backflooding from nearby rivers	Continuing or newly started development of type 3 caves 4. Vertical pipes developing downwards from the top of the gypsum Lateral enlargement of inherited artesian caves at the water table
Exposed denuded	*phreatic,* **water tablevadose**	Heterogeneous: generally high	Descending flow with possible considerable lateral component; localized recharge via superficial sink points; possible backflooding from nearby rivers	Continuing or newly started development of type 3 caves Vertical pits at sink points Lateral enlargement of all cavities at the water table
Exposed open	*phreatic* **water tablevadose**	Heterogeneous: generally low	Descending flow with possible considerable lateral component; localized recharge via superficial sink points; possible backflooding from nearby rivers	Development of type 3 caves Vertical pits at sink points Lateral enlargement of all cavities at the water table

EVOLUTION OF EVAPORITE KARST IN TERMS OF KARST TYPES

Types of karst are viewed as sustainable stages of karst evolution, marked by characteristic settings and styles of karst development (Klimchouk 1996b; Klimchouk & Ford 2000). The most important conditions which determine settings are: hydrostratigraphic arrangement, an overall circulation pattern, recharge modes and recharge/discharge configuration, structural prerequisites for groundwater flow and speleogenesis, groundwater chemistry and degree of inheritance from earlier conditions. Combinations of these conditions and respective intrinsic mechanisms of karst development appear to change considerably and regularly between types of karst.

Fig. 5 outlines the entire sequence of karst settings (stages) that a given formation could experience during its history. In actuality no individual karst is known that displays all of its possible sequence but many have experienced several of the stages. The

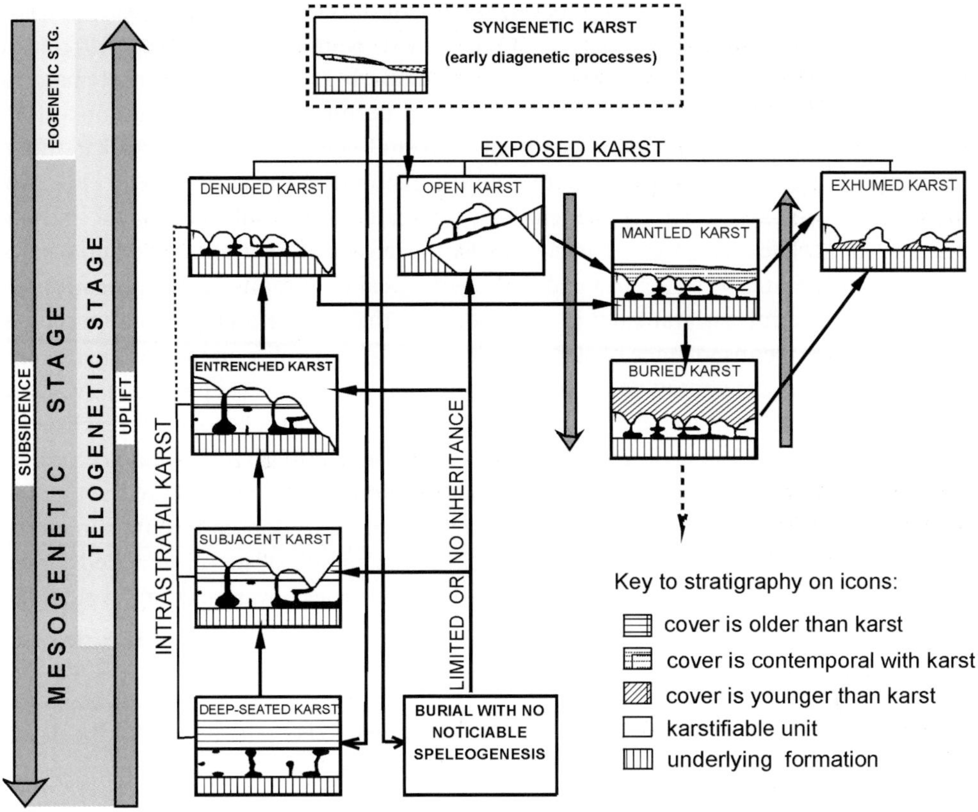

Fig. 5. Evolutionary types of karst (from Klimchouk & Ford 2000).

karst may be completely destroyed, along with its host formation, within the same stage that its development commenced: this is more common for karst in sulphates than in carbonates and is the fate of most salt. In contrast, carbonate karst can survive through several cycles of burial-exposure, being repeatedly fossilised and rejuvenated.

Syngenetic karst in evaporites is limited in extension. Syngenetic karst in ancient evaporites, probably common in continental settings, is sometimes recognized among paleokarst features. Modern syngenetic karst is limited to salt lakes where it develops in the bottom evaporite deposits of various compositions. It is quite prominent in many salt lakes in the pre-Caspian lowland and the Altay region in Russia, in Central Asia, China (the Qinghai-Xizang plateau, Tibet), Middle East and the United States. In addition to various sculpturing forms on freshly exposed surfaces, created by rainfalls and inflowing surface streams, the most typical karst features are "windows", "cauldrons" and holes in the bottom salt masses created by currents of groundwaters rising from aquifers that occur below lakes.

Intrastratal karst is considered to develop within rocks already buried by younger strata, where karstification is later than deposition of the cover rocks (Quinlan 1978). It is by far the predominant karst type in evaporite rocks. Karstification may be initiated at any of the stages of intrastratal development, particularly at some stage en route back to the surface. Where evaporites are encased in poorly permeable clays or shales in a stratified sequence, intrastratal karst may not develop at all and any considerable karstification will not commence until the soluble unit is exposed to the surface. The entire sequence of intrastratal karst types includes deep-seated karst, subjacent karst and entrenched karst. The respective settings differ by the degree of separation of soluble units from the surface and by structural and hydrogeological conditions for karstification.

Deep-seated intrastratal karst is not evident at the surface and the soluble rock is not exposed. As a consequence of standard denudation and uplift on the continents, the deep-seated rocks are shifted with time into progressively shallower positions. At some stage *en route* to the surface, erosional incision into the cover rocks locally breaches the hydrogeological confinement and the aquifer is brought into direct hydraulic connection with the surface (subjacent karst). Further incision causes inversion of the circulation system, drastic changes in recharge-discharge configuration and establishment of the vadose zone and water table conditions within the karstic strata (entrenched karst). At this point the soluble unit is still capped by insoluble rocks over most of the area, the situation that protects gypsum karst from rapid destruction and favour to preserve relict artesian features. Progressive denudation may eventually expose the rock entirely (denuded karst).

Hydraulic and hydrochemical conditions are shown to be quite potent for the development of *deep-seated* evaporite karst in many situations, particularly where gypsum beds are sandwiched between insoluble but pervious formations and where vertical cross-formational hydraulic communication is favoured (Klimchouk 1997a; 2000a). Transverse hydraulic communication, usually ascending, establishes between the two surrounding aquifers across the gypsum unit, giving rise to maze cave patterns provided proper structural prerequisites exist. Outstanding examples are the giant gypsum maze caves in the Western Ukraine, presently relict where entrenched, which include 5 longest gypsum caves in the world totalling in about 500 km of passages (Klimchouk, 2000b). In the deep-seated karst zone of this region (zone IV in Fig.6A) extensive cave systems still develop under confined settings through the transverse circulation mechanism, as evidenced by hydrochemical studies and numerous data from exploratory drilling. This mechanism is unlikely to occur in salt because salt beds of small to moderate thicknesses are not common and because in this rock intrastratal joints readily seal under lithostatic pressure.

Another mechanism of deep-seated karstification, described in the previous section, involves solution attack from the underlying aquifer to the bottom of the evaporite unit and natural convection circulation cells. It may create vast isolated cavities in both gypsum and salt even without forced flow through a soluble unit. Documented examples in gypsum include numerous giant Schlotten-type caves in the Zechstein (the Upper Permian) gypsum in Germany (Kempe 1996, see Fig.7D). Cavities of this type in both

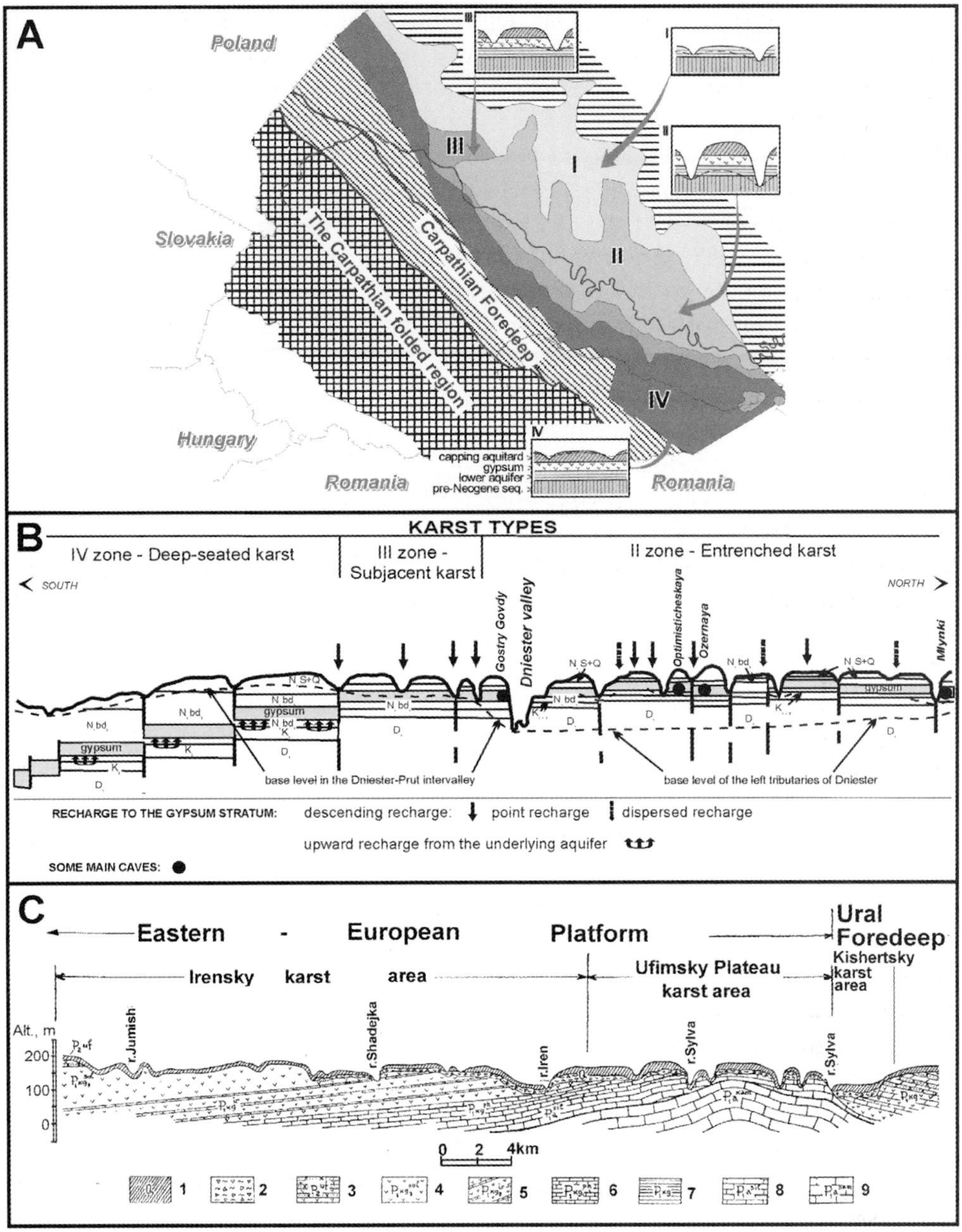

Fig. 6. Zonality of different types of intrastratal gypsum karst in the Western Ukraine (A = schematic map, B = profile) and in the pre-Ural, Russia (C = profile, from Andrejchuk, 1996). See text for explanation. Legend to the profile C: 1 = alluvial and fluvioglacial terrace deposits, 2 = karst-collapse breccia, 3, 5, 7, = terrigenous rocks of different ages, 4 = sulphate rocks (gypsum and anhydrite with limestone and dolomite beds), 6 = carbonate rocks (limestone and dolomite), 8 = reef limestone, 9 = silicified limestone.

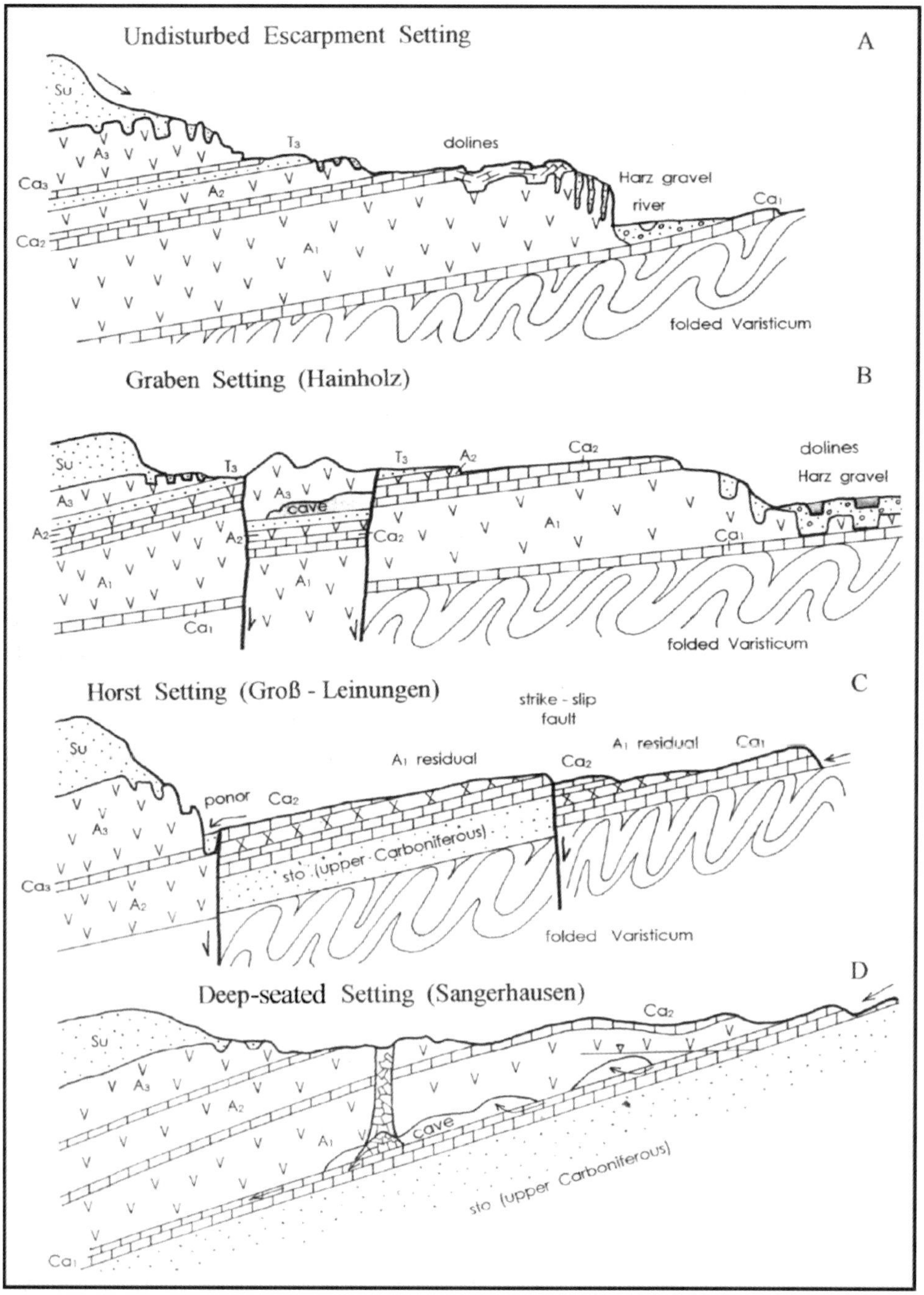

Fig. 7. Profiles illustrating different types of intrastratal gypsum karst at the fringes of the South Harz, Germany, determined by geomorphic and tectonic situation. Denuded, entrenched, and subjacent settings pass into the original deep-seated settings to the left side of the profiles (from Kempe 1996).

gypsum and salt are responsible for initiation of vertical breakdown structures called "breccia pipes", which are abundant in many deep-seated evaporite karsts as illustrated by studies from the United States, Canada, China and Russia. They have diameters ranging from few tens to over 100 m (sometimes even measuring in kilometers) and propagate by upward stopping from the depth as great as 1200 m. When several closely spaced breccia pipes reach the surface, they may give rise to large (measuring from several hundreds meters to tens of kilometers) often elongated depressions termed solution subsidence troughs or solution-induced depositional basins (Quinlan et al. 1986). The later term applies if the rate of sedimentation is approximately equal to the rate of subsidence and depressions do not have strong topographic expression. Such features are reported in Canada, the southwestern United States, Russia (in the Ural and Siberia) and in other regions.

Deep-seated dissolution of salt units may occur from a side if they laterally contact with thick aquifers of active groundwater circulation. The process continuing through lengthy geological times causes the dissolution front to recede along the margins of great intrastratal salt deposits, leaving some of the largest solution-induced basins such as those in the Prairie Provinces of Canada and Montana (the Devonian salt) or in the south of the Siberian platform of Russia (the Cambrian to Devonian sulphates and salt). Prolonged dissolution of evaporite beds may lead to a total destruction of host evaporite beds yet within the deep-seated stage, and to the formation of aerially extensive brecciated horizons and disconformities, the common ultimate result of intrastratal evaporite karst (Klimchouk & Andrejchuk 1996a; Friedman 1997). Disruption and brecciation of the carbonate beds due to intrastratal dissolution of underlying sulphates or salt is an important factor of the deep-seated carbonate karstification in the complex interbedded sequences. Another important factor is the chemical interaction between carbonates and sulphates, which can greatly increase the solubility of dolomite, gypsum, and anhydrite (Palmer 1995).

Reemergence of evaporite units to the relatively shallow subsurface due to uplifts and erosion and respective thinning of the overburden cause an increase of hydraulic gradients and local breaching of the hydrogeological confinement by incision into cover rocks and locally into the evaporites. This signifies the stage of *subjacent karst*, marked by drastic changes of various conditions including structural (lithostatic unloading and increase of fissure widths and frequency), hydrodynamic (activation of upward discharge and overall groundwater circulation) and geomorphologic (formation of karstic features at the surface). Dissolution rates in evaporates increase dramatically owing to either increased flow through previously initiated (*sensu* breakthrough conditions) conduits or because breakthrough conditions have been reached rapidly due to the increase of gradients and opening of fissures. Restrictions on discharge, imposed by hydraulic resistance of the upper aquifer and the confining bed progressively diminish during the stage of intrastratal karst. Where vadose zone and water-table conditions locally establish, dissolution is localized either at underground streambeds or at the water table. The latter localization leads to horizontal notching, a typical feature in many gypsum caves. Geomorphic expression of karst includes collapse and subsidence dolines (which form extensively at this stage due to intense widening of caves, decrease of hydraulic heads and removal of buoyant support), dry valleys and a range of karst hydrology phenomena such as rising springs, sinking streams and ponors, etc. In highly karstified places coalescence of collapse and subsidence dolines gives rise to large karst depressions.

Subjacent karst in evaporites is well expressed if considerable karstification is inherited from the preceding deep-seated stage. Examples include the gypsum karsts of the margins of the Zechstein basin in Europe (north-eastern England and northern and eastern Germany), the south-western part of the Western Ukrainian gypsum karst, the Pre-Ural karst areas and the Pinega region of Russia, the gypsum karst areas in the margins of the Permian Basin (eastern New Mexico, north-central Texas and western Oklahoma) and the predominantly salt karst of northeast Arizona in the United States. Because subjacent karst settings are transitional in terms of karst evolution, respective karst areas are commonly adjacent to the areas of deep-seated or entrenched karst, or to both. They frequently present distinct engineering problems, pronounced subsidence hazard in particular.

Further erosional incision leads to the situation where major valleys largely or entirely drain sub-horizontal gypsum beds that remain capped with protective insoluble beds. This is *entrenched karst*, common with gypsum but rarely occurring with salt as most of medium to thin salt beds in the stratified sequences get dissolved during the previous stages. Entrenched gypsum karst may have relict artesian caves well preserved and accessible (as in the Western Ukraine, the Paris basin in France and the pre-Ural region in Russia) and support the formation of contemporary caves, mainly single-conduit or crudely branching caves that develop from swallow holes on the interfluves towards outlets in the valleys slopes (as in the western Oklahoma in the US and the Pinega and Kuloj regions in Russia). A characteristic feature of many entrenched gypsum karsts are vertical solution pipes ("chimneys" or "comins") that develop from the overlying bed, commonly limestone or dolomite, across the gypsum in places of focused percolation. Their density may be as great as 300 per km^2. Upward stoping of vertical pipes through the overburden is the main mechanism of collapse and subsidence formation in entrenched karst. Large dolines with swallow holes (ponors) form on interfluves where collapse features can capture focused surface flow; dry valleys are also common. Underground streams fed by ponors are commonly superimposed on relict maze networks. A range of forms associated with unloading processes and gravity open fissures may extensively develop within strips of denuded gypsum along river escarpments. They commonly include karst trenches and densely packed funnel-like dolines associated with vertical pipes.

Denuded and open karst types (soluble rocks are exposed to the surface) are characterised by similarly exposed geomorphic settings but differ in their previous karstification history. Whereas denuded karst is former intrastratal karst, which may have considerable karstification inherited from deep-seated and intrastratal stages, open karst represents the "pure line" of exposed development, that is karst evolved solely when the soluble rock has been exposed to the surface, with limited or no inheritance.

Denuded gypsum karst is commonly found as small patches or strips within or adjacent to entrenched karst areas, where protective rocks are entirely removed, or as small to moderately sized isolated massifs in folded regions. However, in cratonic regions denuded gypsum karst may have substantial spread where regionally important thick sequences of sulphate rocks are brought to the denudation surface. Many surface karst landforms evolve due to unroofing of caves that had formed on preceding stages of intrastratal development, so that a style of surface karst landscapes depends on the type of the preceding speleogenesis. Large dolines and cirques form where isolated large caves had been the predominant style of speleogenesis, e.g. in the South Harz region, Germany. Other areas may display a very high intensity of surface karstification because of unroofing of artesian caves or densely packed vertical solution pipes (patches of denuded gypsum in the Western Ukraine, Pinega and pre-Ural regions of Russia). The extensive Gypsum Plain in the west Texas and New Mexico, USA probably also falls into denuded karst category. Contemporary cave development favours linear or crudely dendritic caves to form that commonly convey sank streams. Where exposed sulphate sequence has considerable thickness and a major aquifer at the base, focused upward discharge through the gypsum gives rise to large cavities, collapse features, upwelling springs and karst lakes.

Open karsts are found mainly in arid and semi-arid environments and where evaporite units are quite thick. It differs from denuded karst in that no substantial karstification had occurred until exposure, the common case if evaporite unit had been encased into impervious sediments. Examples of the open gypsum karst include many areas in Spain, the Central Apennines and Sicily in Italy, the Diebel Nador and Oranais areas in the eastern and western Algeria, the Ar Rabitat/Bir area in the northwest Libya, the central and northern Somalia and some mountain areas in the Alps (France and Switzerland), North Caucasus (Russia) and in Central Asia (Uzbekistan and Tajikistan). Many other smaller areas are associated with gypsum caprocks of salt diapirs.

Speleogenesis in open gypsum karst depends on the existence of fissures wide enough for breakthrough to occur quickly. Strongly competitive development in unconfined settings, imposed by the specificity of gypsum dissolution, is evidenced by the fact that linear or crudely branching caves overwhelmingly predominate in open gypsum karsts. Passages quickly develop to accommodate the highest possible discharge, and water table or vadose conditions are established. Surface karst features display a wide range of solutional sculpturing forms. Solution dolines are normally scarce, associated with highly transmissive conduits, i.e. caves. Where the vadose zone is thick, vertical pitches form in gypsum caves, e.g. in the Central Apennines and Sicily in Italy, Sorbas and Vallada in Spain and the Gypsum Plain in the US. As a rule, no epikarst is formed in open gypsum karst. Instead, a kind of sealing crust develops on exposed gypsum in arid climates due to recrystallization in the uppermost layers.

Open karsts in salt are small, most commonly associated with rising diapiric structures. Where extrusion of salt is rapid, diapirs may support dramatic landscapes of local relief up to 900 m with large salt cliffs, deep circus, crevasses and canyons and various karst features. Outstanding examples are the Khodja-Mumyn and Khodja-Sartis salt domes in the Pamir mountains of Tajikistan and salt domes in the Zagros mountains of Iran. In the Tajikistan sites surface karst features are particularly abundant and include numerous dolines, deep collapses and shafts, various karren forms, pinnacles and giant salt "mushrooms" capped with gypsum residual boulders. Caves are also numerous, formed by captured ephemeral streams. They commonly begin with vertical shafts and continue as single sub-horizontal passages, leading to outlets at base level. The largest known assemblage of salt caves is found in Mount Sedom near the Dead Sea, Israel, where over one hundred caves with >20 km of passages have been surveyed, including the largest known salt cave Malham Cave explored for 5.7 km (Frumkin, 2000). Other considerable caves in salt are known from Spain, Romania, Hungary, Russia, Algeria and Chile.

Mantled karst is that covered by significant thicknesses of unconsolidated sediments that accumulate as the karst develops. Most common are soils formed from the insoluble residuum of impure limestones and dolostones (locally derived or "autochthonous" deposits). Mantled karst should be distinguished from *buried karst*, which is a complete infilling and burial by later materials such as transgressive marine sediments, reducing or (usually) terminating the karstification.

Gypsum karst that has been mantled by glacial till, now partly exposed along the rims of river cliffs, is described for Manitoba, Ontario and the Maritime Provinces of Canada (Ford, 1997) and for Pinega and the North Dvina regions of Russia. Characteristic landforms include densely packed small suffosion dolines, vertical solution pipes, pinnacles, shlotten and karst trenches. Similar topographies are known above river cliffs in some entrenched gypsum karsts (pre-Ural, Russia). Where gypsum is deeply mantled, as in other parts of the above-mentioned regions, karst features are represented mainly by collapse dolines and by small caves where the gypsum is locally entrenched by post-glacial rivers. Areas within the fluvial plains in the Erbo Basin in Saragoza region, Spain, exemplify the alluviated subtype of mantled gypsum karst.

REGIONAL EXAMPLES OF GYPSUM KARST EVOLUTION: INHERITANCE AND ZONALITY

In many regions the depth of occurrence of soluble units, the extent of denudational uncovering and depth of erosional entrenchment change regularly in some directions as result of differentiated vertical neotectonic movements and regional geological structure. Such regions commonly display a range of karst types that evolved with time from one to another as the successive stages of karst development. Respective zones change to each other more or less gradually in the direction of regional deep; they are commonly elongated according to the strike of major tectonic structures. Examples of evaporite karsts where successive types of karst are present together are very instructive for an understanding of karst evolution because different stages can be observed simultaneously within the same formation and aquifer. The three examples given below, the gypsum karsts of the Western Ukraine, pre-Ural (Russia) and South Harz (Germany), differ much in general geologic settings and history but they all illustrate well the role of inheritance in evolution of gypsum karst.

Gypsum karst of the Western Ukraine develops on the outskirt of the East-European Platform along the boundary with the Carpathian Foredeep. Evolution of the platform margin since the late Miocene, when the gypsum strata had been deposited and buried, resulted in differentiation of the platform edge into the four zones (Fig. 6A). In the first zone the gypsum strata has been completely removed by denudation. The zones II, III and IV represent the distinct types of intrastratal gypsum karst: entrenched, subjacent and deep-seated. Patches of denuded karst locally intersperse within the zone II. Evolution of karst was guided by differential neotectonic movements on the edge of the platform and entrenchment of the major valley of the Dniester river during the late Pliocene and Pleistocene.

Across the entire region, confined hydrogeological settings with constrained discharge and sluggish flow prevailed during most of the Pliocene, when slow speleogenetic initiation occurred. By the late Pliocene to early Pleistocene the early, shallow and wide fluvial plain of the pre-Dniester had formed. This initial erosional entrenchment into the confining clays increased leakage across them, and activated the transverse groundwater flow within the artesian system. The "great cave belt" of the Podols'ky region lies entirely within the limits of this ancient pre-Dniester Valley.

Since the end of the early Pleistocene and through Pleistocene, continued uplifts in the part of the region resulted in incision of the Dniester and its northern sub-parallel tributaries into the confining sequence and the Miocene aquifer system. Also, the northern tributaries of the Dniester incised rapidly, dividing the area north of the Dniester into elongated sub-parallel interfluve massifs. This led to a substantial acceleration of groundwater circulation within the Miocene artesian system, breaching of its artesian confinement and evolvement of the subjacent karst zone. With further deepening of the valleys during the late Pleistocene, conditions of entrenched karst established along Dniester and to the north of it, and artesian caves became entirely fossilized.

In the area to the south-southwest of the Dniester Valley, overall uplift rates during most of the Pleistocene were much slower, and there was a relative subsidence of some tectonic blocks adjacent to the foredeep. This imposed slow rates of speleogenetic development, which activated only during the late Pleistocene in some of the more uplifted blocks entrenched by the Prut Valley (Zoloushka and Bukovinka caves). The zone of subjacent karst has formed and encompassed the whole Prut-Dniester interfluve, where karst hydrologic features are diverse and contemporary linear caves are developing now. The zone of deep-seated karst has further shrunken toward the foredeep. In the northwestern part of the gypsum belt this zone is wider. Deep-seated speleogenetic processes, induced by incision of valleys into the confining sequence, had been active there in the middle Pleistocene but later uplift has slowed down and even turned into subsidence. Speleogenesis has been reactivated recently in response to Holocene uplifts and increasing anthropogenic impacts such as opencast quarrying and groundwater abstraction.

Intense maze-like karstification of the gypsum strata in this zone is evidenced by borehole hydrogeological data.

On the eastern margin of the huge Eastern-European platform, in Russia, the remarkable pre-Ural region of gypsum karst is located, stretching north to south along the Ural foredeep. The sulphate thickness of the early Permian age with dolomite interbeds is widespread at the platform margin, being underlain by the thick carbonates of the Artynsky formation. Gypsum karst in the Pre-Ural region has undergone complex multicycle development since Mesozoic, when continental conditions established. During this period repeated cycles of uplift and subsidence have occurred, resulted in the presence of several generations of paleokarst features, including thick horizons of karst breccia in the upper part of gypsiferous sequence (Andrejchuk 1996). Contemporaneous karstification in gypsum occurs in deep-seated, subjacent, entrenched and denuded settings, within respective zones that change one to another from west to east according to the depth of the occurrence of sulphates and erosional entrenchment (Fig.6C).

The large structural swell of the Ufimsky Plateau represents the area where sulphates were entirely removed and only karst breccia horizons left, the ultimate result of the intrastratal gypsum karst. On the western slope of the Ufimsky swell various members of the gently sloping sulphate sequence of the total thickness of 100-150 m outcrop or lie close to the surface within the 20-40 km wide belt. Areas of deep-seated, subjacent, entrenched and mantled karst change to each other; the mantle being represented mainly by karst breccia. Development of karst is very intense, with underground and surface features being remarkably diversified owing to dense fissuring, varying (according to the depth and proximity of erosional valleys) hydrogeological conditions and high degree of inheritance from the earlier karst stages. Moreover, upward discharge from the underlying aquifer of the Artynsky carbonate rocks to the lowermost unit of the gypsiferous strata occurs along the strike of the swell flank, adding to the diversity of hydrological settings and karst features. The narrow gypsum area on the eastern slope of the Ufimsky Plateau, which stretches north to south along the foredeep, represents subjacent karst type, which turns into deep-seated karst further to east. Karstification is extremely intense due to massive upward discharge through the gypsum from the underlying carbonates.

In Germany, thick evaporite deposits of Zechstein (the Upper Permian) extend across much of the country at considerable depths. These deposits contain salt (up to 600 m) and several sulphate units of considerable thicknesses separated and underlain by carbonate beds. Sulphates are found close to the surface in several locations but it is the area south of the Harz and Kyffhauser where gypsum karst is best studied and is represented by several types (Kempe 1996).

In deep-seated settings transverse circulation across the gypsum beds was not able to initiate conduits because of considerable thickness of sulphates and scarce and closed fissuring. Instead, caves developed at the base of the lowermost gypsum bed, where aggressive water from the basal aquifer attacked gypsum from below. Caves developed via natural convection mechanism, with return and outflow of saturated water through the underlying aquifer. Depending on local structural pre-requisites, either maze-like ramifying patterns of large passages and rooms form, or giant isolated rooms up to 60 m high. More that 100 such caves were intercepted by mines over the centuries in the Mansfeld and Sangerhausen areas in depths ranging from 70 to 400 m.

Upon the uplift of the South Harz Mountains as a reaction to the Alpine orogeny the Zechstein has outcropped at the fringes. Settings of subjacent, entrenched and denuded karst have evolved along the marginal outcrops, depending on local tectonic and geomorphic situation (Fig.7). Inheritance of deep-seated karstification has played an important role in the subsequent development. Giant artesian cavities gave rise to large and deep collapse sinkholes (locally termed Erdfalle), some of them later evolved into karst cirques. Some of the inherited caves were considerably modified by dissolution at the water table or by sank streams. Because of inherited karstification, considerable losses of concentrated surface flow occur when rivers reach the Zechstein barrier, with this water reappearing as large springs some kilometres away from their points of sinking. Unloading along steep gypsum escarpments has opened fissures and allowed contemporary linear caves to form, as well as karst trenches at the surface.

DISSOLUTION OF GYPSUM FROM FIELD OBSERVATIONS AND INTENSITY OF KARSTIFICATION IN TYPES OF KARST

Based on lab experiments and numerical modelling studies, typical dissolution rates of gypsum under breakthrough conditions are commonly assumed to be of the order of 10.000 μm/a (Jeschke, Vosbeck & Dreybrodt 2000; James 1992; Dreybrodt, Romanov & Gabrovsek 2001), while rates for limestone fall within 100 - 1,000 μm/a (Buhmann & Dreybrodt 1985; Palmer 1991). However, dissolution is unevenly distributed within a karst system. Because of gypsum dissolution rates are sensitive to many factors, which are greatly variable in space and time, actual rates vary within wide ranges. Regime field measurements are useful to appreciate variability of dissolution rates under natural conditions, to obtain and compare typical rates for most common situations of solvent-rock interaction, different flow components and hydrogeological conditions. Reasonable generalization of rates in gypsum is possible owing to extensive field measurements made during recent decades in Italy, Spain and the Western Ukraine (Klimchouk et al. 1996; Klimchouk & Aksem, in press). Dissolution rates in field conditions are obtained by measuring gypsum tablet weight loss (TWL) and by micro-erosion measurements of lowering surface (MEM). More than 3,000 measurements by MEM have been made in Italy in 17 locations during 1993-1995, 22 MEM stations and 13 TWL stations have been operated in Spain during 1991-1994 and 644 measurements have been made by the TWL method in 53 stations in the Western Ukraine during 1984-1992.

Individual measurements are site-specific and are integrating the actual rates for certain (varied) periods of measurement, so that a caution is needed in attempting the extrapolation of results in space and time (Ford & Williams 1989). The field results show dramatic variations of dissolution rates between different environments (flow components in an aquifer system), many of which are also characterised by high rate variations with respect to time. Typical rates reported below (Table 2) are based on generalization of average values from many locations representative for certain environments (situations).

Table 2: *Typical gypsum dissolution rates from direct measurements (TWL and MEM) in various natural environments*

Situations of gypsum dissolution	Relative overall circulation intensity (flow velocity)	Typical dissolution rates, μm/yr
1. Direct exposure to precipitation	variable, generally moderate	100 - 1,000
2a. Surface streams	high to very high	10,000 - 500,000
2b. Cave streams	variable, moderate to high	1,000 - 200,000
3. Localized vertical percolation (trickles and drips in solution pipes)	variable, moderate to high	100 - 10,000
4a. Saturated zone of an unconfined aquifer in gypsum, bulk water body	sluggish	100 - 1,000
4b. Saturated zone of an unconfined aquifer in gypsum, the upper layer of water	moderate	1,000 - 10,000
5a. Confined aquifer in gypsum, sluggish circulation	sluggish	100 - 1,000
5b. Confined aquifer in gypsum, active circulation	moderate	1,000 - 10,000
5c. Confined aquifer, the water entering the gypsum from the lower aquifer and buoyant currents within the bulk water body, rising from the feeding channels	moderate	1,000- 20,000

Dissolution rates on surfaces directly exposed to precipitation show strong dependence on the amount of precipitation. They can be generalized as being within the range of 100 - 1,000 μm/a. For this situation, the Italian dataset allows a comparison between the MEM-based rates for gypsum and limestone, with gypsum dissolution being 30 to 70 times faster. This broadly agrees with theoretical considerations.

The rates in localized surface streams (rivers), derived from the literature (Pecherkin 1969; James 1992) and from our measurements in some spring flows in the Western Ukraine, fall within a range of 10,000 - 500,000 μm/a. Such high and variable rates reflect close dependence of gypsum dissolution on hydrodynamic conditions.

Dissolution rates in the unsaturated vadose zone, generated by free-running streams in caves and by focused vertical percolation (trickles and drips creating characteristic vertical dissolution pipes), are hard to measure and generalise due to great variations in flow regime and chemistry. The rates in streams fall within a range of 1,000 - 200,000 μm/a, in percolation trickles - within 100 - 10,000 μm/a.

Dissolution in the saturated zone of unconfined gypsum aquifers is uneven due to the distinct density (chemical) stratification of water. Measurements in flow pools, which represent the aquifer in maze caves of the Western Ukraine, suggest that dissolution rates in the more aggressive and dynamic uppermost (up to depth of 10 cm) layer of water are typically within a range of 1,000 - 10,000 μm/a, roughly an order of magnitude greater than the rates in the bulk water below (typically 100 - 1,000 μm/a). Greater dissolution rates in the uppermost layer of the saturated zone are responsible for intense widening of passages (horizontal notching) at the water table and for mushroom-like shape of the rocks projecting from the water in pools, common morphological effects in gypsum caves.

Dissolution rates in confined settings have been studied in the Western Ukraine, where in the zone IV an upward transverse circulation pattern in the layered artesian system is responsible for the formation of maze caves in the gypsum layer that separates two original aquifers. Aggressive water comes into the gypsum from the underlying sandy-carbonate aquifer. Such settings are typical for many deep-seated gypsum karsts. The degree of karstification in the study region corresponds to the post-breakthrough conditions, to the late artesian stage of speleogenesis, with maze conduit systems already well developed. Transverse circulation across the gypsum is generally rather sluggish, although in the areas of deep opencast mining it is considerably intensified owing to local breaching of artesian confinement and massive groundwater abstraction.

In both cases dissolution rates are unevenly distributed within the gypsum bed, depending upon spatial position in the cave/fissure system relative to the overall upward circulation pattern and internal currents structure in the conduit system. Currents directly rising from feeding channels in the conduit system may keep rather high dissolution capacity even in the middle part of the gypsum, while the bulk water in fissures and "stagnant" conduits is much less aggressive. Dissolution rates in the "middle" of the gypsum strata are typically within 100 - 1,000 μm/a under natural (sluggish) conditions but they rise about an order of magnitude (1000 - 10,000 μm/a) under active circulation. Dissolution is more intense (up to 20,000 μm/a) in the water that enters the gypsum from the lower aquifer and in buoyant currents that rise from the feeding channels within the bulk aquifer body.

Dissolution rates considered above should not be confused with the solutional denudation, which is determined from solute load data derived from chemographs and hydrographs, related to a basin area. It is commonly expressed as the amount of rock dissolved per unit area of a basin (proportion of a basin underlain by soluble rocks) per unit time ($m^3/km^2/a$), or as an equivalent thickness of rock removed per unit time across a horizontal surface (mm/Ka). Numerical values in these units are the same, as well as values in μm/a used above for dissolution rates from direct measurements.

There are many problems involved in methodology of field measurements of dissolution and their interpretation, for thorough reviews refer to Ford & Williams (1989) and White (2000). Published denudation rates for limestones are abundant; most of them are obtained from exposed karsts and fall within the range of 1 - 100 mm/Ka. Denudation rates from gypsum karsts are scarce; some available values are given in Table 3. It is evident from the table that denudation rates from gypsum karsts are broadly an order of magnitude greater that from limestone karsts.

Table 3: ***Selected solutional denudation rates in gypsum karst areas***

Location, source of information	Type of karst	Denudation rate, mm/Ka
Limestone karsts in different locations, from summary reviews	Predominantly open and denuded	1 - 100, most typically 10 - 80
Pinega, North Russia (Tanasijchuk; cited after Ford & Williams, 1989)	Subjacent and entrenched, locally denuded	220
Kuloj, North Russia (Korotkov, 1974)	Subjacent and entrenched, locally denuded	260 - 280
Perm region, pre-Ural, Russia, various areas (Gorbunova, 1979; Gorbunova et al, 1992)	Deep-seated, subjacent and entrenched, locally denuded	150 - 200
Western Ukraine, the Dniester river basin that encompasses most of the gypsum karst	Deep-seated, subjacent and entrenched	41
Western Ukraine, the Optimistychna Cave block (Dubljansky et al, 1981)	Entrenched karst, deeply drained	13
Western Ukraine, the Jazovsky area (Blotsky, 1982)	Deep-seated, confined conditions locally breached by opencast quarrying, circulation greatly intensified	1,800
Zorbas, South Spain (Pulido-Bosch, 1986)	Open	260
North Caucasus, Russia, three different areas (Ostapenko, 2001)	Open	144 - 853
French Alps (Nikod, 1976)	Open	1,000

Solutional denudation is a composite measure of dissolution processes, which are unevenly distributed within a 3-D karst system. Quantitative partition of the denudation by hydrologic zones and components of a karst system is difficult due to problems inherent in separation of mass balance data and determination of respective areas. The unevenness of dissolution is well illustrated by the measured rates summarized in Table 2 but their use for quantitative partition is again problematic because it is difficult to estimate the respective areas of rock surface. Nevertheless, based on a general concept about relative importance of certain environments in different types of karst and on the respective generalized dissolution rates, it is possible to fairly speculate about intensity of karstification on different stages of gypsum karst evolution.

Dissolution in the deep-seated (confined) conditions of sluggish transverse circulation (situation 5a in the Table 2) is rather slow by "gypsum" standards even after breakthrough but it is substantial if compared with typical rates for limestones. Besides hydrologic mass balance, the intensity of karstification depends on density of fissuring and type of conduit pattern evolved during the early speleogenesis. The latter two conditions determine the effective surface of dissolution in the aquifer. The overall intensity is probably rather low in this setting but it can be greater where structural requisites favour evolvement of maze patterns.

In shallower confined settings, in mature deep-seated or subjacent karsts (situation 5b in the Table 2), karstification enhances according to increasing flow and dissolution surface area. Again, other conditions being equal, overall solutional denudation is greater in the regions with pervasive speleogenesis (e.g. the Western Ukraine or pre-Urals) than in the regions where speleogenesis is more localized in space (e.g. the South Harz). The greatest intensity of karstification is where massive aggressive discharge occurs through sulphate rocks from regional aquifers, e.g. in the slopes of the Ufimsky swell in the pre-Ural. This is "modelled" and illustrated by the Jazovsky area in the Western Ukraine, where massive discharge from the artesian system occurs due to opencast mining and where solution denudation rates are extremely high (1,800 mm/Ka).

In the vadose zone of subjacent and entrenched karst, dissolution rates can be locally very high (situation 3 in the Table 2) but the overall karstification intensity is commonly low because dissolution is highly localized. The least intensity of karstification is in the deeply drained entrenched karst which has an insoluble caprocks and no saturated zone within gypsum. This is the case through the most of the entrenched karst zone in the Western Ukraine, where denudation rate (13 mm/Ka) is the lowest among those presented in Table 3. However, where an overlying aquifer leaks extensively into the densely fissured gypsum bed, creating closely packed vertical dissolution pipes (e.g. in some areas of the Pinega, Kuloj and pre-Ural regions in Russia), karstification can be quite intense in the vadose zone.

Where the saturated zone and water table is present within gypsum (in subjacent, entrenched or denuded karsts), karstification can be very intense, depending (besides of the amount of available aggressive recharge) on inherited cave porosity. Again, the intensity is greater in the regions where fissure and cave porosity is generally high, i.e. in the Pinega, Kuloj and pre-Ural regions where the combined denudation rates for mixed karst types are within 150 - 280 mm/Ka.

Three values for the Western Ukraine in Table 3 are illustrative of distinctions in the solutional denudation between different types of intrastratal karst. The value of 41 mm/Ka is a composite rate obtained for the Dniester basin, which encompasses the zones of deep-seated, subjacent and entrenched karst (see Fig. 6A and discussion in the previous section). A contribution of the entrenched karst zone, with its low karstification intensity, balances much higher denudation rates which can be assumed for the subjacent and deep-seated karst zones. Although the value of 1,800 mm/Ka for the deep-seated Jazovsky area can be considered rather as an exception than a norm for undisturbed conditions, high denudation rates within 150 - 300 mm/Ka are probably characteristic for these zones.

Exposure of gypsum karst to the surface (denuded and open karst types) does not necessarily implies a highest intensity of karstification even if amount of precipitation is considerable. Firstly, dissolution rates on exposed gypsum surfaces are not too high by "gypsum" standards (situation 1 in the Table 2). Secondly, in areas where previous and contemporaneous internal karstification is highly localized, the surface area exposed to the intense dissolution remain modest, and so the overall karstification intensity is modest. Studies in exposed carbonate karst suggest that 65 to 85 % of the dissolution takes place at the rockhead surface which is particularly large in the epikarst. In contrast, gypsum does not favour formation of epikarst, which would increase dramatically the effective dissolution surface and hence karstification intensity in exposed settings. Instead, a kind of a sealing crust commonly develops on exposed gypsum surfaces due to recrystallization processes in the uppermost layers. So, it is not surprising the existence of prominent exposed gypsum massifs in mature landscapes of regions with rather high precipitation (e.g. in Central Apennines and the South Harz) and all the more in more arid climates (e.g. in Sicily and the South Spain). However, open karsts where fracturing has been dramatically enhanced with exposure (such as in the three regions listed in the Table 3) may experience high karstification intensity even in arid climate (Sorbas). Other two examples represent gypsum karsts in the mountain folded regions where, in addition to the high degree of fracturing, annual rainfall is substantial (900 - 1,700 mm). Provided in similar settings, high denudation rates can be even more readily expected for denuded (former intrastratal) karsts, which inherited closely spaced cave porosity from previous stages.

SUMMARY AND CONCLUSION

The particularities of evaporite karst and of its evolution are determined by some specific features of evaporite geology but even more by dissolution chemistry and kinetics. Evaporites widely support different types of intrastratal karst; exposed types of karst (open and denuded) are less common than in carbonate rocks.

The development of conduit porosity in evaporites is extremely sensitive to variations of hydrogeologic and structural conditions. Evolution of geomorphic and hydrogeologic settings is therefore very important in the development of evaporite karst. Moreover, changes due to human activity may induce and dramatically intensify evaporite karst.

Evaporite karst readily commences in deep-seated settings, although in some circumstances evaporites may remain virtually untouched by karstification until exposure and denudation. Style and intensity of the evaporite karst development in shallow and exposed settings, as well as environmental hazards that this karst may present, depend greatly on previous karstification history, i.e. on inheritance. Inheritance, and hence the aspects of evolution, are probably much more important for the contemporary karst development in evaporites than in any other karst-supporting lithologies.

ACKNOWLEDGEMENT

This work was partially supported by the ROSES (Risk of Subsidence due to Evaporite Solution) Project ENV4-CT97-0603 funded by the European Commission Framework IV Programme.

REFERENCES

Andrejchuk, V., 1996: Gypsum karst of the pre-Ural region, Russia. pp.285-292 *In:* Klimchouk, A., Lowe, D., Cooper, A. & Sauro, U. (Eds.): *Gypsum karst of the world. International Journal of Speleology*, Theme issue 25 (3-4).

Birk, S., 2002: *Characterisation of karst systems by simulating aquifer genesis and spring responses: Model development and application to gypsum karst.* Tubingen Geowissenschaftliche Arbeiten, Reine C, 60, p.118, Tubingen.

Bischoff, J.L., Julia, R., Shanks, W.C. & R.J.Rosenbauer, 1994: Karstification without carbonic acid: bedrock dissolution by gypsum-driven dedolomitization.- *Geology*, 22, 995-998.

Buhmann, D. & Dreybrodt, W. 1985. The kinetics of calcite dissolution and precipitation in geologically relevant situations of karst areas: 2. Closed system. *Chem. Geol.*, 53, 109-124.

Carbonates & Evaporites 12 (1), 1997 (a special issue on the Symposium: Evaporite Karst: Processes, Landforms, Examples, and Impacts).

Calaforra, J.M., 1998: *Karstologia de yesos*. Universidad de Almeria, Almeria, 384 pp.

Clemens, T., Huckinghaus, D., Sauter, M., Liedl, R. & G.Teutsch, 1996: A combined continuum and discrete network reactive transport model for the simulation of karst development. pp. 309-318 *In:* Kovar, K. & van der Heijde, P. (Eds.) *Calibration and reliability in groundwater modeling*. IAHS Publ. 237.

Dreybrodt, W., 1990: The role of dissolution kinetics in the development of karst aquifers in limestone: A model simulation of karst evolution.- *Journal of Geology*, 98, 639-655.

Dreybrodt, W., 1992. Dynamics of karstification: A model applied to hydraulic structures in karst terranes.- *Applied Hydrogeol.,* 1, 20-32.

Dreybrodt, W., 1996: Principles of early development of karst conduits under natural and man-made conditions revealed by mathematical analysis of numerical models.- *Water Resources Research,* 32, 2923-2935.

Dreybrodt, W. & L.Eisenlohr, 2000: Limestone dissolution rates in karst environments. pp.136-148 *In:* Klimchouk, A.B., Ford, D.C., Palmer, A.N. & Dreybrodt,W. (Eds.) *Speleogenesis: Evolution of Karst Aquifers*, National Speleological Society, Huntsville, Alabama.

Dreybrodt, W., Romanov, D. & F.Gabrovsek, 2001: Karstification below dam sites: A model of increasing leakage from reservoirs.- *In: Proceedings of the 8th Multidisciplinary Conference on Sinkholes and the Engineering and Environmental Impacts of Karst*, Louisville, Kentucky, USA.

Dubljansky, V.N., Shutov, Yu.I. & M.P.Savchin, 1981: Seasonal peculiarities of the development of gypsum karst in the Pridnestrovskaja Podolia.- *Doklady AN USSR*, B, 6, 435-437 (in Russian).

Ford, D.C. 1997: Principal features of evaporite karst in Canada.- *Carbonates and Evaporites*, 12 (1): 15-23.

Ford, D.C. & P.W.Williams, 1989: *Karst geomorphology and hydrology*. Unwin Hyman, London, 601 p.

Friedman, G.M., 1997: Dissolution-collapse breccias and paleokarst resulting from dissolution of evaporite rocks, especially sulfates.- *Carbonates and Evaporites,* 12 (1), 53-63.

Frumkin, A., 2000: Speleogenesis in salt, the Mount Sedom area, Israel. pp.443-451 *In:* Klimchouk, A.B., Ford, D.C., Palmer, A.N. & Dreybrodt,W. (Eds.) *Speleogenesis: Evolution of Karst Aquifers*, National Speleological Society, Huntsville, Alabama.

Gabrovsek, F., 2000: *The Evolution of Early Karst Aquifers: From simple principles to complex models*. Zalozba ZRC, Ljubljana, p.150.

Gabrovsek, F. & W. Dreybrodt, 2000: Role of mixing corrosion in calcite-aggressive H_2O-CO_2-$CaCO_3$ solutions in the early evolution of karst aquifers in limestone.- *Water Resources Research, 2(5),* 1179-1188.

Gorbunova, K.A., 1977: *Karst in gypsum of the USSR*. Perm university, Perm, 83 p. (in Russian).

Gorbunova, K.A., 1979: *Morphology and hydrogeology of gypsum karst.* Perm University, Perm, 93 p. (in Russian).

Gorbunova, K.A., Andrejchuk, V.N., Kostarev, V.P. & N.G.Maximovich, 1992: *Karst and caves of the Perm region*. Perm University, Perm, 200 p.. (in Russian).

Grimandi, P., 1987: Grotta della Spipola.- *Ipoantropo,* 5, 51-64.

Groves, C.G. & A.D.Howard, 1994a: Early development of karst systems. 1. Preferential flow path enlargement under laminar flow.- *Water Resources Research*, 30, 2837-2846.

Groves, C.G. & A.D.Howard, 1994b: Minimum hydrochemical conditions allowing limestone cave development.- Water *Resources Research*, 30 (3), 607-615.

Howard, A.D. & C.G.Groves, 1995: Early development of karst systems. 2. Turbulent flow. *Water Resources Research*, 31 (1), 19-26.

James, A.N., 1992: *Soluble materials in civil engineering.* Ellis Horwood, Chichester, 435 p.

Jeschke, A., Vosbeck. K. & W.Dreybrodt, 2001: Surface controlled dissolution rates of gypsum in aqueous solutions exhibit nonlinear dissolution kimetics. - *Geochimica et Cosmochimica Acta*, 65 (1), 27-34.

Johnson, K.S., 1997. Evaporite karst in the United States.- *Carbonates and Evaporites*, 12 (1), 2-14.

Kaveev, M.C., 1963: About influence of carbon dioxide, originated during destruction of oil deposits, on development of karst processes.- *Doklady AN SSSR,* 152 (3). (in Russian).

Kempe, S., 1972: Cave genesis in gypsum with particular reference to underwater conditions.- *Cave Science*, 49, 1-6.

Kempe, S., 1996: Gypsum karst of Germany. pp.209-224 *In:* Klimchouk, A., Lowe, D., Cooper, A. & Sauro, U. (Eds.) *Gypsum karst of the world. International Journal of Speleology,* Theme issue 25 (3-4).

Klimchouk, A.B., 1994: Speleogenesis in gypsum and geomicrobiological processes in the Miocene sequence of the Pre-Carpatian region. pp.40-42 *In:* I.D.Sasowsky and M.V.Palmer (Eds.) *Breakthroughs in Karst Geomicrobiology and Redox Geochemistry* (Abstracts and Field Trip Guide for the symposium held February 16-19, 1994, Colorado Springs, Colorado). Karst Water Institute, Special Publications 1.

Klimchouk, A.B., 1996a: Dissolution and conversions of gypsum and anhydrite. pp.21-36 *In:* Klimchouk, A., Lowe, D., Cooper, A. & Sauro, U. (Eds.) *Gypsum karst of the world. International Journal of Speleology*, Theme issue 25 (3-4).

Klimchouk, A.B., 1996b: The typology of gypsum karst according to its geological and geomorphological evolution. pp.49-60 *In:* Klimchouk, A., Lowe, D., Cooper, A. & Sauro, U. (Eds.) *Gypsum karst of the world. International Journal of Speleology,* Theme issue 25 (3-4).

Klimchouk AB., 1997a: Artesian speleogenetic settings. pp. 157-160 *In: Proc. of the 12th Internat. Congr. of Speleol.*, vol.1, La Chaux-de-Fonds, Switzerland.

Klimchouk, A.B., 1997b: Speleogenetic effects of water density differences. pp. 161-164 *In: Proc. of the 12th Internat. Congr. of Speleol.*, vol.1, La Chaux-de-Fonds, Switzerland.

Klimchouk AB., 2000a: Speleogenesis under deep-seated and confined settings. pp. 244-260 *In:* Klimchouk, A.B., Ford, D.C., Palmer, A.N. & Dreybrodt,W. (Eds.) *Speleogenesis: Evolution of Karst Aquifers*, National Speleological Society, Huntsville, Alabama.

Klimchouk AB., 2000b: Speleogenesis of great gypsum mazes in the Western Ukraine. pp.261-273 *In:* Klimchouk, A.B., Ford, D.C., Palmer, A.N. & Dreybrodt,W. (Eds.) *Speleogenesis: Evolution of Karst Aquifers*, National Speleological Society, Huntsville, Alabama.

Klimchouk, A.B., 2000c: Speleogenesis in gypsum. pp. 431-442 *In:* Klimchouk, A.B., Ford, D.C., Palmer, A.N. & Dreybrodt,W. (Eds.) *Speleogenesis: Evolution of Karst Aquifers*, National Speleological Society, Huntsville, Alabama.

Klimchouk, A.B. & S.D.Aksem, in press: Hydrochemistry and solution rates in gypsum karst: case study from the Western Ukraine. - *Environmental Geology*.

Klimchouk, A.B. & V.N.Andrejchuk, 1996a: Breakdown development in cover beds, and landscape features induced by intrastratal gypsum karst. pp.127-144 *In:* Klimchouk, A., Lowe, D., Cooper, A. & Sauro, U. (Eds.) *Gypsum karst of the world. International Journal of Speleology*, Theme issue 25 (3-4).

Klimchouk, A.B. & V.N.Andrejchuk, 1996b: Environmental problems in gypsum karst terrains. pp.145-156 *In:* Klimchouk, A., Lowe, D., Cooper, A. & Sauro, U. (Eds.) *Gypsum karst of the world. International Journal of Speleology*, Theme issue 25 (3-4).

Klimchouk, A.B., Cucchi, F., Calaforra, J.M., Aksem, S., Finocchiaro, F. & P.Forti, 1996: Dissolution of gypsum from field observations. pp.37-48 *In:* Klimchouk, A., Lowe, D., Cooper, A. & Sauro, U. (Eds.) *Gypsum karst of the world. International Journal of Speleology,* Theme issue 25 (3-4).

Klimchouk, A.B. & D.C.Ford, 2000: Types of karst and evolution of hydrogeologic settings. pp. 54-64 *In:* Klimchouk, A.B., Ford, D.C., Palmer, A.N. & Dreybrodt,W. (Eds.) *Speleogenesis: Evolution of Karst Aquifers*, National Speleological Society, Huntsville, Alabama.

Klimchouk, A., Lowe, D., Cooper, A. & U.Sauro (Eds.), 1996: *Gypsum Karst of the World.* International Journal of Speleology, Theme issue 25 (3-4).

Kolodij, V.V., Schepak, V.M., Nudyk, B.I., Gorelova, L.V. & R.P.Pankiv, 1991: *Low-mineralized waters of the deep-seated horizons of oil- and gas-bearing confined basins of Ukraine.* Naukova dumka, Kiev, 184 p. (in Russian).

Korotkov, A.I., 1974: Appraisal of the intensity of karst processes in the Pinego-Dvinsky region. *In: Peshchery Pinego-Severodvinskoj karstovoj oblasti,* 101-102, Leningrad. (in Russian).

Manikhin, V.I., 1966: On the question of solubility of calcium sulfate under high pressures. - *Geokhimicheskie Materialy*, 13, 193-196. (in Russian).

Nikod, J., 1976: Karst des gypses et des evaporites associees. – *Ann. de Geogr.,* 471, 513-554.

Ostapenko, A.A., 2001: *Underground karst forms in the sulphate deposits of the Western Caucasus.* PhD thesis, Kubansky University, Krasnodar. (in Russian).

Palmer, A. N., 1975: The origin of maze caves.- *National Speleological Society Bulletin*, 37, 57-76.

Palmer, A.N., 1981: Hydrochemical controls in the origin of limestone caves. pp.120-122 *In: Proc. of the 8th International Speleological Congress.* Bowling Green, Kentucky,

Palmer, A.N., 1984: Geomorphic interpretation of karst features. pp.173-209 *In:* LaFleur, R.G., ed.: *Groundwater as a geomorphic agent.* Allen & Unwin, Boston.

Palmer A. N., 1988: Solutional enlargement of opening in the vicinity of hydraulic structures in karst regions. pp.3-15 *In*: Assoc. of ground water scientists and enigneers, 2nd Conference on *Environmental Problems in karst Terranes and their Solutions*, Proceedings.

Palmer, A.N., 1991: Origin and morphology of limestone caves.- *Geological Society of America Bulletin,* 103, 1-21.

Palmer, A.N., 1995: Geochemical models for the origin of macroscopic solution porosity in carbonate rocks. pp.77-101 *In*: Budd, A.D., Saller, A.H. & Harris, P.M., eds.: *Unconformities and porosity in carbonate strata.* AAPG Memoir 63, Tulsa, Oklahoma.

Pecherkin, A.I., 1986: *Geodynamics of sulphate karst.* Irkutsk University, Irkutsk, 172 pp. (in Russian).

Pecherkin, I.A., 1969: *Geodynamics of coasts of the Kama reservoirs.* Part II. Perm University, Perm. (in Russian).

Pulido-Bosch, A., 1986: Le karst dans les gypses de Sorbas (Almeria): aspects morphologiques et hydrogeologiques. - *Karstologia Mems,* 1, 27-35.

Quinlan, J.F., 1978: *Types of karst, with emphasis on cover beds in their classification and development.* PhD Thesis, Univ. of Texas at Austin.

Quinlan, J. F., Smith, A. R. & K.S.Johnson, 1986: Gypsum karst and salt karst of the United States. pp.419-420 *In: Atti simposio internazionale sul carsismo nelle evaporiti, Le Grotte d'Italia* 12.

Raines, M.A. & T.A. Dewers, 1997: Dedolomitization as a mechanism for karst generation in permian Blane formation, southwestern Oklahoma, USA.- *Carbonates and Evaporites,* 12 (1), 24-31.

Shternina, E.B., 1949; Solubility of gypsum in water solutions of salts.- *Izvestija sectora fiz.-him. analiza IONH AN SSSR,* 17, 203-206. (in Russian).

Stankevich, E.F., 1970: On a possibility of development of deep-seated karst.- *Voprosy Karstovedeniya*, 2, 43-47, Perm (in Russian).

Turyshev, A.V., 1965: About one possible way of the formation of karst cavities in the big depths.- *Gidrogeologichesky Sbornik*, 4 (Trudy Instituta Geologii UFAN SSSR, 76), Sverdlovsk. (in Russian).

White, W. B., 1977: Role of solution kinetics in the development of karst aquifers. pp.503-517 In: Tolson, J. S. & Doyle, F. L. (Eds.) *Karst hydrogeology. International Association of Hydrogeologists Mem.* 12.

White, W.B., 2000: Dissolution of limestone from field observations. pp.149-155 *In:* Klimchouk, A.B., Ford, D.C., Palmer, A.N. & Dreybrodt,W. (Eds.) *Speleogenesis: Evolution of Karst Aquifers*, National Speleological Society, Huntsville, Alabama.

Address
Institute of Geological Sciences, Natl. Academy of Sciences of Ukraine
P.O.Box 136, Kiev-30, 01030 Ukraine
E-mail: klim@klim.carrier.kiev.ua

Evolution of Karst: From Prekarst to Cessation, 97-114, Ljubljana-Postojna 2002

PALEOKARST: CESSATION AND REBIRTH?

R. ARMSTRONG L. OSBORNE

Abstract
The transformation of active karst into paleokarst by burial, isolation or cessation of process is not necessarily permanent. Paleokarst structures and landforms can be and are exhumed or reactivated, sometimes on numerous occasions. There is not a great deal of similarity between the localities where exhumation and reactivation of paleokarst has been reported. Exhumation and reactivation however have not been reported in many karsts that are similar to those where they have been reported. Exhumation and reactivation appears to be favoured in four situations: - the margins of sedimentary basins overlying grand unconformities, the axes of anticlines, narrow steeply-dipping impounded karsts and where paleokarst fill contains unstable minerals. Six processes are principally responsible for exhumation and reactivation: - per-ascensum speleogenesis, eustatic sea level changes, paragenesis, high density speleogenesis, glaciation, and large-scale meteoric speleogenesis. On some occasions karst landforms, particularly caves or segments of caves, may survive intact and unfilled for geologically significant periods of time. These may be completely isolated from the surface environment, or become reactivated by entrance formation due to breakdown, surface lowering or headward erosion. The intersection and reactivation of ancient open cavities and of exhumed cavities by "modern" caves may be much more common than is currently recognised. If caves have histories as long and as complex as the karsts in which they are developed then many "modern" caves will be composite features composed of interconnected "modern", relict and exhumed cavities excavated at different times by different processes. Unravelling these histories is the new challenge facing cave science. It will require caves to be studied in a much more detailed, thorough and systematic manner and will also require the application of new technologies in surveying, analysis and dating.
Keywords: *Paleokarst,Exhumation, Reactivation*

INTRODUCTION

When does the karst process cease? Does burial under a sedimentary basin or burial and filling with lava put an end to karst forever, or are these just interludes in a long cycle of karst cessation and later rebirth?

There have been an increasing number of reports since the 1960s of karsts in which not only have there been numerous phases of karstification, but also where ancient karst landforms have been exhumed and re-activated. In these cases paleokarst is clearly not the cessation of karst, but only the cessation of one particular phase of karst development.

The following discussion concentrates on the reactivation/exhumation of cavernous paleokarsts related to grand unconformities and on relict karst landforms. *Relict* karst landforms are considered here to be features that have been preserved by isolation from, or cessation of, the processes that formed them. Less emphasis will be given to the more common type of paleokarst; preserved epikarst horizons within carbonate sequences (*intrastratal* paleokarst).

Exhumation is used to describe the process by which filling and covering sediments are removed from a paleokarst feature, particularly a cave or doline, and *reactivation* is used to indicate that karst processes have re-commenced in a feature from which they have been absent for a considerable period of time. While reactivation will generally follow exhumation, it is likely that many paleokarst features (E.g. ancient open cavities and fissures) have never been filled and so can be reactivated without being exhumed.

Young caves may also *intersect* and *expose* parts of ancient open caves. While parts of the ancient cavity system will be completely obliterated by more recent speleogenesis, some exposed forms will be exposed intact, without later modification. The term *young* cave is used to describe any cave that can be entered at the present time. It is important to recognise from the outset that some of these caves may have Palaeozoic origins.

While multiple or polycyclic karstification is common, much paleokarst, particularly intrastratal paleokarst, is never again re-karstified. Some will be subducted, some will never reach the surface and some will be transformed in ways that prevent re-activation. Perhaps the exhumation/reactivation of paleokarst is favoured by particular geotectonic circumstances.

WHERE DOES EXHUMED/REACTIVATED PALEOKARST OCCUR ?

It is not uncommon in the Highlands of southeastern Australia, where my research is based, to find paleokarst deposits and cave forms intersected by, or incorporated into, young caves. However the literature suggests that while multiple karstification is quite common, it is uncommon for young caves to intersect or incorporate paleokarst structures (Osborne, 2000). Cave/paleokarst intersection is reported from a few other localities including:-

- The Transdanubian Ranges of Hungary (Korpás, 1998, Korpás et al, 1999; Bolner-Takács, 1999) (A in Fig. 1),The Bihor Mountains, Romania (Ghergari et. al, 1997; Silvestru & Ghergari, 1994) (B in Fig. 1).
- The gypsum maze caves of western Ukraine (Klimchouk & Andrejchouk, in Press) (C in Fig. 1).
- The Black Hills of South Dakota, USA (Bakalowicz et. al, 1987, Palmer & Palmer, 1995, 2000) (A in Fig. 2).
- The Cayman Islands (Jones, 1992; Jones & Hunter, 1994) (B in Fig. 2).

A first step in understanding how paleokarst caves become exhumed, intersected or reactivated might be to consider the geological and geomorphic setting of these locali-

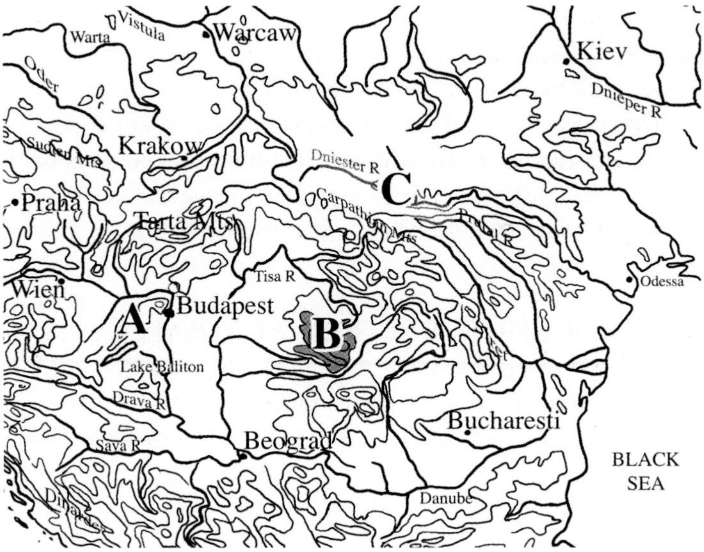

Fig. 1. Central Europe. ***A:*** *The Transdanubian Ranges of Hungary.* ***B:*** *The Bihor Mountains, Romania.* ***C:*** *The gypsum maze caves of western Ukraine*

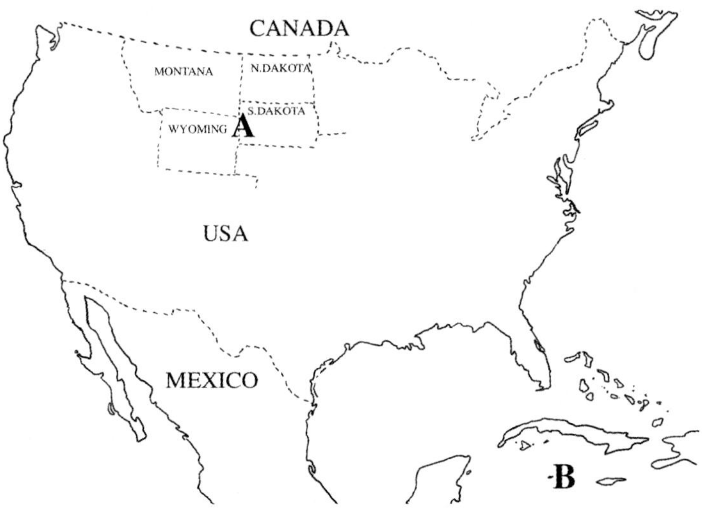

Fig. 2. North America. ***A:*** *Black Hills, South Dakota.* ***B:*** *Cayman Islands, Shading = Kaskaskia Paleokarst after Palmer & Palmer (1995)*

ties. The striking thing about the Highlands of southeastern Australia and the five other localities listed above is that they have in very little in common: -"

- A Palaeozoic fold belt on a passive continental margin. (SE Australia)
- Two Mesozoic European karsts (Hungary & Romania)
- An artesian gypsum karst. (Ukraine)
- A Late Palaeozoic carbonate platform sequence. (USA)
- A tropical carbonate island (Cayman Islands), except that each has undergone some degree of tilting or deformation.

However each is more like other areas where there are no reports of "young" caves being in any way related to ancient ones, E.g.: -

- The Appalachian karsts of the USA.

- The Dachstein Limestone karsts of Austria and Slovenia.
- The gypsum karst of Germany (Kempe, 1996)
- Thousands of tropical carbonate islands.

The discussion that follows draws both on the literature and the author's work in southeastern Australia to illustrate situations favouring interactions between paleokarst and "young" caves. Since many examples will be drawn from southeastern Australia, it will assist to provide a brief summary of its tectonic and geomorphic setting.

THE HIGHLANDS OF SOUTHEASTERN AUSTRALIA

The Highlands of southeastern Australia (Fig. 3) are developed on deformed Palaeozoic rocks of the Tasman Fold Belt and on relatively undeformed Latest Palaeozoic to Meso-

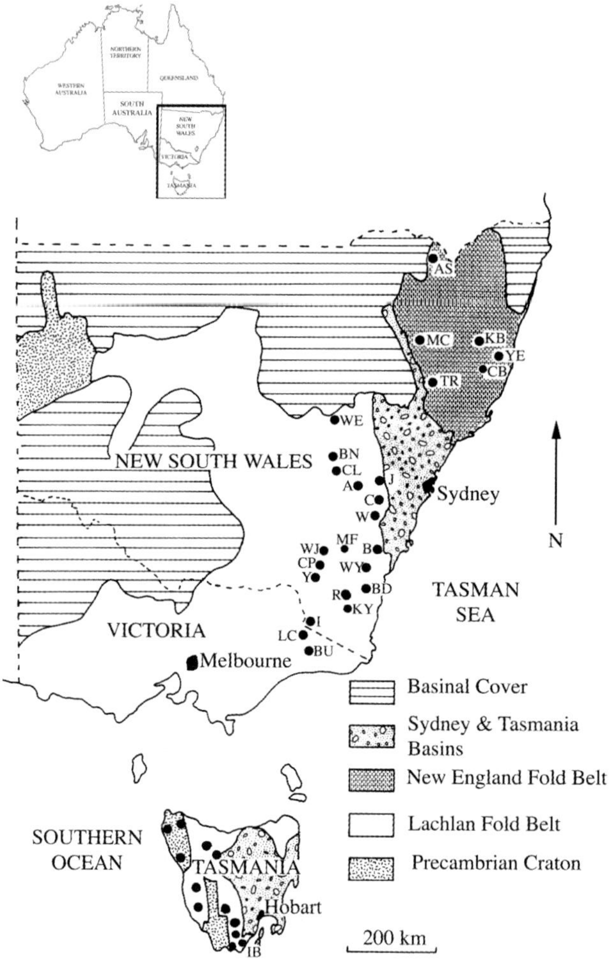

Fig. 3. Geological setting of some cavernous karst developed in Palaeozoic and older carbonates in southeastern Australia. AS = Ashford, MC = Moore Creek, KB = Kunderang Brook, YE = Yessabah, CB = Comboyne, TR = Timor, WE = Wellington, BN = Borenore, CL = Cliefden & Walli, A = Abercrombie, J = Jenolan, C = Colong, W = Wombeyan, B = Bungonia, MF = Mount Fairy, WJ = Wee Jasper, CP = Cooleman Plain, WY = Wyanbene, Y = Yarrangobilly, BD = Bendithera, R = Rosebrook, KY = Kybean, I = Indi, LC = Limestone Creek, BU = Buchan, IB = Ida Bay.

zoic cratonic sedimentary basins which unconformably overly the Palaeozoic sequence. Cavernous karsts are developed in limestones ranging in age from Ordovician to early Permian and also in Proterozoic dolostones in Tasmania. There are no gypsum strata within the Palaeozoic or Mesozoic sequences.

The region became cratonised in the Carboniferous and was subjected to significant glaciation during the Late Carboniferous to Early Permian. The present landscape; with a narrow coastal plain, an continent-long erosional escarpment (the Great Escarpment) and low Highlands consisting of incised plateau surfaces, has its origins in the Cretaceous with uplift associated with the opening of the Tasman Sea. Since Australia did not separate from Antarctica until the Eocene, the present landforms, including caves, have Gondwana origins. The idea that caves of the southern continents may have related histories is by no means new and can be found in the work of Lester King (King, 1959).

Paleokarst has been recognised at unconformities within the folded Palaeozoic sequence, where cratonic basins unconformably overly Palaeozoic limestones, and where Tertiary basalts and sediments overlie Palaeozoic limestones.

With the exception of relatively large areas of outcrop in Tasmania, most of Palaeozoic carbonate rocks in southeastern Australia form elongate north-south trending impounded karsts (karst barre), often with steeply dipping strata. Many of the most cavernous karsts are located directly adjacent to unconformable boundaries between the limestone and overlying siliciclastic or volcaniclastic sediments.

SITUATIONS FAVORING EXHUMATION/REACTIVATION

While the six localities discussed in the introduction may have quite different tectonic settings, there are specific local and regional situations that are favourable to paleokarst cavities being exhumed and/or reactivated.

1. THE MARGINS OF SEDIMENTARY BASINS UNCONFORMABLY OVERLYING SOLUBLE ROCKS

Major unconformities represent significant breaks in the stratigraphic record. The unconformity surface is a buried landscape resulting from an extended period of subaerial exposure. Soluble rocks exposed in these ancient landscapes will develop a suite of surface and underground karst landforms. These landforms will be filled and buried when sedimentation re-commences and the ancient landscape is covered by sedimentary basins. If later in their geological history these sedimentary basins are uplifted and eroded, buried karsts at the basin margins are likely to be re-exposed and subjected to further karstification and possible exhumation/reactivation (Fig. 4).

This situation occurs both in southeastern Australia and in the northwestern USA. In southeastern Australia the Sydney Basin (Permo-Carboniferous to Triassic) and the

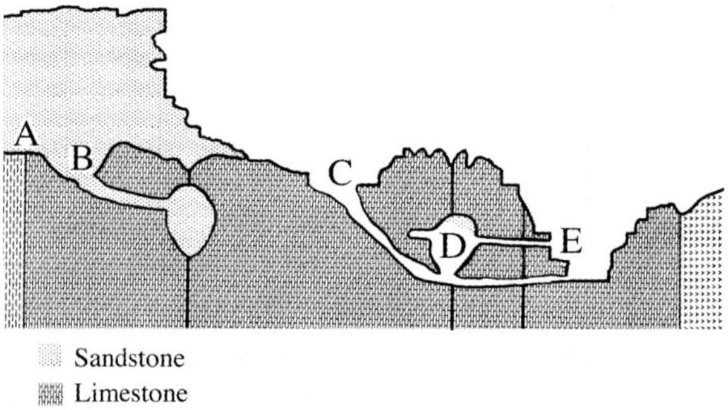

Fig. 4.Paleokarst and unconformities. ***A:*** *Unconformity surface.* ***B:*** *Doline in unconformity surface filled with sandstone.* ***C:*** *"Young" doline and cave invading ancient system.* ***D:*** *Ancient cupola, partly exhumed, intersected at base by "modern" cave.* ***E:*** *Ancient hall from cupola, intersected by valley incision, now forming cave entrance.*

Tasmania Basin (Carboniferous to Permian) both unconformably overlie Early Palaeozoic limestones. The unconformity at the base of the Sydney Basin represents a land surface with a local relief reaching 1 500 m and period of exposure of up to 35 million years. Young caves intersect paleokarst at Bungonia and Jenolan on the southwestern margin of the Sydney Basin and at Ida Bay on the margin of the Tasmania Basin (Fig. 3).

2. THE AXES OF ANTICLINES

Where a buried carbonate sequence has been subjected to regional folding with widely-spaced fold axes, the overlying beds will tend to be preserved along the axes of synclines, often forming ranges of hills, and eroded along the axes of anticlines (Fig.5). Consequently the underlying carbonates will tend to be exposed, and paleokarst reacti-

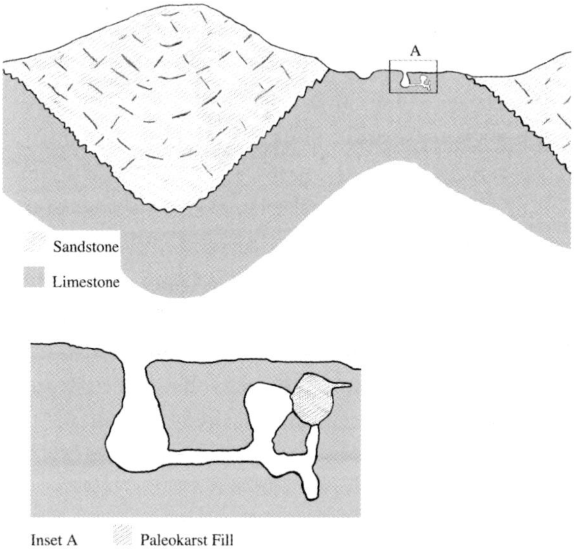

Fig. 5.Paleokarst and Anticlines. Unconformity is between limestone and overlying sandstone. Paleokarst is intersected by modern cave at crest of anticline.

Fig. 6. Vertical paleokarst shaft of probable Late Devonian age, filled with megabreccia, intersecting thinly bedded limestone bedrock. Cathedral Cave, Wellington Caves, N.S.W., Australia.

vated, close to the axes of anticlines. In broad folds close to the anticlinal axis, the orientation of paleokarst structures will be less disturbed than on the limbs. Here vertical paleokarst structures, such as shafts, will approximately retain their original vertical orientation, aiding their reactivation and recognition.

Examples from southeastern Australia include Wellington Caves (Figs 3 & 6) and Wombeyan Caves (Osborne, 1993a).

3.NARROW STEEPLY-DIPPING IMPOUNDED KARSTS

Subsequent phases of cave development are likely to behave differently in steeply-dipping limestone and horizontally-bedded limestone (Osborne, 1999a). When horizontally-bedded karsts are subjected to further periods of karstification and speleogenesis there is ample opportunity for new caves to form on the same inception horizon, adjacent to the older caves but without intersecting them (see Figure 15 in Osborne, 1999a).

Where bedding in thin bodies of limestone becomes steeply inclined following folding, narrow, elongate impounded karsts are produced. In these karsts, laterally adjacent paths may not be available for subsequent phases of speleogenesis. If multiple phases of karstification occur after folding, new caves will most likely form along the same bedding planes as any older paleokarst cavities, possibly at different vertical levels within the bedding planes (Fig. 8). The paleokarst may act as an aquifer and be wholly or partially exhumed, or may act as an aquiclude, forcing new caves to form either above or below it. Consequently it is more likely that new caves will intersect ancient ones in

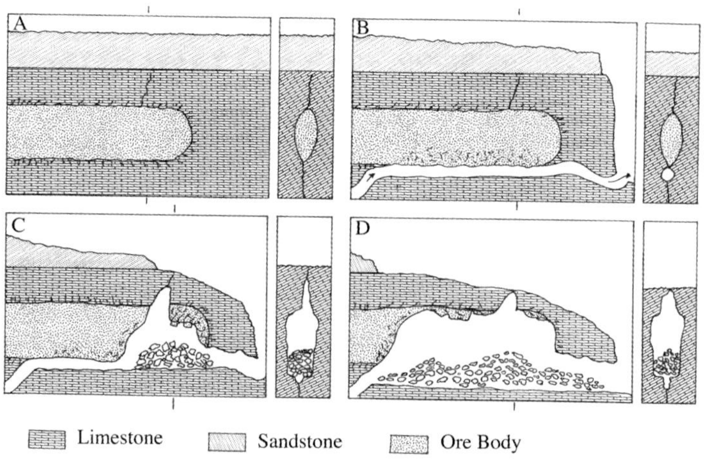

Fig. 7. Cave development by exhumation of ore deposit after Osborne (1996), viewed in cross-section. ***A:*** *Ore body is emplaced in steeply-dipping limestone, which is unconformably overlain by sandstone cap rock.* ***B:*** *Cave development is deflected by ore body which acts as aquiclude in phreatic conditions. Passage develops under ore body.* ***C:*** *Lowering of water table brings deposit into the vadose zone. Stripping back of overlying cap rock increases exposure of unstable minerals to oxygenated vadose seepage water. Deposit begins to weather and fallen material is removed by modern stream.* ***D:*** *Out-of-scale chamber expands as cap rock is further stripped back. Ore body remnants forming substrate for gypsum and aragonite speleothems.*

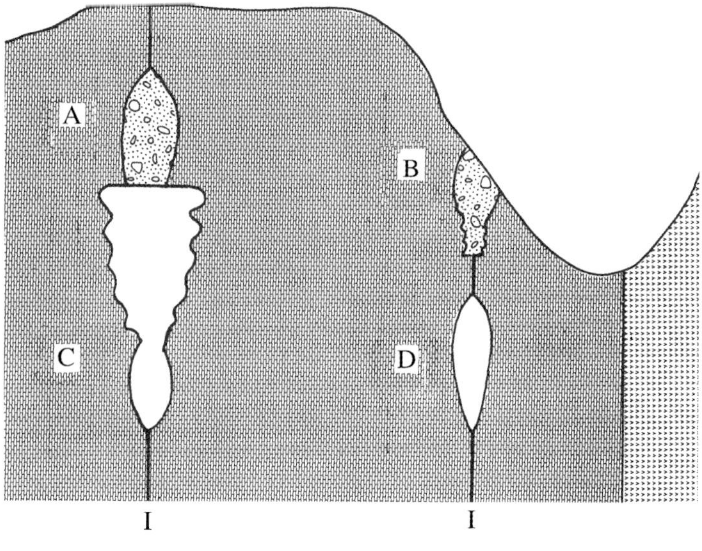

Fig. 8 Intersection of filled cave in steeply dipping limestone as a result of paragenesis after Osborne (1999a). ***A & B:*** *Filled ancient passages, B is exposed by valley incision.* ***C:*** *Young phreatic passage developed on same inception horizon as A works upward due to paragenesis and intersects A.* ***D:*** *Modern phreatic passage developed on same inception horizon as B.*

narrow bodies of steeply-dipping limestone than in extensive masses of horizontally-bedded limestone.

4. WHERE PALEOKARST FILL CONTAINS UNSTABLE MINERALS

Ancient caves are more likely to be exhumed/reactivated if they are filled with materials that become unstable when exposed to vadose conditions. Osborne (1996) noted the close proximity of some cavernous karsts to ore deposits and described how paleokarst fills containing pyrite were weathering in vadose conditions and being rapidly removed from the caves.

This process will over time result in the complete exhumation of ancient cavities (Fig. 7). One significant feature of these exhumed caves will be their lack of integration with the surrounding modern hydrology. If there are streams in these caves they are likely to be out of scale with the cavities through which they flow.

PROCESSES THAT MAY PROMOTE EXHUMATION/REACTIVATION

1. PER-ASCENSUM SPELEOGENESIS

Ford (1995) considered that caves formed by per ascensum processes were more likely to intersect paleokarst than those formed by per descensum processes (descending meteoric water). This is because paleokarst may offer high permeability outflow routes that rising fluids may preferentially follow. Bolner-Takács (1999) described an outstanding example of the intersection of paleokarst by later per ascensum speleogenesis in Beremend Crystal Cave, Hungary. Similarly the gypsum caves of the western Ukraine, formed by artesian processes, frequently intersect paleokarst bodies (Klimchouk & Andrejchouk, in Press).

2. EUSTATIC SEA LEVEL CHANGES

The filling and later exhumation of paleokarst features in the Cayman Islands described by Jones (1992) and Jones & Hunter (1994) are a consequence of eustatic sea level changes. Caves formed during periods of low sea level, were filled during high stands and then intersected and partially exhumed when the sea level fell.

A similar process could occur in areas where sea level changes occur due to both eustatic and volcanic/tectonic processes. Anne Felton is researching raised reef flats on the north shore of Oahu, Hawaii, where young karst features intersect paleokarst, while Grimes (2001) has described possible paleokarst deposits exposed in caves on Christmas Island.

While the formation of paleokarst along the Adriatic coast by Recent marine incursion is well known and documented (Zötl, 1989), there are no reports of caves which were filled during earlier higher level sea stands being exhumed and reactivated.

Both oceanic island and littoral karsts need to be investigated for signs of reactivation/exhumation of paleokarst features that were filled during past high stands and have since been exhumed or reactivated.

3.PARAGENESIS

Paragenesis can be an important process for exhuming and reactivating ancient caves. This is particularly the case where more recent caves have developed in the limestone mass below the level occupied by filled caves. Osborne (1999a) illustrated the operation of this process in steeply dipping limestones (Fig.8). In this case paragenetic excavation, with dissolution acting upwards above a rising clastic fill, causes a cave formed at a lower level in the limestone to intersect an older feature, located higher in the limestone mass. In the narrow impounded karsts of southeastern Australia there is good evidence for multiple phases of paragenesis, resulting in filling, exhumation and overprinting.

Paragenesis is an important process, as it can not only result in young caves intersecting ancient ones, it can also occur repeatedly and by itself produce a complex of overprinted passages.

4. HIGH DENSITY SPELEOGENESIS

Ford (1995) noted that per ascensum caves were more likely to intersect paleokarst than per descensum caves. One possible explanation might be that it is the morphological characteristics of per ascensum caves, rather than their mode of formation, that is responsible for them intersecting paleokarst.

Klimchouk (1996) used the cave index (passage length km/ area of cave field km^2) to distinguish between artesian maze caves (with cave indices of >100) and normal stream caves (with cave indices of <30). Some other caves which intersect paleokarst such as the caves of the Black Hills South Dakota and the Hall and Narrows caves of southeastern Australia (Osborne, 2001a) also have high cave indices.

However, some caves that intersect, or are guided by, paleokarst do not have high cave indices. These include Satorkopuszta Cave in Hungary, the text book example of a point-source hydrothermal cave (Ford & Williams, 1989) and Grill Cave at Bungonia Caves, N.S.W. Australia, a downward-narrowing funnel-shaped cave (Osborne, 2001b). In the case of Grill Cave, paleokarst is intersected in the lowermost, narrow section of the cave, as well as in upper, more expansive sections. In such cases the mode of formation does appear to be crucial.

Irrespective of their mode of formation, however, caves with maze or ramifying morphologies will intersect more of any given limestone mass than a stream cave, considerably increasing the likelihood that they will intersect paleokarst or any other feature preserved in the bedrock.

5. GLACIATION

Ford and Williams (1989, pp 482-490) described a number of processes associated with glaciation that can result in exhumation and reactivation. Dissection of karst landscapes by glacial valleys can both intersect and preserve (by isolation) phreatic caves left as high-level relicts in valley sides or close to summits. While infilling with sediment may inhibit later karst processes, coarse clastic fills may act as post-glacial aquifers, resulting in karst features being exhumed. Karsts with glacial pavements may be converted into confined aquifers when covered by till. Meltwater may be focussed into particular ponors, causing rejuvenation of underground drainage, while raising of the local water tables adjacent to glaciers may flood cavities formerly in the vadose zone. Ford and Williams (1989) also described instances where deep injection of meltwaters into karst aquifers, interstratal karst and paleokarst during crustal isostatic depression or rebound (chiefly the latter) has resulted in rejuvenation of buried karsts as old as the Devonian.

6. LARGE-SCALE METEORIC SPELEOGENESIS

Most stream caves intersect a relatively small volume of limestone, and as previously discussed are less likely to intersect and reactivate paleokarst than caves with more complex structures. Very large stream caves, or stream cave systems consisting of active and abandoned stream channels at different levels (E.g. the caves of the Demanovska Valley, Slovakia) will intersect a greater volume of limestone than will smaller stream caves and so have an increased chance of intersecting ancient karst structures.

If the earlier caves had a network or ramifying nature, or contained large voids (if the earlier karstification was deep seated, artesian, thermal or otherwise *per-ascensum*) then the chance of a large/complex young stream cave intersecting an ancient cave structure (filled or open) should increase.

PRESERVATION WITHOUT FILLING

Ancient caves may be preserved without being partially or completely filled with clastic sediments or precipitates. Some of these will be blind cavities, which have been discovered by excavation or drilling. Others will have gained natural entrances as a result of cliff retreat, surface lowering or other processes that are unrelated to the excavation of the cave.

While it is possible to argue that these relict caves are not truly paleokarst, or that slow deposition of speleothem represents an ongoing vadose process, the caves were principally formed by processes that are no longer active, and fall within a broad definition of paleokarst.

PRESERVATION BY CESSATION OF PROCESS AND ISOLATION

For karst cavities to be preserved in an unfilled, or largely unfilled, condition over a significant period of time: -

- the processes which excavated them must have ceased
  and
- they must remain isolated from active surface processes.

The (relict) great gypsum caves of the western Ukraine (Klimchouk, 1996, 2000) and many of the caves of the Buda Hills, Hungary (Dublyansky, 2000) are good examples of preservation by cessation and isolation. In both cases the speleogenetic process has ceased, i.e. the artesian aquifer has drained and thermal waters no longer circulate. Overlying aquicludes, sealed entrances or lack of entrances isolate them from surface processes.

When caves have no natural entrance, as with most in the Buda Hills, their isolation from at least young surface karst processes is clear. These caves must have had exits (outflow points for thermal waters) when they were active. As a consequence of their size, morphology, position in the landscape or becoming sealed the exits have not acted as entrances, allowing meteoric water or sediment to enter.

Isolation by blocked entrances is another matter. As generations of cavers will attest, digs (sometimes) intersect open caves. Cave sedimentologists have also recognised (E.g. Frank, 1975) that cave entrances will open and close over time.

While deltas and cones of entrance facies sediments (fluvial, talus and aeolian) are the most common forms of cave entrance blockage, caves may also become sealed by speleothem, volcaniclastics and lava flows. The effectiveness of such blockages may also mean that open cavities may survive even when a whole karst is buried under sediments.

The important issue is: - are caves that have been isolated by entrance blockages sufficiently unrelated, old and/or isolated from young karst processes to be considered relict and/or paleokarst? This may be a difficult question to answer, but it is an important question to ask and investigate. Caves discovered by digging have the potential to be much older and more significant than may be initially apparent.

REACTIVATION BY VADOSE INVASION

Caves formed by deep phreatic or per ascensum processes may lie dormant in the landscape due to failure of their fluid supply. Much younger vadose shafts or stream passages may intersect these ancient cavities, leading to their reactivation. It is likely that this has occurred at Bungonia Caves, N.S.W, Australia (Osborne, 1993b) and in Derbyshire, England (Ford, 2000).

I have described invading vadose streams in southeastern Australia (Osborne, 1999b, 2001a). These streams are easily misinterpreted as being responsible for excavating the cavities through which they now flow. Sometimes they are distinctly underfit or the passage morphology below the present water level is different in size and morphology to that above. Often a detailed study of cave pattern, wall morphology and speleogens is required to distinguish between a stream which excavated a cave and one which has been captured into a pre-existing system of cavities.

REACTIVATION BY ENTRANCE FORMATION

Some caves will never have had an entrance opening to the Earth's surface, while others will have lost their entrance due to blockage. The opening of an entrance will allow some limited interaction with the surface and thus a degree of reactivation Surface lowering, cliff retreat, incision and headward erosion can all form new entrances in caves which previously lacked any surface connection (Osborne, 2001a).

From a human point of the view the importance of these entrances is that they allow us to enter the cave. Because these entrances are natural, unlike when we drill or accidentally excavate into a cave, there is a great temptation to incorporate them into our attempts to understand the origin of the cave. Far too often a non-genetic (intercepted) entrance, particularly one produced by cliff retreat, incision or headward erosion is misinterpreted as a hole through which water flowed into or out of the rock mass.

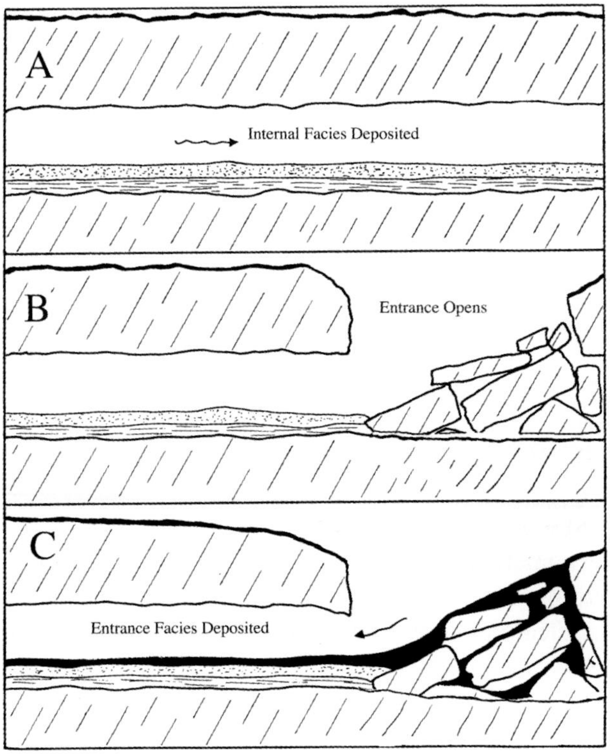

*Fig. 9 Cave entrance development after Osborne (1978). **A:** Closed cave with internal sediments developed. **B:** Non-genetic entrance opens as a result of breakdown. **C:** Entrance facies deposited through entrance.*

If we are to recognise ancient caves that have been preserved by isolation and reactivated by subsequent natural entrance formation then detailed attention must be given to the morphology of the entrances and of the deposits in them. In some cases a distinct facies change will occur between internal and surface-derived sediments, marking the opening of the entrance (Fig. 9) (Osborne, 1978).

EXHUMATION/REACTIVATION WITH NO OBVIOUS CAUSE

A number of environments and processes are likely to be favourable or responsible for young caves intersecting, exhuming or reactivating ancient caves. However in many cases where young caves intersect, exhume or reactivate ancient caves it is by no means clear which characteristic of the environment has been favourable to this occurrence, or what process excavated the new cave.

While there are indications that the "Hall and Narrows" caves of Osborne (2001a), many of which intersect paleokarst, may have formed by per ascensum processes, this is by no means certain. Using intersection of paleokarst as an indicator of per ascensum processes may well turn out to be a circular and fallacious argument.

In some southeastern Australian cases, E.g. Timor Cave, an isolated "phreatic" room, situated high in the landscape, which intersects both flowstone and lava-filled paleokarst (Osborne, 1986), the process by which the young cave was excavated, and its relationship with the surrounding landscape, remains unclear. This will be the case with many localities until there is greater understanding and agreement as to which speleogens, patterns of cave development and cave deposits are truly indicative of particular modes of speleogenesis.

CONCLUSIONS

The extensive literature reporting multiple sequences of karstification makes it no longer possible to imagine that burial, marine transgression or isolation will necessarily result in the permanent cessation of karst processes in any mass of soluble rock.

The important questions are now about: -

- the extent to which ancient and young karst features interact
- the nature of these interactions
- the extent to which ancient karst features are exhumed
- the processes which result in exhumation
- how to recognise exhumed features
- the extent to which ancient karst features survive as unaltered relicts
- the conditions which lead to survival
- how to recognise relict features
  (particularly when they are incorporated in young systems)

Reports of young caves intersecting ancient caves filled with lithified sediment remain relatively uncommon, and therefore probably relate to specific and less-common speleogenetic processes. These features are often quite striking and criteria exist for their recognition (Osborne, 2000).

Exhumed and relict karst features are not often reported as components of young caves. If more than a few caves have histories as long and as complex as the karsts in which they are developed then many young caves will be composite features composed of interconnected young, relict and exhumed cavities excavated at different times by different processes.

Over the years I have recognised exhumed dolines at Yarrangobilly Caves (Osborne, 1996) and exhumed caves at Jenolan Caves (Osborne, 1993c, 1999b). This was possible only because remnants of the former fills remained adhering to the doline and cave walls and because in some caves exhumation can be observed continuing today. If almost all, or all, of the fill had been removed this would have been almost impossible

Recognition of relict cave forms that have never been filled is even more difficult. Out of scale and out of character voids (E.g. convection cupolas forming the ceilings of stream passages) should arouse suspicion.

A more thorough study and understanding of caves is now required including: -

- Detailed metre by metre examination by skilled observers.
- Mineral surveys; including trace element, fluid inclusion and stable isotope studies to determine paragenetic and speleogenetic environments.
- Very detailed geomorphic (speleomorphic) mapping and imaging.
- Particular emphasis will need to be given to ceiling and wall morphologies, and cross-sections. (reflectorless laser instruments, stereo imaging and graphical databases will assist)
- Absolute dating of cave materials over a greater time range than commonly currently applied. (E.g. K-Ar clay dating, U-Pb carbonate dating)
- More research to identify and understand young active speleogenetic environments. This will require field studies in active speleogenetic environments (often by divers, but also by hydrologists and hydrogeologists) along with physical, mathematical and computer modelling.

ACKNOWLEDGEMENTS

This paper was largely written in November 2001 when the author was staying at the Karst Research Institute, Postojna, Slovenia as part of a Special Studies Program, July-November 2001, from the University of Sydney.

I would particularly like to thank:

- The Director of the Karst Research Institute, Dr Tadej Slabe, and staff for assistance, accommodation and for the use of facilities at the Institute.

- Keith Crook and E. Anne Felton for accommodation and field trips to the karst of Oahu, Hawaii in July 2001.
- Alexander Klimchouk and Natalie Yablokova for their hospitality, field trip to the gypsum caves of western Ukraine and insightful discussions in September 2001.
- Derek Ford and Alexander Klimchouk for reading the manuscript and making helpful suggestions.
- P.J. Osborne for assistance while travelling in Hawaii, Brazil and Europe and for reading the drafts.

The paper was presented at the symposium "Evolution of karst: From prekarst to cessation", Karst Research Institute, Postojna, 17-21 September 2002.

REFERENCES

Bakalowicz, M. J., Ford, D. C., Miller, T.E., Palmer, A. N. & Palmer, M.V., 1987. Thermal genesis of dissolution caves in the Black Hills, South Dakota. *Bulletin of the Geological Society of America.* 99: 729-738.

Bolner-Takács, K., 1999. Paleokarst features and other climatic relics in Hungarian caves. *Acta Carsologica.* 28(1): 27-37.

Dublyansky, Y.V., 2000. Hydrothermal speleogenesis in the Hungarian Karst. . *in* Klimchouk, A.B., Ford, D.C., Palmer, A.N. and Dreybrodt, W., *Eds. Speleogenesis: Evolution of Karst Aquifers*, National Speleological Society, Huntsville, Alabama. p. 298-303.

Ford, D.C., 1995. Paleokarst as a target for modern karstification. *Carbonates and Evaporites.* 10(2): 138-147.

Ford, D.C. & Williams, P.W., 1989. *Karst Geomorphology and Hydrogeology*. Unwin Hyman, London.

Ford, T.D. 2000. Vein cavities: an early stage in the evolution of the Castleton Caves, Derbyshire, UK. *Cave and Karst Science.* 27(1): 5-14.

Frank, R.M. 1975. Late Quaternary climatic change: evidence from cave sediments in central eastern New South Wales. *Australian Geographical Studies.* 13(2): 154-168.

Ghergari, L., Tamas, T., Damm, P. & Forray, F., 1997. Hydrothermal paleokarst in Pestera din Valea Rea (Bihor Mountains, Romania). *Theoretical and Applied Karstology.* 10: 115-125.

Grimes, K.G. 2001. Karst features of Christmas Island (Indian Ocean). *Helictite.* 27(2): 41-58.

Jones, B., 1992, Caymanite, a cavity-filling deposit in the Oligocene-Miocene Bluff Formation of the Cayman Islands. *Canadian Journal of Earth Sciences.* 29: 720-736.

Jones, B. & Hunter, I.G., 1994. Messinian (Late Miocene) karst on Grand Cayman, British West Indies: an example of an erosional sequence boundary. *Journal of Sedimentary Research.* B64: 531-541.

Kempe, 1996. Gypsum karst of Germany. *International Journal of Speleology.* 25(3/4): 209-224.

Klimchouk, A.B., 1996. Gypsum karst in the western Ukraine. *International Journal of Speleology.* 25(3/4): 263-278.

Klimchouk, A.B., 2000. Speleogenesis in gypsum. *in* Klimchouk, A.B., Ford, D.C., Palmer, A.N. and Dreybrodt, W., *Eds. Speleogenesis: Evolution of Karst Aquifers*, National Speleological Society, Huntsville, Alabama. p. 432-442.

Klimchouk, A.B. & Andrejchouk, V., In Press. Collapse and breakdown mechanisms from observations in the gypsum caves of the Western Ukraine: implications for subsidence hazard assessment. To be published in *Environmental Geology.*

King, L.C., 1959. Can cave deposits in different parts of the World be correlated*? The Bulletin, South African Spelaeological Association* 3(1): 3-7.

Korpás, L., 1998. Paleokarst studies in Hungary. *Occasional Papers of the Geological Institute of Hungary*. 195: 1-139.

Korpás L., Lantos, M. & Nagymarosy, A., 1999. Timing and genesis of early marine caymanites in the hydrothermal paleokarst system of Buda Hills, Hungary. *Sedimentary Geology.* 123: 9-29.

Osborne, R.A.L., 1978. Structure, sediments and speleogenesis at Cliefden Caves, New South Wales. *Helictite*. 16(1): 3-31.

Osborne, R.A.L., 1986. Cave and landscape chronology at Timor Caves, New South Wales. *Journal and Proceedings of the Royal Society of New South Wales*. 119 (1/2): 55-76.

Osborne, R.A.L., 1993a. The history of karstification at Wombeyan Caves, New South Wales, Australia, as revealed by palaeokarst deposits. *Cave Science*. 20 (1): 1-8.

Osborne, R.A.L., 1993b. A new history of cave development at Bungonia, N.S.W. *Australian Geographer*. 24(1): 62-74

Osborne, R.A.L., 1993c. Geological Note: Cave formation by exhumation of Palaeozoic palaeokarst deposits at Jenolan Caves, New South Wales. *Australian Journal of Earth Sciences*. 40: 591-593

Osborne, R.A.L., 1996. Vadose weathering of sulfides and limestone cave development-Evidence from eastern Australia. *Helictite*. 34(1): 5-15.

Osborne, R.A.L., 1999a. The inception horizon hypothesis in vertical to steeply-dipping limestone: applications in New South Wales, Australia. *Cave and Karst Science*. 26(1), 5-12.

Osborne, R.A.L., 1999b. The origin of Jenolan Caves: Elements of a new synthesis and framework chronology. *Proceedings of the Linnean Society of New South Wales*. 121:1-26

Osborne, R.A.L., 2000, Paleokarst and its significance for speleogenesis. *in* Klimchouk, A.B., Ford, D.C., Palmer, A.N. and Dreybrodt, W., *Eds. Speleogenesis: Evolution of Karst Aquifers*, National Speleological Society, Huntsville, Alabama. p. 113-123.

Osborne, R.A.L., 2001a. Halls and narrows: Network caves in dipping limestone, examples from eastern Australia. *Cave and Karst Science*. 28 (1): 3-14.

Osborne, R.A.L., 2001b. Non-meteoric speleogenesis: evidence from eastern Australia. *Proceedings of the 13th International Congress of Speleology, Brasilia D.F., Brazil, July 15-22, 2001*. Session (S1) Geospeleology. 131-S1, 4 p. Published on CD.

Palmer, A.N. & Palmer, M.V., 1995. The Kaskaskia paleokarst of the northwestern Rocky Mountains and Black Hills, northwestern U.S.A. *Carbonates and Evaporites* 10(2): 148-160.

Palmer, A.N. & Palmer, M.V., 2000. Speleogenesis of the Black Hills Maze Caves, South Dakota, U.S.A. *in* Klimchouk, A.B., Ford, D.C., Palmer, A.N. and Dreybrodt, W., *Eds. Speleogenesis: Evolution of Karst Aquifers*, National Speleological Society, Huntsville, Alabama. p. 274-286.

Silvestru, E. & Ghergari, L., 1994. On the paleokarst in the cave Ghetarul de la Scarisoara (Bihor Mountains, Romania). *Theoretical and Applied Karstology.* 7: 515-161.

Zötl, J., 1989. Paleokarst as an important hydrogeological factor. *in:* P. Bosák, D.C. Ford., J. Glazek & I. Horácek. eds. *Paleokarst. A Systematic and Regional Review.* Elsevier and Academia. Amsterdam and Praha: 483-509.

Address
School of Development and Learning,
A35. UNIVERSITY OF SYDNEY, N.S.W. 2006, AUSTRALIA.
E-mail: a.osborne@edfac.usyd.edu.au

Evolution of Karst: From Prekarst to Cessation, 115-154, Ljubljana-Postojna 2002

BASIC PROCESSES AND MECHANISMS GOVERNING THE EVOLUTION OF KARST

WOLFGANG DREYBRODT & FRANCI GABROVŠEK

Abstract

Models of karstification based on the physics of fluid flow in fractures of soluble rock, and the physical chemistry of dissolution of limestone by CO_2 containing water have been presented during the last two decades. This paper gives a review of the basic principles of such models, their most important results, and future perspectives.

The basic element of evolving karst systems is a single isolated fracture, where a constant hydraulic head drives calcite aggressive water from the input to the output. Non linear dissolution kinetics with order $n = 4$ induces a positive feedback by which dissolutional widening at the exit enhances flow rates thus increasing widening and so on until flow rates increase dramatically in a breakthrough event. After this the hydraulic head breaks down and widening of the fracture proceeds fast but even along its entire length under conditions of constant recharge. The significance of modelling such a single fracture results from the fact that an equation for the breakthrough time specifies the parameters determining the processes of early karstification. In a next step the boundary conditions for isolated fractures are varied by including different lithologies of the rock, expressed by different dissolution kinetics. This can enhance or retard karstification. Subterranean sources of CO_2 can also be simulated by changing the equilibrium concentration of the solution at the point where CO_2 is injected. This leads to accelerated karstification. At the confluence of solutions from two isolated tubes into a third one, mixing corrosion can release free carbon dioxide. Its effect to solutional widening in such a system of three conduits is discussed.

Although these simple models give interesting insights into karst processes more realistic models are required. Combining single fractures into two-dimensional networks models of karst in its dimensions of length and breadth under constant head conditions are presented. In first steps the Ford-Ewers' high-dip and low-dip models are simulated. Their results agree to what one expects from field observations. Including varying lithologies produces a variety of new features. Finally we show that mixing corrosion has a strong impact on cave evolution. By this effect micro climatic conditions in the catchment area of the cave exert significant influence. A common feature in the evolution of such two-dimensional models is the competition of various possible pathways to achieve breakthrough first. Varying conditions in lithologies, carbon dioxide injection or changing hydrological boundary conditions change the chances for the competing conduits.

Karst systems developing at steep cliffs in the dimensions of length and depth are characterized by unconfined aquifers with constant recharge to the water table. Modelling of such systems shows that dissolution of limestone occurs close to the water table. The widening of the fractures there causes lowering of the water table until it becomes stable when base level is reached, and a water table cave grows headwards into the aquifer. When prominent deep fractures with large aperture widths are present deep phreatic loops originate below the water table. A river or a lake on a karst plateau imposes constant head conditions at this location in addition to the constant recharge from meteoric precipitation. In this case a breakthrough cave system evolves along the water table kept stable by the constant head input. But simultaneously deep phreatic loops arise below it.

In conclusion we find that all cave theories such as those of Swinnerton (1932), Rhoades and Sinacori (1941), and the Four-state-model of Ford are reconciled. They are not contradictory but they result from the same physics and chemistry under different boundary conditions.

1. INTRODUCTION

Modelling of the evolution of karst aquifers requires reduction of extremely complex systems to highly idealised simple principles. Fig.1 shows such an idealised concept of a karst system. It represents a limestone terrain with a cliff and a plateau. The limestone is dissected into blocks separated by narrow fissures and fractures. Some of those are prominent (1,2) exhibiting large aperture widths and connect water inputs at the plateau to base level at the river flowing along the foot of the cliff. They may be located along a major bedding plane parting or a master joint. Water also infiltrates from the plateau as evenly distributed seepage from meteoric precipitation and/or from a lake or stream located at the plateau. Due to such water supplies a water table is build up, where continuous dissolutional widening of fractures is activated by water containing CO_2 from the atmosphere or from CO_2 in the vegetated soil covering the plateau.

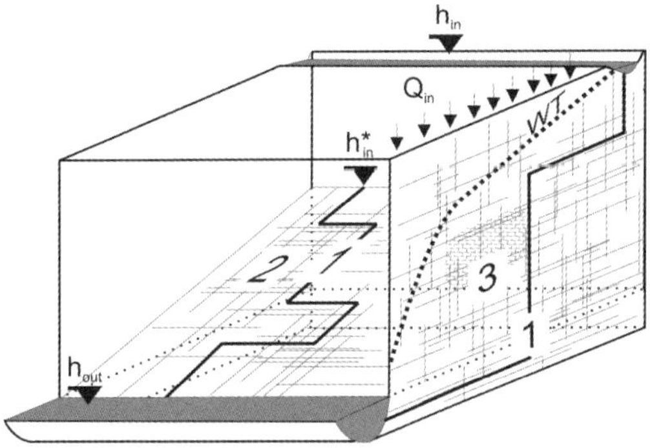

Fig. 1. The basic elements of a karst aquifer discussed in this work. ***1:*** *A single fracture under constant head conditions.* ***2:*** *2D fracture network under constant head conditions.* ***3:*** *Vertical section of an unconfined aquifer with a constant recharge and constant head conditions applied to it. As shown, a dense network of fine fractures and a coarse network of prominent fractures are superimposed to simulate the multiple porosity character of karst aquifers. The thick dashed line WT represents the position of the water table. The hydraulic heads at the inputs and outputs are denoted as* h_{in}, h^*_{in} *and* h_{out}.

Modelling the evolution of such a system in space and time needs several basic ingredients:

1. How does water flow under such conditions through the aquifer? To answer this question we must know the most simple, basic concepts of laminar and turbulent flow through single fractures or conduits.
2. Dissolutional widening depends on the dissolution rates which give the amount of limestone removed from a given area in a known time. These rates usually measured in mol $cm^{-2}s^{-1}$ can be easily converted to retreat of the wall in cm/year by a factor $1.17 \cdot 10^9$ (Dreybrodt, 1988). They depend on many parameters. First of all on the chemical composition of the $H_2O - CO_2 - CaCO_3$ solution. But also on the type of flow and on the widths of the conduits, as we will show later.
3. Dissolutional widening changes the hydrological properties of the aquifer and alters

the flow rates. Therefore flow and dissolutional widening must be coupled, to obtain the evolution in time. These basic ingredients should be combined as a first step in the most simple way by just considering one single conduit. Once the evolution of this basic element of the aquifer is known, combination of many single fractures into a complicated network becomes reasonable. Such networks are not just the sum of their ingredients. They exhibit more complex properties and these give insights into the overwhelming varieties of karst evolution.

We will lead from simple principles to more complex models, and we will try to present the most important processes active in karstification.

2. BASIC INGREDIENTS

2.1 FLOW IN FRACTURES

Fig. 2 illustrates an idealised fracture with plane parallel walls separated by an aperture width a_0. The width of the fracture is b_0 and its length is L. At the left hand side a hydraulic head h injects water into the fracture which leaves at the exit at hydraulic head zero.

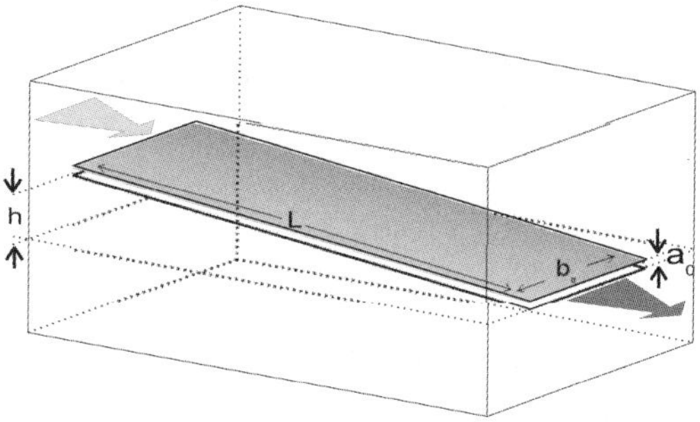

Fig. 2. Uniform fracture with aperture width a_0, *width* b_0 *and length* L. *Calcite aggressive water is driven through it by the time-independent hydraulic head* h. *The goal is to calculate how do the aperture widths and flow rates evolve in time due to dissolutional widening.*

For laminar flow, when each particle in the fluid follows a stable pathway, which never crosses the pathway of any other fluid particle, the flow rate $Q[\mathrm{cm^3 s^{-1}}]$ and the hydraulic head $h[\mathrm{cm}]$ are related by

$$Q = h / R \tag{1}$$

a relation very similar to Ohm's law in electricity, which relates electric current I to voltage V by a resistance R. The resistance R for hydrodynamic flow is well known from the equation of Hagen-Poiseuille (Beek and Muttzall,1975) and is given by

$$R = \frac{12\eta}{\rho g} \cdot \frac{L}{a_0^3 b_0 \cdot M} \tag{2}$$

η is the kinematic viscosity of water, ρ its density, and g earth acceleration constant. M

is a geometrical factor in the order of 1 and depends on the ratio a_0/b_0. For wide fractures $a_0 >> b_0$, $M=1$. For circular conduits one has $a_0 = b_0$ and $M = 0.3$.

After dissolution has changed the profile of a fracture such that the aperture width changes with distance from the entrance. R is then given by a summation over short tubes of length Δx, where $a(x)$ does not change in a significant way. This can be expressed by an integral as

$$R = \frac{12\eta}{\rho g} \int_0^L \frac{dx}{a^3(x)\ b(x) \cdot M(x)} \tag{3}$$

When flow rates exceed a threshold of discharge Q flow becomes turbulent. In this case the motion of each water particle shows large fluctuations from its average flow path and also eddies will occur. As we will see later this has a significant impact on dissolution rates. The threshold when flow becomes turbulent is given by the Reynold's number $\mathrm{Re} = av\,\rho/\eta$, where v is the flow velocity in the conduit.

For smooth fractures and tubes flow becomes turbulent for $Re > 2000$. Then the relation between head and flow rate is no longer linear and the Darcy-Weissbach equation has to be applied (Dreybrodt, 1988). It reads

$$Q = \sqrt{\frac{2gA^2d}{f}} \cdot \sqrt{\frac{h}{L}} \cdot \frac{h}{|h|} \tag{4}$$

where A is the cross-sectional area and d is the hydraulic diameter of the conduit. f is a friction factor given by

$$\frac{1}{\sqrt{f}} = -2 \log_{10} \left[\frac{r}{3.71d} + \frac{2.51\eta}{\rho\sqrt{2gd^3h/L}} \right] \tag{5}$$

r is the roughness of the wall. It is important to note that change to turbulent flow, especially in non-uniform tubes and in nets of tubes alters the distribution of heads and this puts the evolution of karst to a new stage.

2.2 DISSOLUTION OF LIMESTONE

Under conditions of karst where the pH of the solution is about 7 limestone dissolves by the reaction (Plummer et al. 1978)

$$H_2O + CaCO_3 \rightleftarrows Ca^2 + CO_3^{2-} + H_2O \tag{I}$$

If no carbon dioxide is present in the solution saturation is at about 10^{-4} mmol/cm^3. If CO_2 is present the following slow reaction, enhances the solubility of calcite

$$H_2O + CO_2 \rightarrow H^+ + HCO_3 \tag{II}$$

This process delivers a proton which removes the carbonate detached from the mineral by the reaction

$$CO_3^{2-} + H^+ \rightarrow HCO^{3-} \qquad \text{(III)}$$

By this way the ion activity product $\left(CO_3^{2-}\right)\left(Ca^{2+}\right)$ is kept below the solubility constant K_c of calcite. Reactions I to III can be summarized by

$$CaCO_3 + H_2O + CO_2 \rightarrow Ca^{2+} + 2HCO_3^- \qquad \text{(IV)}$$

Thus stoichiometrically for each $CaCO_3$ released from the rock one molecule of CO_2 is consumed by conversion to HCO_3^-. Fig. 3 shows the equilibrium concentration of Ca^{++} with respect to calcite for a solution in equilibrium with a given partial pressure p_{CO_2}. Under such open conditions, where each CO_2 consumed is replaced by one CO_2 entering from the surrounding atmosphere into the solution the equilibrium concentration is given by

$$c_{eq} = 10.75(1-0.139T)\sqrt[3]{p_{CO_2}}\left[\frac{mmol}{cm^3}\right] \qquad (6)$$

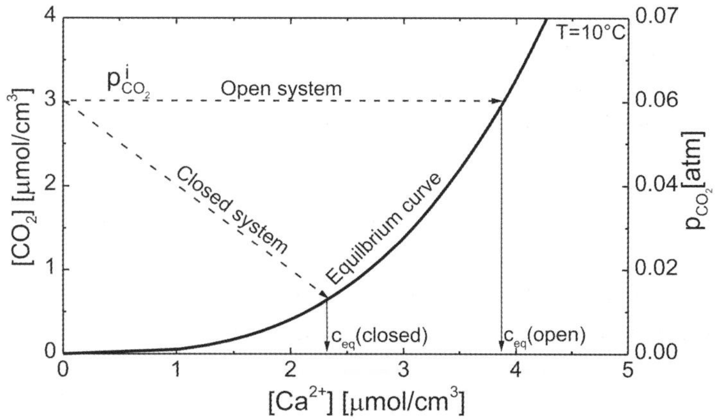

Fig. 3. Chemical pathways of solutions in the open and closed system. The thick line represents the CO_2-Ca^{2+} equilibrium. Dashed lines represent the pathway of solutions in the open and closed system. For each Ca^{2++} released one molecule of CO_2 is needed. For the open system it is replaced from the CO_2 - atmosphere and P_{CO2} stays constant. In the case of the closed system one CO_2 molecule is consumed from the solution. At the intersections between the pathways and the equilibrium curve, the corresponding equilibrium concentrations can be read. The thin solid lines point to these calcium equilibrium concentration.

T is the temperature in °C and p_{CO_2} is in atm. This relation is valid for $p_{CO_2} > 3 \cdot 10^{-4}$ atm. Mostly dissolution in early karstification proceeds under conditions closed to a surrounding atmosphere and CO_2 is not replaced. In this case the CO_2-concentration in the solution drops by the relation

$$[CO_2] = [CO_2]^{\,i} - [Ca^{++}] \tag{7}$$

The straight line in Fig. 3 presents this chemical evolution towards equilibrium. Eqn. 6 is depicted by the lower curve in Fig. 3. The intersection between these two curves represents the equilibrium concentration, when the initial solution was free of Ca und in equilibrium with an initial $p^{i}_{CO_2}$.

Dissolution of limestone in undersaturated water is controlled by three mechanisms:

1. The detachment rate at the surface of the mineral. For karst waters Plummer et al. (1978) experimentally found the following rate

$$F_s = k_3 - k_4 (Ca^{2+})_s (HCO_3^-)_s \tag{8}$$

   k_3 is a constant dependent on temperature, and k_4 depends also on the CO_2-concentration in the solution. The first term k_3 represents dissolution, the second one is the back reaction, which depends on the activities of $(Ca^{2+})_s$ and $(HCO_3^-)_s$ at the surface of the mineral.
2. The ions released must be transported away from this surface into the bulk of the solution, otherwise if they would accumulate there, dissolution would stop. This transport is affected by molecular diffusion. As a consequence concentration gradients build up and the concentrations at the surface are different from those in the bulk.
3. Each CO_3^- detached from the mineral requires one molecule of CO_2 to be reacted to HCO_3^-.

Mass conservation requires that the flux of Ca^{2+} from the surface must be equal to flux of Ca^{2+} transported into the bulk and equal to flux of CO_2 towards the mineral surface. The surface dissolution rates are high, but CO_2-conversion or mass transport may be rate limiting.

CO_2-conversion is a slow process. For pH between 6 and 8 it takes times up to one minute until CO_2 has come to equilibrium with HCO_3^-. If water of volume V dissolves limestone from a surface area *A* mass conservation requires

$$V \cdot \frac{d[CO_2]}{dt} = A \cdot F \tag{9}$$

If the ratio *V/A* becomes small, due to the slow change of $[CO_2]$, which does not depend on *V* or *A* the rates will be limited by CO_2-conversion. Note that for water flowing in a fracture with aperture width 2δ the ratio $V/A = \delta$.

On the other hand if the aperture widths 2δ becomes large the diffusional resistance can also limit rates. Fig. 4 shows dissolution rates for laminar flow in an aperture

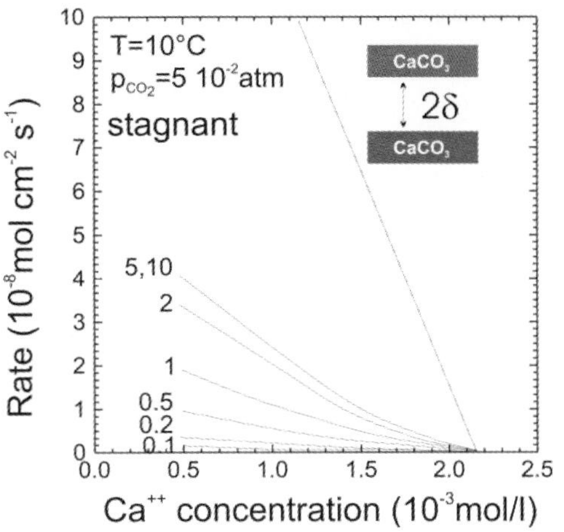

Fig. 4. Dissolution rates from the theoretical model for a free drift run under the conditions of a system closed to CO_2*. The numbers on the curves denote the values of* δ*, i.e, half the distance between the parallel calcite surfaces in* 10^{-3} *cm. For* $\delta = 5 \cdot 10^{-3}$ *cm and* $\delta = 1 \cdot 10^{-2}$ *cm the curves are identical. The uppermost curve gives the rates for fully turbulent motion and* $\delta = 1$ *cm. The insert in the upper right depicts the geometry of the fracture.*

under closed system conditions. The numbers on the curve give the value of δ in 10^{-3} cm. The rates are shown as a function of Ca, how they develop in free drift, when the solution approaches equilibrium. For small $\delta = V/A$, e.g. 10^{-4} cm the rates are very low. This is the region where CO_2 conversion is rate limiting. When δ increases they first increase linearly with δ provided the Ca-concentration is kept constant. With increasing δ the rates approach a limit, where they become almost independent of δ in the region of $5 \cdot 10^{-3}$ cm to 10^{-1} cm. This is of high relevance since this region covers the dimension of initial fracture aperture widths in the early evolution of karst.

All the curves in Fig.4 can be reasonably well approximated by

$$F\,[\text{mol cm}^{-2} s^{-1}] = \alpha\,(c_{eq} - c) \qquad (10)$$

The kinetic constant α [cms^{-1}] is in the order of 10^{-5} cms^{-1} and is listed elsewhere (see Dreybrodt 1988, Buhmann and Dreybrodt 1985). If δ>1cm mass transport becomes rate limiting and the rates are given by

$$F = \frac{\alpha_{\text{lim}}}{1 + 3\,\frac{\alpha_{\text{lim}} \cdot \delta}{D}}\,(c_{eq} - c) = \alpha_D (c_{eq} - c) \qquad (11)$$

where α_{lim} is the kinetic constant at the limit and D is the constant of diffusion for Ca^{2+} ($\approx 10^{-5}$ $cm^2 s^{-1}$). With $\alpha_{\text{lim}} \approx 3.10^{-5}$ cms^{-1} the rates are reduced by a factor of 2 for $\delta \approx 0.3$ cm.

In the early state of karstification flow is laminar, and as we will see later, after short distances of flow away from the entrance the solution comes very close to equilibrium. Close to equilibrium as has been shown experimentally (Svensson and Dreybrodt 1992, Eisenlohr et al, 1997, Dreybrodt and Eisenlohr, 2000) natural calcite carbonates exhibit inhibition of dissolution rates due to impurities in the limestone (e.g. phosphate or silicates). Then the dissolution rates drop by orders of magnitude to a non-linear rate law.

The dissolution rates for limestone are therefore given by

$$F_1 = k_1\,(1 - c/c_{eq}) \text{ for } c \leq c_s,\ k = \alpha c_{eq} \tag{12}$$

$$F_n = k_n(1 - c/c_{eq})^n \text{ for } c > c_s \tag{13}$$

n varies between 3 and 6 and c_s between $0.7c_{eq}$ and $0.9c_{eq}$. It should be noted here that gypsum rocks follow a similar rate law (Jeschke et al, 2001) and that gypsum karst therefore can be modelled the same way as karst in limestone. In the following we use as representative numbers, $k_1 = 4{\cdot}10^{-11}\ mol\ cm^{-2}\ s^{-1}$, $n = 4$, $c_s = 0.9c_{eq}$, and $k_n = 4{\cdot}10^{-8}\ mol\ cm^{-2}\ s^{-1}$ for limestone. It must be stressed here that the values of $k_1 = \alpha c_{eq}$ are constant only for aperture widths from about $5{\cdot}10^{-3}$ cm to 1 mm. According to Eqn.11 they drop for $\delta > 10^{-1}$ cm, as long flow stays laminar. The rate constants k_n are properties of the mineral's surface, solely. Due to inhibition the non linear surface rates close to equilibrium are so low that they become rate limiting. Fig. 5 represents Eqns. 12 and 13. The vertical line separates the region of linear kinetics (n=1) from that of the non linear kinetics ($n = 4$). The dotted line extends the rates of linear kinetics into the non linear region. This visualises the steep drop of inhibited non linear rates in comparison to the linear kinetics.

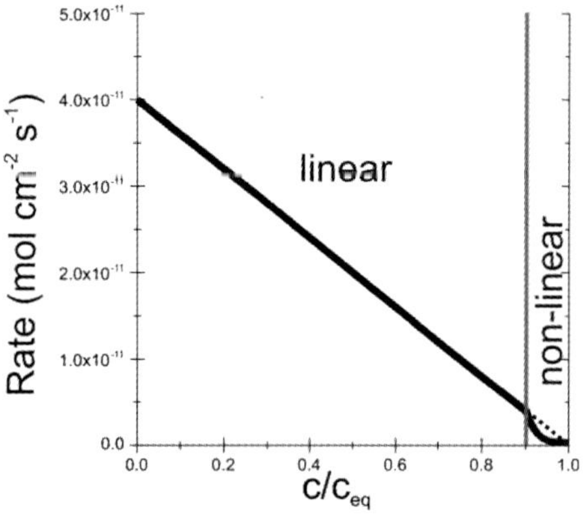

Fig. 5. Dependence of dissolution rates on saturation ratio c/c_{eq}.

When the flow becomes turbulent the bulk of the solution is mixed by the eddies, such that concentration gradients are levelled out. The completely mixed bulk is separated from the surface of the limestone by a diffusion boundary layer (DBL) of thickness ε. Mass transport from the mineral's surface into the bulk and vice versa is affected by molecular diffusion through this layer. The thickness of DBL depends on the hydrodynamic conditions of flow and is given by

$$\varepsilon = a/Sh \tag{14}$$

Sh is the dimensionless Sherwood number given by (Incropera and Dewitt,1996),

$$Sh = \frac{(f/8)\,(\mathrm{Re} - 1000)Sc}{1 + 12.7\sqrt{f/8}\,(Sc^{2/3} - 1)} \tag{15}$$

Re is Reynolds number, f is the friction factor and Sc is the Schmidt number $Sc = \eta/(\rho D)$. For water $Sc \approx 1000$. The resistance to mass transport through the boundary layer is determined also by conversion of CO_2. When the diffusion length of CO_3^{2-}-ions (i.e. the distance a CO_3^{2-}-ion travels from the mineral's surface until it is converted to HCO_3^- ($\lambda \approx 0.02\ cm$) is small compared to ε then diffusion is rate limiting and the effective rate constant k drops with increasing ε. If $\varepsilon \geq \lambda$ than CO_2 conversion becomes rate limiting because it is affected mainly in the boundary layer. Therefore k becomes constant. Detailed numbers are given by Liu and Dreybrodt (1997).

The thickness of the boundary layer Eqn. 14 in our calculations was in the order of several tenth of a mm. Therefore values of $k_1 = 4 \cdot 10^{-11}\ mol/cm^2s$ were used.

3. EARLY KARSTIFICATION OF CONFINED AQUIFERS

3.1 ONE-DIMENSIONAL CONDUITS AT CONSTANT HEAD

As the first basic building block to understand early karst processes, we go back to Fig. 2, which represents some fractures, e.g. a bedding parting. Fig. 6 represents a part of this fracture between x and $x + \Delta x$, where x is the distance from the entrance.

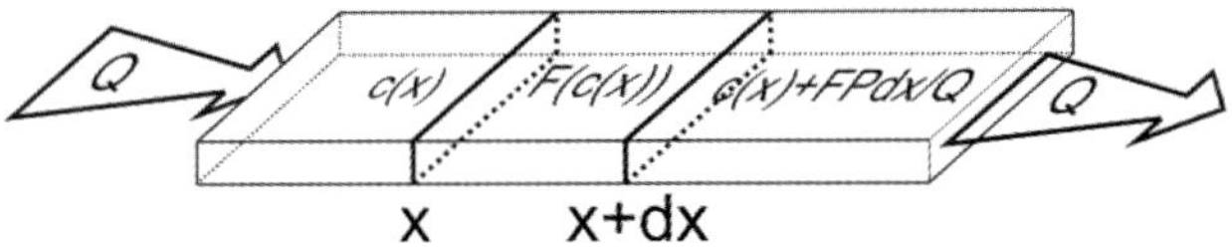

Fig. 6. Mass conservation in the part of the fracture between x *and* x+dx

The widening rate can be calculated by use of Eqns. 12 and 13 everywhere in the fracture if the concentration $c(x)$ along the fracture is known. This can be found as follows. The amount of calcium dissolved from the walls per time unit must be equal to the difference of the amount of calcium entering at x to that leaving at $x + dx$, also related to one time unit. From this we obtain the mass balance equation

$$F(c(x))P(x)dx = v(x) \cdot A(x)dc = Qdc \tag{16}$$

where $A(x)$ is the cross-sectional area at x, $P(x)$ the corresponding perimeter and v the velocity. Due to the continuity of flow the constant flow rate Q through the fracture is given by $v(x) \cdot A(x)dc = Qdc$.

Eqn.16 can be solved if one uses the dissolution rates given in Eqns.12 and13. (Dreybrodt 1996; Dreybrodt and Gabrovšek 2000; Gabrovšek 2000). The solutions are

$$F(x)=\begin{cases} F_1(x)=k_1(1-\frac{c_{in}}{c_{eq}})\ \exp\ (-x/\lambda_1) \text{ for } x<x_s \\ F_n(x)=k_4\left(1-\frac{c_s}{c_{eq}}\right)^n\left(1+\frac{x-x_s}{\lambda_n}\right)^{n/(1-n)} \quad \text{for } x\geq x_s, \end{cases} \tag{17}$$

$$,\lambda_1=\frac{Q\,C_{eq}}{Pk_1} \text{ and } \lambda_n=\frac{Qc_{eq}(1-c_s/c_{eq})^{1-n}}{Pk_n(n-1)}$$

c_{in} is the calcium concentration at the input, P is the perimeter, and x_s is the position where the linear kinetics switches to the non-linear one. Fig. 7 illustrates these solutions. It shows the dissolution rates along a fracture of 1 km length for standard values given in table 1.The solid line shows the dissolution rates for linear kinetics valid up to equilibrium. Note the steep decay in dissolution rates by ten orders of magnitude in the first 5 m of the fracture. Due to such steep exponential decay the rates have dropped to $10^{-30}\,mol/cm^2s$ after the solution has penetrated for 10m, this corresponds to dissolutional widening of 10^{-19} cm/year. Only surface denudation could result then.

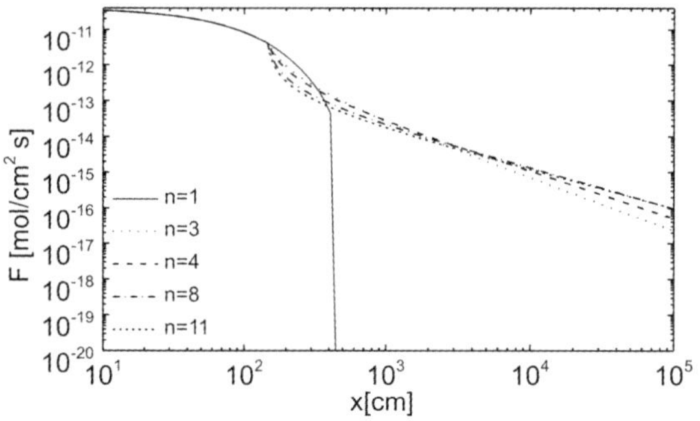

Fig. 7. Dissolution rates along the uniform "standard" fracture for various orders n *of the rate equation as denoted in the figure.*

The dotted lines show the dissolution rates for various n after the rate law has switched to non linearity. Here the rates drop much slower in a hyperbolic way and sufficient dissolution is still active at the exit to widen the fracture with a = *0.02cm* to *0.04cm* in about *100000y*, a geologically realistic time.

The evolution of the fracture widths can now be approached in the following way. In reality a funnel like profile is created because the rates at the input are higher than those at the exit. To a first approach we assume, however, that the rates at the exit are active all along the entire fracture thus maintaining a profile of parallel planes. For this we can use the analytical solutions of Eqn.16. Widening in the fracture is even and given by

$$\frac{da}{dt}=2\gamma\cdot F(L,t) \tag{18}$$

with

$$F(L,t) = k_n \cdot \left(1 - \frac{c_s}{c_{eq}}\right)^n \cdot \left\{\frac{L \cdot a_0^3}{\lambda_{n,t=0}\, a^3(t)} + 1\right\}^{-n/(n-1)} \tag{19}$$

For most relevant cases, when the inflowing solution has a calcium concentration below x_s the summand *1* in the bracket can be safely neglected and Eqn. 18 can be integrated after inserting Eqn. 19.The result is

$$a(t) = a_0 (1 - t / T_B)^{\frac{1-n}{2n+1}} \tag{20}$$

with

$$T_B = \frac{1}{2\gamma} \cdot \frac{n-1}{2n+1} \cdot \frac{a_0}{F(L,0)} \tag{21}$$

Inserting the equation for *F(L,0)* we obtain the relation:

$$T_B = \frac{1}{2\gamma} \cdot \frac{n-1}{2n+1} \cdot \left(\frac{1}{a_0}\right)^{\frac{2n+1}{n-1}} \left(\frac{24\eta L^2 (n-1)}{\rho g h c_{eq}}\right)^{\frac{n}{n-1}} (k_n)^{\frac{1}{n-1}} \tag{22}$$

The evolution *a(t)* is illustrated by Fig. 8. Initially a slow increase is observed. But

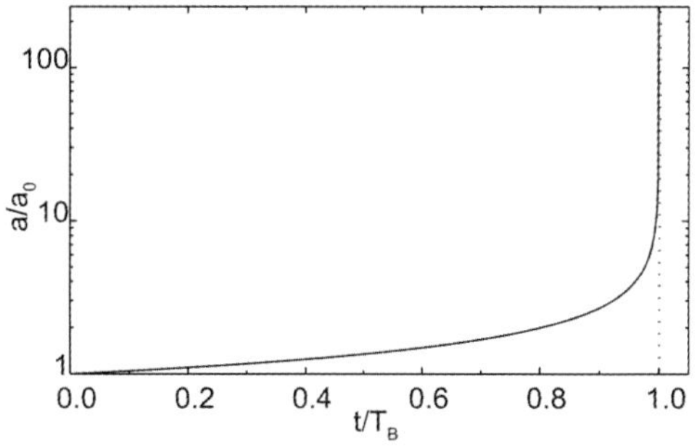

Fig. 8. Evolution of fracture aperture widths at the exit as given by Eqn.20. The dotted vertical line represents the pole of the function a(t).

increasing *a(t)* creates increasing dissolution rates at the exit and vice versa. This positive feedback loop then finally creates the steep increase in a(t) and correspondingly in flow rate *Q* through the fracture.

One point is of utmost importance. The breakthrough time T_B in Eqn. 22 contains the parameters which determine the time scale of early karstification. T_B increases drastically with decreasing aperture width (exponent $(2n+1)/(n-1)$), it increases also with *L* (exponent *2n/n*-1). The dependence on head *h* is less drastic (exponent -*n/*(*n*-1)). A most important chemical parameter is c_{eq}. For bare karst areas, when rainwater with atmospheric P_{CO2} enters into the fractures c_{eq} under closed condition is at about 10^{-4} mmol/cm^3, in contrast to $c_{eq} = 2 \cdot 10^{-3}$ mmol/cm^3 in vegetated areas. This increases breakthrough times by at least one order of magnitude.

The above considerations are only approximative. Numerical solutions of the equations are more exact. Fig. 9 shows the result of digital modelling of our standard case. Its parameters are listed in Table 1.

Description	Name	Unit	Initial or Standard value
Aperture width	a_0	*cm*	*0.02*
Fracture length	L	*cm*	10^5
Fracture width	b_0	*cm*	*100*
Hydraulic gradient	i		*0.05*
Order of non linear kinetics	n		*4*
Linear kinetics constant	k_1	mol/cm^2s	$4\cdot10^{-11}$
Non linear kinetics constant	k_n	mol/cm^2s	$4\cdot10^{-8}$
Concentration of calcium	c	mol/cm^3	
Switch concentration	c_s	mol/cm^3	$1{\cdot}8\cdot10^{-6}$
Equilibrium concentration	c_{eq}	mol/cm^3	$2\cdot10^{-6}$
Viscosity of the solution		g/cms	$1{\cdot}2\cdot10^{-2}$
Density of the solution		g/cm^3	*1*

***Table 1**: Parameters used for the model of the evolution of a single fracture*

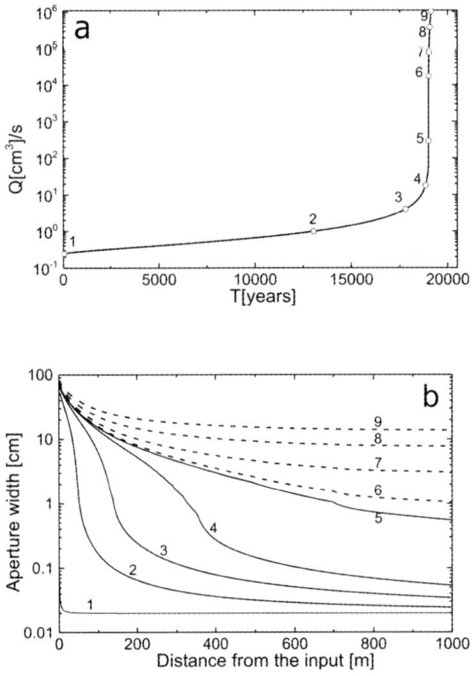

Fig. 9a in a logarithmic plot depicts as a function of time the flow rate through an initially plane parallel fracture with initial parameters as given in Table 1. The flow rate exhibits a slow increase that is enhanced in time until it is drastically accelerated to such an amount that they exceed the water available at the surface. At this breakthrough time T_B the hydraulic head breaks down, and the initial phase of laminar flow through the fracture is terminated. Fig. 9b represents the evolution of the aperture widths along the fracture for various times depicted by points 1 to 9 in Fig. 9a. The widening rates ($2\gamma F$) are shown by Fig. 9c. In the beginning where the fracture widths at the entrance (2-4) are below 1mm the rates are given by Eqns. 12 and 13. They are maximal at $c=0$. Later when the entrance widens, molecular diffusion becomes rate limiting (cf. Eqn. 11) and the rates close to the entrance drop. But they rise downstream as the aperture widths decrease. Finally when 4th order nonlinear kinetics becomes active rates are determined by Eqn.13 and they drop again. After breakthrough when flow is turbulent (dashed lines) the rates become high and even along the conduit. Details of this dynamic behaviour are given in the literature. (Dreybrodt, 1988, 1990, 1996; Dreybrodt and Gabrovšek, 2000). Fig. 9d shows the saturation ratio c/c_{eq} along the fracture. At the beginning the ratio rises steeply until $c=c_s$ where the higher kinetics become active causing a further slow increase. With increasing flow rate the region of first order kinetics ($c<c_s$) penetrates downstream until at breakthrough the concentration drops drastically.

To elucidate the mechanisms of the feedback loop Fig. 9e depicts the head distribution along the fracture. In the beginning when the profile is even $a(x)=a_0$ there is a linear decline from h to zero. The funnel shaped profile at later times distorts this decline. In the widened parts the head becomes close to the boundary value h, and at the bottleneck h declines from this value to zero at the output. Thus the hydraulic gradient increases as this bottleneck becomes shorter. Consequently flow velocity increases and dissolution rates at the exit are enhanced. After breakthrough flow becomes turbulent and the head distribution changes (dashed curves) and the decline along the fracture becomes more even. This is also important for 2 or 3-dimensional nets, because after breakthrough this new distribution of heads determines the further evolution of the aquifer.

So far we have considered that the inflowing solution is allogenic water far

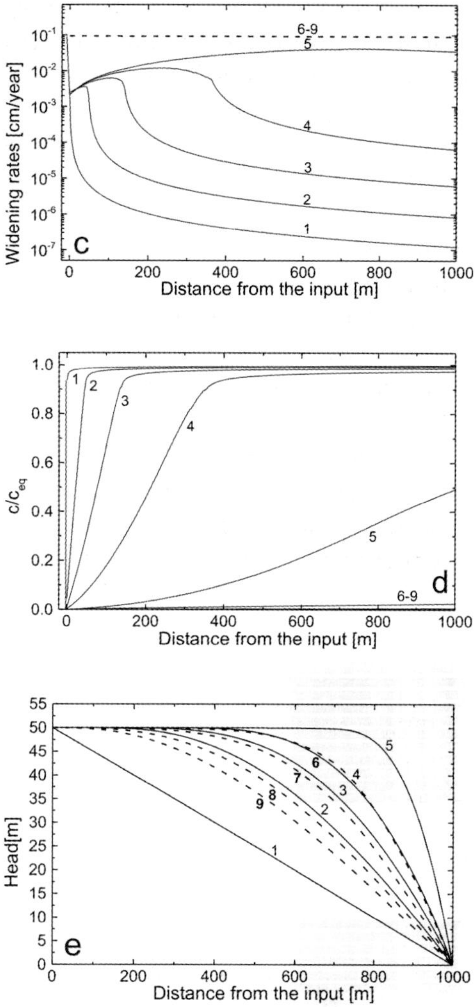

Fig. 9. Evolution of a single fracture. ***a)*** *Evolution of the flow rate as a function of time. Open circles mark the points where the profiles in Figs. 9b-9e are shown. The steep increase of the flow rate marks breakthrough time. Note the logarithmic scale on* Q(t). ***b)*** *Profiles of the aperture widths* a(x) *recorded at various times: 0,13.1ky, 17.8ky, 18.85ky, 19.01ky, 19.014ky, 19.032ky, 19.082ky, 19.152ky, labeled from 1-9 respectively. Full lines indicate laminar flow and dashed lines turbulent flow.* ***c)*** *Widening rates along the fracture at times given above.* ***d)*** *Concentration profiles.* ***e)*** *Distribution of hydraulic heads along the fractures at the given times.*

away from equilibrium with respect to calcite. We now ask the question: What happens if the inflowing solution is closer to equilibrium. To answer this we consider Eqn. 17, which gives the dissolution rates along a plane parallel fracture. When c_{in} approaches c_{eq}, the penetration length λ_n approaches infinity and the rates become almost constant along the entire fracture, close to the maximal value at the input. Further increase in flow, will further increase the value of λ_n without significant influence to the rates. The reason is that the second term in the bracket of Eqn.17 becomes small with respect to the summand 1. Therefore one expects that the feedback loop gradually looses influence when c_{in} approaches c_{eq}.

This is shown by Fig. 10. It depicts the flow rates versus time for a single conduit with differing input concentrations. Curves 1 to 5, with input concentrations equal or below $0.95c_{eq}$, clearly exhibit breakthrough behaviour. When c_{in} comes closer to c_{eq} as in curve 6 ($c_{in} = 0.975c_{eq}$) flow rates increase steadily because dissolutional widening becomes even along the entire tube at maximal possible rate $k_n \cdot (1 - c_{in}/c_{eg})^n$ during the entire time of evolution. In that case karstification becomes very slow, but it may create horizons of increased permeability, which later, when geological conditions change may be utilised for conduit growth. Such horizons have been suggested by Lowe and Gunn (1997).

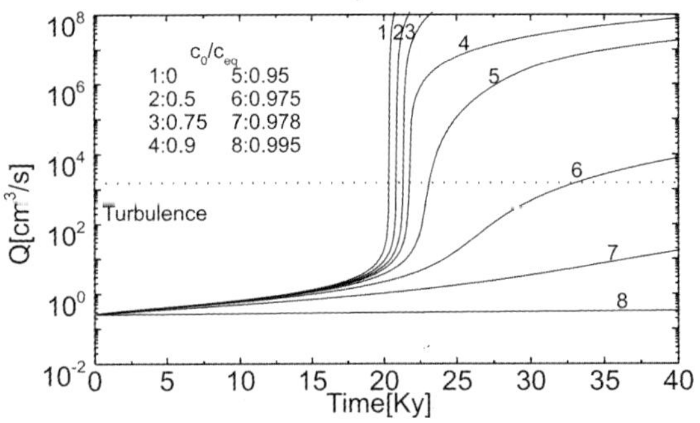

Fig. 10. The evolution of flow rate in the standard fracture for various values of c_0/c_{eq} *as denoted in the figure.*

3.2 THE HETEROGENEOUS FRACTURE

In the examples discussed up to now all chemical parameters c_{eq}, k_n, n were assumed as constant along the entire fracture length. This is highly idealistic. In nature karst conduits may have sections of varying lithology and therefore with varying values of n and k_n. Subterranean sources of CO_2 could enter into fractures and increase the solubility of limestone reflected by an increase of c_{eq}. In this section we will shortly discuss the influence of such new conditions on breakthrough time (Gabrovšek et al., 2000, Gabrovsek, 2000).

Fig. 11 depicts the heterogeneous standard fracture, which exhibits different properties, such as different dissolution kinetics or differing c_{eq}, in its entrance part for $x \leq KL$ and the exit region for $x > KL$.

First we assume differing dissolution kinetics with $k_{n1} = 4 \cdot 10^{-8}$ *mol/cm²s* and $n_1 = 4$ in the first half of the fracture (K = 0.5) and $k_{n2} = 4 \cdot 10^{-6}$ *mol/cm²s* and $n_2 = 6$ in the remaining part.

Fig. 12 shows the numerical results for the standard fracture with $n_1 = 4$ and $n_2 = 6$ (a,b,c) and for the reverse case, when $n_1 = 6$ and $n_2 = 4$ (d,e,f). Both fractures show breakthrough behaviour, but at quite different time scales.

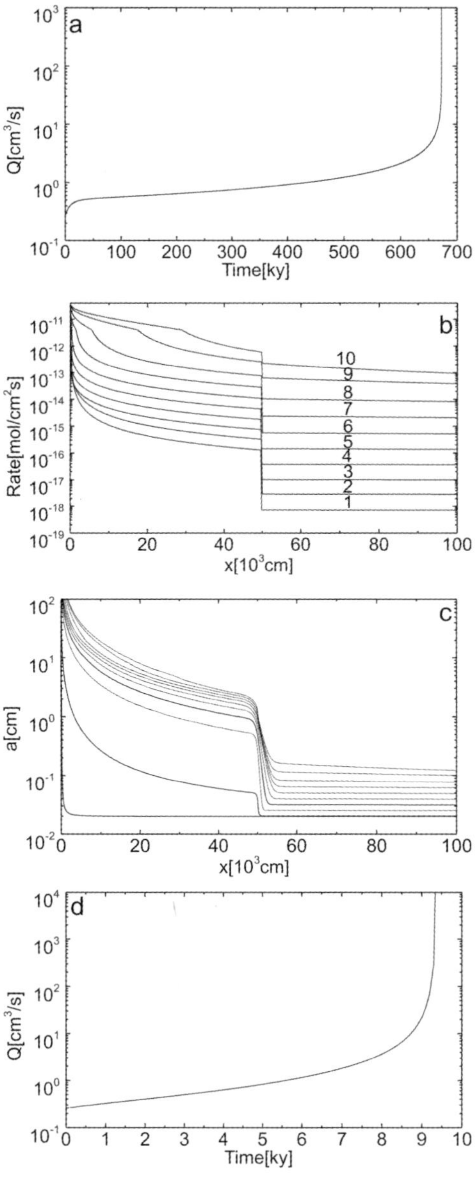

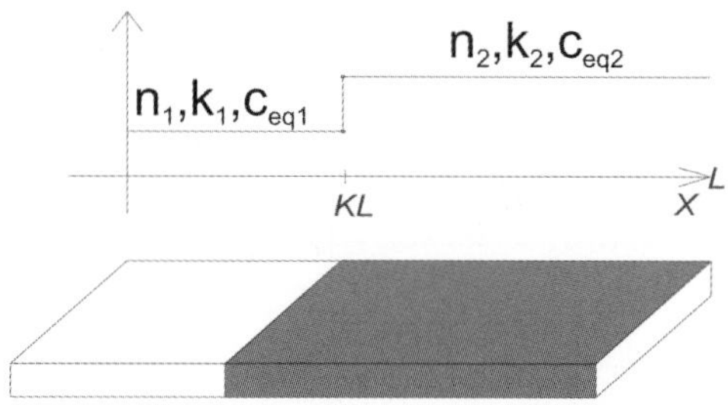

Fig. 11. Conceptual model of a heterogeneous fracture with change of kinetic properties (n, k_n) *or equilibrium concentration at* x=KL.

For $n_1 < n_2$ the dissolution rates drop drastically when the solution encounters the border of changing lithology. Since the solution is close to saturation the dissolution rates, shown by Fig. 12b, remain constant from then on. After the time of 45ky the first half of the fracture has opened up to such an extent that the hydraulic head remains close to the input head and the head loss from h to base level zero is along the second half. With increasing widths of this half flowrates increase such that the concentration at the boundary becomes sufficiently high to switch on the feed back loop causing breakthrough. Breakthrough time is greatly influenced by the low dissolution rates at the exit of the fracture and is substantially longer than in the homogeneous standard fracture (cf. Fig. 9).

For $n_1 = 6$ and $n_2 = 4$ (Fig. 12 d-f) the dissolution rates are boosted up when the solution meets the border. Due to the significantly lower dissolution rates in the entrance half the concentrations remain sufficiently high such that breakthrough is dominated by the kinetics with $n_2 = 4$ in the exit part. Compared to the first case the initial rates at the exit are higher by

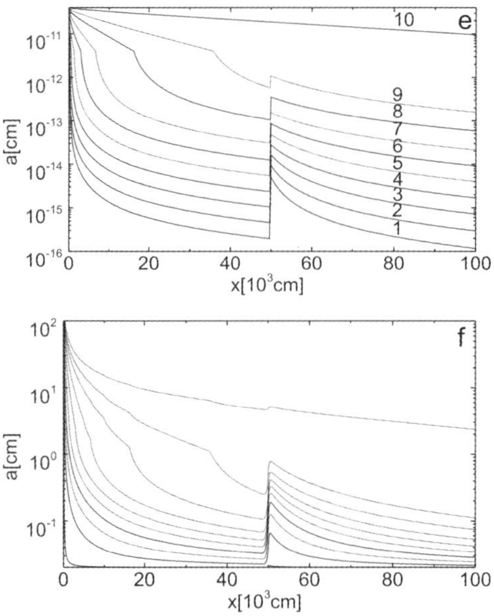

*Fig. 12. **a)** Evolution of flow rates in time for the standard fracture with* $n_1 = 4$, $n_2 = 6$ *and* $K = 0.5$ ***(b,c)** Profiles of dissolution rates and aperture widths for* $n_1 = 4$, $n_2 = 6$ *and* $K = 0.5$ *plotted at 0.1, 45.8, 452.1, 599.4, 649.1, 665.5, 670.9,672.5, 673 and 673.1ky marked from 1-10 respectively. **d)** Evolution of flow rate in time for the standard fracture with* $n_1 = 6$, $n_2 = 4$ *and* $K = 0.5$. ***e,f)** Profiles of dissolution rates and aperture widths for* $n_1 = 6$, $n_2 = 4$ *and* $K = 0.5$ *at 0.1, 3.3, 5.8, 7.3, 8.2, 8.7,9, 9.2, 9.3 and 9.4 ky marked from 1-10 respectively.*

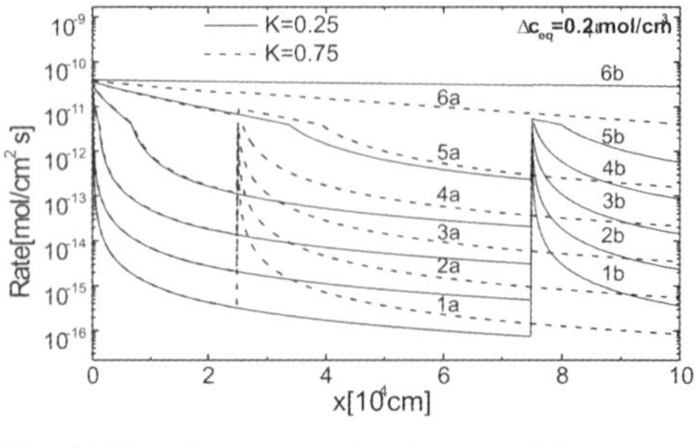

Fig. 13. Dissolution rates for the point CO_2 *input at* $K = 0.25$ *(dashed lines) recorded at 0.1, 6.5, 9.4, 10.13, 10.35, 10.39 ky (labeled from 1a to 6a respectively) and the for the input at (full lines) recorded at 0.1, 6.93, 10.19, 11.07, 11.27, 11.31 ky (labeled from 1b to 6b respectively).*

two orders of magnitude. Therefore breakthrough time is only 10ky, even less than that of the standard fracture. These examples show that differing lithologies have a strong impact on karstification and cannot be neglected. More details on this issue are reported by Gabrovšek (2000), and by Dreybrodt and Siemers (2000).

We now turn to the case where c_{eq} changes step like by injection of subterranean carbon dioxide. Fig. 13 shows the numerical results of the dissolution rates along the standard fracture for two cases. **a)** $K = 0.25$ and **b)** $K = 0.75$. At these positions $c_{eq} = 2 \cdot 10^{-6}$ mol/cm^3 increases by $\Delta c_{eq} = 2 \cdot 10^{-7}$ $mol\ cm^{-3}$. With an increase of c_{eq} the rates are enhanced, where CO_2 is injected into the fracture and consequently dissolutional widening becomes faster

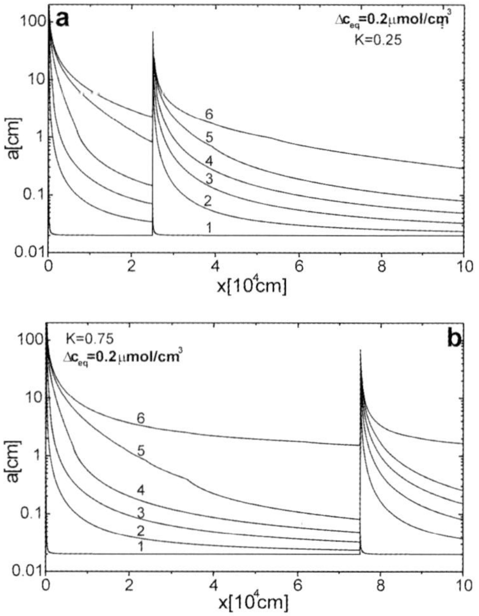

*Fig. 14. **a)** Profiles of aperture widths for the input of* CO_2 *at* $K=0.25$*, recorded at the times given in Fig. 13, labeled from 1-6. **b)** Profiles of aperture widths for the input of* CO_2 *at* $K=0.75$*, recorded at the times given in Fig. 13, labeled from 1-6.*

there. The fracture profiles are depicted by Fig. 14 for both cases. Fig. 15 illustrates the breakthrough behaviour for the cases *K=1* (standard fracture), *K = 0.25* (Fig. 14a), *K = 0.75* (Fig. 14b), and *K = 0.9*. In all cases of CO_2- injection breakthrough times are reduced. Further details are published by Gabrovšek et al. (2000). It should be noted here that also injection of solutions with different chemical composition can increase c_{eq}, e.g. mixing corrosion, and reduce breakthrough times.

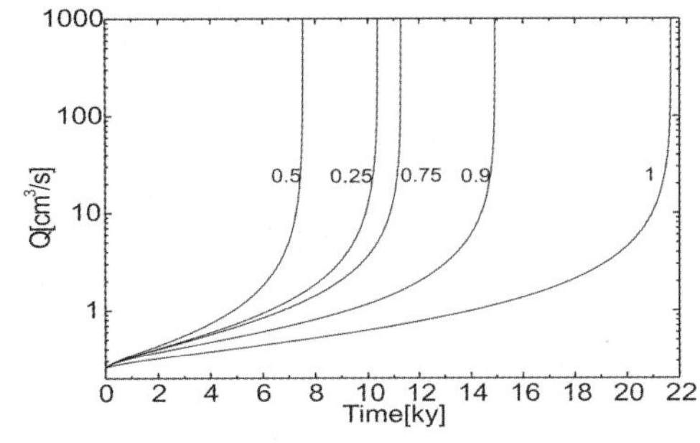

Fig. 15. Breakthrough times for the standard fracture with CO_2-input at x=KL for various values of.

3.3 EVOLUTION OF CAVES IN 2-DIMENSIONAL NETS OF FRACTURES

To approach further to reality we consider a confined aquifer consisting of a limestone bed dipping downward, which is dissected by narrow initial fractures. This is shown schematically by the model domain in Fig. 16. The bed dips from left to right. The left hand side has input points, where the head and the chemical composition of the inflowing water can be defined individually for each input point. The left hand side is at base level, i.e. *h=0*. The aperture width of each fracture can be assigned individually. By this way it is possible to model the statistical properties of fracture widths. In the following we use a log-normal distribution of fracture widths with average $\overline{a}_0 = 0.02$ cm and $\sigma = 0.01$ cm. It is also possible to use bi-modal distributions to simulate a coarse net of wide fractures embedded into a dense net (continuum) of narrow fractures to account for the double-porosity properties of karst aquifers (Sauter, 1992).

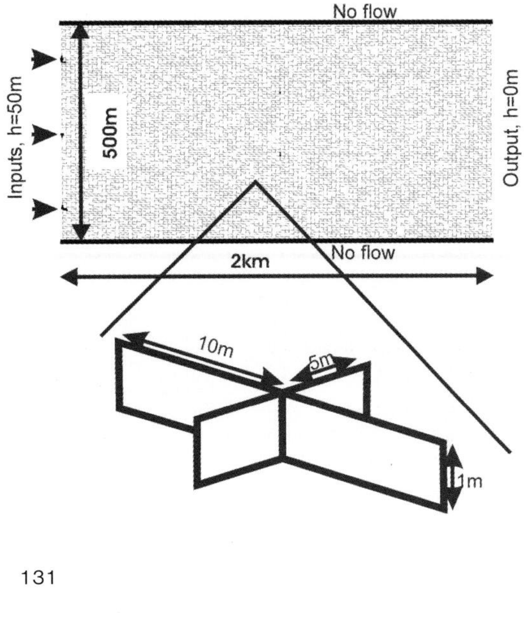

Fig. 16. Modelling domain of its 2-dimensional fracture network. The length of the domain is 2km, the width 500m. Fracture spacing is 10m x 5m. Each fracture has uniform initial aperture width, which is determined by a log-normal distribution over the entire set of fractures. There are three inputs on the left side of the domain at h=50 m and a series of outputs on the right hand side at h=0.

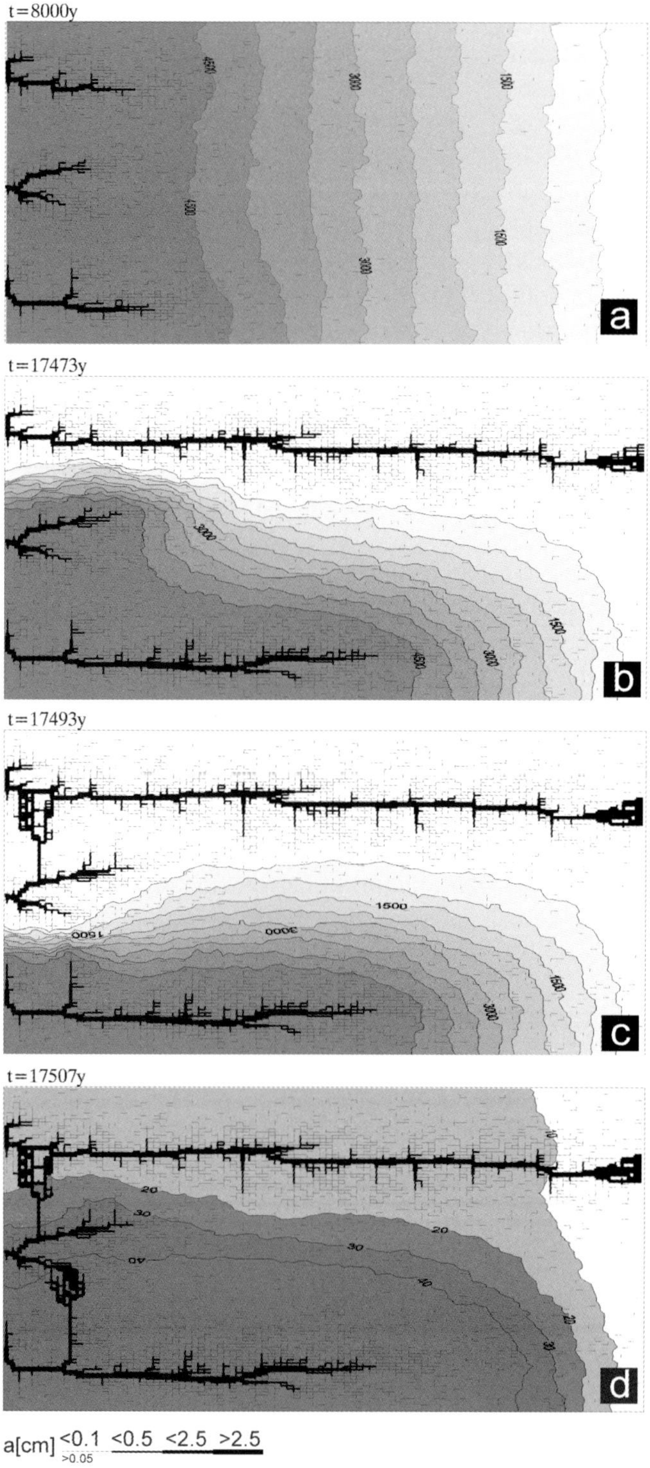

To model the evolution of conduits in such nets one has to calculate the distribution of hydraulic heads at all the nodes in the net and from these the flow rate through each fracture. Furthermore one must know the chemical composition of the solution at each node to couple the flow to the chemical dissolution model in each single fracture. Technical details of this procedure

Fig. 17. Distribution of aperture widths and hydraulic head isolines at various times for the domain presented in Fig.16. Hydraulic head at the left hand side is set to 50m and 0 at the right-hand side. Water at all inputs is in equilibrium with pCO_2=0.05atm. All fractures smaller than 0.05 cm have been omitted. The bar code indicates the numerical values.

are described by Siemers and Dreybrodt (1998) and by Gabrovšek (2000). The parameters of the model domain are $\overline{a}_0 = 0.02$ cm, $\sigma = 0.01$ cm, h = 50 m, the length L of the domain is 2km and its width 500 m. The upper and the lower boundaries are impermeable.We first apply our modelling efforts to the high-dip model of Ford and Ewers (see Ford and Williams, 1989). Fig. 17 shows the evolution with 3 inputs with equal chemical composition and equal heads.

Fig. 17a depicts the situation after 8000 years. Several conduits have grown downstream. At approx. 17470 (Fig. 17b) years the upper has reached base level and breakthrough occurs. Therefore the constant head boundary condition at this input is replaced by a constant flow rate at that input. Thus the hydraulic head in this conduit drops to values close to base level, as can be seen from the pressure isolines in the figures. This directs flow from the conduits which have not reached base level towards the master conduit. Therefore they integrate into a common system. When such a conduit reaches the leading one breakthrough occurs (Fig. 17c and d) and again the constant head condition at the input is changed to constant flow. The distribution of flow rates within the network is illustrated by Fig. 19.

The rates are depicted in units of Q_{max} which is the maximal flow rate through a fracture which occurs in the net. Note that Q_{max} increases in time. As one visualises from Fig. 19a flow is widely distributed over the net initially. As the conduits grow down head the flow is radiating into the net from their tips. After breakthrough flow is concentrated in the mayor conduits (Figs. 19b-d). The evolution of the flow rates through the aquifer is depicted by Fig. 18 (curve1), which also shows the subsequent breakthrough events. This scenario shows a competition between the growing conduits. Prior to breakthrough each of these propagates down head. The breakthrough time for such single 1-dimensional channels is therefore similar as in Eqn. 22, where a_0 has to be replaced by the average initial aperture width along the conduit and L must be replaced by its total length. Since these values, due to the statistical distribution of fracture widths are different for each of the evolving conduits the one with shortest breakthrough time wins the race. Siemers and Dreybrodt (1998) have shown by a sensitivity analysis to the various parameters that Eqn.22 is applicable for the breakthrough time in two-dimensional nets

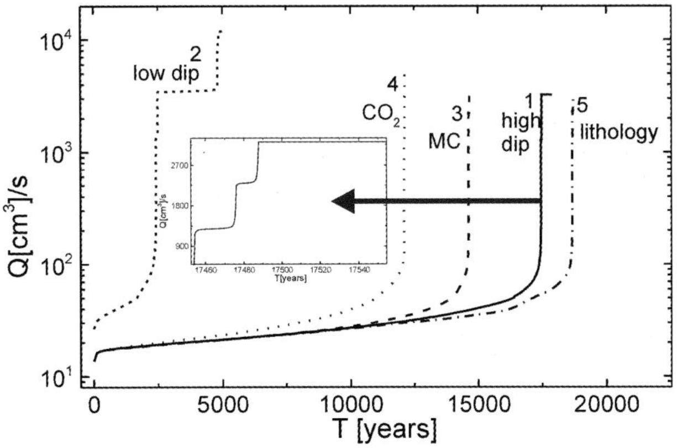

Fig. 18. Evolution of total flow through the network in time for all 2-dimensional cases. Insert shows the sequential breakthroughs in the high-dip model (Figs. 17 and 19).

under constant head conditions. It should be noted here, that the breakthrough time for a defined conduit, where length and average a_0 are exactly known, can be significantly shorter, than that of an isolated one-dimensional conduit. The reason for this is that a conduit embedded into a net of fractures looses fluid into the net (see Fig. 19a,b). Therefore under constant head

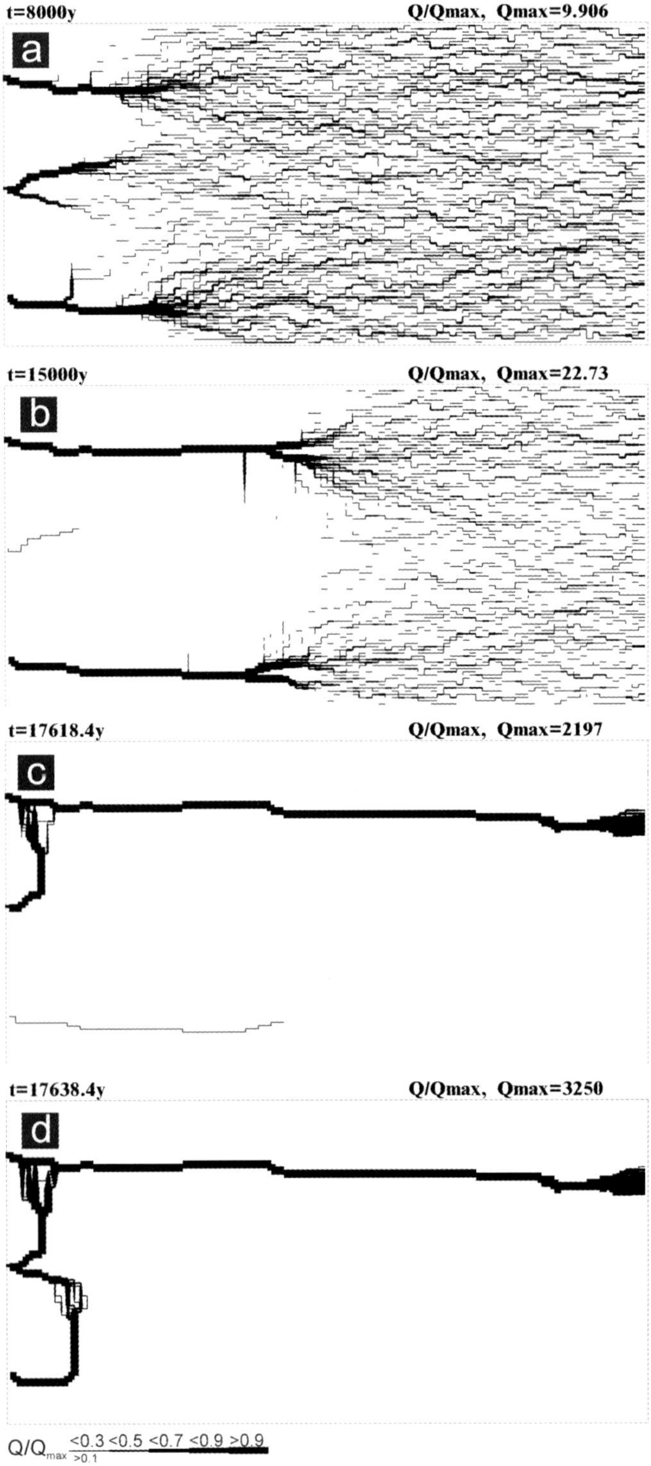

Fig. 19. Flow pattern in the network at the same times as in Fig. 17. Line's thickneses in the bar code represent the values of Q/Q_{max}, where Q_{max} is the flow rate through the fracture with highest flow.

conditions more aggressive solution enters into this fracture and enhances dissolutional widening (Romanov et al. 2002a).

As a next example we discuss the low-dip-model by Ewers and Ford. In this case two additional inputs are placed in the central section of the aquifer, both with equal heads and equal chemical composition of the solutions as those at the left hand side of the domain. This is illustrated by Fig. 20. After 2000 years (a) channels from these inputs have propagated downstream. No conduits can grow from the inputs at the left hand boundary, because these have only negligible head difference to the central region. After 2470 years (b) the conduits exhibit a breakthrough and integrate together similar as in the high dip case. This changes the hydraulic head distribution and conduits from the inputs at the left hand side grow towards these channels. Each row of inputs behaves similar as the high-dip model, and an integration of their conduit systems grows upwards (Figs. 20 c,d).

At each breakthrough event the constant head condition at the corresponding input is replaced by constant flow. This causes changes in the distribution of hydraulic heads, which direct growing channels towards conduits of constant flow rate, or in other words head zero. The evolution of flow rates is depicted by Fig. 18, curve 2.

During the early evolution of a karst aquifer prior to breakthrough the concentrations of the solutions within the karst aquifer are very close to saturation (cf. Fig 9c, single fracture). If the chemical composition of the waters at the inputs are different with respect to initial P_{CO2} and these waters mix somewhere within the aquifer mixing corrosion will boost up dissolution rates. To show the impact of mixing corrosion to the evolution of karst we have changed the chemical composition at the central input in the high-dip model shown by Fig. 17 and have left everything else unchanged. Fig. 21 shows the result.

In contrast to the evolution with equal input chemistry in Fig.17, where the outer conduits grow simultaneously, now the middle conduit has advanced significantly. The outer conduits have stopped growth at 12000y. The reason for this is that during the early phase of evolution water from the two outer inputs injected into system of narrow fractures mixes with water from the central input. Therefore dissolutional widening by mixing corrosion increases the average fracture widths to such an extent that the central conduits gain sufficient advantage to reach base level first. After breakthrough growth of the outer channels is directed towards the central one. The evolution of flow rates is shown in Fig. 18, curve 3.

This example shows that changes in the chemical parameters are of utmost importance. Changes in vegetation can alter the chemical composition of the input waters and can divert the evolving cave patterns to a high extent. By this way climate can effect cave evolution. Details on the effect of mixing corrosion are reported by Gabrovšek and Dreybrodt (2000) and Romanov et al. (2002b).

When subterranean sources of CO_2 either by volcanic origin or by microbial activity are present in the aquifer dissolutional widening is enhanced in the regions neighbouring such inputs. Therefore these regions favour the evolution of conduits growing to

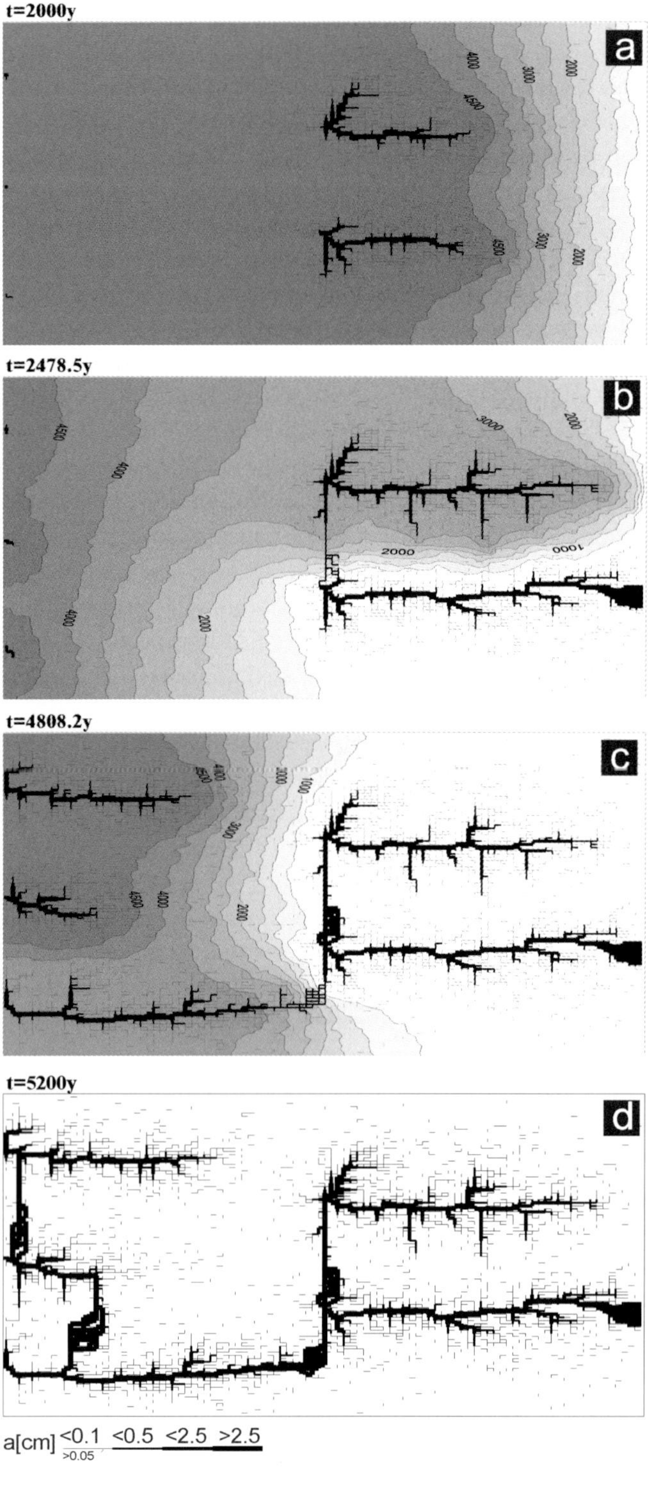

their direction.Fig. 22 shows such an example. Here a point source of CO_2, which raises c_{eq} by ten percent is located in the middle of aquifer. From this input points due to the enhanced dissolution rate a channel grows down head, which is joined by the upper conduit.

Comparison of the evolution compared to that in Fig. 17 shows the strong influence of subterranean

Fig. 20. Aperture widths and hydraulic heads at various time for the low-dip model. Same settings as in Fig.17, but two inputs at h=50m are added to the middle of the domain.

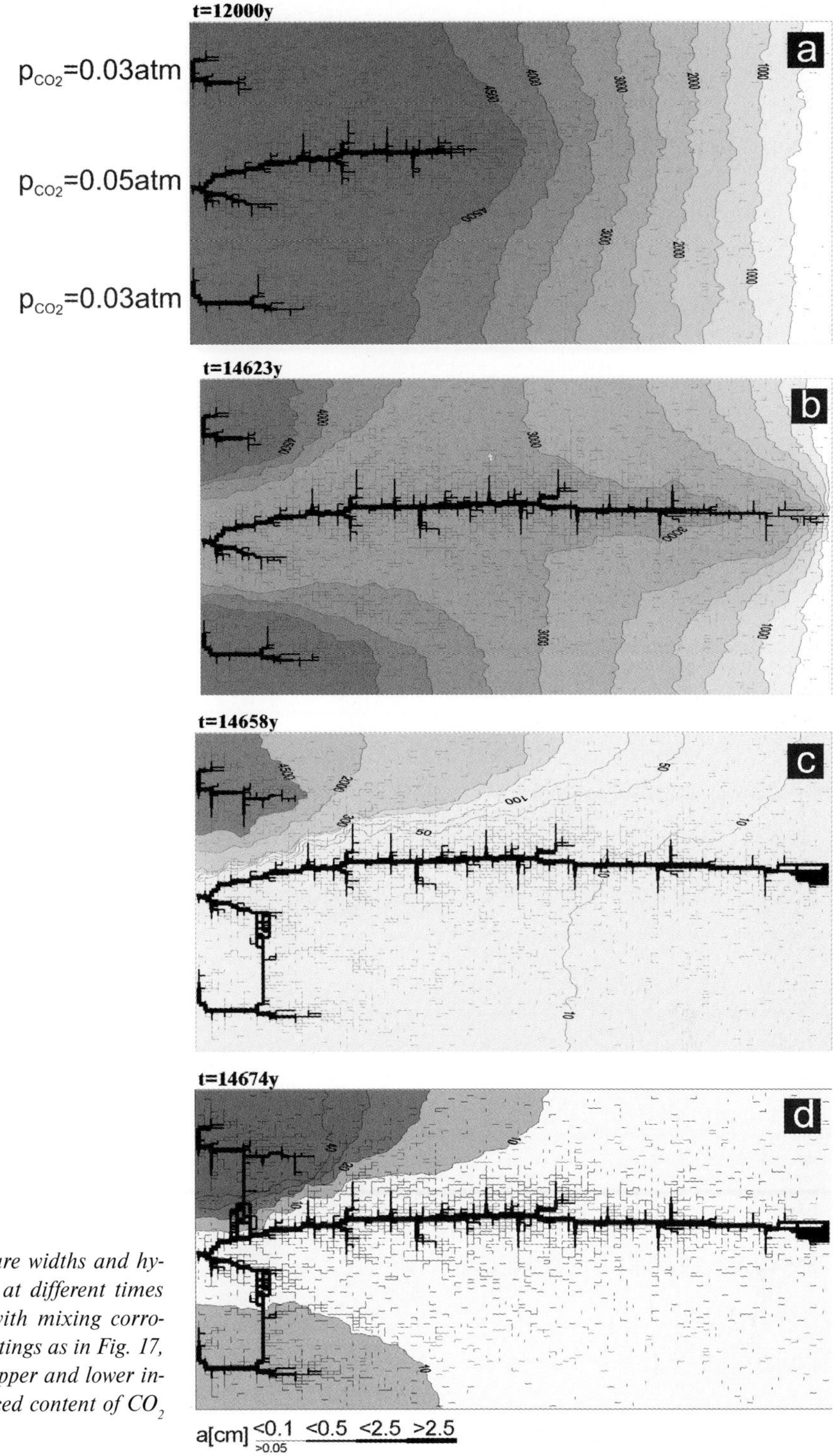

Fig. 21. Aperture widths and hydraulic heads at different times for the case with mixing corrosion. Same settings as in Fig. 17, but water at upper and lower inputs has reduced content of CO_2 (pCO_2=0.03)

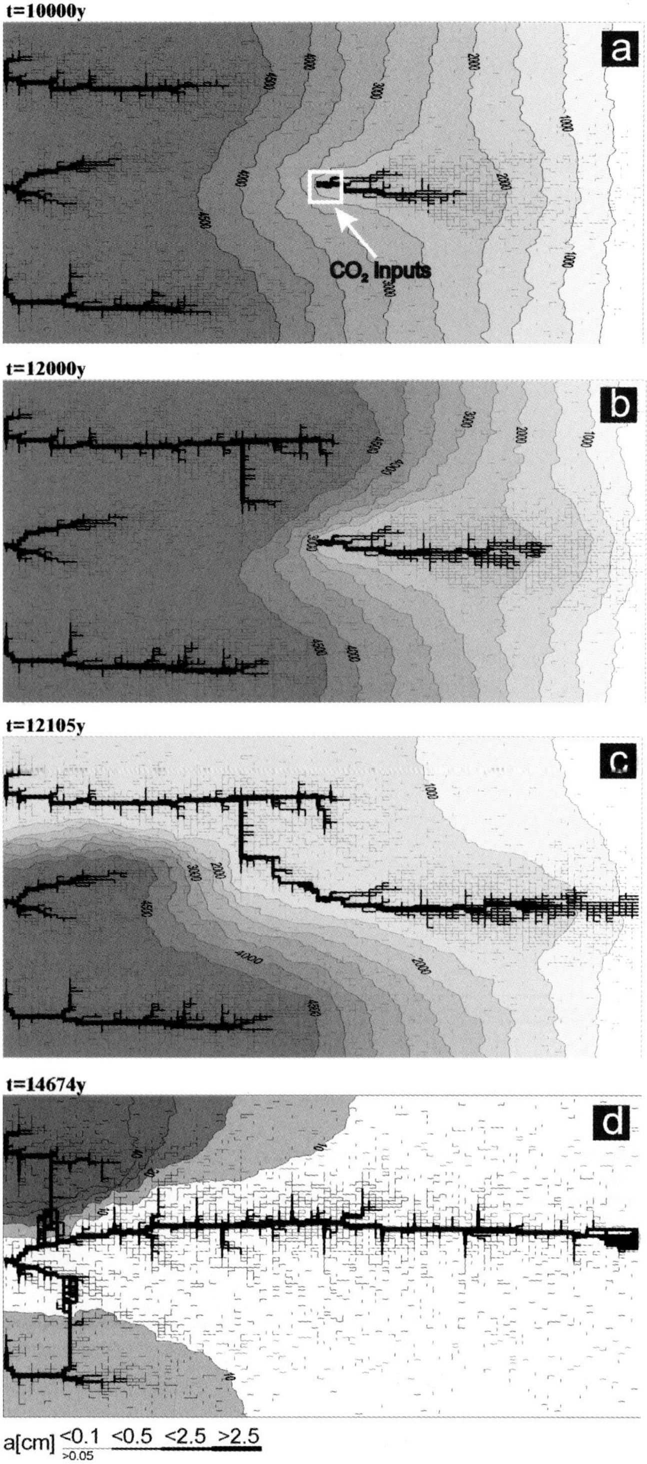

Fig. 22. *High-dip model (Fig. 17) with a CO_2 input. pCO_2 in the region marked in Fig. 22a is set to 0.05atm.*

CO_2 sources. This is also reflected by the evolution of the flow rates shown in Fig.18, curve 4. Further details have been published by Gabrovšek and Dreybrodt (2000).

Varying lithology can change the parameters of the dissolution kinetics (Eisenlohr et al. 1999). Fig. 23 shows the evolution of the aquifer, when its middle part is composed of limestone with $n = 6, k_n = 4 \cdot 10^{-6} mol / cm^2 s$ whereas the outer parts remain unchanged with n=4. Due to the altered kinetics dissolutions rates in the middle part drop, when they are encountered by the solution and channels grow only in the input part with n=4. When such a channel has reached the border between the two lithologies channels grow down head until a first reaches base level and breakthrough occurs. The flow rates for this case are shown by Fig.18, curve 5.

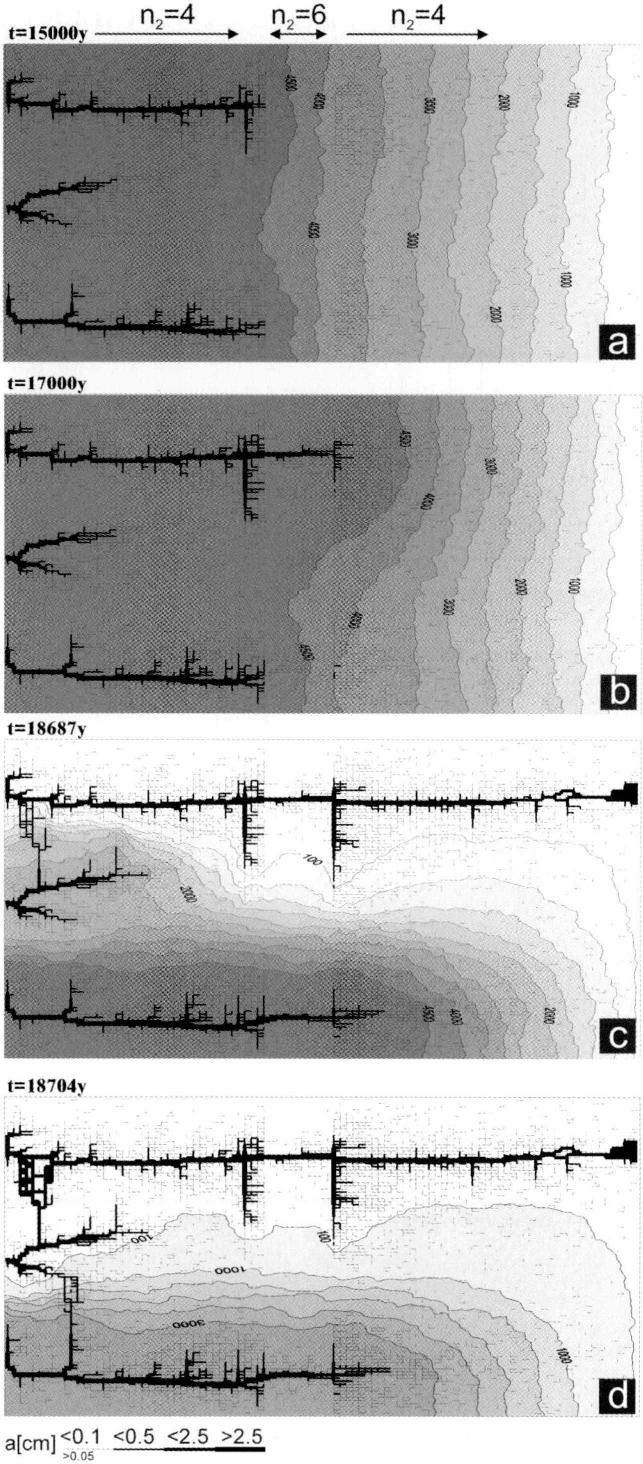

Fig. 23. High-dip (Fig. 17) model with changing lithology. As marked in Fig. 23a, the kinetic order changes within the network from 4 to 6 and back to 4.

4. MODELLING UNCONFINED AQUIFERS IN THE DIMENSION OF LENGTH AND DEPTH

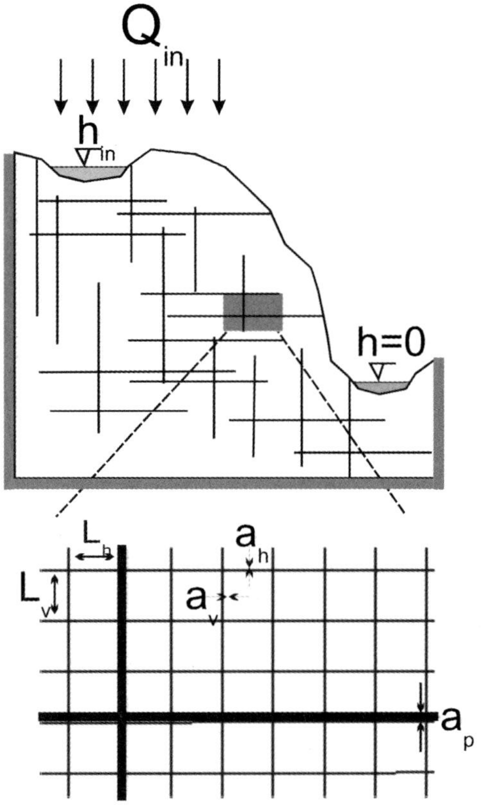

Fig. 24. Schematic representation of a cross-section through the limestone plateau. At the top a combination of constant recharge and constant head conditions can be applied. Thick grey lines show impermeable boundaries. The lower picture is an enlargement showing the parameters of the fracture systems.

So far we have discussed confined aquifers subjected to constant head conditions. By use of this modelling concept the evolution of caves in the dimension of length and breadth can be studied. Now we project one dimension to depth to investigate cave evolution in length and depth. In this projection of reality new boundary conditions must be envisaged.

The aquifer need no longer be confined and a water table may be present. Furthermore input conditions of constant recharge must also be considered. In the following we will present the conceptual frame for such models.

Fig. 24 shows a vertical section of a limestone plateau down cut by a valley on its right-hand side. The massif is dissected by fractures of various initial aperture widths. Prominent fractures are shown in the massif. The enlargement shows a net of fine fractures that are evenly distributed throughout the aquifer. Fig. 25 shows a simplified version of the cross-section representing the modelling domain discussed in this chapter. The model plateau is rather small, 200m long and 30m high. The hydraulic conductivity represented by the rectangular net of fine fractures with aperture widths a_0=0.005 cm is about 10^{-7}*cm/s.*

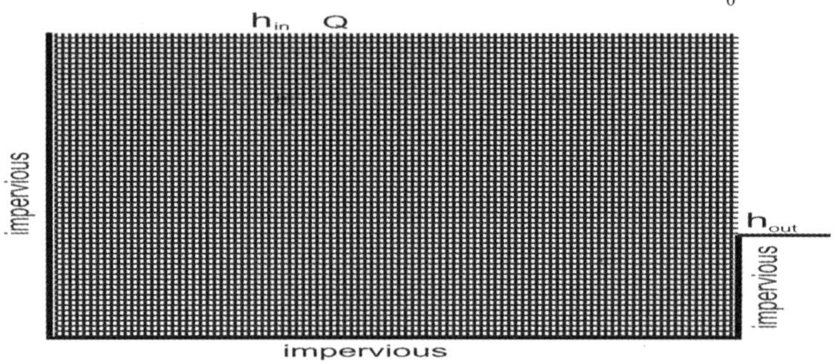

Fig. 25. The model domain with its boundary conditions.

Prominent fractures with aperture widths in the order of few tenth of a millimetre can be incorporated into the system of narrow fractures. A recharge of 450mm/year is evenly distributed at the surface of the plateau and "offered" to the aquifer. The left-hand side, the base and the lower right-hand side are assumed impermeable. This is marked by thick solid lines in Fig.25. The hydraulic head h_{out} at base level is set to zero. The cliff on the right represents a seepage zone where the water leaks from the aquifer. Constant head conditions can be applied additionally on the top, e.g. an allogenic river flows over the massif. Table 2 presents the parameters used in the model and their typical values.

Our model implies an unconfined aquifer, i.e. an aquifer with a water table (WT) which divides a saturated phreatic and an unsaturated vadose zone (see Fig. 1). Recharge is infiltrating through the surface and the vadose zone down to the phreatic zone at the WT. The position of the WT depends on recharge.

Table 2: *Parameters of unconfined model*

Description	Name	Unit	Standard or Initial value
Aperture width	a_0	*cm*	*0.006*
Aperture width of prominent fractures	a_p	*cm*	*0.02*
Length of vertical and horizontal fractures	L_v, L_h	*cm*	*50, 200*
Hydraulic conductivity	K	ms^{-1}	10^{-7}
Annual recharge	Q	*mm/year*	*450*

To obtain the flow through the fractures, the position of the WT must be known, since it defines the boundary conditions for flow and separates the saturated zone from the unsaturated one.

The position of the WT and the height of the seepage face is calculated by the following procedure:

1. An initial guess for the WT is assumed, f.i. the surface of the plateau.
2. A recharge defined by precipitation is equally distributed to the points of the assumed WT.
3. The heads of all the net-points below and at the assumed WT are calculated with the boundary conditions defined by the assumed WT and seepage face, i.e. $h=z$.
4. The heads of the points on the WT are checked for the boundary condition. Their head must be, within a given error, equal to their elevation. If this condition is valid for the point, the WT is kept there, otherwise the WT is either shifted to the point above, if $h > z$ or to the point below if $h < z$. Thus a new approximation for the WT is obtained.
5. Procedure 1-3 is iterated until all the points on the assumed WT fulfil the condition $h = z$.

Once the WT and the seepage zone are obtained, the flow through the fractures in the phreatic zone is calculated and the transport-dissolution model is applied. This is done in the same way as described for confined networks.

Chemical parameters used are those given in Table 1. During percolation through the vadose zone, the solution already attains some saturation state. This is taken into account by taking c_0 between c_s and $0.97c_{eq}$, so that the initial concentration rises linearly with the depth of the water table. The choice of the parameter c_0 is rather arbitrary. It influences the evolution of an aquifer, but does not change the results conceptually. A broad sensitivity analysis has not yet been done. Details are given in Gabrovšek and Dreybrodt (2001) and in Gabrovšek (2000).

4.1 THE EVOLUTION OF FINE FRACTURE SYSTEMS. NO PROMINENT FRACTURES:

Constant recharge

The aquifer consists of system of narrow fractures. No prominent fractures are present in the modelling domain. We assume a constant recharge of 450mm/year evenly distributed to the surface of the plateau. Fig.26a shows the situation at the onset of karstification. The phreatic zone is indicated by fat fracture lines, and the vadose zone by thin interrupted ones. In this way the position of the WT is clearly presented. The colours show the fracture aperture widths increasing from dark blue to red as denoted in the figure. a_0 is the initial width of the vertical fractures. Fig.26b shows the situation after 5ky. The WT has dropped due to the increasing fracture widths in the aquifer. After 10ky the WT reaches the lowest output fractures. This is presented in Fig.26c. By continuous dissolution along the base level a conduit develops and grows headwards (Fig.26d) until it reaches the left boundary after 20ky. Inspection of the colours in Fig.26d reveals that the hydraulic conductivity increases by about 2 orders of magnitude, leaving a highly permeable vadose zone as is observed in nature. Dissolutional widening is most active close to the water table at all times, since the solution quickly approaches equilibrium when penetrating into the net. Therefore close to the WT a narrow region of higher permeability is established which attracts flow. In Fig.26a a small light blue fringe indicates this zone. Later the fringe becomes wider and is composed of fractures with apertures up to $16a_0$. With increasing time the water table drops, leaving behind the vadose region of increased conductivity. The phreatic zone below still has low hydraulic conductivity. In such an aquifer most of the flow is directed along the water table.

After 15ky the conduit at the WT has reached an average width of 1cm. The fracture widths in the vadose zone above are between 0.01-0.1cm, with the wide fractures close to the final WT.

Fig.27a shows the flow rates through the fractures at 5 ky and clearly illustrates (green, yellow, red fractures) that the flow is restricted close to the water table. Dissolution rates shown in Fig.27b also exhibit a maximum close to the water table and drop significantly below. As the water table drops dissolution becomes active in the lower parts of the aquifer. Once the water table has reached a stationary position dissolution stays active close to it and large conduits can grow. This corresponds to the ideal water

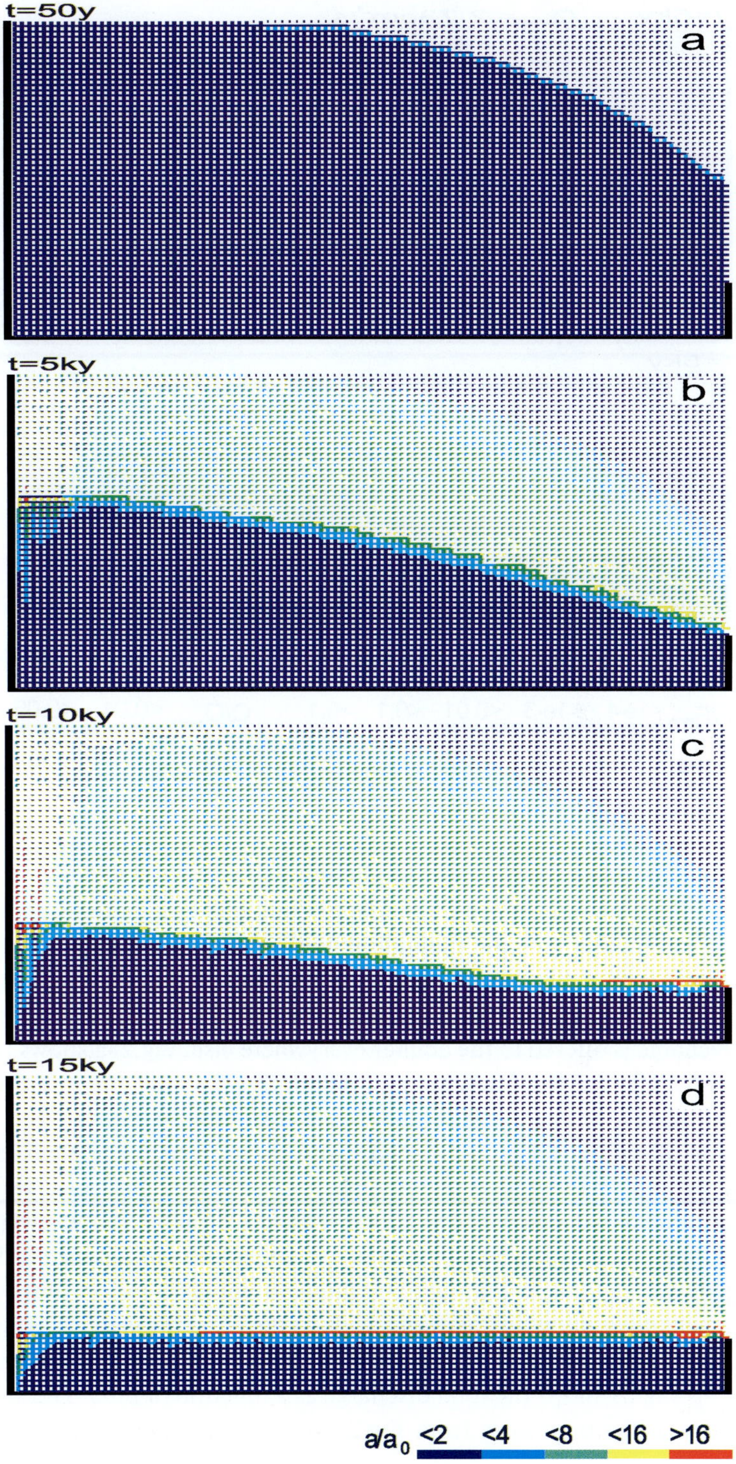

*Fig.26. Evolution of an aquifer with evenly spaced fine fractures and constant recharge. Distribution of fracture widths after 50y (**a**), 5ky (**b**), 10ky (**c**) and 15ky (**d**). The colours represent the widths of the fractures in units* $a(t)/a_0$, *where* a_0 *is the initial width of vertical fractures. Fractures designated by full squares represent the phreatic zone, those by open angles the vadose zone. By this way the water table is clearly presented.*

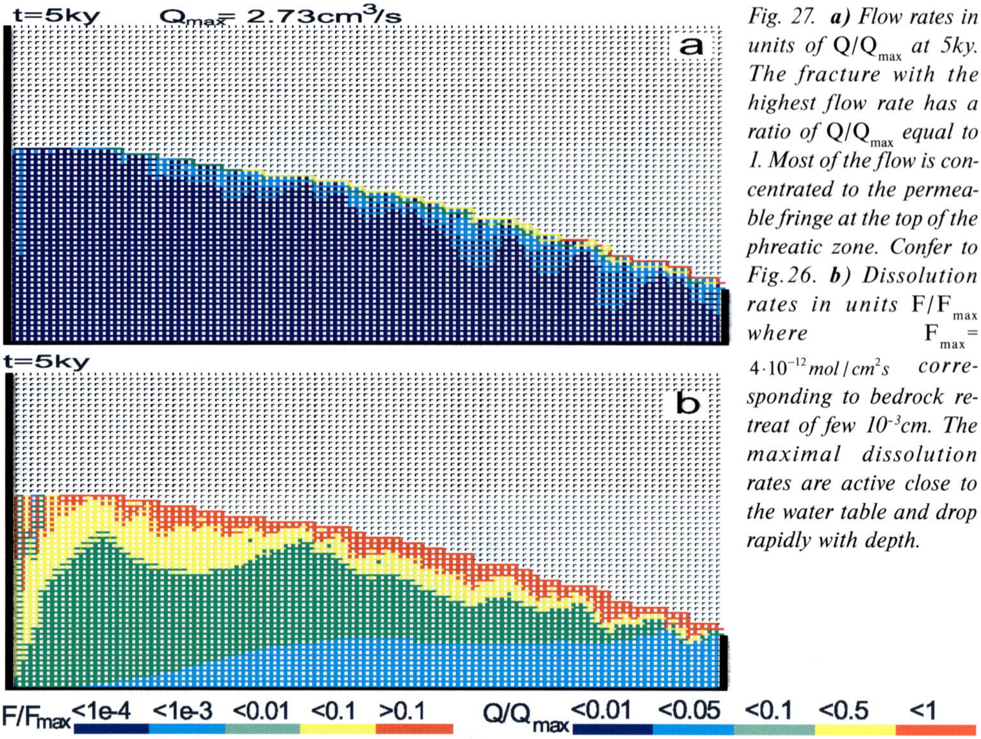

*Fig. 27. **a)** Flow rates in units of Q/Q_{max} at 5ky. The fracture with the highest flow rate has a ratio of Q/Q_{max} equal to 1. Most of the flow is concentrated to the permeable fringe at the top of the phreatic zone. Confer to Fig.26. **b)** Dissolution rates in units F/F_{max} where $F_{max} = 4 \cdot 10^{-12} mol/cm^2 s$ corresponding to bedrock retreat of few 10^{-3}cm. The maximal dissolution rates are active close to the water table and drop rapidly with depth.*

table cave in the model of Swinnerton (1932) and Rhoades and Sinacori (1941) which requires high and even fissuring of the rock.

Combined conditions: constant recharge and constant head

Often constant head boundary conditions and those of constant recharge exist simultaneously. This for example is the case when allogenic rivers are present. Fig.28 shows such a case where a constant head equal to the elevation at the upper left boundary is imposed (see Fig. 28a). Other parameters are equal to those in Fig.26. Constant recharge is offered to the aquifer everywhere else. Fig.28a shows the water table and the distribution of the fracture aperture widths 1ky after the initial state. In the region of constant recharge the water table drops towards the seepage face, whereas in the condition of constant head it coincides with the surface at the platform. Dissolution occurs only in a small banded region close to the WT as illustrated by Figs.28a, b, c. In the constant head region, the water table cannot drop below the surface, therefore the head difference along the WT increases. A permeable fringe along the WT offers an effective pathway draining the water from the constant head region to the output. The feedback mechanism along this pathway leads to the breakthrough at 2.1ky. A wide zone of high conductivity has been created which carries flow from the constant head area.

Fig.29 shows the total discharge as a function of time. The arrows indicate the flow rates at the time steps from Fig.28. This resembles a typical breakthrough behaviour

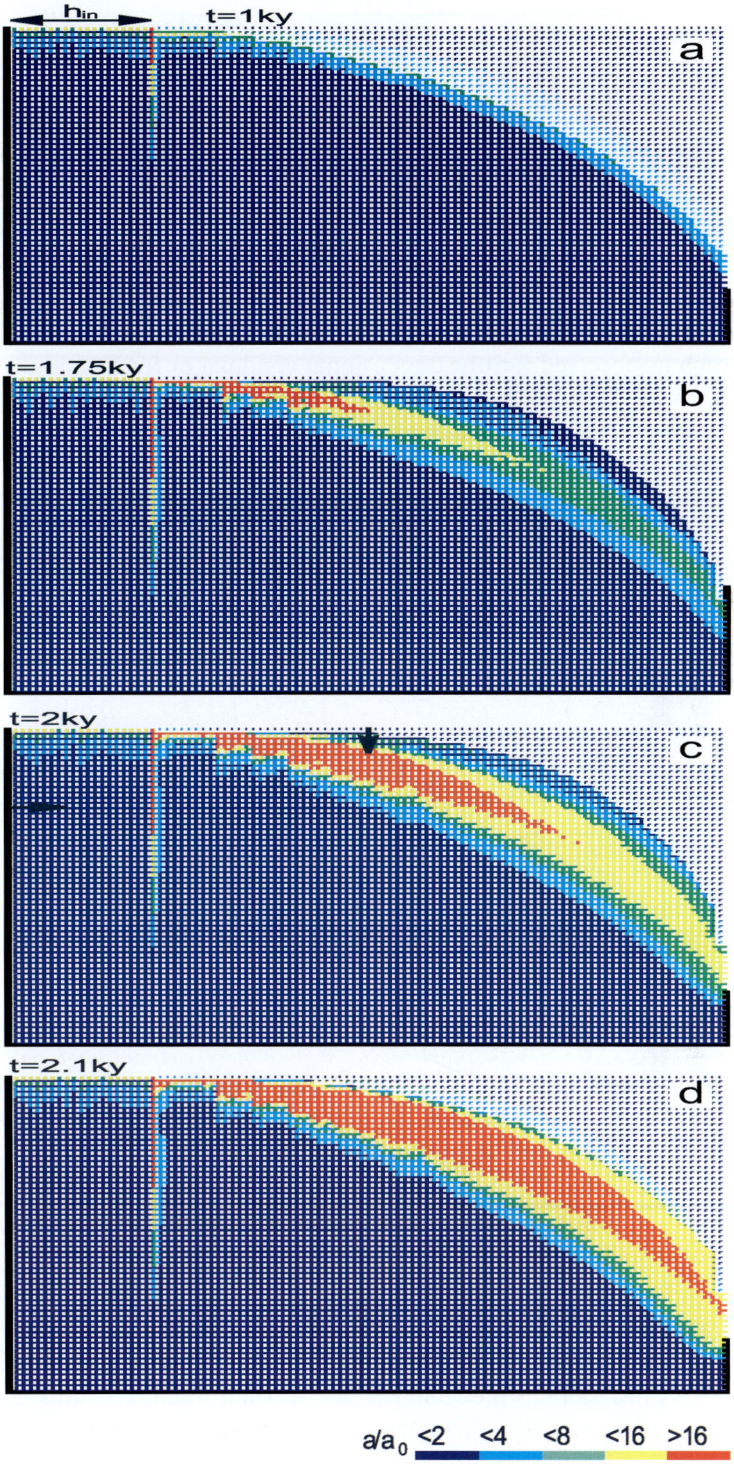

Fig. 28. Evolution of a fine fracture system with combined constant recharge and constant head conditions at the top. The constant head region is marked in figure a. The WT is fixed due to the constant head. Dissolution is mainly active in the fringe close to the water table. The arrows on figure c denote the position of the profiles presented in figure 30.

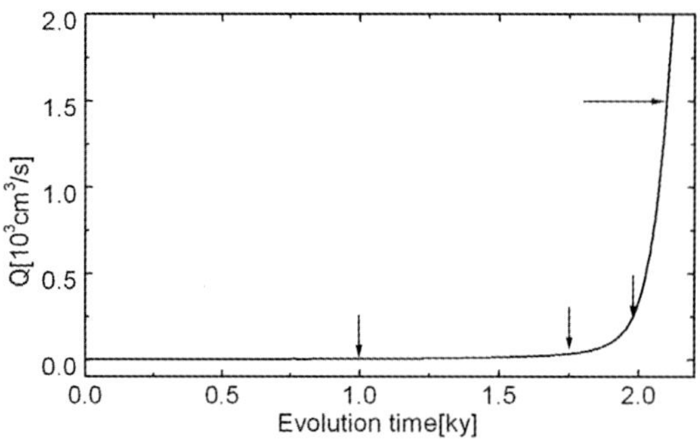

Fig. 29. Evolution of flow rate through the network in Fig.29. Arrows indicate times when aperture distributions in Fig.28 are presented.

such as observed for one-dimensional conduits or for nets under constant head conditions. To obtain some information on the widths of the fractures Fig. 30 depicts the aperture width profiles along a vertical and horizontal cross-section as indicated by the arrows in Fig. 28c.

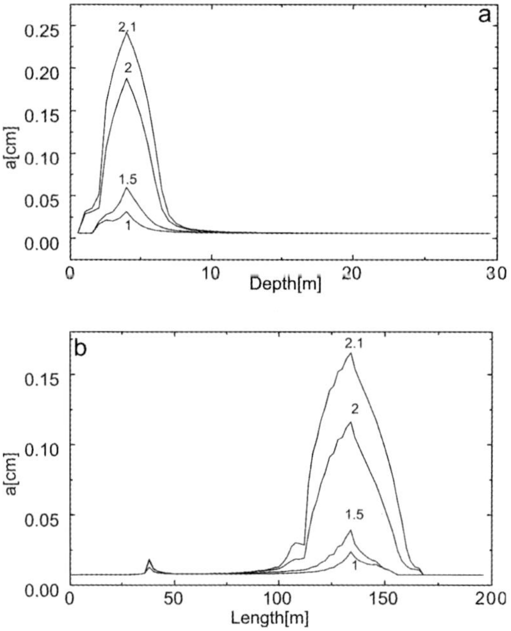

Fig. 30. Distribution of the fracture widths for a horizontal and vertical cross-section of the aquifer as indicted by arrows in Fig. 28c. The numbers on the curves indicate the time of the aquifer evolution in ky. ***a)*** *Widths of the vertical fractures in the vertical cross-section for various times indicated in ky. The region of maximal widths corresponds to the red area in Fig.28.* ***b)*** *Widths of the horizontal fractures in the horizontal cross-section for various times. The small peak at about 30m corresponds to the vertical channel, which develops at the border between constant head and constant recharge regions. Note that the increase of aperture widths accelerates in time.*

4.2 AQUIFERS WITH A NET OF PROMINENT FRACTURES

To create a more realistic karst aquifer we now superimpose a net of prominent fractures to the system of fine fractures. The following procedure is used:

- Divide the net of fine fractures into a coarse net of 5 by 5 dense fractures
- With a random procedure assign to each fracture of this coarse net the aperture width a_p, of a prominent fracture. If the random number chosen for each fracture is

smaller than *p*, the fracture has an aperture width a_p, else its aperture is that of the fine net fractures.

This initial scenario is similar to the approach of a double continuum model of Clemens et al. (1996),(1997), (1999) but it avoids calibration parameters, which are difficult to specify. It is also close to the approach of Kaufmann and Braun (1999,2000) who model the initial aquifer by a superposition of a prominent fracture net within a rock matrix with homogeneous initial conductivity. The most important difference in our approach is that dissolutional widening is regarded in both parts of the aquifer, whereas Clemens et al. and also Kaufmann and Braun disregard dissolution in the dense fractures or in the matrix respectively.

Boundary conditions of constant recharge

As pointed out dissolution in our model is active in the prominent fractures as well as in the continuum of narrow fractures. The question arises, where does permeability arise in the competition of gaining flow from the surface.

This is shown by Fig.31. It depicts an aquifer with a network of prominent fractures (p=0.8) with aperture widths of 0.04 *cm*. To get a more pronounced pattern, recharge is increased to 700*mm/year*. Fig.31a represents the fracture widths after 30k*y*. Fig.31b depicts the flow rates and consequently the flow path at that time. In addition to the conduit growth along the water table, deeper phreatic loops form along prominent fractures below the water table.

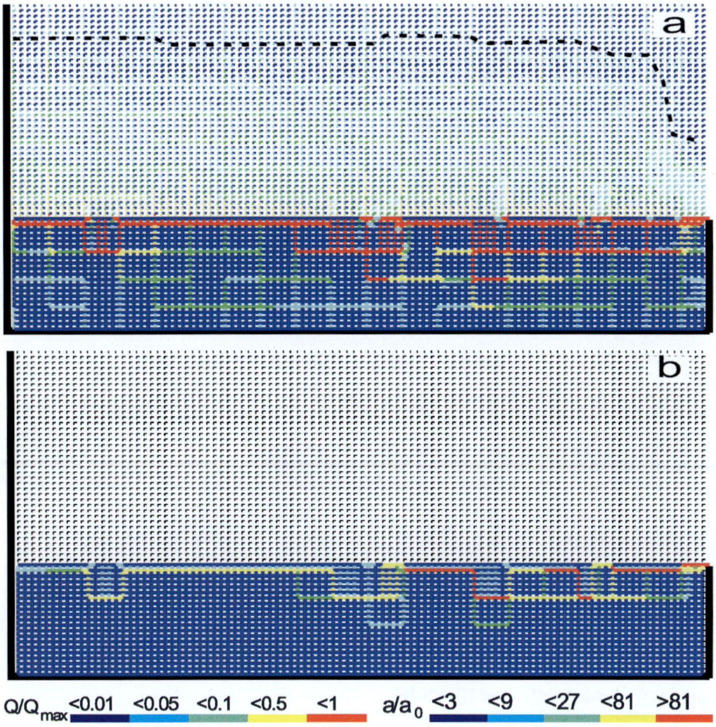

*Fig. 31. Aquifer with a percolating net of prominent fractures (a_p = 0.04cm). Annual precipitation is 700 mm/year. **a)** Distribution of fracture widths after 30ky. Conduits grow along the base level and along the phreatic loops. Note the change in the colour code with respect to other figures. The widths designated by red are above 0.5cm. The dashed line depicts the initial WT. **b)** Distribution of flow rates at 30ky.*

Constant head and constant recharge conditions

The boundary conditions for the case in Fig.32 are the same as in Fig.28: constant head at the left-hand upper side and constant recharge on its right hand side. Fig. 32a shows the widths close to the onset of the evolution after 200 years. After 1ky (Fig. 32b) a complex net of conduits has developed along the prominent fractures. The region of constant head becomes connected to the area of constant recharge by increasing hydraulic conductivity, caused by both, widening of the fine fractures and also connection to the prominent ones. Consequently the water table rises. Close to the water table a

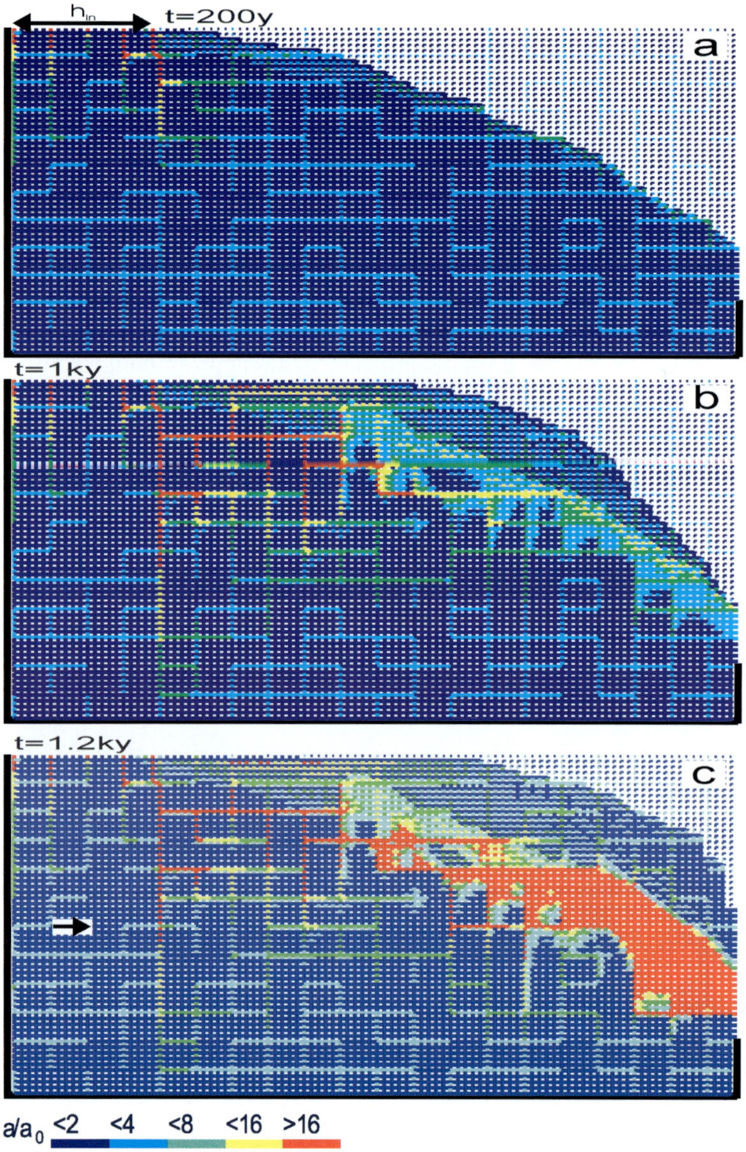

Fig. 32. Evolution of an aquifer with combined - constant recharge and constant head - boundary conditions and a percolation network of prominent fractures appended to the dense fracture network. The initial aperture width of prominent fractures is 0.02cm (light blue). Other parameters are the same as in Fig. 28. ***a)*** *0.2ky,* ***b)*** *1ky,* ***c)*** *1.2ky.*

region of higher conductivity connects the prominent fractures to the seepage face. This change of conductivity and hydraulic heads enhances the evolution of the conduits along the prominent fractures.

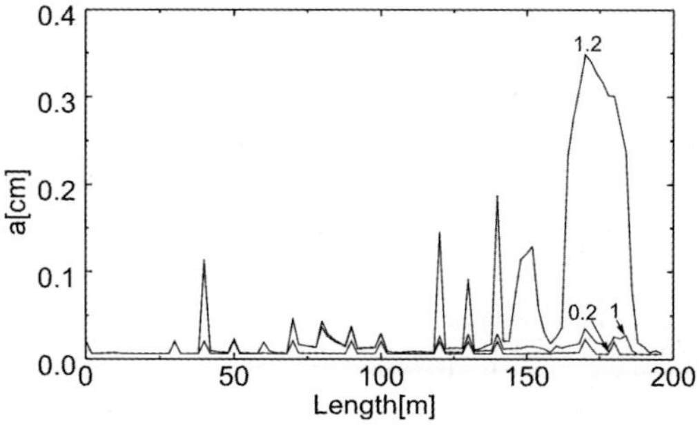

Fig. 33. Profiles of horizontal fractures along a cross-section as indicated by an arrow in Fig. 32c.

After 1.2ky breakthrough occurs (Fig. 32c), with prominent fracture aperture widths on the order of a few millimetres. To illustrate the distribution of fracture widths as they evolve in time, Fig. 33 depicts these along a horizontal cross-section as indicated by an arrow in Fig. 32c. The widening of the fracture accelerates by feedback and consequently the discharge through the aquifer shows the characteristic breakthrough behaviour. This event terminates the early evolution of the aquifer. The constant head condition breaks down and must be replaced by constant recharge. Flow becomes turbulent. Nevertheless, the complicated pattern of vertical and horizontal conduits and a high permeability region close to the spring will design the future structure of the mature karst aquifer. It should be stressed at that point, that constant head conditions are crucial for the evolution of such complicated structures as shown in Fig.32.

Another point of interest is that two processes proceed simultaneously: The evolution of conduits along the prominent fractures and creation of increasing permeability in the continuum, as shown by the red region in Fig 32c. Such a behaviour cannot be obtained if dissolutional widening is restricted to the prominent fractures.

4.3 TIME DEPENDENT BOUNDARY CONDITIONS: DOWN CUTTING OF THE CLIFF

In nature the boundary conditions are changing during the evolution of a karst aquifer. The precipitation rate Q, the chemical parameters of the inflowing solution and also the hydrological boundary conditions may alter. All these variations can be applied to the model presented. We present a case where the base level of an aquifer is down cut during the evolution.

In a first scenario we assume that a "sudden" incision of a valley lowers the base level. This is presented in Figs.34 a and b. The model is the same as used in Fig.31 but the position of base level is kept at 15m during the first 10ky and than it is down cut to 25m immediately. In Fig. 34a, which shows the situation at 9.8ky, a water table cave has developed and as in Fig.31 the system of conduits evolves below the base level.

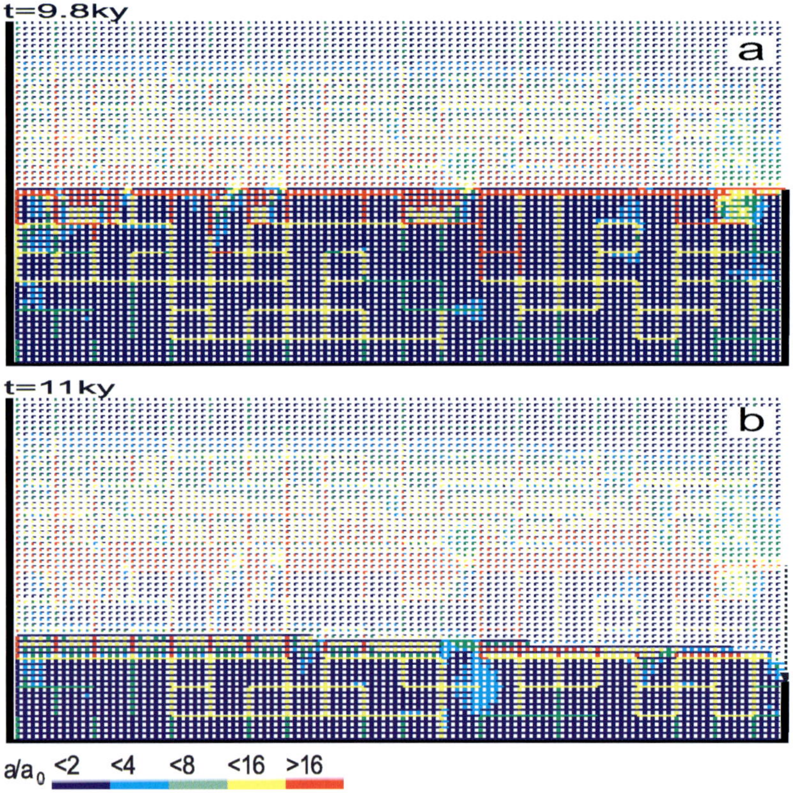

Fig. 34. Evolution of an aquifer with a net of prominent fracture under constant recharge condition with step down cutting of the base level.

After the down cutting the WT adopts to the new base level in a short time. This is presented in Fig.34b. After 11ky a new water table cave is already evolving. Between both base levels the hydraulic conductivity is relatively small since the WT has dropped fast due to the phreatic loops which have evolved prior to down cutting.

Probably more realistic than the step down cutting is a gradual down cutting. Such a scenario is shown on Fig.35. The initial base level is almost at the top of aquifer and is being lowered in steps of two nodes (1m) every 5ky. The mechanisms are similar to those for the step down cutting. The formation of phreatic conduits below base level forces the WT to adapt promptly to the temporary base level. Fig.35a and b show the aquifer at 6ky and 12ky, respectively. The vadose zone exhibits a relatively high permeability since the region of fast widening at the WT was gradually lowered together with the slow down cutting. A slower down cutting produces higher permeability in the vadose zone.

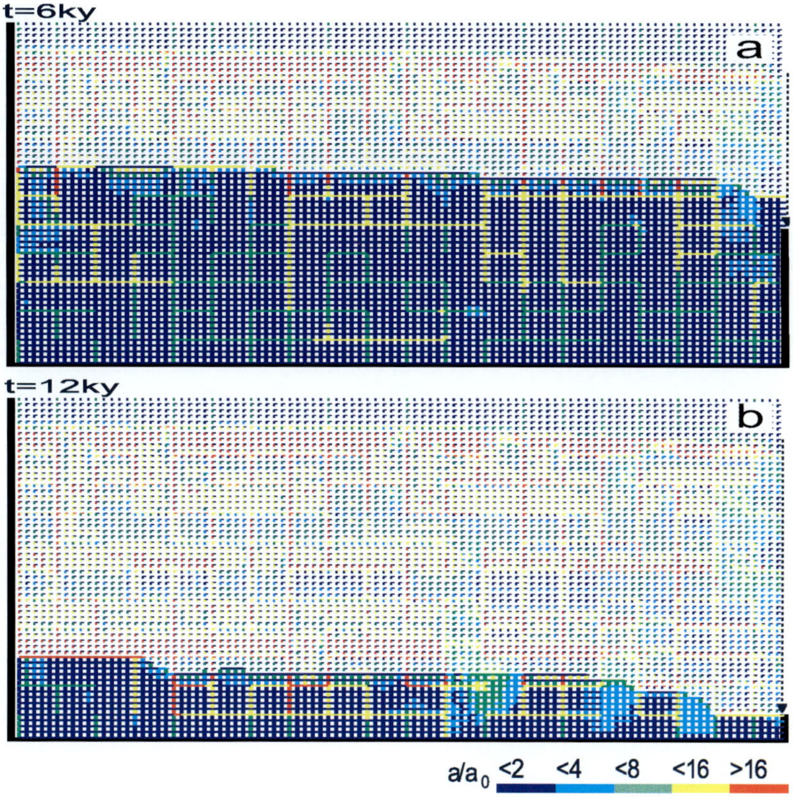

Fig. 35. Evolution of an aquifer with a net of prominent fracture under constant recharge condition with gradual down cutting.

5. CONCLUSION

The basic element in modelling the early evolution of karst is a single 1-dimensional fracture which is widened by dissolutional attack of calcite-aggressive water. Under constant head conditions flow increases slowly at the beginning but then is enhanced dramatically and breakthrough occurs. The breakthrough times depend on the initial aperture width, the length and the hydraulic head acting on the entrance of the fracture. But they also depend on chemical parameters c_{eq}, k_n, n, which determine the dissolution kinetics. When these chemical parameters vary within a single fracture, f.i. c_{eq} by injection of subterranean carbon dioxide or k_n and n by varying lithology of the rock comprising the fracture, breakthrough times are changed significantly. Thus even for one-dimensional systems a great variety of boundary conditions determines the time scale of karst evolution.

A further step to model karst is the combination of one-dimensional fractures into a two-dimensional net either on length and breadth or on length and depth. By this way two-dimensional projections of karst aquifers can be modelled. In such nets due to the interaction of flow one-dimensional fractures can inject flow into this net and therefore enhance dissolutional widening by increased input flow of calcite aggressive solution. Consequently a prominent fracture embedded into a net of narrow fractures can exhibit breakthrough much earlier than if it were isolated. Furthermore boundary conditions in networks become more complex. Differing chemical compositions of input waters at various input regions cause mixing corrosion, where those waters mix, deep in the aquifer. This creates increased permeability which attracts further flow and directs conduits towards such regions. Therefore solely by chemical boundary conditions of the input waters karst aquifers with or without mixing corrosion (i.e. with or without differing chemical composition of the inflowing water) will develop entirely different. A large impact to the evolution of cave systems is caused also by different rock lithologies within the aquifer. Finally the hydrological boundary conditions, i.e. constant head inputs and their location and/or constant recharge to the surface of the aquifer exert significant influence.

Due to our lack of knowledge on all these various boundary conditions and their change in time it is not possible to explain a specific cave system by modelling. The aim of karst modelling is to understand the processes operating in the evolution of karst aquifers.

REFERENCES

Beek, W.J. & Mutzall, K.M.K., 1975: Transport Phenomena.- Wiley, New York

Breznik, M. 1998. Storage reservoirs and deep wells in karst regions.- A.A. Balkema, p.251, Rotterdam

Buhmann, D. & W. Dreybrodt, 1985: The kinetics of calcite dissolution and precipitation in geologically relevant situations of karst areas: 2. Closed system.- Chem. Geol., 53, 109-124

Clemens, T., Hückinghaus, D., Sauter, M., Liedl, R., Teutsch, G., 1997: Modelling the genesis of karst aquifer systems using a coupled reactive network model.- In: Hard Rock Geosciences. IAHS Publ., 241, p. 3-10, Colorado

Clemens, T., Hückinghaus, D., Sauter, M., Liedl, R. and G. Teutsch, 1996: A combined continuum and discrete network reactive transport model for the simulation of karst development.- In: Calibration and Reliability in Groundwater Modelling. -IAHS Publ, 237., 309-318. Colorado

Clemens, T., Hückinghaus, D., Liedl , R., Sauter, M., 1999: Simulation of the development of larst aquifers.- The role of epikarst. Int. Journal of Earth Sciences, 88, 157-162

Dreybrodt W., 1988: Processes in karst systems - Physics, Chemistry and Geology.- Springer Series in Physical Environments 4, Springer, , 288 p., Berlin, New York

Dreybrodt, W., 1990: The role of dissolution kinetics in the development of karstification in limestone: A model simulation of karst evolution.- Journal of Geology, 98, 639-655

Dreybrodt, W., 1996: Principles of early development of karst conduits under natural and man-made conditions revealed by mathematical analysis of numerical models.- Water Resources Research, 32, 2923-2935

Dreybrodt, W., & F. Gabrovšek, 2000, Dynamics of the evolution of a single karst conduit.- In: Klimchouk, A., Ford, D.C., Palmer, A.N., and Dreybrodt , W., (Editors), Speleogenesis: Evolution of karst aquifers. -Nat. Speleol. Soc.,USA,184-193

Dreybrodt, W. & J.Siemers, 2000: Cave evolution on two-dimensional networks of primary fractures in limestone.- In: Klimchouk, A., Ford, D.C., Palmer, A.N., and Dreybrodt , W., (Editors), Speleogenesis: Evolution of karst aquifers.- Nat. Speleol. Soc.,USA, 201-211

Eisenlohr, L., Madry, B., W. Dreybrodt, 1997: Changes in the dissolution kinetics of limestone by intrinsic inhibitors adsorbing to the surface. - In: Proceedings of the 12th Int. Cong. of Speleology , La Chaux de Fonds, Switzerland, Vol II, pp 81-84, La Chaux de Fonds, Switzerland.

Eisenlohr L., Meteva, K., Gabrovšek, F. and W. Dreybrodt, 1999: The inhibiting action of intrinsic impurities in natural calcium carbonate minerals to their dissolution ki-netics in aqueous H_2O-CO_2 solutions.- Geochimica et Cosmochimica Acta, 63, 989-1002

Ford, D.C. Williams, P.W., 1989. Karst geomorphology and hydrology. -Unwin Hyman, p.601, London

Gabrovšek, F., 2000. Evolution of early karst aquifers: From simple principles to complex models.- Založba ZRC, p.150, Ljubljana, Slovenia

Gabrovšek, F., Menne, B. and W. Dreybrodt, 2000: A model of early evolution of karst conduits affected by subterranean CO2 sources. -Environmental Geology, 39, 531-543.

Gabrovšek, F. & W.Dreybrodt, 2000: The role of mixing corrosion in calcite aggressive H_2O-CO_2-$CaCO_3$ solutions in the early evolution of karst aquifers.- Water resources research, 36, 1179-1188

Gabrovšek,F., & W. Dreybrodt, 2001: A model of the early evolution of karst aquifers in limestone in the dimensions of length and depth.- J. Hydrol 240, str. 27-34

Incropera, F., & D. DeWitt, 1996 : Fundamentals of Heat and Mass Transfer.- John Wiley & Sons, 4rd edition, p.912, New York

Kaufmann, G., Braun, J., 1999: Karst aquifer evolution in fractured rocks. -Water Resources Research 35: 3223-3238

Kaufmann, G., Braun, J., 2000: Karst aquifer evolution in fractured, porous rocks. -Water Resources Research 36: 1381-1391

Liu Z. & W.Dreybrodt, 1997: Dissolution kinetics of calcium carbonate minerals in H_2O-CO_2 solutions in turbulent flow: The role of the diffusion boundary layer and the slow reaction . - Geochimica et cosmochimica acta, 61, 2879-2889

Lowe, D.J., & J. Gunn, 1997: Carbonate speleogenesis: An inception horizon hypothesis.- Acta Carsologica,26,2, 457-491, Ljubbljana

Plummer, L.N., Parkhurst, D.L., and T.M.L. Wigley,1978: The kinetics of calcite dissolution in CO_2 systems at 25°C to 60°C and 0.0 to 1.0 atm CO_2.- American Journal of Science, 278, 179-216

Rhoades, R., Sinacori, M.N., 1941: The pattern of ground-water flow and solution. - Journal of Geology, 49, 785-794

Romanov, Dreybrodt, W. & F. Gabrovsek, 2002a: Interaction of fracture and conduit flow in the evolution of karst aquifers. -In: Martin,J.B., Wicks,and I.D. Sasowsky (Editors), Proceedings of the Symposium on Karst Frontiers: Florida and Related Environments. KWI Special Publication No. 7

Romanov, D., Gabrovšek, F., Dreybrodt, W.,2002b: The impact of hydrochemical boundary conditions on the evolution of karst aquifers in limestone terrains. - Submitted to Journal of Hydrology.

Sauter, M., 1993: Double porosity models in kartified limestone aquifers: field validation and data provision.- In Gültekin, G., Johnson, I.A., Hydrogeological Processes in Karst terraines. IAHS Publication 207, 261-279

Siemers, J. & W. Dreybrodt,1998: Early development of karst aquifers on percolation networks of fractures in limestone. -Water resources research, 34, 409-419

Swinnerton, A.C., 1932: Origin of limestone caverns. - Geological Society of America Bulletin, 34, p. 662-693

Svensson, U. & W.Dreybrodt, 1992: Dissolution kinetics of natural calcite minerals in CO2 -water systems approaching calcite equilibrium. -Chem. Geol, 100, p.129-145

Address

Wolfgang Dreybrodt
University of Bremen, Germany
E-mail: dreybrod@physik.uni-bremen.de

Franci Gabrovšek
Karst Research Institute ZRC SAZU, Postojna, Slovenia
gabrovsek@zrc-sazu.si

Evolution of Karst: From Prekarst to Cessation, 155-190, Ljubljana-Postojna 2002

KARSTIFICATION AND GROUNDWATER FLOW

LASZLO KIRALY

Abstract

One of the principal aims of hydrogeology is to propose a reasonably adequate reconstruction of the groundwater flow field, in space and in time, for a given aquifer. For example, interpretation of the chemical and isotopic composition of groundwater, understanding of the geothermal conditions (anomalies) or forecasting the possible effects of industrial waste disposals and of intensive exploitation nearly always would require the knowledge of the regional and/or local groundwater flow systems. The problem of estimating the groundwater flow field in fractured and karstified aquifers is approached within the framework of a conceptual diagram showing the relationship between groundwater flow, hydraulic parameters (aquifer properties and boundary conditions), distribution of voids and geological factors.

Autoregulation between groundwater flow and karst aquifer properties, duality of karst, nested model of geological discontinuities, scale effect on hydraulic parameters and use of numerical finite element models to check the interpretation of the global response of karst springs are some of the subjects addressed by the author. Inferences on groundwater flow regime with respect to the stage of karst evolution can be made only if the hydraulic parameter fields and the boundary conditions are known by direct observations, or estimated by indirect methods for the different types of karst. Practical considerations on the monitoring strategies applied for karst aquifers, and on the interpretation of the global response obtained at karst springs will complete the paper, which throughout reflects the point of view of a hydrogeologist.

1 INTRODUCTORY REMARKS

1.1 RELATION BETWEEN GROUNDWATER FLOW FIELD, HYDRAULIC PARAMETERS AND GEOLOGICAL FACTORS.

In hydrogeology we do not study karstification or karst evolution for themselves: we are interested in them only in so far as they exert an influence on the groundwater flow field. The reconstruction of a regional groundwater flow field, which is consistent with a given hydraulic conductivity field and with given boundary conditions, nearly always requires the use of numerical models. Presently we have a wide variety of equations describing the groundwater movement in various domains (see, for example, for saturated/unsaturated flow and groundwater/surface-water interaction Tregaro 2000; Ababou et al. 1998) and we can solve them quite accurately by numerical models if we know, in the modelled region, the field of the relevant hydraulic parameters (hydraulic conductivity, storage coefficient, efficient porosity, etc., in each point of the aquifer), as well as the initial and the boundary conditions (mainly infiltration and fixed head values, such as altitude of springs, lakes or rivers).

With the use of numerical models explicitly appears a very important fact: as groundwater flow depends only on hydraulic parameters and on boundary conditions, the geological, geomorphological and climatic factors will exert their influence on the groundwater movement solely through the hydraulic parameter fields and the boundary conditions. If we could measure, for example, the value of the hydraulic parameters everywhere in the Earth's crust, we ought not to bother about fractures, faults, karst channels, lithologies and other geological factors: we could simulate and predict the behaviour of the groundwater flow systems without geology. In other words, if we will give a hydrogeological meaning to the geological, geomorphological or climatic factors, if we will examine their influence on the groundwater flow field, then we have to "translate" them (if possible, explicitly) into boundary conditions and hydraulic properties of the aquifer.

Evidently enough, geology will influence the hydraulic conductivity and porosity through the distribution of "voids": increase of **density**, **opening** and **connectivity** of the voids will increase the hydraulic conductivity and the porosity. If fracture or microfracture families show well defined, preferred **orientation**, the hydraulic conductivity may become anisotropic, thus conducting groundwater better in a direction than in another. At this stage sedimentation, diagenesis and tectonic deformations are the principal processes influencing the void distribu-tion in sedimentary rocks.

Complications may appear in carbonate rocks, which are soluble in water: the groundwater in movement may dissolve the limestone around the existing voids, thus increasing their opening and the hydraulic conductivity of the aquifer. The amount of dissolved limestone, the enlargement of fractures depend obviously on the chemical composition of the rock and of the water, but the relative karstification of the various fracture families will depend mainly on the direction and the magnitude of the groundwater flux density vector $\vec{q}$, [K], $\vec{grad}\ h$ given by Darcy's law, where [K] is the hydraulic conductivity tensor and h is the hydraulic head (Bedinger 1966; Kiraly et al. 1971). Considering that

1. $\vec{q}$ depends on the hydraulic conductivity and the hydraulic gradient,
2. the hydraulic conductivity depends on the opening of pores and fractures,
3. the opening of karstified pores and fractures is strongly influenced by the direction and magnitude of $\vec{q}$ during the previous stages of the groundwater flow field,

we arrive in a very important and characteristic feed-back loop of the karstification process. It shows, that in karst aquifers the hydraulic conductivity field and the void distribution result not only from the geological history of the rocks, but also from the whole history, from the whole evolution of the groundwater flow systems: the present state of the groundwater flow field and the hydraulic conductivity field is the result of successive, short-term and long-term autoregulations between the fields $\vec{q}$, [K], $\vec{grad}\ h$, and the boundary conditions (infiltration, altitude of discharge areas, etc.). Indeed, we have to emphasize, that geographical position of the recharge and discharge areas represent boundary conditions for the flow field $\vec{q}$ and their evolution in time (paleo-geography, geomorphology) could influence karstification and hydraulic conductivity field as much as other geological factors (facies, structure, etc.).

All these conceptual relations between groundwater flow systems, hydraulic parameters, void distribution and geological factors are represented as a partly self-regulating system in the diagram of figure 1. The feed-back of the flow field on the hydraulic conductivity field will produce it's effect only after a "certain time", thus giving an important role to the "duration", to the "history" in the karstification process. This means, that understanding the karstification in a given aquifer would require the knowledge of the "paleo-hydraulic" conditions, as it was proposed by (Mandel 1966) and (Kiraly et al. 1971).

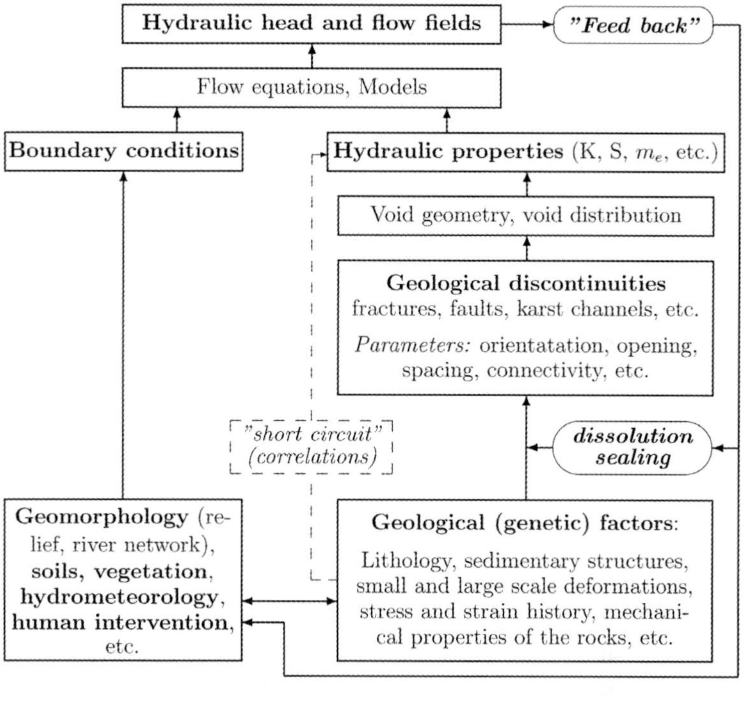

Fig. 1. Schematic representation of the relations between groundwater flow field, hydraulic properties and geological factors in karst aquifers (after Kiraly 1975, modified).

1.2 DUALITY OF KARST AQUIFERS

The partly self-regulating system of Fig. 1 is, in fact, a graphic representation of the karst development according to the ideas of (Rhodes and Sinacori 1941; Swinnerton 1949; LeGrand and Stringfield 1966; Mandel 1966; Bedinger 1966). They assume that dissolution starts in non karstified fractured rocks where the heterogeneity of the permeability field is not very important (1 to 50 ?). Groundwater flow will enhance the dissolution particularly in fractures which are sub-parallel to the local hydraulic gradient and which are in the vicinity of the free groundwater table (Bedinger 1966). The heterogeneity of the hydraulic conductivity field increases (up to 1 to 1 million!) and the zones with higher permeability will represent discharge regions with respect to the lower permeability volumes.

The competition for the drainage between high-conductivity zones will lead to the capture of the slower developing branches and will contribute to the unification of the karst channel network and to the "concentration" of the discharge areas: the karst springs will be less in number but more important as far as the discharge is concerned. The hydrogram of the remaining springs becomes more and more "karstic", i.e. the reaction of the springs to input events will become more and more "violent", with rapidly increasing and rapidly decreasing peak-flow. This is a sign that infiltration becomes strongly heterogeneous, too, with an always growing part of concentrated infiltration. Thank to the works of (Burger 1957; Schoeller 1967; Berkaloff 1967; Forkasiewicz and Paloc 1967; Drogue 1967; Mangin 1975) we may consider the hydrogram of karst springs as one of the most important indirect indicators on the structure of the hydraulic conductivity field and on the heterogeneity of the infiltration in a karst aquifer.

In this "mature" karst aquifer we may speak of the "duality of karst" (Kiraly 1994). Indeed, the organized heterogeneity of the hydraulic conductivity field may be schematized by a high permeability, generally unknown channel network with kilometer wide "meshes", which is "immersed" in a low permeability fractured limestone volume, and is well connected to a local discharge area, the karst spring. The duality of karst aquifers is a direct consequence of this structure:

- duality of the infiltration processes ("diffuse" or slow infiltration into the low permeability volumes, "concentrated" or rapid infiltration into the channel network);
- duality of the groundwater flow field (low flow velocities in the fractured volumes, high flow velocities in the channel network) ;
- duality of the discharge conditions (diffuse seepage from the low permeability volumes, concentrated discharge from the channel network at the karst springs).

Note that besides the rivers disappearing in sinkholes, the concentrated infiltrations could be enhanced by the rapid drainage in a high conductivity "skin" at shallow depth: the epikarst (Mangin 1975).

The above presented karst development assumes a very simple and favorable hydrogeological setting, i.e. open or denuded karst. For more complicated hydrogeological settings the reader should consult the beautiful book edited by (Klimchouk et al. 2000), particularly the papers between pages 45 and 100. In the following chapters of the present paper we will present some of the important hydrogeological consequences of the duality of karst aquifers.

2 THE NESTED STRUCTURE OF THE GEOLOGICAL DISCONTINUITIES.

2.1 QUALITATIVE OBSERVATIONS IN THE FIELD

Geological discontinuities exist at all scales: intragranular cracks not longer than a few microns, microfractures of a few millimetres or centimetres, fractures (in the usual sense) of metric or decametric length, faults of a few hectometres, kilometres or tens of kilometres, big fault zones extending over several hundreds of kilometres, or cave systems with length of tens of kilometres. In sedimentary rocks the bedding planes (stratification) represent very persistent, closely spaced (from a few centimetres to a few meters) discontinuities of considerable lateral extent (several kilometres). Geologists have developed a rather complicated genetic terminology of their own to designate rock discontinuities, but this terminology will not be used here. Following the International Society of Rock Mechanics Suggested Methods for Quantitative Description of Discontinuities in Rock Masses (Brown, 1981), we use only the generic term discontinuity and the somewhat more specific term fracture, to designate discontinuities of metric or decametric length.

Fig. 2.: Illustration of the nested model concept (after "Feuille d'Avis de Neuchâtel)

In most cases the enumerated discontinuities are not randomly oriented, but form families, even if the orientation of a family may change from place to place. This is quite normal given the fact that the orientation of the discontinuities must somehow be related to the rather complicated, past or present, regional and local stress fields (Chinnery 1965; Gramberg 1965). If the lateral extent of the discontinuities is greater than their spacing, it seems reasonable to suppose that families with different orientations will form more or less connected networks of discontinuities, with "meshes" of different magnitudes (Jamier and Simeoni 1979; Rouleau 1985). As the networks of different magnitudes coexist in the real systems, the fractured and karstified medium should be characterized by its nested structure of discontinuities. Even if the nested structure concept is a qualitative mental picture only, it allows to ask some important questions when we are investigating flow and mass transport in fractured and karstic media:

- Which magnitudes of the discontinuities are of interest for the investigated phenomena and which may be neglected.
- Which magnitudes could be averaged and which not (is it possible to combine the "discrete fracture" approach with the continuum approach).
- How could we quantify the nested structure of the discontinuities (if required).
- How do the presently used quantitative methods respect the existence of nested structures in the real systems (in randomly generated fracture or karst channel networks, for example).
- And finally, the most important question: could the nested structure of the geological discontinuities determine a nested structure of the hydraulic conductivity field?

Many of these questions will remain unanswered here. In spite of this fact, they deserve attention from a heuristic point of view.

2.2 THE SCALE EFFECT IN NESTED STRUCTURES

There is an abundant scientific literature on scale effect in fractured media. The interested reader will find the more recent references in Bear et al. (1994) or in Lee and Farmer (1993). In most of these papers the scale effect is investigated by applying the percolation theory or the renormalization theory to a schematic representation of the fractured aquifers. As the above theories don't apply to nested structures, all the schematic discontinuities are of the same order of magnitude, even if there is a certain statistical distribution allowed about the mean fracture length, the mean fracture orientation and the mean fracture opening. The obtained scale effect is related to the clustering of the interconnected discontinuities in randomly generated networks.

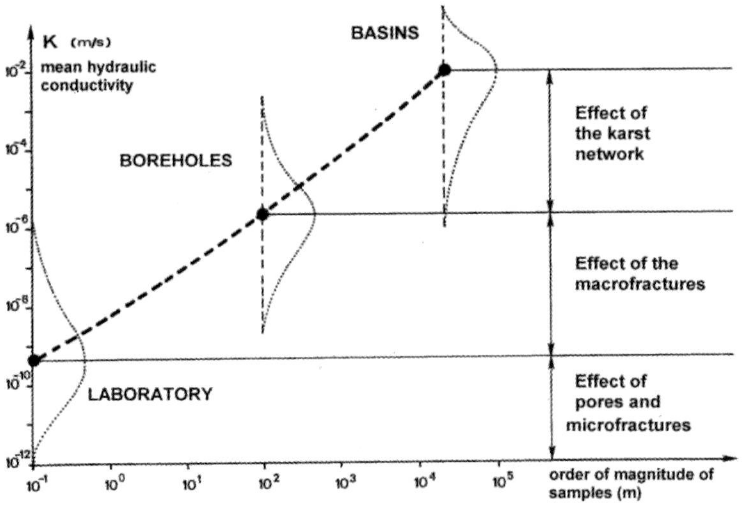

Fig. 3. Scale effect on the hydraulic conductivity in fractured and karstified limestone aquifers (after Kiraly 1975, modified).

A different kind of scale effect could appear in the above described nested structures. The idea was developed for fractured and karstic limestone aquifers located in the Jura mountains (Switzerland), in the early seventies (Tripet 1972; Kiraly 1973, 1975), but the principle might well apply for non-carbonate aquifers, too. In these karstic aquifers, besides the common fracture network with "meshes" of a few meters, there must be a high-permeability channel network with wide, kilometric intervals, which is well connected to a discharge area, the karstic spring. Between the channels, the fractured rock mass has a low hydraulic conductivity, about 10^{-6} to 10^{-7} [m/s], values obtained by pumping tests in 300 to 400 m deep boreholes. Regional numerical models showed, that at a basin-wide scale the overall hydraulic conductivity must be 2000 to 5000 times higher than the "local" conductivity values measured in the boreholes (see Figure 3). This important scale effect is due to the very high hydraulic conductivity of the widely spaced karst channel network. As most of the boreholes are located between the karst channels, the locally measured hydraulic conductivity values don't give any information on the existence of this scale effect. Basin-wide water balance studies and the use of regional numerical models are necessary to put forward the phenomenon.

In non-carbonate fractured aquifers there is no karstic network. Nevertheless, it could happen that large discontinuities with a wide spacing have a higher hydraulic conductivity than closely spaced smaller ones, and in this case there will be a certain scale effect on the hydraulic conductivity: local values will not be the same as the overall regional values. This kind of scale effect is very different from what we obtain with the percolation or renormalization theory: it is the consequence of the nested structure of the hydraulic conductivity field inferred from the nested structure of the fractured and/or karstified medium.

The idea on the nested structure of the hydraulic conductivity suggests to go back to the real systems and check it. Instead of doing statistics on anonymous conductivity values, it would be far more interesting to obtain information about the spacing of the high-permeability zones, about the lateral extent of the high-permeability zones and about the connectivity of the high-permeability zones. Then it would be possible to compare the structure of the hydraulic conductivity field with the structure of the geological discontinuities. Because presently we are not yet able to answer such fundamental questions as how to predict actually water conducting zones from statistical information about geological discontinuities. Although based on qualitative observations and on inferences, the general ideas developed in these first pages will help to critically evaluate the techniques presented without many comments in the next sections.

2.3 PERMEABILITY TENSOR FOR FRACTURES AND INTERSECTIONS OF FRACTURES

The estimation of the hydraulic conductivity tensor from fracture geometry was proposed by Romm and Pozinenko (1963). Snow (1969) presented a general method for individual fractures and Kiraly (1969) proposed to estimate the permeability tensor for both fractures and intersections of fractures. We have to emphasize that using the hydraulic conductivity tensor transforms the discontinuous real aquifer into an equivalent continuum.

Let us define N families of idealized fractures in the delta-neighbourhood of a point. The mean plane of the i-th family is characterized by $\vec{n}_i$ unit normal of the plane; f_i = average number of fractures in the direction of the normal; d_i = average aperture of the i-th family. In Darcy's law given by $\vec{q}$ = - [K], $\vec{grad}\, h$ the hydraulic conductivity tensor [K] may be calculated for the N families of fractures by

$$[K] = \frac{\rho g}{12\mu} \sum_{i=1}^{N} f_i d_i^3 \left[I - \vec{n}_i \otimes \vec{n}_i\right] \tag{1}$$

where ρ = density of water; g= acceleration due to gravity; μ= dynamic viscosity; ⊗ is the tensor product and I is the unit matrix. The geometric or intrinsic permeability [K] is easily identified: it depends only on the fracture parameters f_i, d_i and $\vec{n}_i$.

Let us idealize the intersections of two families of fractures by a bundle of tubes, which is characterized by $\vec{m}_i$ = unit vector parallel to the i-th bundle; F_i = number of tubes per unit surface perpendicular to $\vec{m}_i$; D_i = average diameter of the tubes in the i-th bundle. Making use of the Hagen-Poiseuille formula we obtain the global hydraulic conductivity tensor for M bundles of intersections by

$$[K] = \frac{\rho g \pi}{128\mu} \sum_{i=1}^{M} F_i D_i^4 \left[\vec{m}_i \otimes \vec{m}_i\right] \tag{2}$$

Knowing the fracture parameters for N families of fractures allows to estimate the parameters for the M bundles of intersections:

$$M = \frac{N(N-1)}{2} \qquad \text{(number of bundles)}$$

$$\vec{m}_k = \frac{\vec{n}_i \times \vec{n}_j}{\left|\vec{n}_i \times \vec{n}_j\right|} \qquad \text{(orientation of k-th bundle)}$$

$$F_k = f_i f_j \left|\vec{n}_i \times \vec{n}_j\right| \qquad \text{(density of intersections)}$$

where × is the vector product; $i \le j$; $i = 1 \cdots (N-1)$. Obviously, the most ticklish problem is to estimate D_k when $d_i \neq d_j$.

The idealized representation of the geological discontinuities, which allowed to estimate the permeability tensor, is never totally realized in the real systems. Real fractures are not evenly spaced, their aperture is not constant in the fracture plane, they are not strictly parallel to each other even in the same family, their lateral extent ("length") may vary, in a word: the fractured medium is not only anisotropic, but heterogeneous, too. If the δ-neighbourhood for which we estimate the permeability tensor is "big" with respect to the local heterogeneities, the [K] tensor will not correctly describe the behaviour of the real system. This simply indicates that one [K] tensor alone cannot describe a whole region and the δ-neighbourhood has to be diminished. In this case the heterogeneities will appear clearly in the interior of the region. A last remark: the continuity of the fractures is required only in the δ-neighbourhood, not over the entire region.

2.4 THE "SERIAL TYPE MODEL" OF THE VOID GEOMETRY IN FRACTURED ROCKS

In three orthogonal and equally developed fracture families, or intersection bundles, the hydraulic conductivity is isotrope and its magnitude depends on the spacing $x = 1 / f$ (or $X = 1 / \sqrt{F}$) and the aperture d (or D). In a diagram log d versus log x

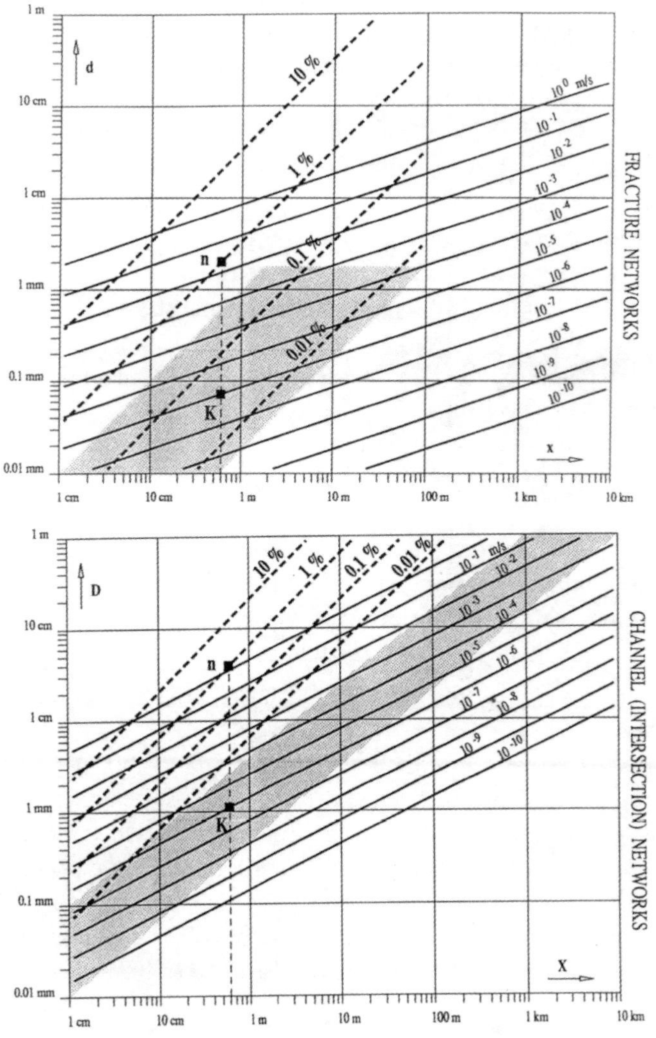

Fig. 4. Hydraulic conductivity and efficient porosity values for various networks of fractures (above) and intersections of fractures or karst channels (below).

(or, for the intersections: log D versus log X) constant permeabilities or constant porosities appear as straight lines (see the diagrams of figures 4a and 4b). These diagrams allow to rapidly estimate the permeability value for more or less connected networks of discontinuities, with "meshes" of different magnitudes. The dark zones represent spacing and aperture values which seem reasonable in real fractured or karstic aquifers and show an important scale-effect on the hydraulic conductivities (but not, or less, on the efficient porosities) with progressive karstification.

In the Swiss Jura Mountains we have field measurements on the permeability (about 10^{-6} m/s), on the efficient porosity (about 0.4 to 1%) and on the fracture spacing (about 0.6 m). If we represent these values on the diagrams of figure 4a and figure 4b (see points K and n), we cannot find a unique fracture aperture or channel diameter which could "explain" both the permeability value and the efficient porosity value. In other words, the void geometry which determines the permeability is not the same as the void geometry which determines the efficient porosity. The efficient porosity value requires large openings in the fracture planes (up to 1 mm aperture) but the permeability value shows that these large voids are not well interconnected.

Combining the "fracture model" with the "intersection model" may represent a solution to the problem: the permeability is determined by the intersections of fractures (required diameter: about 1 mm) and the efficient porosity is determined by the larger voids in the plane of the fractures (required aperture: about 1 mm). The large openings are well connected to the intersections where the groundwater flows, but are poorly connected to each other. The above described void geometry is schematically represented in figure 5, which is not more than the "serial type model" of (Scheidegger 1963) adapted to the three-dimensional fractured medium (Kiraly 1994). The idea was taken up later by (Hauns and Jeannin 1998) who applied it to big karst channels by simulating the changes in width and in depth of the underground rivers. Interestingly enough, the "serial type model" of the void geometry could explain all particularities of the empirical break-through curves observed in fractured and karstic rocks (particularly the "tailing" of the break-through curves), without adsorption and desorption phenomena, and without molecular diffusion into the "immobile water". The above presented example shows that even theoretical and very schematic representations may be useful, provided they are confronted with the observations made in the real system.

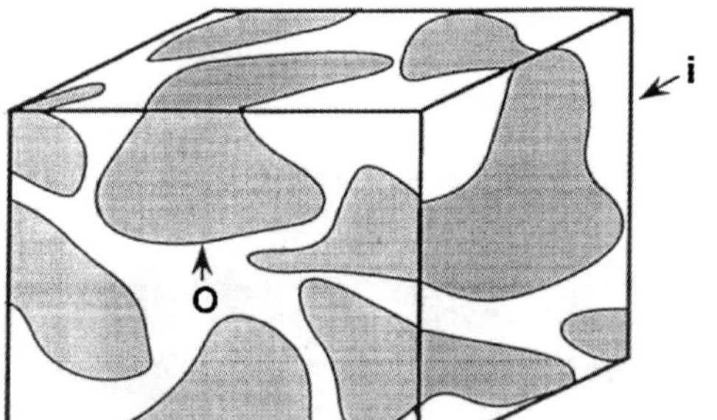

Fig. 5. "Serial type model" of the void geometry in fractured rocks: large voids in the fracture planes (O), well connected to the intersections or channels (i).

3 INTERPRETATION OF KARST SPRING HYDROGRAPHS BASED ON THE GLOBAL METHODS

3.1 THE GLOBAL RESPONSE OF KARST AQUIFERS

In the previous chapters we briefly presented the general nested structure of geological discontinuities and the duality of karst aquifers. How do their consequences manifest in the global response of real karst springs?

The behaviour of the karst spring (hydrograph, water temperature, chemical or isotopic composition, etc.) represents the ***"global response"*** of the karst aquifer to input events. As the available data on the three-dimensional distribution of the hydraulic parameters are very limited, the more easily obtained global response is often used to make inferences (sometimes even contradictory inferences) on the infiltration and groundwater flow processes, as well as on the hydraulic parameter fields and the degree of karstification of the aquifer. In most cases, interpretations are based on the analysis of recession hydrographs by using different hydrograph separation methods (Burger 1957; Forkasiewicz and Paloc 1967; Drogue 1972; Mangin 1975; Bonacci 1987, 1993), statistical analysis of the whole spring hydrograph (Mangin 1984; Dreiss 1982; Labat 2000), or analysis of transfer functions between input (infiltration) and output (spring hydrograph) obtained by black-box or grey-box models. A quick overview of these methods is presented by (Eisenlohr et al. 1997) and a more detailed presentation is found in (Jeannin and Sauter 1998). In this paper we will only propose a few critical remarks concerning some of the usual interpretations.

Figure 6 represents the hydrograph of a typical karst spring, the Areuse spring in the Jura mountains (Switzerland) for 1979, as well as the registered electric conductivity

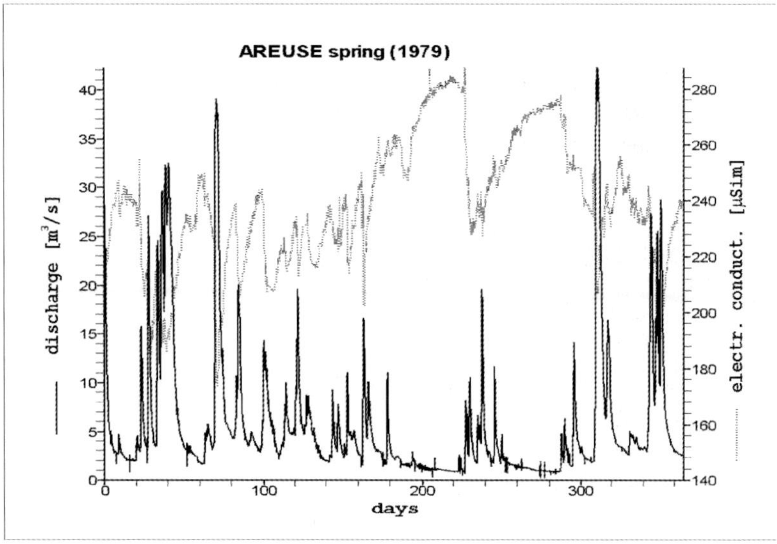

Fig.6. Hydrograph and electric conductivity registered for Areuse spring (Jura mountains, Switzerland) in 1979.

curve giving an indirect indication on the mineralization of the spring water. The most striking features are the rapid variation of the spring discharge and the generally observed dilution effect of storm or snowmelt events on the spring-water chemistry. This suggest not only a well developed karstification of the aquifer, but also, that an important part of the infiltrations should be drained rapidly toward the high permeability karst channel network and the spring. Another important fact is the contrast between the rapidly decreasing recession curve after the peak flow, and the very slowly decreasing recession curve in the domain of feeble discharges. The interpretation seems intuitively evident: the two parts of the recession curve represent the rapid emptying of the high-permeability karst channels and the slow emptying of the low-permeability fractured volumes. All these observations seem more or less evident in the light of the duality of karst aquifers and we can guess, at least qualitatively, how the karst springs could react with increasing karstification. This is attempted in figure 7 proposed by (Hobbs and Smart 1986) where the relations between input and output are represented very schematically as depending on the duality of infiltration, storage and groundwater flow.

3.2 ANALYSIS OF RECESSION HYDROGRAPHS

The recession curve is that part of the spring hydrograph which extends from a peak to the start of the next rise. The first aim of analysing the recession hydrograph was to estimate the volume of groundwater which could be drained by the karst spring in case of drought. As the last part of the slow recession curve can nearly always be approximated by an exponential, it is easy to integrate the approximated discharge from an arbitrary t_0 till "infinity" and get a number for the groundwater volume which could flow out at the spring. The method says naturally nothing about the groundwater volume which is below the spring level, but all the same, it allowed a kind of quantitative comparisons between karst aquifers.

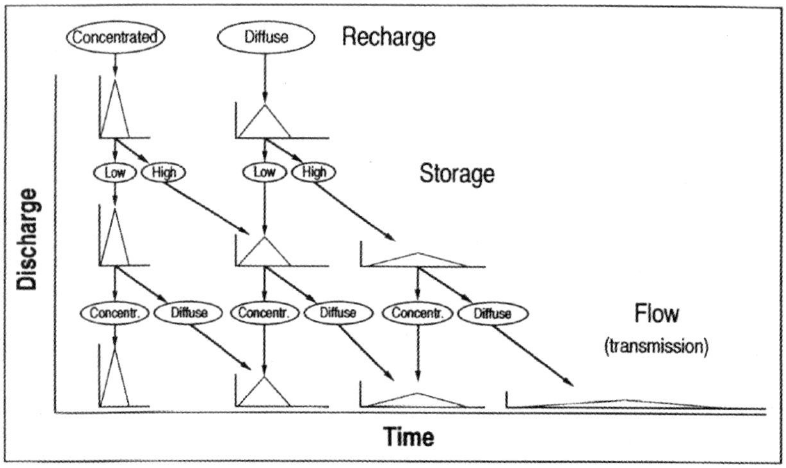

Fig. 7. Possible effects of the duality of recharge, storage and flow on the hydrograph of karst springs (from Hobbs and Smart 1986; in Jeannin and Sauter 1998).

(Forkasiewicz and Paloc 1967) proposed that the total recession curve be represented as the sum of two, three or more exponential functions:

$$Q(t) = \sum_{i=1}^{N} Q_{0i}\, e^{-\alpha_i t}$$

where N is the number of exponentials, t is the time, Q_{0i} are the discharges at t=0 and α_i are the recession coefficients for each exponential (see Fig. 8 and 9). In the interpretation, each exponential is thought to represent the depletion of a reservoir, the hydraulic conductivity of the reservoir being proportional to the recession coefficients α_i.

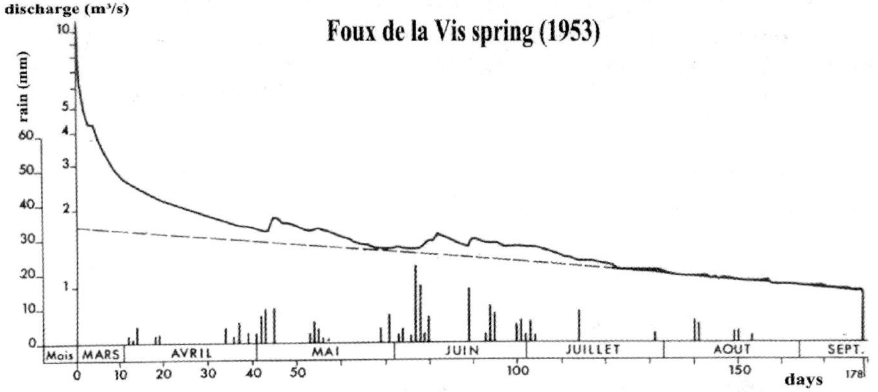

Fig. 8. Foux de la Vis spring (south of France): observed hydrograph during spring and sommer of 1953. The last part of the slow recession curve is approximated by an exponential (after Forkasiewicz and Paloc 1967).

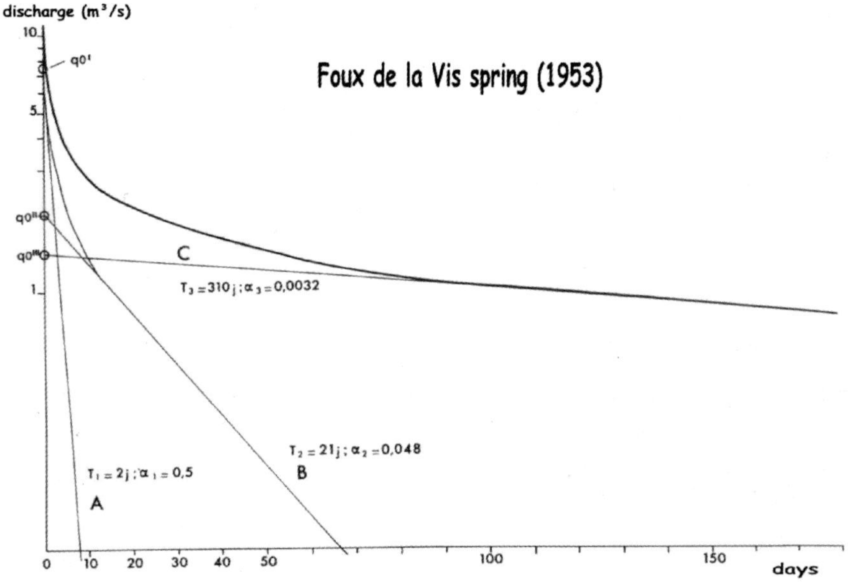

Fig. 9. Illustration of the hydrograph separation method of (Forkasiewicz and Paloc 1967) as applied to the hydrograph of Fig. 8.

According to this interpretation, the exponential with the highest recession coefficient (α_1 in Fig. 9) would represent the rapid depletion of the high permeability karst channels and the exponential with the lowest recession coefficient (α_3 in Fig. 9) would correspond to the ***baseflow,*** i.e. to the slow depletion of the low hydraulic conductivity fracture network. Intermediate exponentials (see α_2 in Fig. 9) are thought to represent the emptying of aquifer volumes with intermediate values of hydraulic conductivity. If the interpretation of the first and last exponential seems reasonable, the interpretation of the intermediate exponential is not necessarily true, as it was shown by (Kiraly and Morel 1976). Fig. 10 shows the separation of a theoretical hydrograph simulated by an oversimplified 2-D finite element model. There are only two classes of hydraulic conductivity in the model, i.e. there is no aquifer volume with an intermediate hydraulic conductivity, the depletion of which causes the appearance of an intermediate exponential, yet the separation gives three exponentials. The intermediate exponential could simply be the result of transient phenommena in the vicinity of the high hydraulic conductivity channel network as we proposed it in (Kiraly and Morel 1976).

The models show that the last exponential represents the depletion of the low hydraulic conductivity fractured volumes, exactly as assumed in the generally accepted interpretation. It is, however, not true that the last recession coefficient α of the baseflow depends on the hydraulic properties of the only low permeability volumes. In fact, it depends greatly on the geometry, the hydraulic conductivity and the density of the high permeability channel network. Fig. 11 shows two nearly exponential recession hydrographs simulated by 2-D finite element models (see Fig. 12). The same geometry and

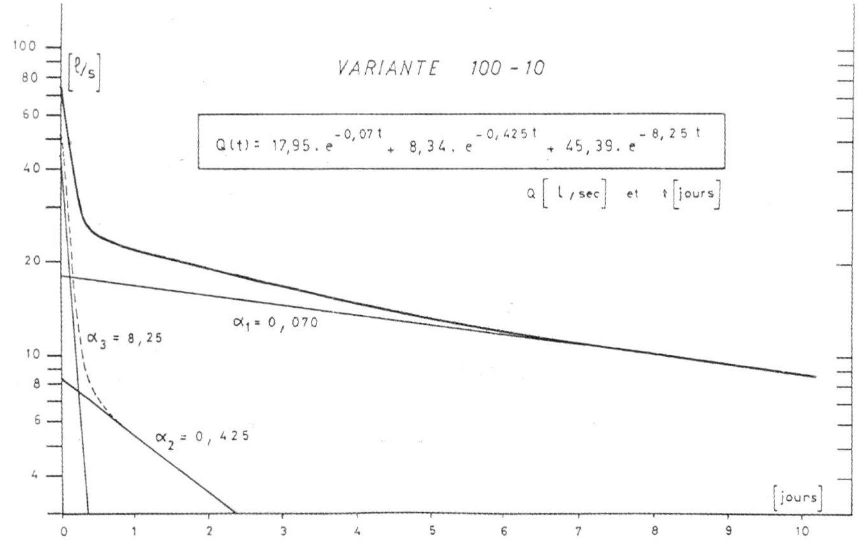

Fig. 10. Separation of a theoretical hydrograph simulated by finite element model. There are only two classes of hydraulic conductivity in the model, yet the separation gives three exponentials (after Kiraly and Morel 1976).

the same hydraulic conductivities are used for the two models, only the channel network is more dense in model K3. The recession coefficient is greater for K3, although the low permeabilities are the same for K1 and K3.

It should be understood that the recession coefficient α is a global parameter and will depend on the global configuration of the karst aquifers (even on their form and their extension). Using it to compute the hydraulic properties of the low permeability volumes could end up with very misleading conclusions.

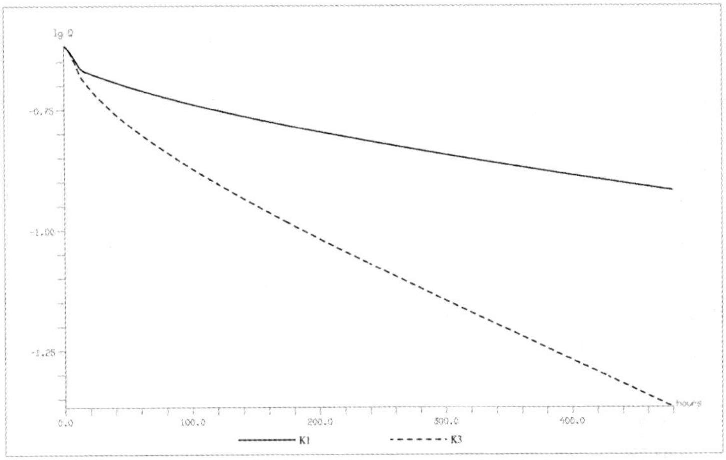

Fig. 11. Two nearly exponential recession hydrographs simulated by 2-D finite element models (see Fig. 12). The same geometry and the same hydraulic conductivities are used for the two models, only the channel network is more dense in model K3.

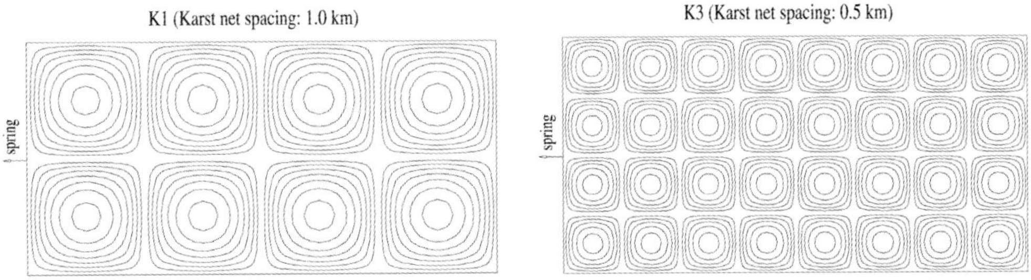

Fig. 12. Two finite element models with the same geometry and the same hydraulic conductivities, but with different channel network densities. Fig. 11 shows that depletion and "base-flow" are very different for the two "aquifers".

3.3 CRITICAL REMARKS ON THE CHEMICAL OR ISOTOPIC HYDROGRAPH SEPARATION METHODS

Fig. 6 showed the generally observed dilution effect of storm or snowmelt events on the spring-water chemistry. This suggests that an important part of the infiltrated "fresh-water" should be drained rapidly toward the high permeability karst channel network and the spring. Fig. 13 and 14 show the dilution phenomenon in detail in the case of a single peak flow of the Areuse spring. Careful sampling of the spring water before, during and after the peak flow allowed to visualize the variation of the calcium content, represented in Fig. 14. It shows that during the slow depletion of the low permeability volumes the karst channels are filled up with highly mineralised water characterizing the base-flow. Concentrated infiltration of fresh water determines the dilution effect during the peak flow, by mixing "old" water and "new" water in the karst channels. The "diluted" water is evacuated from the karst channels during the rapid recession and is progressively replaced by the "old" water of the base-flow (samples 100 to 104 in Fig. 14). These observations do not contradict the general ideas on the duality of karst and careful sampling (rising and falling limbs of peak hydrographs) and chemical analysis of spring water during input events appear as very important auxiliary methods for the understanding groundwater flow.

The idea of taking advantage of the quite general dilution effect by separating the whole hydrograph of a river or a karst spring into a "new-water" component and an "old-water" component was popularised in the mid 1970s and remained more or less widely used for the last 25 years (Martinec et al. 1974, 1979, 1982; Fritz et al. 1976; Dreiss 1989; Harum and Fank 1992; Gu 1992). The principle is simple, but many underlying hypotheses remain implicit, never clearly stated.

Let us define Q = spring discharge, C = concentration of a "substance" in the spring

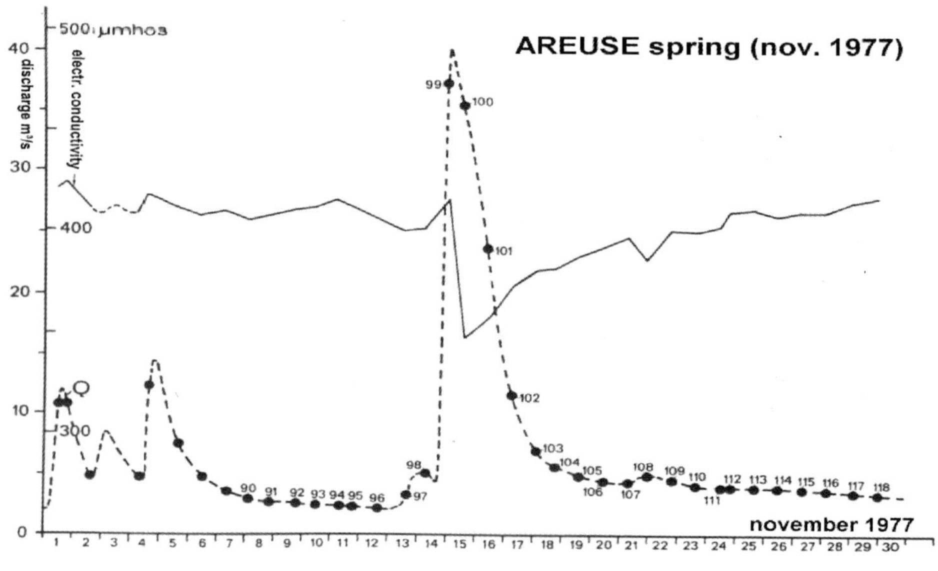

Fig. 13. Single discharge peak of the Areuse spring and dilution effect shown by the electric conductivity curve. Small black, numbered circles represent spring-water samples for chemical analysis (after Kiraly and Muller 1979).

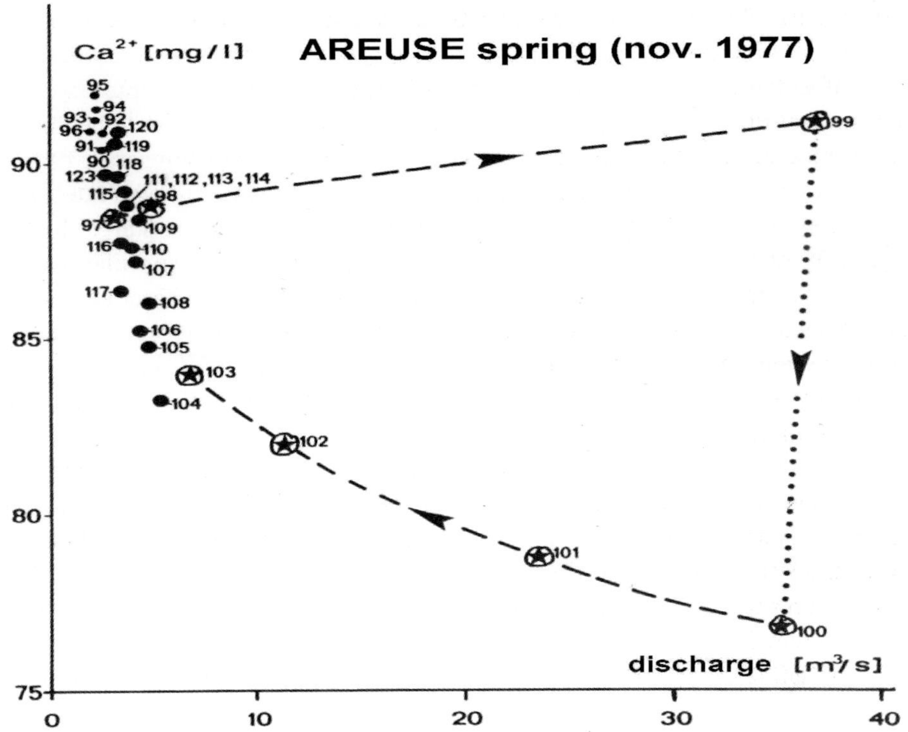

Fig. 14. Ca^{2+} concentration versus discharge for the single peak shown in Fig. 13. Observe the dilution between samples 99 and 100 and the clustering of points located on the slow recession hydrograph (after Kiraly and Muller 1979).

water, Q_{old} = old water component, C_{old} = old water concentration, Q_{new} = new water component, C_{new} = new water concentration. Most authors start from a very simplified mass balance:

$$\boxed{QC = Q_{old}C_{old} + Q_{new}C_{new}} \quad \text{with } Q = Q_{old} + Q_{new} \tag{3}$$

expressing Q_{old} we have

$$Q_{old} = Q\frac{(C - C_{new})}{(C_{old} - C_{new})} \quad \text{with } C_{old} \neq C_{new}\,.$$

This is a classical end member mixing analysis (EMMA) with C_{old} and C_{new} as end members. In most cases C_{old} is chosen to be the concentration of the base-flow and C_{new} is the concentration of the storm or snowmelt water. When applied to real cases, the method gives nearly always a very important old water component: up to 60% or 70% of the peak flow. As long as the chemical or isotopic hydrograph separation is restricted to the "old water" and "new water" concept, there is nothing to say about these definitions.

What should be however severely criticized, is the commonly accepted hydrologic and hydrogeologic interpretation of the components. As C_{old} was taken to be the tracer concentration of the base-flow (Martinec et al. 1974, 1979, 1982; Fritz et al. 1976) and many others do not hesitate to equate the old water component Q_{old} with the hydrodynamic base-flow Q_B, i.e. with the groundwater discharge into the rivers or with the discharge of the low-permeability fractured volumes into the karstic network. The old water component is then compared (and opposed) to the "conventional" base-flow estimate, generally obtained by the backward extrapolation of an exponential recession curve (see, for example, Fig. 9).

The comparison nearly always shows a high proportion of "old water" in the river or karst spring discharge even during flood events: Q_{old} may be as important as 60% or 70% of the total discharge Q during peak flow, much more than the "conventional" base-flow estimate. Equating Q_{old} with the base-flow Q_B leads many authors to accept a much higher infiltration rate into the aquifers or into the low-permeability (!!) fractured volumes than the "conventional" estimates, the infiltrations being supposed to increase the hydraulic gradients and to force the older groundwater to rapidly discharge into the rivers or into the high-permeability karstic channels (see, for example, Martinec et al. 1982). Unfortunately the authors do not produce any empirical gradient and permeability measurements which would allow, together with the drainage length, for the hydraulic proof of the above mentioned interpretation. As a matter of fact it can be shown very easily, even with an oversimplified double reservoir model, that old water component and base-flow are two concepts totally different.

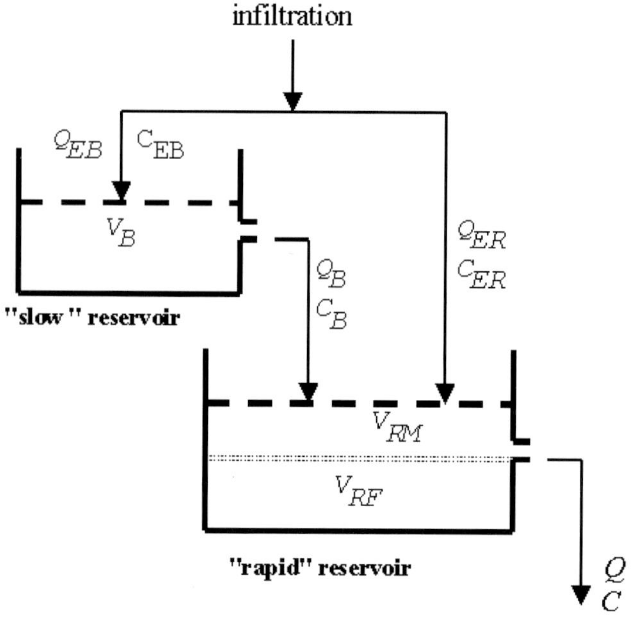

Fig. 15. Simplified double reservoir model for karst aquifers

Let us represent a karst aquifer by the simplified two-reservoir model of Figure 15. The slow reservoir simulates the low per-meability fractured volumes and the rapid reservoir represents the karst channels. The variables are defined as follows:

Q_{EB} = infiltration into slow reservoir; C_{EB} = concentration in Q_{EB}, but it will not be used for the slow reservoir; V_B = ground-water volume in the slow reservoir; Q_B = base-flow; C_B = concentration of the base-flow; Q_{ER} = direct infiltration into the karst channels; C_{ER} = concent-ration of the direct infiltration; V_{RM} = volume of groundwater which is located above the spring level (it can flow out); V_{RF} = volume of groundwater below the spring level (the volume is fix); Q = discharge of the spring; C = concentration of the spring-water. It appears clearly that C_B is C_{old} and C_{ER} is C_{new}. Due to the important residence time of the groundwater in the slow reservoir it is assumed that C_B is more or less constant. We assume, in addition, an exponential depletion (emptying) for each reservoir and in this case the recession coefficient α is the ratio between the discharge and the volume of the reservoir: $\alpha = Q/V$ and we can pass from Q to V or from V to Q easily. Two differential equations will describe the "flow problem":

$$\frac{dV_B}{dt} = Q_{EB} - Q_B = Q_{EB} - \alpha_B V_B \tag{4}$$

$$\frac{dV_{RM}}{dt} = Q_{ER} + Q_B - Q = Q_{ER} + \alpha_B V_B - \alpha_{RM} V_{RM} \tag{5}$$

A third differential equation will describe the mass balance for the "tracer", where the total mass of tracer in the rapid reservoir is $M = C(V_{RM} + V_{RF})$:

$$\frac{dM}{dt} = \frac{d}{dt} C(V_{RM} + V_{RF}) = Q_B C_B + Q_{ER} C_{ER} - QC$$

or

$$(V_{RM} + V_{RF})\frac{dC}{dt} + \frac{dV_{RM}}{dt} C + \boxed{QC = Q_B C_B + Q_{ER} C_{ER}} \tag{6}$$

Equation 6 will reduces to the dashed box, i.e. to equation 3, if the first two terms are zero. But this would imply that there is **no water in the karst channels** ($V_{RM} + V_{RF}$ is zero!), and/or the concentration in the spring water is constant. These are unrealistic conditions, thus equation 3 cannot be used to calculate, even approximately, the base-flow.

Replacing dV_{RM}/dt and rearranging the terms we obtain

$$\frac{dC}{dt} = Q_B \frac{(C_B - C)}{(V_{RM} + V_{RF})} + Q_{ER} \frac{(C_{ER} - C)}{(V_{RM} + V_{RF})} \tag{7}$$

Equations 4, 5 and 7 are three simultaneous differential equations which can be solved by the Runge-Kutta method for Q_B, Q and C if we give α_B, α_{RM}, Q_{EB}, Q_{ER}, and V_{RF}. It must be emphasized that in this simplified model the groundwater volume below the spring level, V_{RF}, does not influence the spring discharge, but it will greatly influence the variation of C, i.e. the dilution effect. For the same base-flow hydrograph or spring hydrograph, for example, very different dilution effects, thus very different "old water" components, could be obtained depending on the volume of V_{RF}. This is the case which is illustrated in Fig. 16.

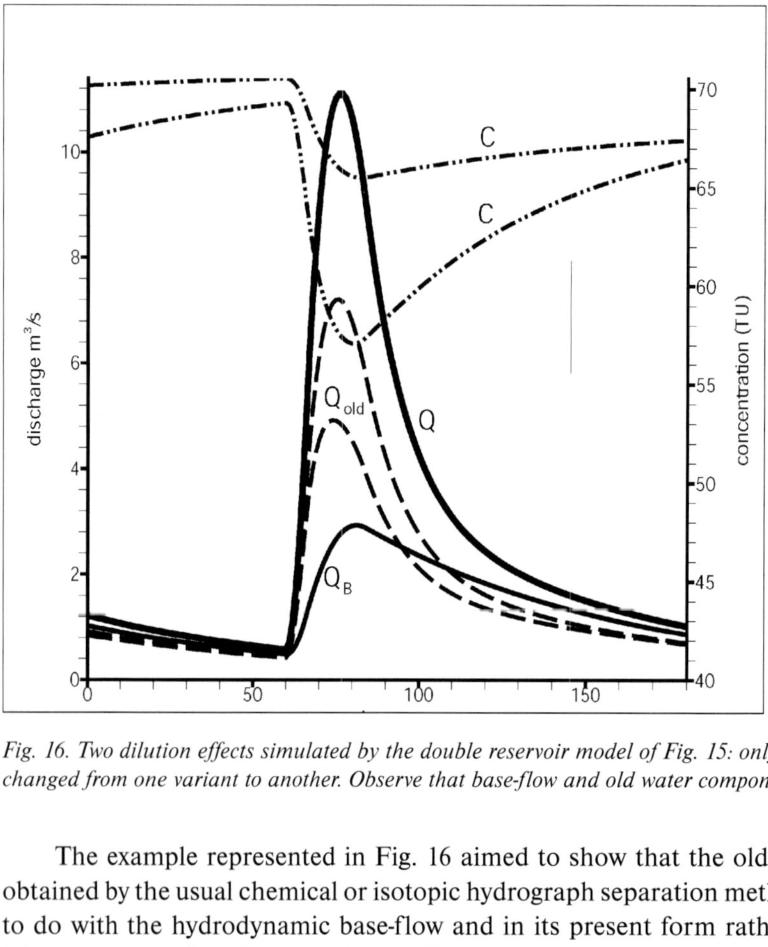

Fig. 16. Two dilution effects simulated by the double reservoir model of Fig. 15: only the fixed volume V_{RF} changed from one variant to another. Observe that base-flow and old water components are not the same.

The example represented in Fig. 16 aimed to show that the old water component obtained by the usual chemical or isotopic hydrograph separation methods has not much to do with the hydrodynamic base-flow and in its present form rather leads to invalid inferences regarding the groundwater flow processes. In the double reservoir model the ratio between the recession coefficients of the slow reservoir and the rapid reservoir is about 1 to 10, and 50% of the infiltration is "diffuse", into the slow reservoir, and 50% is "concentrated", into the rapid reservoir. Both infiltration functions are triangular: 4 hours for rising limb and 18 hours for the falling limb. The "tracer" is tritium: the concentration is 80 TU for the old water and 40 TU for the new or storm water. An important parameter for the dilution is V_{RF}, the volume of water in the karst channels located below the spring level. It is probably the principal responsible for the high old water content obtained by the chemical and isotopic hydrograph separation methods and the misinterpretation of the results. The ratio between the volumes V_{RF} used for the two variants was

1 to 4. Increasing the fixed volume diminishes the dilution and increases the old water component (see the C curves and the dashed old water curves in Fig. 16), while the base-flow does not change at all.

In spite of the many critical remarks presented above, we hope that this important dilution effect could be used, perhaps in the framework of a different paradigm, for a better understanding of karst and karstification. It deserves a better destiny than the only separation in a somewhat arbitrary new water and old water component.

4 MODELING KARST AQUIFERS

4.1 AIMS OF THE MODELING

Analysing the global response of karst springs stimulates our imagination and incites to make hypotheses about the structure of the aquifer, about the hydraulic parameter fields, about the groundwater flow processes, often about karstification and sometimes about the evolution of karst in the interior of the aquifer. The direct verification of the consequences our hypotheses by field measurements in the interior of the karstic medium is, obviously, very difficult, if not impossible. The so called "global models", such as the double reservoir model used in the previous chapter, do not help much either, because we have no information on the spatial distribution of the variables and the parameters.

An indirect method of verification would consist in introducing the inferred karstic structures into a deterministic numerical model and then simulate the supposed processes and their effect on the "global response" of the aquifer (for example, the spring hydrograph), on the groundwater flow field, on the hydraulic head distribution, etc. The simulated behavior of the theoretical aquifer could then be compared to the usually accepted ideas on the groundwater flow processes in karst aquifers. This is the way followed by the research team of CHYN (Centre d'Hydrogéologie de l'Université de Neuchâtel) for years.

The aim of this chapter is to present the effect of the karst channel network and the epikarst zone on groundwater flow processes, as obtained by numerical finite element models simulating a few "theoretical" and oversimplified karst aquifers. The results, although "theoretical", have important practical consequences on the monitoring strategies applied for karst aquifers, on the interpretation of the global responses obtained at karst springs and on the estimation of the recharge of the low conductivity "capacitive" volumes. They suggest to ask such fundamental questions as: what is the meaning of "groundwater level" observations in boreholes when separated from hydraulic conductivity measurements; what is the meaning of "groundwater level" observations in boreholes when separated from hydraulic conductivity measurements; what is the meaning of the "groundwater table" represented by isolines (equipotentials) in karst aquifers; what is the hydraulic meaning of the "components" obtained by chemical or isotopic hydrograph separation methods; etc

4.2 MODEL AND REALITY

The reconstruction of a regional groundwater flow field, which is consistent with a given hydraulic conductivity field and with given boundary conditions, nearly always requires the use of numerical models. A model is not the reality, it is only the realization of a schematic and symbolic representation of the real system. The relations between "real system", "abstract scheme" and "numerical model" are represented in Fig. 17, which also shows the principal problems in modeling groundwater flow.

Starting from incomplete information on the aquifer to be modeled, a *schematic representation of the real system* has to be worked out first. Generally, the flow of the groundwater is represented by differential equations, which may change depending on the type of problem to solve (saturated-unsaturated flow, constant or variable density flow, multiphase flow, etc.). The flow equations contain a few parameters depending on the aquifer properties (hydraulic conductivity, specific storativity, effective porosity, etc.) and the real medium will be represented by the field of these parameters, i.e. by giving a parameter value to each point of the modeled region, even there where we have never made any observation.

As the available data on the hydraulic parameters are very limited, it appears clearly that indirect estimation of the parameters and interpolation or extrapolation of the measured values will be unavoidable when modeling real aquifers (see Fig. 18). It must be emphasized that fractured and karstified media may present additional difficulties due to the strong local heterogeneity of the parameter fields. The karst channel network existing in the real system, for example, is never entirely known. Finally, the imposed and initial conditions complete the schematic representation, sometimes also termed the "conceptual model".

The second problem is related to the *realization of a computer code* based on numerical methods which allow to solve the equations defined in the abstract scheme. The problem is far from beeing simple and in most cases the numerical model is only a more or less imperfect realization of the abstract scheme.

The third, very important problem in modeling groundwater flow is the *transfer of the simulated results onto the real system*. Strictly speaking, the simulated results are not "valid" but in the highly simplified scheme or numerical model, and their meaningful transfer onto the real system requires that simplifying assumptions and uncertainties on the data explicitly do appear as uncertainties on the results. This could help to avoid such ridiculous situations as trying to simulate observed piezometric heads to within a few centimeters, even though the schematized hydraulic conductivity field "ignores" the strong local heterogeneities existing in the real system.

As a matter of fact, schematic representation of the real system, numerical modeling and experimental field work should go hand in hand. The numerical models might be used from the very moment where the first hypotheses on geometry, hydraulic parameters and boundary conditions are explicitly formulated. Whatever may be the value of these hypotheses, the numerical model will give a "response", which represents the verifiable consequences of our inevitably hypothetical and schematic representation of the

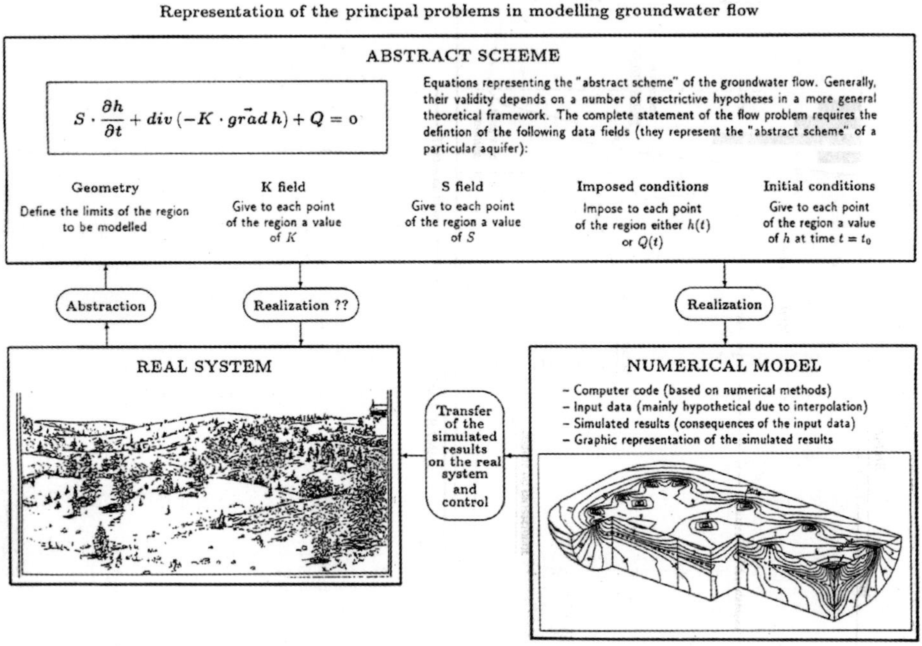

Fig. 17. Principal problems in modeling groundwater flow. Observe that experimental methods should be used to check if the real system may be actually considered as a realization of the schematic representation (after Kiraly 1994, modified)

real system. Ultimately, it is the observed behaviour of the aquifer which will decide if our hypotheses are acceptable or not.

Finally it must be emphasized that modeling is not just curve-fitting. As it was pointed out by Klemes (1986): "For a good mathematical model it is not enough to work well. **It must work well for the right reasons**. It must reflect, even if only in simplified form, the essential features of the physical prototype." This is particularly recommended in modeling karst aquifers.

4.3 COMBINED DISCRETE CHANNEL AND CONTINUUM APPROACH BY USING FINITE ELEMENT MODELS

The nested model concept of the geological discontinuities was presented in the previous chapters. The modelling of this kind of nested structures nearly always requires the combination of the continuum approach with the discrete fracture or discrete channel model. At a regional scale, for example, the discrete fracture (or channel) model alone could not be realized at all, because of the tremendous amount of discontinuities (of different orders of magnitude) which ought to be introduced into the model.

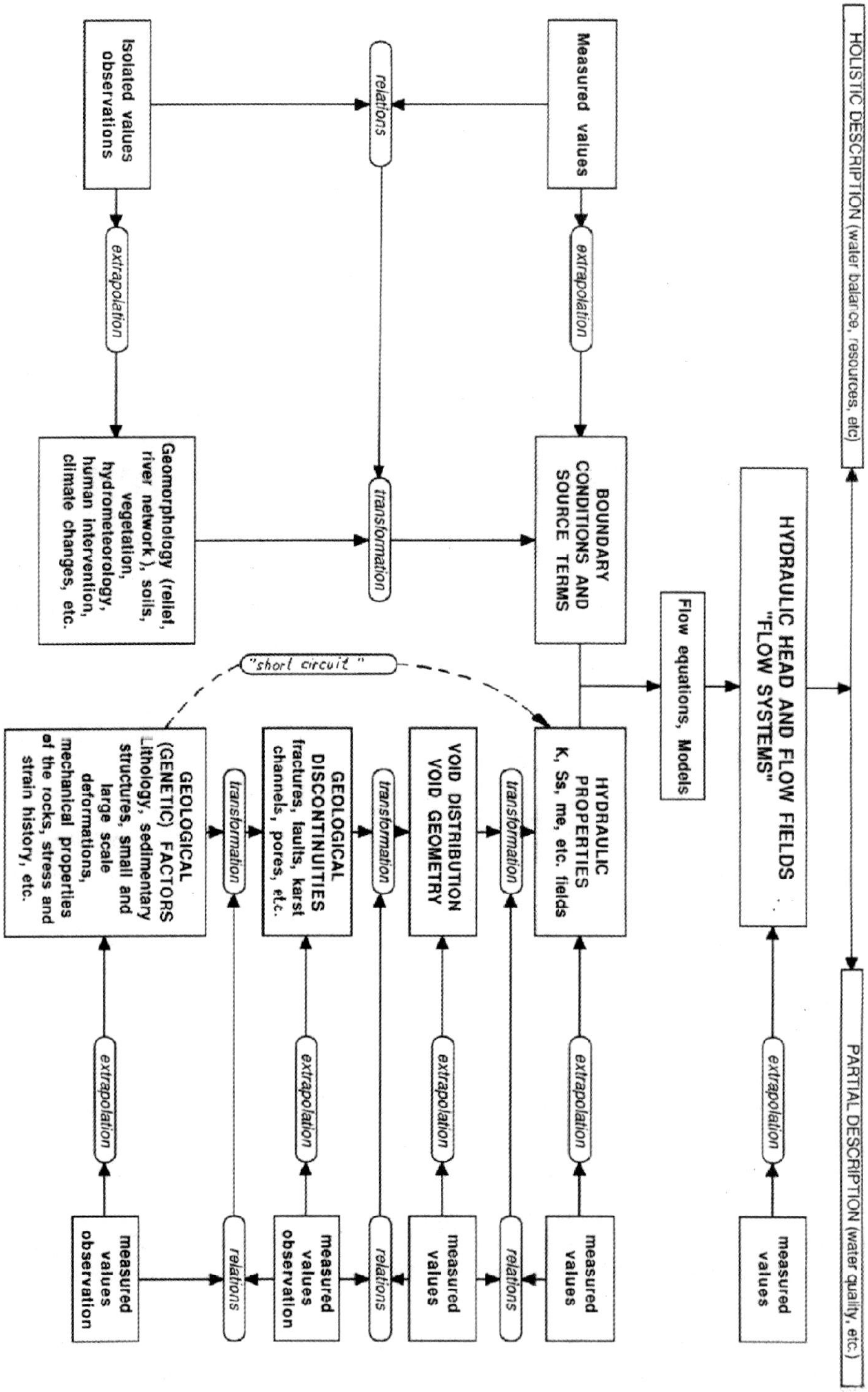

Fig. 18. Problems related to the reconstruction of hydraulic parameter and flow fields (after Kiraly 1975, modified)

On the other hand, the equivalent continuum approach alone would not show the effect of the regional fault zones or the regionally developed karst networks on the groundwater flow systems. So it seems reasonable to model the regional faults or karst networks by 2-D or 1-D "discrete" zones, whereas the volumes between them (which contain only lower order fractures or channels) might be modelled by a 3-D equivalent continuum. As a matter of fact, every discontinuity, which is "big" with respect to the size of the modelled region, should be represented by a discrete zone.

Numerical models using the finite element method are excellent for the combined discrete channel (or discrete fracture) and continuum approach, particularly if they allow for the combination of 1-D, 2-D and 3-D finite elements, as it was proposed by Kiraly (1979, 1985, 1988, 1995) and Helmig (1993). In this case, the high conductivity karst channel network is simulated by 1-D linear or quadratic finite elements, which are "immersed" between 2-D or 3-D linear or quadratic elements representing the low conductivity fractured limestone volumes.

The simulations presented in this paper were carried out by the computer codes FEN1 and FEN2. They have been developed at the Centre d'Hydrogéologie de Neuchâtel and simulate steady-state and transient, one-, two- or three-dimensional saturated groundwater flow by the finite element method. The computer programs allow for the incorporation of one-, two- or three-dimensional linear or quadratic elements within a three-dimensional network. The saturated, constant density, transient groundwater flow is represented by equation (8)

$$S_s \frac{\partial h}{\partial t} + div(- [K]\, \overrightarrow{grad}\, h) + Q = 0 \tag{8}$$

where S_s is the specific storage coefficient, [K] is the hydraulic conductivity tensor, h is the hydraulic head and Q represents the general source/sink terms (infiltration, well discharges, etc.).

The formulation for the finite elements is based on the Galerkin weighted residual approach and the resulting system of linear equations is solved by the frontal elimination technique of Irons (1970). The time dependent problem is solved in FEN2 by using the robust Crank-Nicholson implicit time-stepping scheme. UFEN1 is a code derived from FEN1 and simulates saturated/unsaturated steady-state groundwater flow. In this paper it is used to simulate the free groundwater table in a theoretical "shallow" karst aquifer. The computer codes allow the modeller to "concatenate" several aquifers into one model and this facility is used to link the epikarst with the mean aquifer.

The computer codes allow the modeller to "concatenate" several aquifers into one model and this facility is used to link the epikarst with the mean aquifer. A slightly modified version of FEN2 offers another facility when used to simulate karst aquifers. By giving the identification number of the nodal points located on the karst channels, the program calculates the contribution of each 3-D element (i.e. low conductivity fractured volume) to the karst net. The sum of these contributions is simply the base-flow which can be compared to the total spring hydrograph. Using the linear Darcy's law to simulate the groundwater flow in saturated karst channels represents only a crude approximation of the real system, but our aim was to obtain a rapid and rather "qualitative" indication on the effect of the enormous contrast between the hydraulic conductivities of fractured limestones (10^{-6} m/s) and karst channels (10 m/s or more). The conclusions presented in this paper will not be changed qualitatively with the simulation of turbulent flow: the effects due to concentrated infiltration into the channel network (inversion of gradients, negative base-flow, etc.), for example, will be only increased.

5 PRESENTATION AND DISCUSSION OF A FEW RESULTS.

5.1 THE 2-D APPROACH: SOME EARLY RESULTS.

In the 1970s it was possible to introduce 1-D elements between 2-D finite elements, and thus simulate the karst channel network in 2-D karst aquifers (Kiraly and Morel 1976a, 1976b). These early and very simplified 2-D karst models delivered quite interesting results.

- The simulation of the typical hydrograph of the karst springs (see Fig.6), with the non-exponential rapid recession and the exponential slow recession, nearly always requires the introduction of a high permeability karst channel network in an otherwise low permeability aquifer volume.
- The duality of the hydraulic conductivity field causes an important scale effect in the model: nearly the whole aquifer volume has a very low hydraulic conductivity, however the global structure behaves as a highly transmissive system. Qualitatively it is the right type of structure: we are not very far from karst! We get even closer to karst with the infiltration problem.
- If the chosen spacing of the karst channels allowes to simulate correctly the exponential part of the recession curve of springs, the correct simulation of the peak-flow and the rapidly decreasing non-exponential part of the recession curve requires, however, that more than 50% of the infiltration arrive in "concentrated" form, directly into the high conductivity channels. The concentrated infiltration in the model must have a physical counterpart in the real system. A sound hypothesis would be to suppose, that besides small rivers disappearing in sinkholes, an important part of the infiltration is drained rapidly, probably already at shallow depth in a thin high conductivity layer, towards the karst channel network and the karst spring. This would be the epikarst zone of Mangin (1975).
- The important concentrated infiltration, i.e. the duality of infiltration, has a very important consequence: the temporary inversion of the hydraulic gradients between the channels and the low permeability volumes.
- The temporary inversion of hydraulic gradients has an even more important consequence: the temporary reduction of the base-flow to zero in the vicinity of the peak-

flow. And this is not good news for those who equate the old water component of a karst spring with the base-flow.

- At least, we have to mention that the recession coefficient of the last, exponential part of the depletion curve depends as much (if not more) on the conductivity and the density of the karst channels than on the hydraulic properties of the low permeability volumes.

Although very simple, these 2-D models were very good from a heuristic point of view. Even if in a very simplified and naive form, they had the most important properties of a karst aquifer (duality of the hydraulic conductivity field, duality of the infiltration processes, duality of the groundwater flow field, concentrated discharge at the karst spring). The problems we met with them were actually relevant to the study of karst aquifers and suggested further investigations on the theoretical level, as well as in the domain of empirical field works.

5.2 THE 3-D APPROACH: THE EPIKARST MODEL

Earlier numerical experiments with 2-D Finite Element models showed the necessity to impose a high proportion of concentrated infiltrations in order to generate the typical "karstic" storm hydrographs (Kiraly and Morel 1976a, 1976b). It was supposed, that besides the rivers disappearing in sinkholes, the concentrated infiltrations would result from the rapid drainage in a high permeability "skin" at shallow depth: the epikarst (Mangin 1975). However, the epikarst layer could not be explicitly included in these 2-D models. To indirectly show its role, we explicitly introduced the epikarst layer in a "synthetic" 3-D Finite Element model and varied the proportion of the diffuse infiltrations with respect to the concentrated infiltrations resulting from the rapid drainage in the epikarst zone. As the model is transparent for the modeller, the simulated behaviour of the theoretical karst aquifer will clearly show the effect of epikarst not only on the spring hydrograph, but also on the baseflow component of the spring discharge, on the variation of hydraulic heads and fluxes during recharge and recession periods, as well as on the recharge conditions of the low permeability fractured volumes. The detailed results are presented in (Kiraly et al. 1995), we show hier only a few diagrams without many comments.

The diagram of Fig. 19 show the 3-D geometry of a theoretical "half-syncline" drained by a very simplified high-permeability karst channel network. The karst channels are simulated by quadratic 1-D elements introduced "in sandwich" between the quadratic 3-D elements simulating the low-permeability fractured volumes. The epikarst is simulated by a 2-D finite element layer which will discharge into the channel network of the 3-D syncline, such as represented in Fig. 19. The hydraulic heads are imposed at the base of the epikarst model (where the channels intersect the 2-D layer), and the calculated discharges are injected at each time-step into the channel network of the 3-D model. This will represent the concentrated infiltration function for the mean aquifer.

The hydraulic parameters are the same for all variants of the epikarst model. The hydraulic conductivities K are realistic: 5 * 10-6 [m/s] for the low-permeability fractured volumes and 100 [m/s] for the high-permeability karst channels. In the 2-D epikarst layer the transmissiv*ity* T is relativly high: about 5 * 10-2 m2/s. Linear Darcy's law is used throughout the models.

The specific storage coefficients S_s are kept artificially low in order to "accelerate" the evolution of the simulated hydraulic head and flow field. In the channel network the values of S_s are 400 to 500 times higher than in the low-permeability fractured volumes.

Finally it must be emphasized that we use in the model a very simplified karst channel network. In real systems the karst network is hierarchically organized, with lower and higher order branches having lower and higher hydraulic conductivity values. In the above described model all branches of the karst network are of the same order of magnitude and have the same hydraulic conductivity.

The volume of the total infiltrations remains the same in each variant, but the proportion of the diffuse and concentrated infiltrations will change from one variant to another. Four cases have been simulated:

DSYN0:	100% diffuse infiltration	0% drained by the epikarst
DSYN20:	80% diffuse infiltration	20% drained by the epikarst
DSYN50:	50% diffuse infiltration	50% drained by the epikarst
DSYN100:	0% diffuse infiltration	100% drained by the epikarst

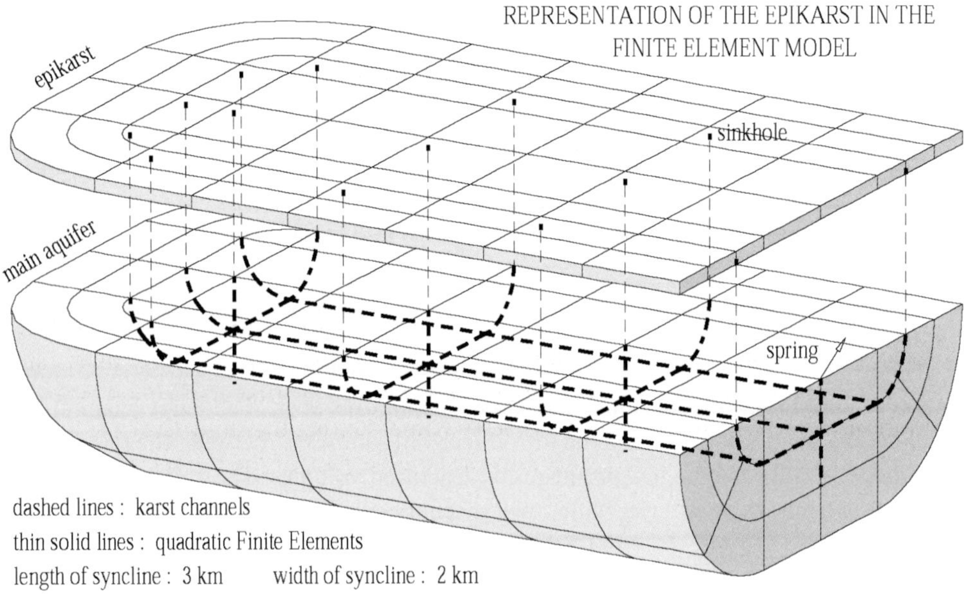

Fig. 19. Representation of the epikarst in the finite element model.

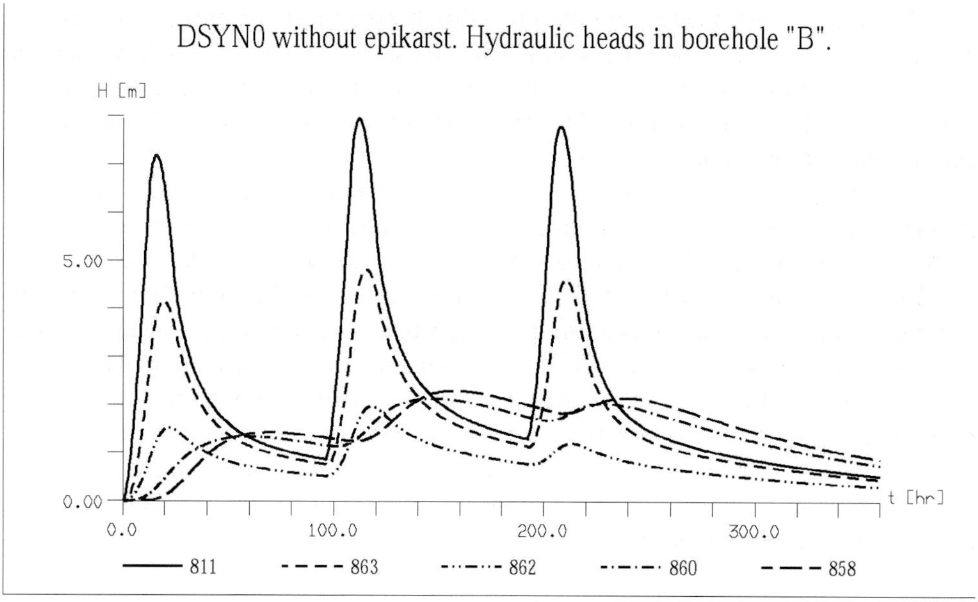

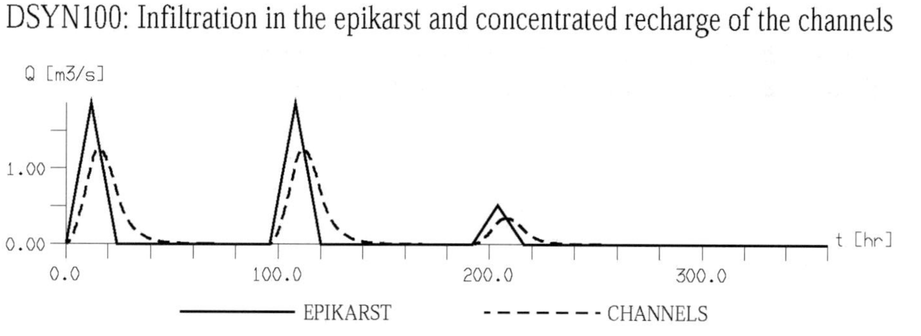

Fig. 20. Total recharge function of the epikarst and concentrated recharge function of the karst channels for variant DSYN100.

Figure 20 represents the total recharge function of the epikarst and the concentrated recharge function of the karst channels for variant DSYN100. There are three input events ("storms"), of a duration of 24 hours each. During the first and second event the infiltrations are distributed over the whole syncline. During the third "storm", infiltration takes place only on a small stripe in the middle part of the model, representing about 30% of the total infiltration area.

5.3 EFFECT ON THE SHAPE OF THE SPRING HYDROGRAM AND ON THE HYDRAULIC HEADS.

Figure 21 is self-explanatory: it represents the spring hydrographs for different proportions of infiltration drained by the epikarst into the high-permeability channel network. It appears clearly that without some kind of concentrated infiltrations we cannot simulate the typical karstic reactions of the spring. The rise of the groundwater table in the low-permeability volumes cannot "press" enough water into the karst channels to cause a typical karstic storm hydrograph at the spring. It seems reasonable to admit that in most "open" karst aquifers more than 40% of the infiltrations should be drained rapidly into the karst channels (also see Kiraly and Morel 1976a).

Earlier numerical experiments with 2-D finite element models suggested that concentrated infiltrations might cause an inversion of the gradients between karst channels and low-permeability volumes (Kiral and Morel 1976a, 1976b). These 2-D models cannot show, however, the vertical distribution of the hydraulic heads in a borehole. Taking advantage of the 3-D model, we "registered" the simulated heads in an imaginary borehole "B", the location of which is presented in figure 23. The borehole intersects a karst channel and the hydraulic heads are measured at 7 points between the top and the base of the aquifer.

The results are represented for variants DSYN0 (no concentrated infiltrations, see Fig. 22) and DSYN100 (100% of the infiltrations are concentrated, see Fig. 22). Again, the figures are self-explanatory and need not many comments.

During the recharge period there is nearly always an inversion of gradients between the karst channel and the low-permeability volumes located below the channel. The concentrated infiltrations must be really important to produce the same inversion with respect to the low-permeability volumes located above the channel. The bloc-diagrams

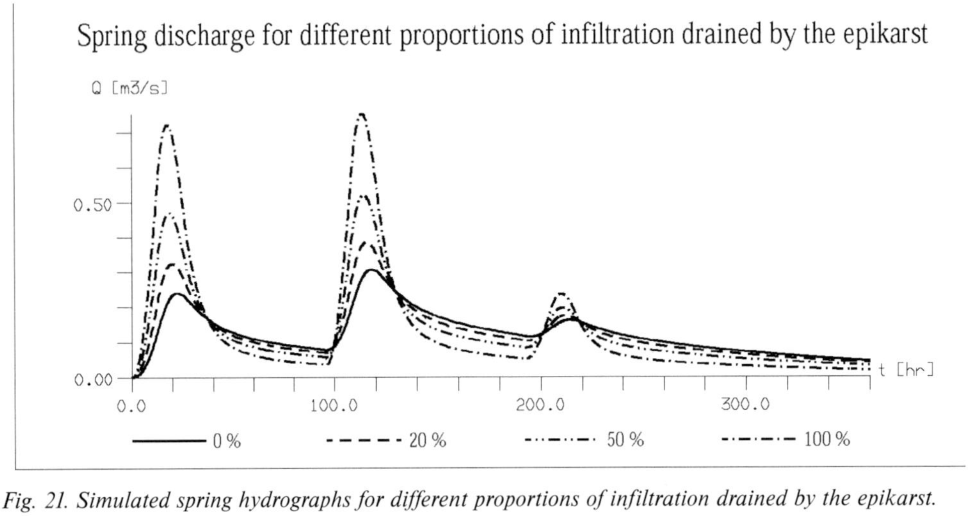

Fig. 21. Simulated spring hydrographs for different proportions of infiltration drained by the epikarst.

of Fig. 23 clearly show the recharge and drainage mechanism with epikarst and concentrated infiltration.

The practical consequences of these theoretical results are important: the hydraulic heads should be measured separately in the high-permeability segments and in the low-permeability segments of boreholes or piezometers. If we measure only one "groundwater level" in an otherwise heterogeneous borehole, the results will be rather misleading than helpful. Other practical consequences are related to the determination of the base-flow component, to the recharge mechanism of the low permeability fractured volumes, to the interpretation of the chemical or isotopic composition of the spring-water, etc.

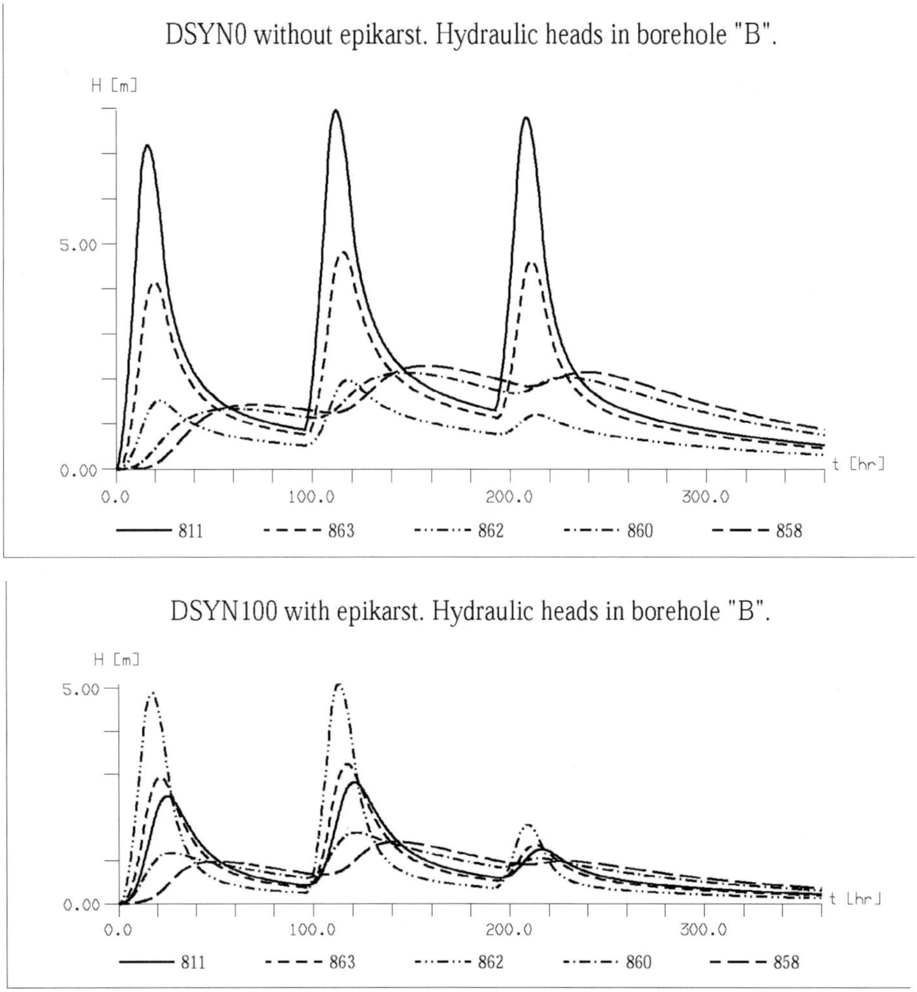

Fig. 22. Variation of the hydraulic head in borehole "B" for DSYN0 and DSYN100

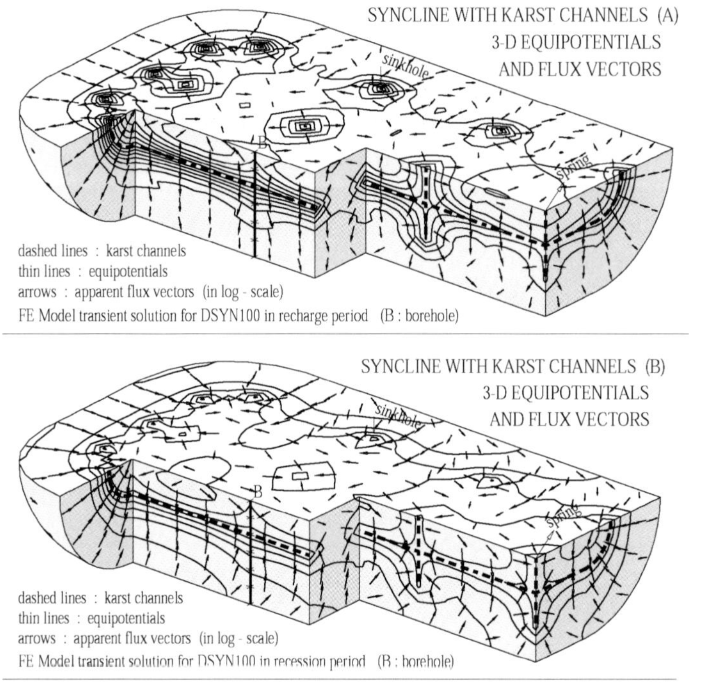

Fig. 23. Variation of the hydraulic head for DSYN100 in recharge periode and in recession periode. Location of borehole "B" shown on the figures.

5.4 EFFECT OF THE EPIKARST ON THE "BASE-FLOW" COMPONENT OF KARST SPRINGS.

In spite of the fact, that the inversion of gradients between karst channels and low-permeability volumes is well known by many karst hydrogeologists, most of the graphically obtained base-flow hydrographs don't show the logical consequence, namely the zero (or negative) base-flow value during recharge periods. One of the few exceptions is found in Tripet (1972), who suppressed the base-flow component of the Areuse spring during the recharge periods.

Taking advantage of the possibility to calculate the contribution of the low-permeability 3-D elements to the nodes located on the 1-D karst channels, we computed the baseflow component for each variant. The dramatic effect of the concentrated infiltrations on the base-flow component is presented in Fig. 24 for variants DSYN0, DSYN50 and DSYN100. The appearance of negative base-flow during the recharge period indicates that the karst channels inject more water into the low-permeability volumes than they drain. The volume of this recharge might not be very important, but the fact that the low-permeability volumes may be recharged "from the interior" should not be overlooked.

Another consequence of the negative baseflow appears when estimating the "rapid infiltration" from the spring hydrograph. Generally this is done by substracting the graphically determined baseflow component from the total discharge curve. Now, when the baseflow is negative, it should be added to the spring discharge, otherwise the intensity of the rapid or direct infiltration will be systematically underestimated (see Fig. 24).

As the model allows for the independent estimation of the baseflow and of the rapid or concentrated infiltration into the karst channel network (which will be called [

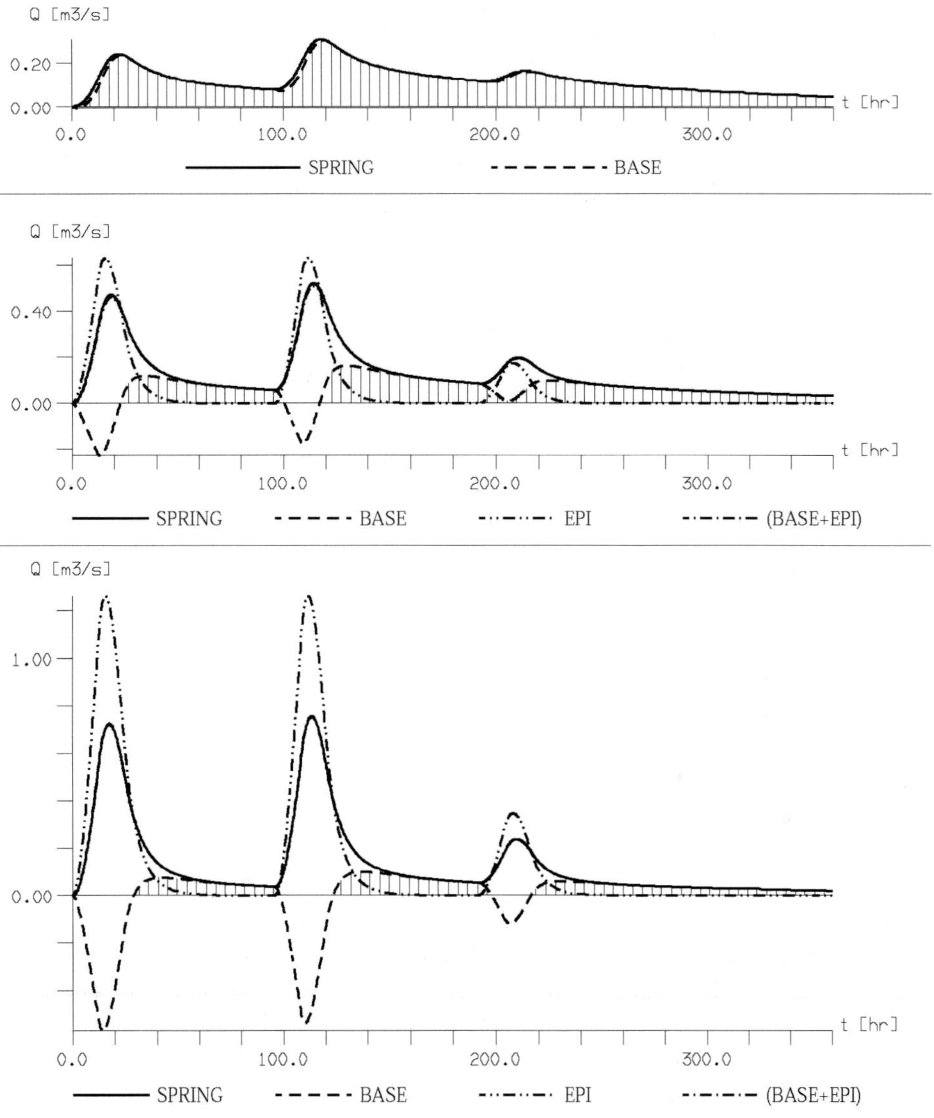

Fig. 24. Springflow, baseflow, epiflow and (epiflow+baseflow) for variants DSYN0 (above), DSYN50 (middle) and DSYN100 (below). Note that concentrated infiltration (epiflow) may be greater, or even much greater than the spring discharge. The curve (baseflow+epiflow) is not visible, because it coincides almost exactly with the springflow.

"epiflow", for short, in the following), we can take a critical look at the usually accepted chemical or isotopic hydrograph separation methods.

Fig. 24 show, that the "new water component" obtained by the End Member Mixing Analysis (EMMA) could not be identified with the "rapid recharge to the conduit system after a storm", as it was stated by Dreiss (1989, page 121). Indeed, the "new water component" obtained by EMMA must be always smaller than the spring discharge, but figures 13a and 13b indicate clearly that the rapid recharge into the karst channels, noted as the epiflow, may be greater (or even much greater) than the spring discharge.

5.5 REMARKS ON THE RECHARGE OF THE LOW CONDUCTIVITY VOLUMES: THE "FARADAY CAGE" EFFECT OF EPIKARST

The huge low permeability fractured limestone volumes are often designated as the "capacitive" part of karst aquifers. They might contain important groundwater resources, and their recharge mechanism may have important practical consequences on the groundwater management problems (base-flow of karst springs, exploitation of groundwater by pumping wells or galleries, etc.).

Figure 6 ("deep" karst syncline) and figure 7 ("shallow karst") suggest that a well developed epikarst layer enhancing the concentrated infiltration into the high conductivity karst channel network will "short-circuit" the low conductivity volumes and will play the role of a "Farady cage" with respect to the main aquifer. Depending on the importance of this "Faraday cage" effect, the recharge of the low conductivity volumes could be much smaller than in the case of pure diffuse infiltration, with the above mentioned important consequences on the ground-water management problems. In the "deep syncline" configuration the inversion of gradients will always contribute to recharging the low conductivity volumes "from the interior", but in the "shallow karst" configuration the "short-circuit" of the low permeability volumes might be almost total.

6 CONCLUSION AND OUTLOOK

Karst aquifers are 3-D systems and cannot be reduced to 2-D objects without losing important informations on the infiltration processes and the distribution of hydraulic heads. Numerical experiments with a 3-D finite element model using the combined discret channel and continuum approach, and simulating the infiltration and groundwater flow processes in a highly simplified theoretical karst aquifer, allowed to show the importance of the existence or non-existence of an epikarst zone enhancing concentrated infiltration. The effect of the epikarst on the hydraulic head and the groundwater flow field has practical consequences on the monitoring strategies applied for karst aquifers, on the interpretation of the global responses obtained at the karst springs and on the estimation of the recharge of the low conductivity "capacitive" volumes. Hydraulic head measurements should always be related to zones of known hydraulic conductivity and the "piezometric maps" of karst aquifers should always indicate the hydraulic conductivity at the measurement points (see, for example, Jeannin 1995).

Future research is needed in the simulation of transient, turbulent Fflow at a basin-wide scale, using the discrete channel and continuum approach. The comparison of a spring hydrograph simulated with turbulent channel flow, and another spring hydrograph simulated with linear channel flow would certainly improve the interpretation of empirical karst spring hydrographs.

ACKNOWLEDGEMENTS

Some of the computer codes used for the groundwater flow simulation and some of the ideas presented in this paper were developed in the framework of earlier research projects supported by the Swiss National Foundation for Scientific Research. Our most sincere thanks to this Institution.

REFERENCES

Bedinger M.S., 1966: Electric analog study of caveformation. Nat. speleol. Soc. Bull. Vol. 28, No 3: 127-132.

Bonnet M., Margat J., Thiery D., 1976: Essai de représentation du comportement hydraulique d'un systčmekarstique par modčle déterministe: application ŕ la"Fontaine de Vaucluse". Annales scientifiques de l'Université de Besançon, fasc. 25, 3e série: 79-95., Deuxičme colloque d'hydrologie en pays calcaire.

Dreiss S.J., 1989: Regional scale transport in a Karst aquifer: 1. Component separation of spring flow hydrographs. Water Resources Research, Vol. 25, 1: 117-125.

Helmig R., 1993: Theorie und Numerik der Mehrphasenströmungen in geklüftet-porösen Medien.Institut für Strömungsmechanik und Elektron.Rechnen im Bauwesen der Universität Hannover, Bericht Nr 34/1993, 186 p.}

Irons B.M., 1970: A frontal solution program for Finite Element analysis. Int. Journ.Num. Meth. Eng., 2: 5-32.

Jeannin P.-Y., Grasso A., 1995: Recharge respective des volumes de roche peu perméable et des conduits karstiques, rôle de l'épikarst. Bulletin du Centre d'Hydrogéologie, No 14: 95-111.

Jeannin P.-Y., Maréchal J.-C., 1995: Lois de pertes decharge dans les conduits karstiques: base théorique etobservations. Bulletin du Centre d'Hydrogéologie, No 14: 149-176.

Jeannin P.-Y., 1995: Comportement hydraulique mutuel des volumes de roche peu perméable et des conduits karstiques: conséquences sur l'étude des aquifčres karstiques. Bulletin du Centre d'Hydrogéologie, No 14: 113-148.

Kiraly L., 1973: Notice explicative de la carte hydrogéologique du canton de Neuchâtel. Supplément du Bulletin de la Société neuchâteloise des sciences naturelles, Tome 96, 16 p. + carte.

Kiraly L., Morel G., 1976a: Etude de régularisation de l'Areuse par modčle mathématique. Bulletin du Centre d'Hydrogéologie, 1: 19-36.

Kiraly L., Morel G., 1976b: Remarques sur l'hydrogramme des sources karstiques simulé par modčles mathématiques. Bulletin du Centre d'Hydrogéologie, 1: 37-60.

Kiraly L., 1978: La notion d'unité hydrogéologique. Bulletin du Centre d'Hydrogéologie, 2: 83-216.

Kiraly L., 1979: Remarques sur la simulation des failleset du réseau karstique par éléments finis dans les modčles d'écoulement. Bulletin du Centre d'Hydrogéologie, 3: 155-167.

Kiraly L., 1984: Régularisation de l'Areuse (Jura suisse) simulée par modčle mathématique. in: Hydrogeology of karstic terrains. Case histories., Burger A., Dubertret L. editors, International Contributions to Hydrogeology, No 1: 94-99.

Kiraly L., 1985: FEM301 - A three dimensional model for groundwater flow simulation. NAGRA Technical Report 84-49, 96 p.

Kiraly L., 1988: Large scale 3-D groundwater flow modelling in highly heterogeneous geologic medium. in: Groundwater flow and quality modelling, E. Custodio et al. (eds), pp 761-775, NATO ASI series Vol.224.

Kiraly L., Perrochet P., Rossier Y., 1995: Effect of the epikarst on the hydrograph of karst springs: a numerical approach. Bulletin du Centre d'Hydrogéologie, 14: 199-220.

Klemes V., 1986: Dilettantism in hydrology: transition or destiny? Water Resources Research, vol. 22, No 9: 177S-188S.

Mangin A., 1975: Contribution ŕ l'étude hydrodynamique des aquifčres karstiques. Thčse, Université de Dijon, 124 p.

Mohrlok U., 1996: Parameter-Identifikation in Doppel-Kontinuum-Modellen am Beispiel von Karstaquiferen. Dissertation an der Geowissentschaftlichen Fakultät der Universität Tübingen, TGA, Reihe C, Nr. 31, 125 p.

O.E.C.D., 1988: The International HYDROCOIN Project. Level 1: code verification. OECD Publications, Paris, 198 p.

Schoeller H., 1967: Hydrodynamique dans le karst. Chronique d'Hydrogéologie, No 10: 7-21.

Tripet J.-P.., 1972: Etude hydrogéologique du bassin de la source de l'Areuse. Mat. carte géol. de la Suisse, série Hydrologie, 21, 183 p.

Trösch J., Zurbrügg C., 1995: Turbulent flow in high permeable karst. Bulletin du Centre d'Hydrogéologie, 14: 235-240.

Wollrath J., Helmig R., 1991: SM-2, Strömungsmodell für inkompressible Fluide, Theorie und Benutzerhandbuch. Institut für Strömungsmechanik, Universität Hannover, Techn. Bericht 1991.

Address
Centre d'Hydrogéologie, University of Neuchâtel, Switzerland
e-mail: Laszlo.Kiraly@unine.ch

Evolution of Karst: From Prekarst to Cessation, 191-223, Ljubljana-Postojna 2002

KARST PROCESSES FROM THE BEGINNING TO THE END: HOW CAN THEY BE DATED?

PAVEL BOSÁK

Abstract

Determining the beginning and the end of the life of a karst system is a substantial problem. In contrast to most of living systems development of a karst system can be „frozen" and then rejuvenated several times (polycyclic and polygenetic nature). The principal problems may include precise definition of the beginning of karstification (e.g. inception in speleogenesis) and the manner of preservation of the products of karstification. Karst evolution is particularly dependent upon the time available for process evolution and on the geographical and geological conditions of the exposure of the rock. The longer the time, the higher the hydraulic gradient and the larger the amount of solvent water entering the karst system, the more evolved is the karst. In general, stratigraphic discontinuities, i.e. intervals of nondeposition (disconformities and unconformities), directly influence the intensity and extent of karstification. The higher the order of discontinuity under study, the greater will be the problems of dating processes and events. The order of unconformities influences the stratigraphy of the karst through the amount of time available for subaerial processes to operate. The end of karstification can also be viewed from various perspectives. The final end occurs at the moment when the host rock together with its karst phenomena is completely eroded/denuded. In such cases, nothing remains to be dated. Karst forms of individual evolution stages (cycles) can also be destroyed by erosion, denudation and abrasion without the necessity of the destruction of the whole sequence of karst rocks. Temporary and/or final interruption of the karstification process can be caused by the fossilisation of karst due to loss of its hydrological function. Such fossilisation can be caused by metamorphism, mineralisation, marine transgressions, burial by continental deposits or volcanic products, tectonic movements, climatic change etc. Known karst records for the 1st and 2nd orders of stratigraphic discontinuity cover only from 5 to 60 % of geological time. The shorter the time available for karstification, the greater is the likelihood that karst phenomena will be preserved in the stratigraphic record. While products of short-lived karstification on shallow carbonate platforms can be preserved by deposition during the immediately succeeding sea-level rise, products of more pronounced karstification can be destroyed by a number of different geomorphic processes. The longer the duration of subaerial exposure, the more complex are those geomorphic agents.

Owing to the fact that unmetamorphosed or only slightly metamorphosed karst rocks containing karst and caves have occurred since Archean, we can apply a wide range of geochronologic methods. Most established dating methods can be utilised for direct and/or indirect dating of karst and paleokarst. The karst/paleokarst fills are very varied in composition, including a wide range of clastic and chemogenic sediments, products of surface and subsurface volcanism (lava, volcaniclastic materials, tephra), and deep-seated processes (hydrothermal activity, etc). Stages of evolution can also be based on dating correlated sediments that do not fill karst voids directly. The application of individual dating methods depends on their time ranges: the older the subject of study, the more limited is the choice of method. Karst and cave fills are relatively special kinds of geologic materials. The karst environment favours both the preservation of paleontological remains and their destruction. On one hand, karst is well known for its richness of paleontological sites, on the other hand most cave fills are

complete sterile, which is true especially for the inner-cave facies. Another problematic feature of karst records is the reactivation of processes, which can degrade a record by mixing karst fills of different ages.
Key words: *karst, speleogenesis, dating methods, geochronology*

Principle: The time scale for the development of karst features cannot be longer than that of the rocks on which they form. (White 1988, p. 302)

INTRODUCTION

The beginning and the end of the life of living organisms (plants, animals) are really clear thresholds (insemination/pollination →→ death) that can be precisely determined and described. On the other hand, to establish the beginning and the end of the life of a karst system is a substantial problem. In contrast to mots of living systems, the development of karst systems can be „frozen" (halted) and then rejuvenated, often for several times.

Fossilisation and rejuvenation of karst can be viewed according to thermodynamic principles (Eraso 1989): when the external dissipation function of the system, which represents the velocity of entropy production, reaches a minimum, the system is in a stationary state - water circulation and its chemical potential for rock dissolution has ceased - and the karstification is interrupted. The introduction of new energy (hydraulic head) to the system may cause reactivation of karstification. Polycyclicity of karst formation is a typical feature (e.g., Panoš 1964; Ford & Williams 1989). The polygenetic nature of many karsts that evolved in several different steps should be stressed, too (Ford &Williams 1989), e.g., overprint of cold karst processes on earlier deep-seated/hydrothermal products, which themselves followed meteoric early diagenesis (e.g., Bosák 1997).

The dating of karst evolution poses philosophical problems, principally (1) the precise definition of the beginning of karstification, and (2) modes of preservation of any karstification products, recognising that karst rocks are more easily soluble than other rock types under specific conditions that differ with the individual lithologies (limestones, dolomites, gypsum, anhydrite, rock salt, quartzite). The role of preservation is very important because karstlands function as traps or preservers of the geologic and environmental past, especially of terrestrial (continental) history where correlative sediments are mostly missing, but also of evidences in the marine records (Horáček && Bosák 1989).

Karstification of the host rocks may start during their formation phases - diagenesis - changing the soft sediment to a consolidated rock shortly after deposition itself. Such karstification is a consequence of the emergence of part of a depocenter (sedimentary basin) and the introduction of meteoric water to the diagenetic system. The formation of a freshwater lens and a halocline zone related to the surface relief and sea-level changes is the result. The early stages of origin of dissolutional (karst) porosity by meteoric diagenesis in carbonate rocks have been described in numerous sedimentological and paleokarst studies (e.g., Longman 1980; James & Choquette 1984; Tucker & Wright 1990; James & Choquette, Eds. 1988; Wright, Esteban & Smart, Eds. 1991; Moore 1989, 2001). Some authors suppose karst to be merely the facies of meteoric diagenesis (Esteban & Klappa 1983).

The evolution of a karst depends especially on the time available for processes to operate and on the geographical and geological conditions of rock exposures. The longer the time available, the higher the hydraulic gradient and the larger the quantity of solvent water entering the system, the more evolved will be the karst in all its modes of occurrences (exo- and endokarst). In general, we can state that the kind of stratigraphic discontinuities, i.e. intervals of nondeposition (disconformities and unconformities; see Esteban 1991), directly influences the intensity and extent of karstification. The higher the order of discontinuity under study, the bigger are the problems to be expected when dating the processes and events.

The end of karstification can also be viewed also from various perspectives. An undisputed end of karstification occurs at the moment when host- rock together with its karst phenomena is completely eroded/denuded, i.e. at the end of the karst cycle *sensu* Grund (1914; see also Cvijić 1918). In such a case, nothing is left to be dated. Karst forms of individual stages of evolution (cycles) can also be destroyed also by other, non-karst processes of erosion or by the complete filling of epikarst and burial of karst surfaces by impermeable sediments, without the necessity of destroying an entire sequence of karst rocks (the cycle of erosion of Davis 1899; see also Sawicki 1908, 1909). Temporary and/or final interruption of karstification can be caused by fossilisation due to the loss of the hydrological function of the karst (Bosák 1989, p. 583). The fossilisation can be caused by metamorphism, mineralisation, marine transgressions, burial by continental deposits or volcanic products, tectonic movements, climatic change etc. (see Bosák 1989).

The principal question in this paper is: *Can we date karst processes at all?* The answer is given at the end. The paper deals mostly with karst in carbonate rocks, although the geochronologic methods and some of approaches reviewed are universal.

UNCONFORMITIES: THE TIME FRAME

The beginning and the end of karst is clearly associated with conformities, unconformities and disconformities. Esteban (1991) in an excellent review following the sequence stratigraphic approach outlined the role of nondepositional events (stratigraphic discontinuities) in karst evolution. Different ranks of stratigraphic discontinuity represent the differing time gaps in deposition that have been available for dissolution (karstification; see also Moore 1991, pp. 247-264).

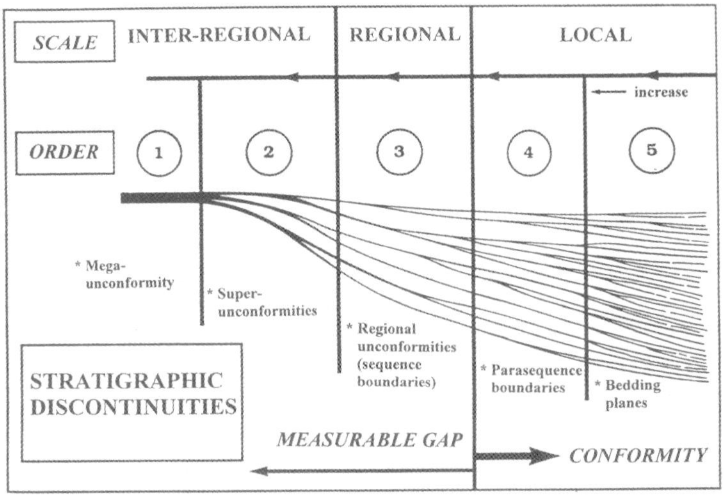

Fig. 1. Hierarchy of stratigraphic discontinuities (modified after Esteban 1991).

The stratigraphic discontinuity (gap, lacuna) represents the chronostratigraphic interval(s) missing through nondeposition (hiatus) and/or lithostratigraphic interval(s) missing through erosional truncation. Excluding conformities, Esteban (1991) proposed classification of unconformities into (1) single (SUK) and (2) composite (CUK), both with measurable stratigraphic gaps. Conformities have no measurable stratigraphic gap and correspond to bedding planes or parasequence boundaries. The single unconformity represents a stratigraphic gap equivalent to a sequence boundary and the composite one is formed by the stacking or superposition of single unconformities (Esteban 1991, p. 92). A hierarchy of stratigraphic discontinuities was proposed, too (Fig. 1). Most (paleo)karsts are composite unconformities, representing long timespans without deposition.

STRATIGRAPHY OF KARST

The order of unconformities influences the stratigraphy of the karst due to the time involved in subaerial processes (Table 1). There are two general systems of the karst stratigraphy based on: (1) the carbonate sedimentological/sequence stratigraphic approach (Choquette & James 1988), and (2) general karst models (Bosák, Ford & Głazek 1989).

Choquette & James (1988) distinguished: (1) *depositional karst*, (2) *local karst*, and (3) *interregional karst*. They noted, that to distinguish the products of local and interregional karsts may be difficult in some cases. Esteban (1991) stressed that the depositional karst of Choquette & James (1988), which is associated with parasequence boundaries (single unconformities) reflects a *Caribbean model* of karst development, while interregional karst resulting from complex evolution producing composite unconformities represents the *general* (non-Caribbean) *model* of karst.

STRATIGRAPHIC DISCONTINUITIES		ORDER	TIME GAP SCALE		CORRESPONDING STRATIGRAPHIC UNITS	STRATIGRAPHY OF KARST	
			Ma	Chronostratigr.		James & Choquette, Eds. 1988	Bosák et al., Eds. 1989
UNCONFORMITIES SINGLE COMPOSITE	E. UNCONFORMITY	1	200	ERATHEM	MEGASEQUENCE		
	MEGAUNCONFORMITY		>60	SYSTEM	SUPERSEQUENCE SET	INTER-REGIONAL	KARST
	SUPERUNCONFORMITY SET		30	SERIES	SUPERSEQUENCE	KARST	PERIOD
	SUPERUNCONFORMITY	2	4-12	STAGE			
	REGIONAL	3			DEPOSITIONAL		
	UNCONFORMITIES		~1	BIOZONE	SEQUENCE		
	(sequence boundaries)					LOCAL	
CONFORMITIES	SYNTECTONIC	3-4	0.0X-1	Variable		KARST	KARST
	UNCONFORMITIES						PHASE
	BOUNDARY OF	4	0.0X	Not	PARASEQUENCE		
	SHOLAING			recognisable			
	CYCLES					DEPOSITIONAL	
	BEDDING PLANE	5	0.00X		BED	KARST	

***Table 1**. Stratigraphic discontinuitetes, time gaps (modified after Esteban 1991) and stratigraphy of karst.*

The *Caribbean model* (Esteban 1991, p. 93) is characterised by brief exposure time, unstable carbonate mineralogy, shallow burial, minor tectonics, minor deep (freshwater) phreatic zone, with primary and fabric-selective porosities predominant, restriction to tropical to semi-arid environments, diffuse recharge-diffuse flow only, affected by mixing marine zone processes but not by hydrothermal mixing. However, geothermal-driven convection of groundwater has been detected in some Caribbean-type of settings (e.g., Rougerie & Wauthy 1993).

The *General model* (Esteban 1991, p. 93) is characterised by longer exposure time, stable mineralogy, deep burial, one or several tectonic events, an important deep phreatic zone, secondary and fracture porosities predominant, a wider range of climatic environments, confluent recharge, pipe and confined flow, absence of mixing marine zone effects and presence of hydrothermal mixing.

Local karst forms when part of a carbonate shelf is exposed, usually because of tectonism, drops in sea level or synsedimentary block tilting. Depending on the length of time involved, the effects of exposure can vary from minor to extensive with the development of exo- and endokarst (Choquette & James 1988, pp. 16-17).

Interregional karst is much more widespread, is related to major eustatic-tectonic events, and results in karst terranes that may exhibit profound erosion, a wide variety of karst features, and deep, pervasive dissolution (Choquette & James 1988, p. 17).

Depositional karst forms as a natural consequence of sediment accretion at and around sea level. It is to be expected within the sediment packages that typify carbonate platforms. It is most commonly associated with meter-scale depositional cycles (Choquette & James 1988, p. 16).

Bosák, Ford & Głazek (1989) distinguished between: (1) the *karst phase*, and (2) the *karst period*. The connection to individual types of unconformities clearly proves the temporal relationships between all types of the karst, which may be mutually correlated (Table 1).

Karst period defines long-lasting times of groundwater circulation and continental weathering, which were terminated by an ensuing marine transgression. They are recognised by higher order unconformities or disconformities (= *interregional karst* of Choquette & James (1988). Their karst features can usually be divided into several generations (→ → karst phases). Głazek (1989a) defined the tectonic conditions for karst periods as being induced by orogenies. Those lengthy periods are caused by the post-collisional uplift of orogens and their fringes. The periods are marked by unconformities and disconformities over broad areas and need not to be confined to individual modern continents. These long periods display diachronicity and many lesser phases. They are longest in duration and most complex at former mountain crests and become gradually shorter on the former mountain slopes and their broad fringes along adjacent continents. These periods result from major changes of plate motion patterns and they divided structural complexes corresponding to orogenic cycles (Głazek 1973).

A karst *phase* is caused by a geodynamic or major climatic change, e.g., uplift or downwarping, sea-level change, a phase of permafreezing, etc. (Bosák, Ford & Głazek 1989). From the tectonic point of view, Głazek (1989a) distinguished two kinds of karst phases: (1) represented as unconformities within the limited areas of one past shallow marine platform and its continental fringes, or of one continent created by the collision of two plates (= *local karst* of Choquette & James 1988); and (2) disconformable or paraconformable surfaces resulting from glacial-eustatic fluctuations of sea level or from local tectonic events (= *depositional karst* of Choquette & James 1988).

Interregional (paleo)karst and products of karst periods can be linked with composite unconformities of the 1st and 2nd orders *sensu* Esteban (1991). Such products can be correlated over extensive regions, e.g., post-Kaskadia and post-Variscan karstifications in North America and Europe, respectively (Głazek 1989a). Local (paleo)karst and products of type 1 of karst phases (*sensu* Głazek 1989a) are common products during single unconformities and syntectonic unconformities, i.e. of the 3rd order. Karst forms created during the 4th and 5th order unconformities (conformities) correspond to depositional (paleo)karst and to Type 2 karst phases.

KARST RECORD

The principal differences between the Caribbean karst model and the general karst model are concerned with exposure time. The former is associated with brief exposures to subaerial agents, i.e. with stratigraphic discontinuities of 3rd to 5th order with durations

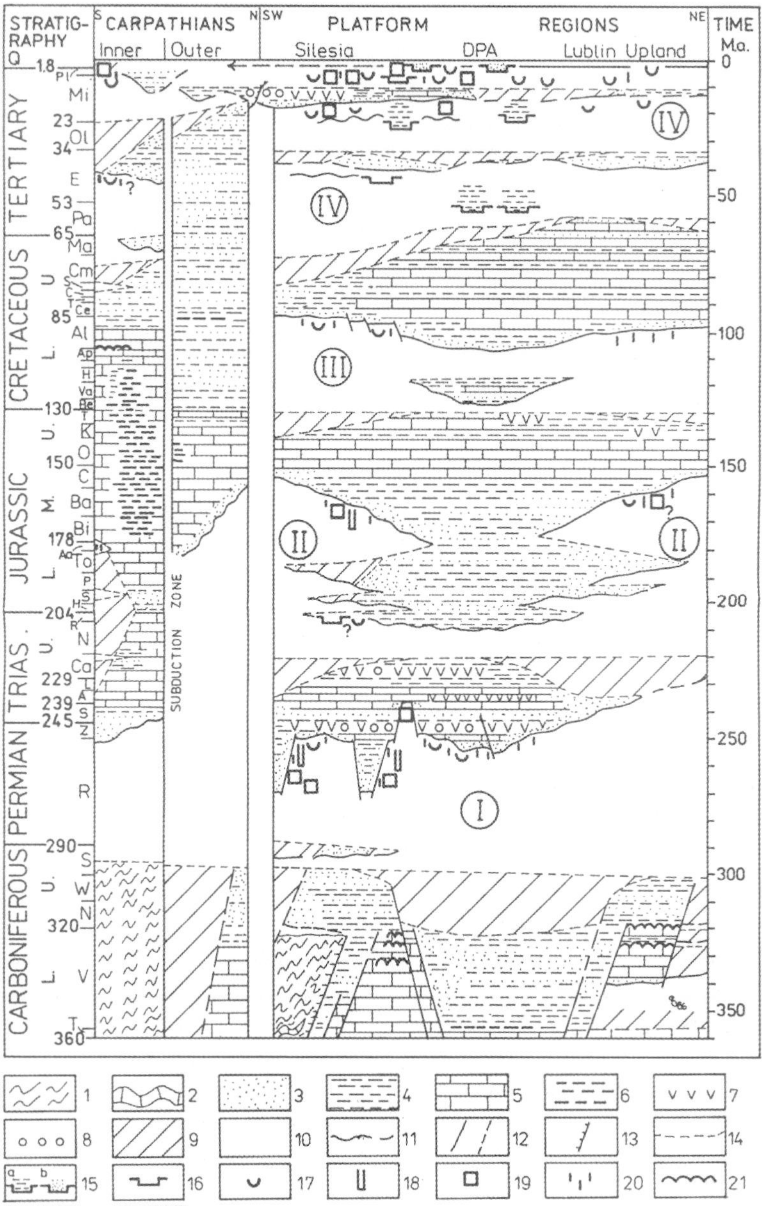

Fig. 2. Time distribution of paleokarst phenomena and sediments in Poland (from Głazek 1989b; with permission). Metamorphosed basement: 1 - silicate rocks, 2 - marble lenses; Sedimentary rocks: 3- psammites and psephites, 4 - silts, clays, marls, 5 - carbonates, 6 - deep-sea carbonate-silicate, 7 - sulphates, 8 - salts, 9 - unknowns deposits (eroded), 10 - subaerial degradation; Boundaries: 11 - unconformable cover, 12 - synsedimentary faults, 13 - synsedimentary overthrusts, 14 - supposed limits of deposition, 15 - subrosion depressions with fills (a. brown coal, b. drift deposits), 16 - poljes, 17 - sinkholes, 18 - shafts, 19 - caves, 20 - minor solution forms, 21 - syngenetic caves, 22 - karst corrosion surfaces, 23 - maximal extent of Pleistocene glaciers, I to IV - periods of karstification.

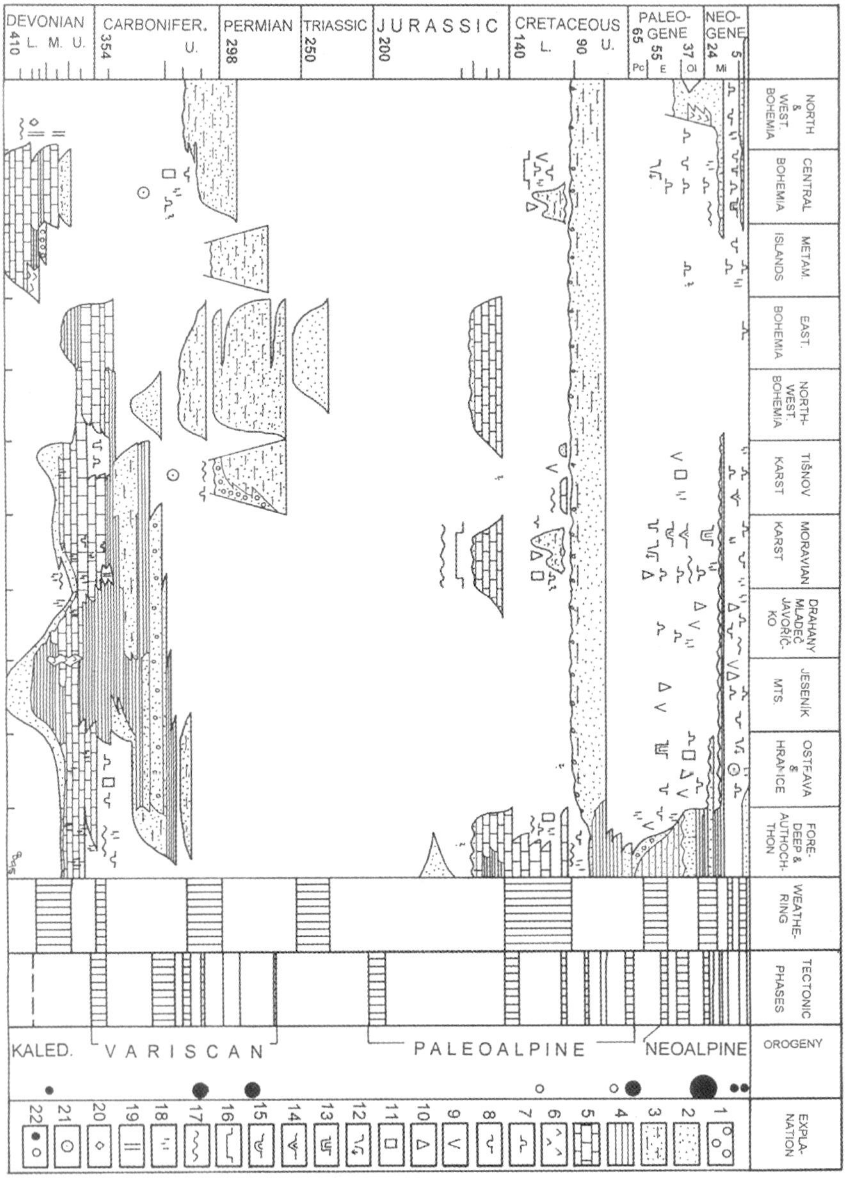

Fig. 3. Distribution of paleokarst and sediments in selected sections of the Bohemian Massif (simplified and schematized; modified after Bosák 1997). Lithology: 1 - conglomerates, 2 - sandstones, 3 - lithologically variable siliciclastics (redbeds, alternation of sandstones, siltstones, sandstone, etc.), 4 - shales, 5 - carbonate rocks, 6 - volcanics and volcanoclastic rocks; Karst forms: 7 - caves, 8 - dolines, 9 - geological organs, 10 - karst cones, 11 - karst inselbergs, 12 - collapse shafts, 13 - canyons, 14 - V shaped valleys, 15 - U shaped valleys, 16 - poljes and large karst depressions, 17 - corrosional surfaces, 18 - karren and minor solution forms, 19 - neptunian dykes, 20 - meteoric diagenetical vugs, 21 - hydrothermal karst, 22 - volcanic activity, black Bohemian Massif, circle Outer Western Carpathians adjacent to the Bohemian Massif, circle diametre approximately covers the time span of volcanic activity.

of 0.00X to about 1 Ma, the latter with lengthy exposures corresponding to stratigraphic discontinuities of 2nd and 1st order; i.e. with times of $X0^0$ to $X0^2$ Ma (Table 1).

The karst record of 1st and 2nd order stratigraphic discontinuities on the East European Platform and epi-Variscan Central European Platform in Poland was identified by Głazek, Dąbrowski & Gradziński (1972) and Głazek (1973, 1989a). It encompasses a maximum of 50 to 60 % of the geological time elapsed since deposition of the rocks (Fig. 2). Analysis of the Bohemian Massif (epi-Variscan Platform; Bosák 1987, 1997; Tab. 2, Fig. 3) showed that 12 to 45 % of geological time since the regression of Paleozoic seas in the Upper Devonian/Lower Carboniferous is in such records and 55 to 88 % of time is not recorded in the preserved marine or continental sequences (Bosák 1987).

Table 2: *Review of temporal data for the evolution of the Bohemian Massif since the Paleozoic regression (after Bosák 1987, 1997)*

Regional geologicalunit	Duration since regression (Ma)	Record preserved (Ma)	Record incontinental deposits(Ma)	Record (%)	Gap without record (%)
Moldanubicum	375	45	45	12	88
Bohemicum	375	48	36	13	87
Saxothuringicum	420	52	40	12	88
Brunovistulicum					
a. in outcrops	320	75	36	23	77
b. covered by Carpathian Foredeep	320	100-145	2	31-45	69-55

These two examples of platform areas differ in the time recorded in the subsequent cover sediments. The Bohemian Massif is a relatively young body resulted from amalgamation of individual terranes during the Variscan Orogeny. Since that time uplift has prevailed over subsidence as a consequence of the tectonic stress caused by the Alpine Orogeny in its foreland. Platform sediments are rather rare there (Upper Jurassic and Upper Cretaceous regional transgressions, several minor Oligocene and Miocene transgressions covering only margins of the massif; see Fig. 3). The Polish territory is composed of slightly older elements in a different geotectonic setting, and the geologic structure is little affected by younger orogenies. Platform cover is developed more continuously and individual stratigraphic discontinuities are shorter. Therefore, there is a significant difference in the preserved record of time in the two regions, i.e. 12-45 % vs. 50-60 %. Some old cratonic units can be nearly completely without any platform cover (e.g., Scandinavian Shield), partly as a consequence of glacial isostasy. In such terranes, the time recorded can represent less than 10 %. On some recent and fossil carbonate platforms, time recorded in sediments represents only 5 to less than 10 % (Great Bahama Bank, Devonian carbonate platform on Moravia; Bosák et al. in print).

It can be readily asserted that the shorter the time available for karstification, the greater is the probability of preservation of the karst phenomena in the stratigraphic record. While products of short-lived karstification on shallow carbonate platforms can be preserved by deposition during the sea-level rise following immediately after, products of more pronounced karstification may be destroyed by a variety of geomorphic processes. The longer is the duration of subaerial exposure, the more complex are those geomorphic agents. Further, individual long periods of subaerial exposure (stratigraphic discontinuities of the 1st and 2nd orders - karst periods) may coalesce, being separated only by a short interruption (e.g., marine transgression/ingression).

Products of paleokarst evolution are best preserved directly beneath a cover of marine or continental sediments, i.e. under the deposits, which terminate the periods or phases of karstification. The longer the duration of the stratigraphic gap the more problematic is the precise dating of the paleokarst, unless it can be chronostratigraphically proven. Therefore, the ages of particular paleokarsts have been assigned mostly to times shortly before the termination of the stratigraphic gap (Bosák 1997). This fact can be easily illustrated in the Bohemian Massif for preCenomanian age paleokarst, for preCallovian in the Moravian Karst or for Westphalian/Stephanian in central Bohemia (see Fig. 3). An identical situation occurs in Poland (Głazek 1989b; see Fig. 2)

Some processes can destroy karst features in relatively short time, leaving planated surfaces with little or no traces of previous karstification, e.g., the effect of marine transgressions. This can be illustrated from recent karst in the coastal zone of Palawan Island (Philippines) and the Lower Devonian of the Koněprusy area, Czech Republic. On Palawan, Longman & Brownlee (1980) described wave and surf action destroying or undercutting recent shore cliffs up to 30 m high that were composed of highly karstified limestones with dense networks of pinnacle karren, leaving only a flat abrasion platform with only rare relics of truncated solution fissures and sinkholes in their place. An identical situation is detected at the boundary between Koněprusy Limestones (Pragian) and Suchomasty Limestones (Dalejan, Lower Devonian) at Koněprusy. The truncation plane, which is nicely exposed in Koněprusy Caves, is smoothed by marine abrasion and shows no trace of karst, although the limestones contain distinct traces of meteoric diagenesis and the formation of neptunian dykes correlated with the hiatus, which lasted about 5-6 Ma.

MINIMUM TIME FOR SPELEOGENESIS

The evolution of a conduit is rather complicated set of events facing numerous critical thresholds (for summary see White 1988 and Ford && Williams 1989). At the present time, two phases of speleogenesis has been generally accepted: (1) initiation - initial enlargement of a fracture to a critical size, and (2) enlargement - growth of a protoconduit to full conduit size (White 1988, p. 287). The initial fracture permeability and/or rock porosity has connected apertures on the order of 50 -500 mmm and the diameter of a dissolutional proto-conduit reaches 5-15 mm (White 1988, Ford & Williams 1989). At diameters of 0.5 to 5 cm there is a kinetic breakthrough (Dreybrodt & Gabrovšek 2000) and flow may change from laminar to turbulent (White 1988, p. 291; Ford && Williams 1989).

The duration of a typical *initiation phase* was calculated to about 3-5 ka (White 1988) based on experiments of Howard & Howard (1967) and calculations of Palmer (1981). They stated that the maximum dissolution rate is 0.14 $m.a^{-1}$. Palmer (1991) calculated the initiation phase to minimum of 10 ka under favourable conditions. Dreybrodt & Gabrovšek (2000) estimated the duration of the initiation (gestation) phase for realistic cases from 1 ka to 10 Ma. The time depends critically on the length and the initial width of the fracture.

The *enlargement phase*, i.e. the time in which protoconduit enlarges into full size (of 1-10 m or more) is expected to be 5 - 20 ka up to 100 ka in many geologic settings (White 1988). Ford & Williams (1989, p. 166) suggested that conduits can expand to diameters of 1-10 m in a few thousands of years (see also Palmer 1991), or even in a few hundreds years in high relief, wet terrains. Palmer (1991) calculated the maximum wall retreat to 0.01-0.1 $cm.a^{-1}$ in a typical meteoric groundwater cave. For hydrothermal caves, times on the order of 10^5 to 10^6 years are required to produce caves of traversable size (Palmer 1991, p 18). Data of Ford (1980) and Palmer (1984) suggest that an extension time of 10 to 100 ka per kilometre of the conduit may have prevailed in a majority of karst settings. White (1984) obtained an extension rate of 3-5 ka per kilometre. Dreybrodt & Gabrovšek (2000) estimated the velocity of enlargement of a conduit under phreatic conditions to about 200 $mm.ka^{-1}$, so a phreatic passage of 30 m diameter can be developed within 100 ka. Of course, all those estimates are only illustrative as the velocity of speleogenesis is affected by numerous thresholds (see e.g., White 1988) and agents including geologic conditions (lithology, primary and secondary porosity), climatic conditions (temperature, precipitation, water volumes), hydrochemical conditions (concentration and kind of solvent agents), etc.

Theoretical assumptions have been proven by field observations. Mylroie & Carew (1986, 1987) dated the origin of Lighthouse Cave (San Salvador Island, Bahamas) between 85 ka (cementation of eolianite host rock) and 49 ka (U-series datum from a stalagmite), i.e. 36 ka available for the cave formation along the halocline. Numerous data from North America or Ireland indicate the post-glacial origin of caves perfectly adjusted to recently deranged surface landscapes and hydrologic regimes, i.e. caves developed during the last 8-15 ka (e.g., Mylroie && Carew 1986, 1987; White 1988; Ford && Williams 1989).

Determining the age of a cave is a problem because the dating is based on cave deposits (both clastic and chemogenic). In most cases we are able to date only the last few events of cave filling. Cases where the original syngenetic cave fill is preserved are rare, e.g., phreatic clays and silts, hydrothermal speleothems quasi-synchronous with phreatic speleogenesis. The dynamic character of karst results in repeating infilling and excavation of cave fills, under differing specific conditions. For example, in the Czech Karst only young Middle and Late Pleistocene deposits are preserved in the caves, with older Quaternary and pre-Quaternary fills found in some vertical corroded fissures as result of sequences of cave fills and exhumations (Ložek & Skřivánek 1965). In the Moravian Karst (Czech Republic), the situation is very similar (Kadlec et al. 2001), although the principal caves in both karst regions are at least of Early Miocene age. Complex watertable caves with pronounced flood histories offer only the age of the last cave fill episode. In Slovenia, Trhlovca and Divaška Caves (Classical Karst) contain sedimentary fill about 0.7 to 1.1 Ma old (Brunhes/Matuyama boundary and Jaramillo subchron; Bosák et al. 2000; Pruner & Bosák 2001), representing the last flood-derived fills. The system of Domica-Baradla Cave (Slovakia-Hungary), although pre-Pliocene in age, is filled only by the Late Pleistocene sediments (magnetostratigraphy and U-series dating; Pruner & Bosák 2001 and yet unpublished data of Bosák/Pruner and D.C. Ford teams). So the age of the cave itself (void within the rock) is very far from obtained dates.

INCEPTION: THE START OF A CAVE?

The preceding discussion has summarised the characteristic time scale for the development of a conduit. The same scale (i.e. 10 to 100 ka) is demanded for the development of a surface landform (White 1988, p. 304). Nevertheless, for caves concepts of legacy karst (V.P. Wright 1991; Wright & Smart 1994) or inception (Lowe 1999) have also been proposed that suggest that there exist pre-requisities guiding at least some speleogenesis.

Legacy karst according to V.P. Wright (1991) and Wright && Smart (1994) refers to dissolution occurring at the present or in the past whose distribution is controlled by an earlier (paleo)karst system. *Inception* according to Lowe (1999, 2000) is limited to a minor subset of all stratigraphic partings, those which dominate initially, imprinting incipient guidance for the later cave development. The weaknesses are imprinted within carbonate sequences during or soon after diagenesis, and certainly pre-tectonically. According to Waltham (2000) the inception horizon is a feature within the limestone structure that is a favourable site for the critical first phase of cave enlargement. The feature may be physical or chemical - a fracture, a mineralised fault, a shale bed containing pyrite, or a contrast in limestone chemistry. It is the initial inception stage and not the subsequent development stages, that provides the key to understanding where caves lie. The inception is a part of the initiation phase of cave formation (Lowe & Gunn 1997). It can be commented, that long ago, Ford (1971) stated that some planes or contacts are preferred *locii* of initiation in some caves. In that view the concept of inception, which states the same, seems to be rather complicated.

Taking these concepts into account, reflecting the polycyclic and polygenetic nature of much karst, we are facing a serious problem: how to define the age of origin of caves (protoconduits)? We have two possibilities of approach: (1) to accept all previous paleokarst features as the beginning of speleogenesis (even meteoric diagenesis), or (2) to accept only the result of the last speleogenetic phase (where it is the phase that created the known cave), ignoring all previous events. The second option seems to offer some problems in specific settings.

For example, the origin of the Lighthouse Cave (San Salvador Island, Bahamas;

Mylroie & Carew 1986, 1987) was as a single event piece of speleogenesis in upper Pleistocene rocks (~125,000 years in age) without any legacy karst; there is no problem to place the beginning of speleogenesis after that age. On the other hand, speleogenesis in the Koněprusy region (Czech Republic; Bosák 1996, 1997, 1998) identified by the analysis of hundreds of cored boreholes in Lower Devonian limestones indicate that each succeeding phase of karstification utilised previously karstified („prepared") space, starting with Lower/Middle Devonian diagenetic (mostly meteoric) vuggy porosity and neptunian dykes, followed by late Variscan hydrothermal karst (Carboniferous/Permian), Lower/Middle Cretaceous karstification and finally by a complex set of confined hydrothermal/cold karstification during Paleogene/Miocene time = the complex and prolonged history of polycyclic and polygenetic karst with many interruptions in formation and many changes of geologic and climatic conditions. Where is the beginning of speleogenesis to be dated?

GEOCHRONOLOGIC METHODS

Owing to the fact that unmetamorphosed or only slightly metamorphosed karst rocks have existed since the Proterozoic, we are facing the wide range of application of geochronologic methods. The oldest karst forms with caves and cave deposits are known from Early Proterozoic of Transvaal, South Africa (2.2 Ga; Martini 1981). Karst breccias of Archean age are known in the Canadian Shield (D.C. Ford, pers. comm. 2002). Somewhat younger are paleokarst surfaces in Canada (Belcher Island - 1.7 Ga, Ontario and Quebec - 1.4 Ga; Ford 1989). Upper Proterozic karst is also known from several locations on old cratons and platforms, e.g., in China (Zhang Shouyue 1989), Russia (Tsykin 1989) or Australia (Rowlands et al. 1980).

Most of the methods outlined below can be utilised for direct and/or indirect dating of karst and paleokarst processes. Karst/paleokarst fills are highly variable in origin and composition, including a wide range of clastic and chemogenic sediments, products of surface and subsurface volcanism (lava, volcaniclastic materials, tephra), and deep-seated processes (hydrothermal activity, etc). During burial, paleokarst forms can be cut or penetrated by products of younger deep-seated processes (volcanic or hydrothermal - ore - veins). Evolutionary karst stages can be based also on dating of correlative sediments, which do not fill karst voids directly, i.e. glacial deposits, river terraces, eolian and lacustrine sediments, marine deposits and fossils. Certain dating methods cannot be used for karst events at all, especially those requiring magmatic and/or metamorphic lithologies as suitable materials.

Colman & Pierce (2000) reviewed the range of geochronologic methods for the Quaternary period. Their conclusions can be adapted also for older chronologic units. The methods are grouped into six categories: (1) *sidereal* (calendar or annual) methods, which determine calendar dates or count annual events; (2) *isotopic* methods, which measure changes in isotopic composition due to radioactive decay and/or growth; (3)

radiogenic methods, which measure cumulative effects of radioactive decay, such as crystal damage and electron energy traps; (4) *chemical and biological* methods, which measure the results of time-dependent chemical or biological processes; (5) *geomorphic* methods, which measure the cumulative results of complex, interrelated, physical, chemical, and biologic processes on the landscape; and (6) *correlation* methods, which establish age equivalence using time-independent properties. Results of dating can be classified into four groups as follows: *numerical-age*, *calibrated-age*, *relative-age*, and *correlated-age* (Colman & Pierce 2000, p. 3). They also proposed to abandon the term *absolute date* in favour of *numerical date*.

The application of individual dating methods depends on their timespans. In general, we can state that the older is the subject of our study, the more limited are the methods of dating available. The nature of geologic materials to be dated represents another

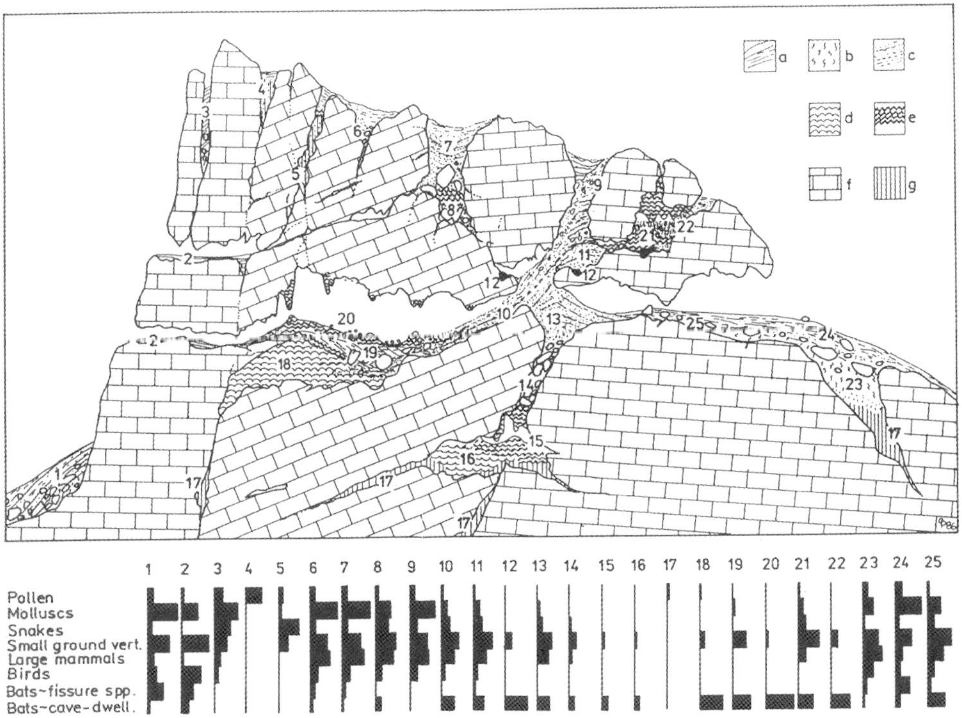

Fig. 4. A sketch of common types of karst infills and their fossil content. Note the appearance of remains of ancient fills of the inner-cave facies (12) preserved in wall niches, which may lie in the direct contact with much younger deposits (11) or those preserved in different but neighbouring cavities (21 vs. 11). Collapse of sedimentary plugs and redeposition may also occur in caves (10), which may also cause serious confusion unless detailed lithological studies are done (see e.g., situation on sites 19 and 10). A - Holocene soils and related deposits, b - loess base of Holocene deposition, c - sequence of Pleistocene and earlier surface deposits, d - former infill of the inner-cave facies, frequently fluvial, e - flowstones, f - carbonate rock, g - ancient residua of strongly weathered surface or subsurface sediments, mosty non-calcareous (from Kordos & Horáček 1989, with permission).

threshold. Not all geologic materials are suitable for numerical dating. On the other hand, most of materials are suitable to attempt correlated-age.

Karst and cave fills are relatively special kinds of geologic materials. The karst environment favours both the preservation of paleontological remains and their destruction. On one hand, karst is well known for its wealth of paleontological sites (see e.g., Horáček & Kordos 1989), on the other hand most cave fills are completely sterile, especially for the inner-cave facies. Another problematic feature of karst records is that there may be reactivation of processes, which degrades the record into an unreadable form, often mixing karst fill of different ages (collapses, redepositions, etc., e.g., Horáček & Bosák 1989; Fig. 4).

Evaluation of dating results of karst records depends, as in other geologic records, on uncertainties, which vary with the geologic context, age range, and methods applied (Sowers & Noller 2000, p. 8-9). According to these authors, sources of uncertainty can be found in: (1) analytical error; (2) natural variability in sample quality and suitability; (3) geologic context errors; (4) calibration errors, and (5) violations of assumptions.

The best reviews of dating methods are offered by Geyh & Schleicher (1990), Noller, Sowers & Lettis (Eds., 2000), and Bradley (1999); some useful data can be found also in Faure (2001).

NUMERICAL-AGES

Numerical-ages are generally subdivided to isotopic, radiometric and sidereal (Colman & Pierce 2000, p. 3). Geyh & Schleicher (1990) divided only the radiometric methods, recognising those using (1) parent/daughter isotope ratios; (2) dating based on radioactive disequilibrium of the U, Th, and Pa decay series, and (3) age determinations using radiation damage. Methods (1) and (2) of the Geyh & Schleicher (1990) classification correspond to isotopic methods of Colman & Pierce (2000), and method (3) is the equivalent of radiometric methods. The U-Pb method was recently applied to about 92 Ma old spar fill in paleokarst in Guadelupe Mts., U.S.A. by Lundberg, Ford & Hill (2001).

ISOTOPIC METHODS

Isotopic methods measure changes in isotopic composition due to radioactive decay and/or growth (Colman & Pierce 2000). The *methods of parent/daughter isotope ratios* (Tab. 3) are based on radioactive decay: for each parent atom that decays, a stable daughter isotope is formed, either directly or as the end-product of a decay series (Geyh & Schleicher 1990, p. 51). The number of decays depends on the quantity of parent nuclides. The decay of each radionuclide is characterised by (1) the kind(s) of radiation they emit (alpha, beta, spontaneous fission, beta-plus decay and orbital electron capture), (2) the energy(ies), and (3) the half-life (Geyh & Schleicher 1990, p. 25). Various radioactive isotopes have different half-lives ranging from several years (^{210}Pb) to billion

Table 3: *Review of isotopic dating methods I - parent/daughter isotope ratios*

Dating Method	Dating range	Suitable materials
$^{138}La/^{138}Ce$	>Ga	Basic rocks, acid rocks, pegmatites
$^{138}La/^{138}Ba$	>Ga	REE-bearing minerals
$^{207}Pb/^{206}Pb$	>Ga	igneous, metamorphic rocks, sulfides
$^{176}Lu/^{176}Hf$	>500 Ma	REE-bearing minerals
$^{187}Re/^{187}Os$	>200 Ma	meteorites, molybdenite, ultrabasic magnatic rocks
U/Xe_{sf}	U-minerals > 100 Materrestrial rocks > 1 Ga	U-bearing minerals; terrestrial rocks
Xe_{sf}/Xe_n	> 100 Ma	U-bearing minerals
$^{40}K/^{40}Ca$	> 60 Ma	high K content, low Ca content (K/Ca>50) - lepidotite, muscovite, biotite, K-fedspars, salt minerals
$^{147}Sm/^{143}Nd$	> ca 50 Ma	old, especially basic igneous rocks, high grade metamorphics, whole-rock and mineral samples, great resistance of the system
$^{87}Rb/^{87}Sr$	> 10 Ma	minerals and whole-rock samples, magmatic and metamorphic rocks, sediments with limitations (authigenic clay minerals)salt minerals - problems low temperature of metamorphism
Kr_{sf}/Kr_n	> 10 Ma	U-bearing minerals
$^{129}Xe/^{136}Xe$	5-100 Ma	U-bearing minerals
Common Lead Method	> Ma to Ga	Pb-bearing minerals with low or no U content, whole-rock (igneous)
$^{238}U/^{206}Pb$ $^{235}U/^{207}Pb^2$ $^{232}Th/^{208}Pb$	< 0.1 - > 1 00 Ma	U- and Th-bearing minerals in igneous and metamorphic rocks (esp. zircon and monazite), U-bearing opal and paleokarst calcite
$^{40}K/^{40}Ar$	> 100 ka (K-feldspars)> 3-5 Ma (alunite, jarosite)	K-bearing minerals from igneous, metamorphic and sedimentary rocksfeldspars, mica, amphibole, glauconite, clay minerals, whole-rock materials - volcanic rocks, particularly basalts
$^{39}Ar/^{40}Ar$	ka-4.5 Ga	K-bearing minerals from igneous and metamorphic rocks with low Ca content (mica, alunite, amphibole), sedimentary rocks suitable sometimes (glauconite, clay minerals), K-bearing sulfides

Note: The table was compiled according to data in Geyh & Schleicher (1990); Noller, Sowers & Lettis (Eds. 2000); Faure (2001); White (1988), and Ford & Williams (1989). Some data were kindly provided by H. Hercman (Warsaw, Poland).

of years (^{187}Re). This makes geochronological studies possible over the entire range of possible ages. The methods are based on long-lived radionuclides, therefore the application to Quaternary studies is almost excluded (Geyh & Schleicher 1990, p. 53).

The *method of dating with cosmogenic radionuclides* (Tab. 4) is based on nuclear reaction of cosmic rays with gas molecules in the stratosphere and troposhere producing many radionuclides. Samples must have existed in closed system conditions since the beginning of the aging period, i.e. since the geochronological clock was reset to zero (Geyh & Schleicher 1990, p. 158). Most methods are based on, first, the insolation of the material and then its burial at depths too great for cosmic ray penetration (e.g. in most caves or karst deposits).

***Table 4:** Review of isotopic dating methods II - cosmogenic radionuclides*

Dating Method	Dating range	Suitable materials
^{129}I	3-80 Ma	buried organic matter and its derivatives
^{53}Mn	1-10 Ma	meteorites, ice and pelagic sediments
$^{26}Al/^{10}Be$	0.1-10 Ma	ice, marine and lacustrine sediments, corals, organic matter, manganese nodules
^{81}Kr	0.05-10 Ma	groundwater and ice
^{26}Al	0.1 - 5 Ma	ice, pelagic sediments, manganese nodules
^{36}Cl	0.1-3 Ma	old groundwater, soils, ice, glacial materials
^{10}Be	0.01-15 Ma	carbonate-free pelagic sediments, ice, manganese nodules, quartz pebbles
$^{10}Be/^{36}Cl$	X0-X00 ka	Ice
^{41}Ca	20-400 ka	bones, secondary carbonates
^{14}C	0.3-30 (55) ka	organic matter, peat, humus, bones, tissues, carbonate shells, corals, travertines, speleothems, soils, groundwater, ice
^{39}Ar	0.1-2 ka	Ice
^{32}Si	0.1-1.5 ka	marine siliceous materials
^{3}H	< 100 a	Groundwater
$^{3}H/^{3}He^{3}He$	< 100 a	Ice
^{22}Na	1-30 a	shallow groundwater

Note: The table was compiled according to data in Geyh & Schleicher (1990), and Noller, Sowers & Lettis (Eds. 2000). Some data were kindly provided by H. Hercman (Warsaw, Poland).

The *methods of radioactive disequilibrium of the U, Th, and Pa decay series* are based on radioactive disequilibrium utilising the time-dependence of geochemical disturbances of the radioactive equilibrium between parent and daughter isotopes of the natural radioactive decay series of ^{238}U, ^{235}U and ^{232}Th, whose end members are stable lead isotopes (Ivanovich & Harmon, Eds. 1992; Geyh & Schleicher 1990, p. 213).

The principle of all isotopic methods is that the system has to be closed after deposition, only under such conditions can radioactive equilibrium be gradually established. It means that any disturbance occurring during the evolution of the equilibrium (starting with the closure of the system) can lead to the stopping or resetting of the radiometric clocks. The nature of the „disturbance" depends on the sensitivity of the system, which mostly closes during the crystallisation of rock-forming minerals from magmas or solutions. The geochronometer can be stopped by heating, recrystallisation, diagenetic processes such as leaching, or corrosion leading to opening of the system or adjustment to new conditions (e.g., heating/cooling).

The review of isotopic methods is given in Tables 3-5 summarising only principal data of each method (dating range and suitable materials).

RADIOMETRIC METHODS

The methods are based on the interaction of non-conducting solids with ionising alpha, beta, gamma, and cosmic radiation changes their physical and chemical proper-

***Table 5**: Review of isotopic dating methods III - radioactive disequilibrium of the U, Th, Protactinium decay series*

Dating Method	Dating range	Suitable materials
U/He	< 30 Ma	non-recrystallised aragonite (marine fossils, corals)
$^{234}U/^{238}U$	50 ka - 1.5 Ma	marine molluscs, corals, lacustrine and pelagic sediments, speleothems
$^{230}Th/^{234}U$	< 100 a - 600 ka	fossils, bones, travertines, speleothems, oolite, manganese nodules, marine phosphorites, marine hydrothermal deposits
$^{230}Th_{excess}/^{232}Th$ $^{230}Th/^{238}U$	0.1 - 300 ka < 1 Ma	marine carbonates, manganese nodules, glass shards (volcanic ash), fish bones+teeth, lacustrine sediments with clay mineralsigneous rocks phosphorite deposits
$^{230}Th_{excess}$	< 300 ka	deep sea sediments, manganese nodules
$^{231}Pa/^{235}U$	0.1-200 ka	fossils, bones, oolite, manganese nodules, marine phosphorites, less often travertines, speleothems U-content several ppm
$^{231}Pa/^{230}Th$	0.1-200 ka	U-rich marine carbonate (corals mollusc shells)
^{226}Ra	< 200 ka	marine sediments, ice
$^{231}Pa_{excess}/^{230}Th_{excess}$	< 150 ka	pelagic sediments
$^{231}Pa_{excess}$	< 150 ka	pelagic sediments, corals, manganese nodules
^{210}Pb	< 150 a	lacustrine, fluvial and coastal marine sediments, coral, peat, ice
^{224}Ra ^{228}Ra	< 100 a	corals, Fe-Mn nodules in lakes
$^{228}Th_{excess}/^{232}Th$	< 10 a	High rate deposition in lakes, deltas, estuaries, along coast
Ra/Rn	30 - 100 days	groundwater residence time
$^{234}Th_{excess}$	< 100 days	short-term reworking and diagenesis

Note: The table was compiled according to data in Geyh & Schleicher (1990); Noller, Sowers & Lettis (Eds. 2000); White (1988), and Ford & Williams (1989). Some data were kindly provided by H. Hercman (Warsaw, Poland).

ties (e.g., deffects in crystal lattice). The changes are known as radiation damage. The age determinations are based on two types of damage: (1) electron shell phenomena, and (2) lattice phenomena (Geyh & Schleicher 1990, p. 253-255). The review of methods is given in Table 6.

Fission-track method is a radiogenic method of age estimation based on accumulation of damage trails left by nuclei that are expelled during fission decays of ^{238}U. The method can be applied to minerals with relatively high U content (e.g., apatite, zircon, sphene, volcanic glass). It can be used for direct age determination and for indirect date estimates. Tracks in apatite are partially or entirely erased by increased temperature (110-135 °C), which corresponds to a depth of 3-6 km at normal geothermal gradient. This behaviour has been utilised for dating of unroofing, as lesser heat causes reduction in fission-track ages and reduction of fission tracks (Dumitru 2000).

Thermoluminescence methods are based on lattice defects in common minerals (e.g., quartz, feldspars) fromed during crystallisation or from exposure to nuclear radiation. Heating of sediments causes vibration of mineral lattice and eviction of timer-stored electrons from traps (Forman, Pierson & Lepper 2000). Geyh & Schleicher (1990, p.

257) cite different age ranges for different materials and there can be numerous errors resulting from different sources for the materials and their exposure (see review in Forman, Pierson & Lepper 2000).

Electron spin resonance is based on lift of electrons by ionising radiation from the valence band to a conduction band. Some electrons fall into quasi-stable traps at "forbidden" energy levels. Traps occupied by a single electron act as paramagnetic centres, whose density can be measured by ESR (Geyh & Schleicher 1990, p.273).

Table 6: *Review of radiogenic dating methods*

Dating Method	Dating range	Suitable materials
Fission Track	20 ka-2.7 Ga	Direct age -minerals, obsidian, glass (natural and man-made), tectites, petrified wood, etc.) indirect - age of cooling of some minerals - uplift and erosional history
Thermolumi-nescence	< 500 ka	archeological objects, quartz and feldspars, flint tools, shells, bones teeth, polymineral fine-grained samples, lava (plagioclase), tectites, volcanic glas, loess, travertine and speleothems, fossil calcite shells
Optically simu-latedLumine-scence	1-700 ka	eolians, fluvial, glacial sediments, quartz, zircon
Electron spin Resionance (ESR and EPR)	25-50 ka to > 1 Ma (?100 Ma)	fossils, speleothems, travertine, caliche and vein fillings, pelagic sediments, ceramics, cooling ages of quartz, feldspars, silicates, glass, apaptite etc., crystallization age of gypsum
Exo-electron Method (TSEE)	< 100 ka	bones and dentin
Thermally simu-latedcurrent (TSC)	1-2 Ma	basalts only
Alpha-recoil track	> 100 ka	crystallisation of rock-forming minerals (esp. mica), ages of bones and dentin, low U content

Note: The table was compiled according to data in Geyh & Schleicher (1990); Noller, Sowers & Lettis (Eds. 2000); White (1988), and Ford & Williams (1989). Some data were kindly provided by H. Hercman (Warsaw, Poland).

Numerical-ages are provided also by numerous other methods, which have been applied especially in Cenozoic geochronology (see in Noller, Sowers & Lettis, Eds. 2000). *Dendrochronology* is based on variations in annual growth rings of trees. There are records extending back more than 7 ka. *Varve dating* in laminated sediments is based on annual depositional cycles, especially in lakes. The method can be applied for sediments 18 ka old, i.e. deposited since the last glacial maximum. *Sclerochronology* is the measurement or estimation of ages or time intervals from the growth patterns or inclusions contained in the mineralised biogenic deposits of animals and plants. The method has been applied on corals, molluscs, fish otoliths. Historical records are useful for dating historical events (e.g., collapses, earthquakes).

CALIBRATED-AGES, RELATIVE-AGES

Calibrated-age methods can provide approximate numerical ages. Relative-age methods provide an age sequence and most also provide some indication of the magnitude of age differences between the members in a sequence (Colman & Pierce 2000, p. 4). The methods of this type are specially chemical and biological methods and geomorphic ones.

Chemical and biological methods are based on the assumption that certain reaction rates (e.g., diffusion, exchange, oxidation, hydration) are at least nearly constant. The age is estimated from the initial and end concentrations of suitable reactants or products (Geyh & Schleicher 1990, p. 345). The *amino-acid racemization method* is based on the slow conversion of amino acids after an organism has died. The *amino-acid degradation method* is based on the natural degradation (mainly dehydration) of the ABA acid (Geyh & Schleicher 1990, p. 355). In the *obsidian hydration method* glasses adsorb water on the surface, where it becomes chemically bound, forming a hydrated layer. The process is diffusion controlled, so the layer grows very slowly. The diffusion front of the hydrated layer is a sharp boundary (Geyh & Schleicher 1990, p. 362). Dating of bones by the *nitrogen and collagen method* is based on the rate of protein decomposition, which is influenced by numerous natural factors. The *fluorine-chlorine-apatite method* in combination with the collagen method was modified by Wyszocański-Minkowicz (1969) to relative dating of bones identifying climatic conditions of bone fossilisation. Nevertheless, the recent data indicate that the expectations are very far from the reality and the method does not function. The *fluorine or uranium methods* utilises the fact that skeletal remains continually take up F and U from groundwater via an irreversible ionic exchange. Both methods are very rough with low precision (Geyh & Schleicher 1990, p. 356-357 and 336-370). There are also other methods, like rock-varnish method, lichenometry, soil chemistry applied in Quaternary geochronology (see in Noller, Sowers & Lettis, Eds. 2000, p. 241-292) or chemical electron-spin-resonance dating, molecular (protein and DNA) clocks, Ca diffusion and cation-ratio methods (see in Geyh & Schleicher 1990, p. 359-369).

Table 7: *Review of chemical and biological methods*

Dating Method	Dating range	Suitable materials
Amino-acid racemization	< 500 ka theoretical range < 5 Ma	dating fossils matter that contains amino acids:bones, teeth, foraminifera, coprolites, mulluscs, land snails, marine phosphorites, tuffs, carbonate mud and oolite, speleothems, wood
Amino-acid degradation	up to Miocene	molluscs, foraminifers
Obsidian hydration	0.01->1 Ma	obsidian, ignimbrite, basaltic glass, fused shale, slag, vitrophyre, other natural glasses
N and collagen dating bones	< 100 ka	skeletal materials
F and U datingBones	up to Pliocene	skeletal materials

Note: The table was compiled according to data in Geyh & Schleicher (1990); Noller, Sowers & Lettis (Eds. 2000); White (1988), and Ford & Williams (1989).

CORRELATED-AGES

Correlated-ages are based on the methods of classical geology, geochemistry, geophysics, paleontology and, archeology, e.g., paleontology and stratigraphy, paleomagnetism and magnetostratigraphy, climatic correlations and stable isotope studies, astronomical correlations, tephrochronology, archeology. Principles of these methods are summarised in various textbooks (e.g., for Quaternary in Noller, Sowers & Lettis, Eds. 2000). Combinations of methods have been often applied, e.g., paleontology/stratigraphy with magnetostratigraphy or stable isotope studies or astronomical variations. Particularly useful is the combination of correlated-age methods with numerical-age determination of some marker horizons.

The methodology applied to obtain correlated-age results depend on the nature of the geologic material filling the (paleo)karst and on the types of karst. The fills of exokarst landforms such as sinkholes offer more possibilities for the preservation of fossil fauna and flora than do cave interiors. Troglobitic fauna and flora are usually much too small in number and volume to be significant (Ford & Williams 1989, p. 367). Therefore, fossil remains within a cave that come from the surface (carried in by sinking rivers) or from trogloxenes (e.g., bats, some birds, some mammals) are more important. Airborne grains (pollen, volcanic ash) can only be important when favourable air-circulation patterns are developed within a cave.

There are also numerous *geomorphic methods*, applied especially to young - Cenozoic - landscape and coast evolution. Methods are in general summarised in Noller, Sowers & Lettis (Eds., 2000).

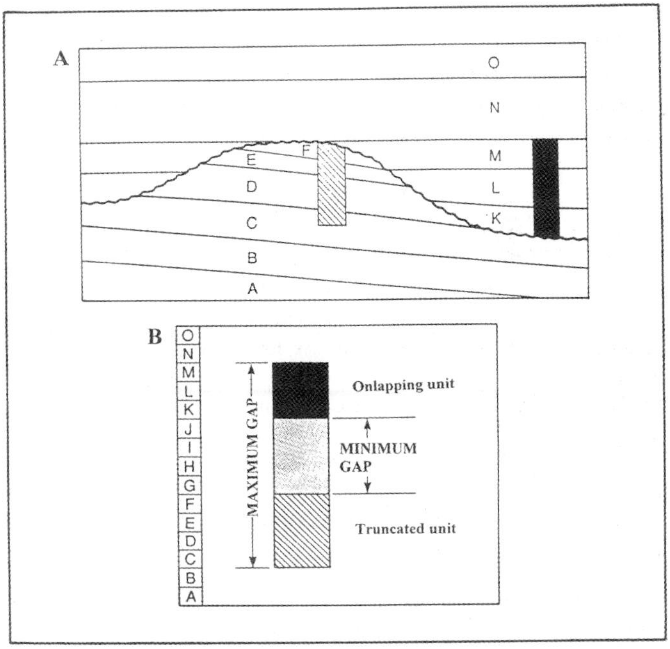

Fig. 5. Chronostratigraphic representation of an unconformity (modified after Esteban 1991).

Stratigraphy. The duration of stratigraphic unconformity can be determined by its chronostratigraphic representation (Esteban 1991, p. 92) based on (1) minimum gap (the time interval not represented by the sedimentary record in the area, caused either by complete erosional removal or by nondeposition. The minimum gap corresponds to the difference between the youngest age of the truncated section and the oldest age of the onlapping section, and (2) maximum gap (the maximum time interval absent in the sedimentary record in the area. The maximum gap corresponds to the difference between the age of the truncated section and the age of the youngest bed of the onlapping section; Fig.5).

The stratigraphic order in sedimentary sequences is governed by the *law of superposition*, according to which under normal tectonic settings the overlying bed is younger than the underlying one. The law is valid for the majority of sedimentary sequences. However, the karst environment represents one exception. Owing to the dynamic nature of karst, its polycyclic and polygenetic character, karst records can be damaged by the simple process of redeposition. In several places in the Czech Karst (Czech Republic) during the Early Quaternary (Biharian stage), destruction of the roofs of some caves and re-opening of fossilised vertical shafts (drawdown vadose connections) caused the excavation of pre-Quaternary fossil-bearing sediments and their deposition into younger caves. In Koněprusy Caves, such re-deposited fill from a vertical chimney was washed into a block collapse in the form of pseudo-matrix (see Bosák, Horáček & Panoš 1989). Contamination of younger deposits by re-deposited fossil-bearing sediments has been known elsewhere in caves (e.g., re-deposition of Cretaceous forams in Pleistocene deposits in the Moravian Karst). In Castleguard Cave (Canadian Rocky Mts.) there are Cretaceous pollen in basal varve layers of Würmian age (D.C. Ford, pers. comm. 2002). Well-known are also sandwich structures, described by Osborne (1998). Younger beds are inserted into voids in older ones. Those processes degrade the record in karst conservers (Horáček & Bosák 1989). *Biostratigraphy.* Reinforcing the law of superposition are the use of *index fossils* (a widely distributed fossil that occurs only in one stratigraphic horizon), and the concept of *facies* (different conditions can at one and the same time create different assemblages at different sites, while almost identical assemblages may derive from different time periods). Biostratigraphy is based on vertical subdivision of geologic time according to fossil fauna and flora, which dominated at the studied time. Biostratigraphic systems may be defined either as a *range zone*, i.e. by means of the first and the last appearance dates of suitable index forms, or as an *assemblage zone* if based on specific characteristics of community structure. The time interval of individual biozones depends on the general evolution velocities of living organisms, therefore intervals shorter than 0.3 Ma can scarcely be recorded by biozonation and the common resolution is 0.7 Ma (Jindrich Hladil, pers. comm. 2002). A useful correlation is given in Haq, Hardebol & Vail (1988) and Berggren et al. (1995) indicating that the resolution of individual biozones of different kinds of fossils range from more than 6.5 to about 0.3 Ma. For biostratigraphic zonation, the application of fauna/flora evolution differs for marine and terrestrial records: nevertheless the principles of zonation in marine and lacustrine sediments are very similar. Fauna and flora in the terrestrial domain are often facies dependent, influenced especially by climate. In the Cenozoic, mammalian biozones (MQ, MN) differ in duration in different regions as a consequence of migration velocities and routes (see Horáček & Kordos 1989). There is also known "mixing" of flora of Carboniferous and Permian affinities, e.g., in Czech Upper Paleozoic limnic basins; arid facies contain Permian flora deeply below Carboniferous/Permian boundary.

Submerged caves may be characterised by peculiar biotopes containing very old elements with close ties to deep-sea fauna (e.g., recently in the Caribbean area). Caves can serve as refuges over very long time-spans, with highly conservative faunal assemblages. Such situations need to be recognised during the biostratigraphic interpretation of marine organisms found in cave facies, especially when studying transgressive tracts on karst surfaces (see also Horáček & Kordos 1989, p. 610).

Paleomagnetism and magnetostratigraphy. The method is based on variations in the polar declination, inclination and intensity of the Earth´s magnetic field. The changes are recorded in rocks by the orientation of magnetic minerals during their deposition or crystallisation. Use of records of ancient variations as a dating tool relies on matching the curves of declination and inclination in a given deposit with established curves (standard time-scales) that have been dated by independent methods (e.g., Ford & Williams 1989). The method faces numerous constraints and thresholds, especially where there is no independent dating of deposits by numerical-ages.

The complete reversals (excursions) of the field occur at 10^5-10^6 years establish the principal time units (chrons). Nevertheless, there were periods when the polarity was stable for very long times, e.g., in the Cretaceous from about 107 to about 83 Ma (see e.g., Haq, Hardebol & Vail 1988). Most normal- or reverse-polarised deposits contain short-lived changes of polarity (subchrons) with durations from 10^0 to 10^2 ka. The combination of detailed micropaleontology with dense sampling for paleomagnetic analysis can result in high-resolution scales, e.g., a precision of about 5 ka on the Jurassic/Cretaceous boundary in the Tethyan realm (Houša et al. 1999) or even better for reversals in Pleistocene record combining paleomagnetism and thermoluminescence dating (Zhu & Tschu, Eds. 2001).

The application of the method for dating clastic cave sediments has been limited by the complex conditions underground, i.e. it is often necessary to combine it with other methods offering numerical- relative- or correlate-ages. Moreover, the character of cave deposition results in numerous breaks in deposition, in which substantial timespans can be lost (Bosák et al. 2000; Pruner & Bosák 2001). The example of correlation of magnetostratigraphy results from selected caves in Slovakia and Slovenia is presented in Figure 6. Paleomagnetic and magnetostratigraphic studies have been successfully applied also on calcite speleothems (e.g., Latham, Schwartz & Ford 1979, 1986).

The secular variations are quasi-periodic changes in declination and to lesser extent also of inclination. The changes are of smaller magnitude than those described as excursions and appear to be merely regional in extent. They presumably result from changes in the non-dipole component of the magnetic field. If the changes are dated independently, they can be used in chronostratigraphic time scales (Bradley 1999). The study of magnetosusceptibility of different age periods when adjusted to numerical- or correlate-ages represents is also a useful tool for correlation or dating. The method can be used in deep-sea sediments, carbonate platforms, loess accumulations, etc. The content of ferro- and paramagnetic minerals is studied. Their contents are fixed during deposition and/or early diagenesis. Magnetosusceptibility stratigraphy has been applied to some Devonian carbonate sequences (Crick et al. 1997; Hladil et al. 2002) or for some Quaternary deposits (Kadlec et al. 2001). The changes in magnetosusceptibility are believed to be influenced by climatic conditions (temperature, humidity, winds) and, maybe, by Milankovich cycles.

Astronomical correlations. Orbital perturbations, known also as Milankovich cycles, reflect the astronomical cycles: the precession of the equinoxes (with a periodicity of 19 and 23 ka), obliquity of the ecliptic (41 ka) and eccentricity of the orbit (100 ka). It is widely believed that the orbital-forcing, Milankovich-rhythm mechanism is responsible for continental icesheet build up and the consequent sea-level changes, which can be

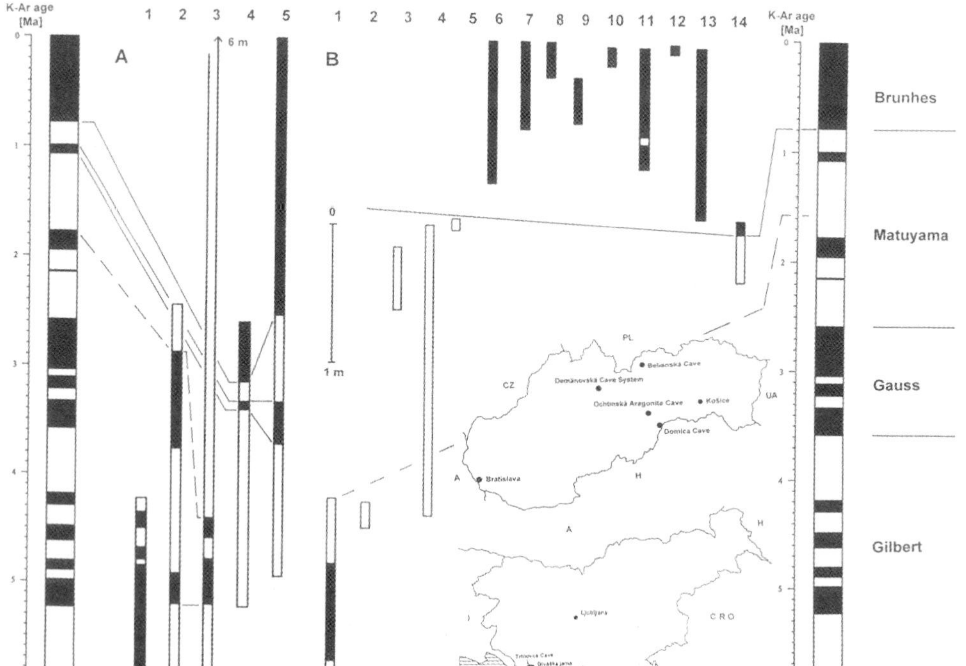

Fig. 6. Measured magnetostratigraphic profiles in some of Slovenian (A) and Slovak caves (B) and their correlation with the magnetostratigraphic chart of Cande & Kent (1995; after Pruner & Bosák 2001). A. Slovenia: 1 - Črni Kal-Černotiče, 2 - Kozina profile, 3 - Divača profile, 4 - Divaška Jama, 5 -Trhlovca Cave; B. Slovakia 1-2 - Belianská Cave, 3-7 - Demänovská jaskyňa Slobody, 8-9 - Demänovská jaskyňa Mieru, 10-13 - Domica Cave, 14 -Ochtinská Aragonite Cave.

recorded e.g., in Caribbean-model shallow marine carbonate sequences as erosional/karst surfaces and meteoric diagenetic changes (e.g., Tucker & Wright 1990). Astronomical cycles are well preserved both in marine and continental deposits, especially in laminated sequences and profiles with cyclic patterns. Most of studies indicate cycles of about 20-23 ka, 40-41 ka, 100 ka and 400-405 ka, which can be mutually superimposed. The detailed study of cyclicity of sediments, i.e. calibration of sedimentary cycles, or other cyclic variations in the geological record, to computed time series of the quasi-periodic variations of the Earth´s orbit, can result in cyclostratigraphic sequential scales. When calibrated by numerical dating (e.g., Ar/Ar single grain) they can substantially contribute to the construction of geological time scales (e.g., Neogene astrochronology in the Mediterranean; Krijgsman et al. 2002; Abdul Aziz et al. 2002) and to the improvement of previous models, e.g., the standard geomagnetic polarity timescale of Cande & Kent (1995) for the Cenozoic was age-corrected by astrochronology (Abdul Aziz et al. 2002).

Stable isotopic studies. Oxygen isotopic studies provide data to understand past environmental conditions, especially paleotemperatures. Relative abundance of oxygen ^{16}O and ^{18}O, the $^{18}O/^{16}O$ ratio, is compared with that in standards (PDB belemnite for solids and standard mean oceanic water - SMOW - for liquids; e.g., J.D. Wright 2000). If variations of marine stable isotope records are compared with numerical-ages and correlated-ages, a chronostratigraphic time scale can be constructed (Emiliani 1955; Shackleton & Opdyke 1973; Hays, Imbrie & Shackleton 1976; Imbrie et al. 1984). The oxygen isotope curve shows temperature changes influenced by glaciations. The time scale for the whole Quaternary has been established by this means. It is composed of 22 stages, with boundaries numerically dated by ^{14}C, K/Ar, Ar/Ar and U series dates and compared with paleomagnetic records and orbital variations. The stable isotope time scale has been often used for karst studies (e.g., Mylroie & Carew 1986; see also Ford & Williams 1989).

CORRELATION OF CAVE LEVELS AND RIVER TERRACES

Correlation of cave levels with river terraces has been relatively common in the past. Speleogenetic models of extensive areas were based on such correlation (e.g., the Czech Karst with the Berounka River, Czech Republic; Hromas 1968). Nevertheless, most of these correlations were limited to nearby rivers rather than to entire drainage areas (White 1988, p. 318). Sawicki (1909) defined so-called *evolution level*, i.e. connected with the piezometric surface and oriented towards the base level (see also Bögli 1981). This view allows to determined „cave levels" even for deep phreatic or bathyphreatic systems, see Hölloch Cave System (Muotatal, Switzerland; Bögli 1966) with three main levels of bathyphreatic caves correlated with principal interglacials of the Alps.

White (1988) mentioned several examples of cave levels (watertable *sensu* Ford 1968 or epiphreatic caves *sensu* Jennings 1985) correlated with the entrenchment of rivers, especially of the Mammoth Cave System (U.S.A.), where cave sediments showed good agreement between magnetostratigraphy and the model for its Tertiary-Quaternary evolution. Detailed analysis of factors influencing the interpretation of cave levels was summarised by Palmer (1984). Sharply defined cave levels with narrow vertical ranges (e.g., Mammoth Cave, Kentucky, USA) appear to have formed in response to intermittent episodes of rapid valley entrenchment, probably by headward erosion, followed by lengthy periods of virtually static base level.

Maybe the most conspicuous example of correlation of river terraces and cave levels has been in the Demänová Cave System (Demänovská Valley, Low Tatras Mts., Slovakia) developed by Droppa (1966) and mentioned in numerous textbooks (e.g., Bögli 1981, p. 116-119; Jennings 1985, p. 243-244). Droppa (1966) recognised 9 cave levels and correlated them to the well-developed terrace system of the Váh River. Recent detailed magnetostratigraphic (Pruner & Bosák 2001) and U-series dating of cave sediments and speleothems (Hercman et al. 1997) in the 4th and 5th cave levels (*sensu* Droppa 1966) has shown that the cave fill of these passages is older than the age of correlated terrace of the Váh River. From the combination of results, the 4th cave level was dry already at about 700 ka (the base of speleothem is ca 685 ka), although previous correlation with river terraces assumed the age of speleogenesis to Mindel 2, i.e. to ca 330-500 ka (Droppa 1972). Magnetostratigraphic data from highler cave levels from both Demänovská and parallel Jánská Valley indicate that the age of cave fill can be correlated with the age of sediments covering river terraces of the Váh River. Caves formed under phreatic and reworked under vadose conditions are therefore older. From the longitudinal sections of the cave system it is concluded that the evolution of passages followed the four state model of Ford (1968, 1971) and Ford & Ewers (1978). Upper levels represent rather deep phreatic caves with multiple deep loops later modified by vadose entrenchment and bypassing, while the lower cave levels can be correlated with nearly ideal watertable cave with minor shallow phreatic loops. Therefore, the cave levels should be correlated with the positions of respective karst springs rather than with terrace surfaces of the same or similar elevation, which can be lowered by subsequent erosion.

CONCLUSIONS

The precise dating of events during karst initiation, evolution and destruction is a highly risky task. Owing to the fact that karst and caves have been developing since the Archean, nearly all known dating methods can be applied. Paleokarst features can be fossilised by infilling and/or cover with a broad variety of rocks: marine and continental chemical and siliciclastic deposits, mineral deposits produced e.g., by weathering or hydrothermal activity, products of volcanism (lava, volcaniclastics). Recent karst surfaces and accessible caves can be covered/filled by a very similar spectrum of fills.

The methods determining the age of fills directly are based on physical, chemical and biological methods, plus methods of classical geology and stratigraphy. There are also indirect means of dating - correlation with correlative sediments not occurring in the karst itself. The range of age data produced by individual groups of methods substantially differs. There are geochronologic methods giving real dates - numerical-ages and ages based on correlation - calibrated (or relative)-age and correlate-age. The principal problem of dating of paleokarst features is in determining the duration of stratigraphic discontinuities. The longer are the discontinuities, the greater is the proportion of time is not recorded in any correlated sediments (40 to 90 % of time can be missing in old platforms). Results of paleokarst evolution are best preserved directly beneath a cover of marine or continental sediments, i.e. under sediments, which terminated karstification periods or phases. The longer the stratigraphic gap the more problematic is precise dating of the age of the paleokarst, if it cannot be chronostratigraphically proven. Therefore, ages of paleokarsts has been associated chiefly with periods just or shortly before the termination of the stratigraphic gap. The characteristic time scale for the development of a karst surface landform or a conduit is 10 to 100 ka (White 1988, p. 304).

The dating of cave initiation and evolution, i.e. the origin of the void within the bedrock is more problematic. The age of the erosional cave falls between the age of the host rock and that of the oldest dated fill. With the inception theory, the true start of speleogenesis can hardly be estimated. Many caves contain only very young fills, older ones having been excavated during repeating cave exhumations/rejuvenations caused by changes in hydraulic conditions, spring position, climate, etc. The minimum age for the cave initiation phase is estimated to be a minimum of 10 ka and cave enlargement up to accessible diameters usually takes about 10-100 ka under favourable conditions.

The end of karstification occurs at the moment when host-karst rock together with its karst phenomena is completely eroded/denuded - the end of the karst cycle. In such case, nothing can be dated, all has been denuded. Karst forms of individual evolutionary stages (cycles) can be destroyed by erosion, denudation and abrasion, complete filling of epikarst and covering of karst surface by impermeable sediments, without the necessity of destroying the entire sequence of karst rocks (the cycle of erosion). Temporary and/or final interruption of karstification is caused by the fossilisation of karst due to loss of the hydrological function of the karst. Nevertheless, in contrast to living organisms, the development of the karst system can be „frozen" and rejuvenated even for a multiplicity of times (polycyclic and polygenetic nature of karst). Further, the dynamic nature of karst can cause redeposition and reworking of classical stratigraphic order, making the karst record unreadable and problematic for interpretation.

The final answer to the question posed in the introduction is: according to my long-lasting experience, yes we can date karst processes and events; under extremely favourable conditions we can date the products of some processes very precisely by numerical dating and/or a combination of methods, but in a majority of cases we have to handle a number of unknown factors. To solve the problem we apply complex approaches, including geopoetry, more or less successfully depending on talent of student of the karst.

ACKNOWLEDGEMENT

The compilation of this review was supported by the Grant Agency of the Academy of Sciences of the Czech Republic (Grant No. A3013201) and the Research Plan of the Institute of Geology of the Czech Republic (No. CEZ Z 03-013-912). The author especially acknowledge the contribution of Derek C. Ford (McMaster University, Canada), who carefully and critically reviewed the manuscript. Helena Hercman (Institute of Geological Sciences, Polish Academy of Sciences, Warsaw) supported special data concerning numerical dating in karst sciences. Jindrich Hladil (Institute of Geology, Academy of Sciences of the Czech Republic, Prague) contributed by some critical comments and data.

REFERENCES

Abdul Aziz, H., W. Krijgsman, F.J. Hilgen, D.S. Wilson, C.G. Langereis & J.P. Calvo, 2002: An astronomical polarity time scale for the Middle Miocene based on continental sequences. - Geophysical Research Abstracts, 4 (CD ROM).

Berggren, W.A., D.V. Kent, C.C. Swisher II. & M.-P. Aubry, 1995: A revised Cenozoic geochronology and chronostratigraphy. - In: Geochronology time scales and global stratigraphic correlation, SEPM Special publication, 54, 129-212.

Bögli, A., 1966: Karstwasserfläche und unterirdischer Karstniveaus. - Edrkunde, 20, 11-19.

Bögli, A., 1981: Karst hydrology and physical speleology. - Springer, 284 pp, Berlin.

Bosák, P., 1987: Paleokarst - key to paleogeography and stratigraphy of continental periods. - 3. Pracovni seminár z paleoekologie. Sbor. Konf., 2-14, Brno. (in Czech)

Bosák, P., 1989: Problems of the origin and fossilization of karst forms. - In: Bosák, P., D.C. Ford, J. Głazek & I. Horáček, Eds.: Paleokarst. A Systematic and Regional Review, 577-598, Elsevier-Academia, Amsterdam-Praha.

Bosák, P., 1996: The evolution of karst and caves in the Koněprusy region (Bohemian Karst, Czech Republic) and paleohydrologic model. - Acta Carsologica, 25, 57-67, Ljubljana.

Bosák, P., 1997: Paleokarst of the Bohemian Massif in the Czech Republic: an overwiev and synthesis. - International Journal of Speleology, 24, 1995, 1-2, 3-40, L´Aquila.

Bosák, P., 1998: The evolution of karst and caves in the Koněprusy region (Bohemian Karst, Czech Republic), part II: hydrothermal paleokarst. - Acta Carsologica, XXVII/2, 3, 41-61, Ljubljana.

Bosák, P., D.C. Ford & J. Głazek, 1989: Terminology. - In: Bosák, P., D.C. Ford, J. Głazek & I. Horáček, Eds.: Paleokarst. A Systematic and Regional Review, 25-32, Elsevier-Academia, Amsterdam-Praha.

Bosák, P., I. Horáček & V. Panoš, 1989: Paleokarst of Czechoslovakia. - In: Bosák, P., D.C. Ford, J. Głazek & I. Horáček, Eds.: Paleokarst. A Systematic and Regional Review, 107-135, Elsevier-Academia, Amsterdam-Praha.

Bosák, P., J.E. Mylroie, J. Hladil, J.L. Carew & L. Slavík, in print: Blow Hole Cave: Unroofed cave on San Salvador Island, the Bahamas, and its importance for detection of paleokarst caves on fossil carbonate platforms. - Acta Carsologica, 31.

Bosák, P., P. Pruner, A. Mihevc & N. Zupan Hajna, 2000: Magnetostratigraphy and unconformities in cave sediments: case study from the Classical Karst, SW Slovenia. - Geologos, 5, 13-30, Poznań.

Bradley, R.S., 1999: Quaternary paleoclimates. Methods of paleoclimatic reconstruction. - Unwin Hyman, 472 pp., Boston.

Cande, S.C. & D.V. Kent, 1995: Revised calibration of the geomagnetic polarity timescale for the Late Cretaceous and Cenozoic. - Journal of Geophysical Research, 100, B4, 6093-6095.

Choquette, P.W. &N.P. James, 1988: Introduction. - In: James, N.V. & P.W. Choquette, Eds., Paleokarst, 1-21, Springer, New York.

Colman, S.M. & K.L. Pierce, 2000: Classification of Quaternary geochronologic methods. - In: Noller, J.S., J.M. Sowers & W.R. Lettis, Eds., Quaternary Geochronology. Methods and Applications, American Geophysical Union, 2-5, Washington.

Crick, R.E., B.B. Ellwood, A. El Hassani, R. Feist & J. Hladil, 1997: magnetosusceptibility event and cycloctratigraphy of the Eifelian-Givetian GSSP and associated boundary sequences in North Africa and Europe. - Episodes, 20, 3, 167-175.

Cvijić, J., 1918: Hydrographie souterraine et evolution morphologique du Karst. - Rec. Travaux du Institute de Geographie Alpine, 6, 4, 376-420.

Davis, W.M., 1899: The geographical cycle. - Geographical Journal, 14, 481-504.

Dreybrodt, W. & F. Gabrovšek, 2000: Dynamics of the evolution of single karst conduits. - In: Klimchouk, A.A., D.C. Ford, A.N. Palmer & W. Dreybrodt, Eds., Speleogenesis. Evolution of karst aquifers, National Speelological Society: 184-193, Huntsville.

Droppa, A. 1966: Correlation of some horizontal caves with river terraces. - Studies in Speleology, 1, 186-192, Brno.

Droppa, A., 1972: Geomorphology of Demänovská Valley. - Slovenský kras, 10, 9-46, Martin. (in Slovak)

Dumitru, T.A., 2000: Fission-track geochronology. - In: Noller, J.S., J.M. Sowers & W.R. Lettis, Eds., 2000: Quaternary Geochronology. Methods and Applications, American Geophysical Union, 131-155, Washington.

Emiliani, C., 1955: Pleistocene temperatures. - Journal of Geology, 63, 539-578.

Eraso, A., 1989: Foreword. - In: Bosák, P., D.C. Ford, J. Głazek & I. Horáček, Eds.: Paleokarst. A Systematic and Regional Review, 13-14, Elsevier-Academia, Amsterdam-Praha.

Esteban, M., 1991: Palaeokarst: Practical Applications. - In: Wright, V.P., M. Esteban & P.L. Smart, Eds., Palaeokarsts and Palaeokarstic Reservoirs, P.R.I.S. Occassional Publication Series, 2, 89-119, Reading.

Esteban, M. & C.I. Klappa, 1983: Subaerial exposure environments. - In : Scholle, P.A., D.G. Bebout & C.H. Moore, Eds., Carbonate depositional environments, 1-54, Amer. Assoc. Petroleum Geologists, Tulsa.

Faure, G., 2001: Origin of igneous rocks. The isotopic evidence. - Springer, 496 pp., Berlin.

Ford, D.C., 1968: Features of cavern development in Central Mendip. - Transactions of Cave Research Group of Great Britain, 10, 1, 11-25.

Ford, D.C., 1971: Geologic structure and a new explanation of limestone caverns. -Transactions of Cave Research Group of Great Britain, 13, 2, 81-94.

Ford, D.C., 1980: Threshold and limit effects in karst geomorphology. - In: Coates, D.L. & J.D. Vitek, Eds., Thresholds in Geomorphology, 345-362, Allen & Unwin, London.

Ford, D.C., 1989: Paleokarst of Canada. - In: Bosák, P., D.C. Ford, J. Głazek && I. Horáček, Eds., Paleokarst. A Systematic and Regional Review, 313-336, Elsevier-Academia, Amsterdam-Praha.

Ford, D.C. & R.O. Ewers, 1978: The development of cave systems in dimensions of length and depth. - Canadian Journal of Earth Sciences, 15, 1783-1789.

Ford, D.C. && P.W. Williams, 1989: Karst Geomorphology and Hydrology. - Unwin Hyman, 601 pp, London.

Forman, S.L., J. Pierson & K. Lepper, 2000: Luminescence dating. - In: Noller, J.S., J.M. Sowers & W.R. Lettis, Eds., 2000: Quaternary Geochronology. Methods and Applications, American Geophysical Union, 157-176, Washington.

Geyh, M.A. & H. Schleicher, 1990: Absolute age determination. - Springer, 503 pp, Berlin.

Głazek, J., 1973: The importance of karst phenomena in paleogeographic and paleotectonic reconstructions. - Pregląd Geologiczny, 21, 10, 517-523, Warszawa.

Głazek, J., 1989a: Paleokarst of Poland. - In: Bosák, P., D.C. Ford, J. Głazek & I. Horáček, Eds., Paleokarst. A Systematic and Regional Review, 77-105, Elsevier-Academia, Amsterdam-Praha.

Głazek, J., 1989b: Tectonic conditions for karst origin and preservation. - In: Bosák, P., D.C. Ford, J. Głazek & I. Horáček, Eds., Paleokarst. A Systematic and Regional Review, 569-575, Elsevier-Academia, Amsterdam-Praha.

Głazek, J., T. Dąbrowski & R. Gradziński, 1972: Karst of Poland. - In: Herak, M. & V.T. Stringfield, Eds., Karst. Important Karst Regions of the Northern Hemisphere, 327-340, Elsevier, Amsterdam.

Grund, A., 1914: Der geographische Zyklus im Karst. - Ges. Erdkunde, 52, 621-640.

Haq, B.U., J. Hardenbol & P.R. Vail, 1988: Mesozoic and Cenozoic chronostratigraphy and cycles of sea-level changes. - In: Sea-level changes-An integrated approach, SEPM Special Publication, 42, 71-108.

Hays, J.D., J. Imbrie & N.J. Shackleton, 1976: Variations in the Earth´s orbit: pacemaker of the ice ages. - Science, 194, 1121-1132.

Hercman, H., P. Bella, M. Gradziński, J. Głazek, S.E. Lauritzen & R. Lovlie, 1997: Uranium-series dating of speleothems from Demänova Ice Cave: A step to age estimation of the Demänova Cave System (The Nízke Tatry Mts., Slovakia). - Annales Société Geol. Polon., 67, 4, 439-450.

Hladil, J., P. Pruner, D. Venhodová, T. Hladilová & O. Man, 2002 : Towards an exact age of Middle Devonian Čelechovice corals: past problems in biostratigraphy and present solutions complemented by new magnetosusceptibility measurements. - Coral Research Bulletin, 7, 65-71, Dresden.

Horáček, I. & P. Bosák, 1989: Special characteristics of paleokarst studies. - In: Bosák, P., D.C. Ford, J. Głazek & I. Horáček, Eds., Paleokarst. A Systematic and Regional Review, 565-568, Elsevier-Academia, Amsterdam-Praha.

Horáček, I. & L. Kordos, 1989: Biostratigraphic investigations in paleokarst. - In: Bosák, P., D.C. Ford, J. Głazek & I. Horáček, Eds.: Paleokarst. A Systematic and Regional Review, 599-612, Elsevier-Academia, Amsterdam-Praha.

Houša, V., M. Krs, P. Pruner, D. Venhodová, F. Cecca, M. Piscitelo, F. Olóriz & J.M. Tavera, 199: Magnetostratigraphy and micropaleontology across the J/K boundary in The Tethyan Realm. - Geologica Carpathica, 50, 3, 33-35.

Howard, A.D. & B.Y. Howard, 1967: Solution of limestones under laminar flow between parallel boundaries. - Caves and Karst, 9, 25-38.

Hromas, J. 1968: New discoveries in Koněpruské Caves in the Bohemian Karst. - Československý kras, 20, 51-62. Praha. (in Czech)

Imbrie, J., J.D. Hays, D.G. Martinson, A. McIntyre, A.C. Mix et al., 1984: The orbital theory of Pleitocene climate: support from a revised chronology of the marine $\delta^{18}O$ record. - In: A.L. Berger, J. Imbrie, J.D. Hays, G. Kukla & B. Saltzman, Eds., Milankovitch and climate, I, 269-305, Reidel, Dordrecht.

Ivanovich, M. & R.S. Harmon, Eds., 1982: Uranium series disequilibrium. Applications to environmental problems. 2nd Ed. - Clarendon, 910 pp, Oxford.

James, N.V. & P.W. Choquette, 1984 : Diagenesis 9. Limestones - the meteoric diagenetic environment. - Geoscience Canada, 11, 161-194.

James, N.V. & P.W. Choquette, Eds., 1988: Paleokarst. - Springer, 416 pp, New York.

Jennings, J.N., 1985: Karst geomorphology. - Blackwell, 293 pp. Oxford.

Kadlec, J., H. Hercman, V. Beneš, P. Šroubek, J.F. Diehl & D. Granger, 2001: Cenozoic history of the Moravian Karst (northern segment): cave sediments and karst morphology. - Acta Musei Moraviae, Sci. geol., LXXXV, 111-161, Brno.

Krijgsman, W., F.J. Hilgen, K. Kuiper, J.R. Wijbrans & D.S. Wilson, 2002: Neogene astrochronology: applications for Ar/Ar dating and sea-floor spreading rates. - Geophysical Research Abstracts, 4 (CD ROM).

Latham, A.G., H.P. Schwartz & D.C. Ford, 1979: Palaeomagnetism of stalagmite deposits - Nature, 280, 5721, 383-385.

Latham, A.G., H.P. Schwartz & D.C. Ford, 1986: The palaeomagnetism and U-Th dating of Mexican stalagmite, DAS2. - Earth and Planetary Science Lettres, 79, 195-207.

Longman, M.W., 1980: Carbonate diagenetic textures from near-surface diagenetic environments. - American Association of Petroleum Geologists Bulletin, 63, 4, 461-487, Tulsa.

Longman, M.V. & D.N. Brownlee, 1980: Characteristics of karst topography, Palawan, Philippines. - Zeitschrift für Geomorphologie, N.F., 24, 3, 299-317.

Lowe, D.J., 1999: Why and how are caves „organized": does the past offer a key to present. - Acta Carsologica, 28/2, 7, 121-144, Ljubljana.

Lowe, D.J., 2000: Role of stratigraphic elements in speleogenesis: the speleoinception concept. - In: Klimchouk, A.A., D.C. Ford, A.N. Palmer & W. Dreybrodt, Eds., Speleogenesis. Evolution of karst aquifers, National Speelological Society: 184-193, Huntsville.

Lowe, D.J. & J. Gunn, 1997: Carbonate speleogenesis: An inception horizon hypothesis. - Acta Carsologica, 26/2, 38, 457-488, Ljubljana.

Ložek, V. & F. Skřivánek, 1965: The significance of fissures and their fills for dating of karst processes. - Československý kras, 17, 7-22, Praha.

Lundberg, J., D.C. Ford & C.A. Hill, 2001: A preliminary U-Pb date on cave spar, Big Canyon, Guadalupe Mountains, New Mexico, U.S.A. - Journal of Cave and Karst Studies, 62(2), 144-148.

Martini, J.E.J., 1981: Early Proterozoic paleokarst of the Transvaal, South Africa. - Proceedings 8th International Congress of Speleology, I, 4-5, Huntsville.

Moore, C.H., 1989: Carbonate Diagenesis and Porosity. - Developments in Sedimentology, 46, 1-338, Elsevier, New York.

Moore, C.H., 2001: Carbonate Reservoirs. Porosity Evolution and Diagenesis in a Sequence

Stratigraphic Framework. - Developments in Sedimentology, 55, 1-444, Elsevier, Amsterdam.

Mylroie, J.E. & J.L. Carew, 1986: Minimum duration for speleogenesis. - Comunicacions 9° Congreso Internacional de Espeleologia, Vol. I: 249-251, Barcelona.

Mylroie, J.E. & J.L. Carew, 1987: Field evidence of the minimum time for speleogenesis. - National Speleological Society Bulletin, 49,2, 67-72, Huntsville.

Noller, J.S., J.M. Sowers & W.R. Lettis, Eds., 2000: Quaternary Geochronology. Methods and Applications. - American Geophysical Union, 582 pp., Washington.

Osborne, R.A.L., 1998: Lateral facies changes, unconformities and stratigraphic reversals: their significance for cave sediment stratigraphy. - Cave Science, 11, 3, 175-184.

Palmer, A.N., 1981: Hydrochemical controls in the origin of limestone caves. - 8th International Speleological Congress Proceedings, 120-122, Bowling Green.

Palmer, A.N., 1984: Geomorphic interpretation of karst features. - In: LaFleur, G.A., Ed., Groundwater as a Geomorphic Agent, 173-209, Allen & Unwin, London.

Palmer, A.N., 1991: Origin and morphology of limestone caves. - Geological Society of America Bulletin, 103, 1-21.

Panoš, V., 1964: Der Urkarst in Ostflügel der Böhmishen Masse. - Zeitschrift für Geomorphologie, N.F., 8, 2, 105-162.

Pruner, P. & P. Bosák, 2001: Palaeomagnetic and magnetostratigraphic research of cave sediments: theoretical approach, and examples from Slovenia and Slovakia. - Proceedings, 13th International Speleological Congress, 4th Speleological Congress of Latin America and the Carribean, 26th Brazilian Congress of Speleology, Brasilia, July 15-22, 2001. CD ROM.

Rougerie, F. & B. Wauthy, 1993: The endo-upwelling concept: from geothermal convection to reef reconstruction. - Coral Reefs, 12, 1, 19-30, Berlin.

Rowlands, N.J., P.G. Blight, D.M. Jarvis & C.C. Von Der Borch, 1980: Sabkha and playa environments in late Proterozoic grabens, Willouran Ranges, Australia. - Journal of Geological Society of Australia, 27, 1, 55-68.

Sawicki, L., 1908: Skizze des slowakischen Karstes und der geographische Zyklus im Karst überhaupt. - Kosmos, 6-7, 395-444, Lwów. (in Polish)

Sawicki, L., 1909: Ein Beitrag zum geographischen Zyklus im Karst. - Geographisches Zeitschrift, 15, 185-204, Wien.

Shackleton, N.J. & N.D. Opdyke, 1973: Oxygen isotope and paleomagnetis stratigraphy of equatorial Pacific V28-238: Oxygen isotope temperatures and ice volumes on a 10^5 and 10^6 year scale. - Quaternary Research, 3, 39-55.

Sowers, J.M. & J.S. Noller, 2000: The essence of Quaternary geochronology. - In: Noller, J.S., J.M. Sowers & W.R. Lettis, Eds., 2000: Quaternary Geochronology. Methods and Applications, American Geophysical Union, 5-10, Washington.

Tsykin, R.A., 1989: Paleokarst of the Union of Soviet Socialist Republics. - In: Bosák, P., D.C. Ford, J. Głazek & I. Horáček, Eds.: Paleokarst. A Systematic and Regional Review, 2253-295, Elsevier-Academia, Amsterdam-Praha.

Tucker, M.E. & V.P. Wright, 1990: Carbonate Sedimentology. - Blackwell, 482 pp, Oxford.

Waltham, T., 2000: Caves is where you find "em". - Caves & Caving, Spring/Summer 2000, 26-29.

White, W.B., 1984: Rate processes: Chemical kinetics and karst landforms development. -

In: LaFleur, G.A., Ed., Groundwater as a Geomorphic Agent, 227-248, Allen & Unwin, London.

White, W.B., 1988: Geomorphology and Hydrology of Karst Terrains. - Oxford University Press, 464 pp, New York.

Wright, J.D., 200: Global climate change in marine stable isotope records. - In: Noller, J.S., J.M. Sowers & W.R. Lettis, Eds., 2000: Quaternary Geochronology. Methods and Applications, American Geophysical Union, 427-433, Washington.

Wright, V.P., 1991: Palaeokarst types, recognition, controls and assocations. - In: Wright, V.P., M. Esteban & P.L. Smart, Eds. Palaeokarsts and Palaeokarstic Reservoirs, P.R.I.S. Occassional Publication Series, 2, 56-88, Reading

Wright, V.P., M. Esteban & P.L. Smart, Eds., 1991: Palaeokarsts and Palaeokarstic Reservoirs. - P.R.I.S. Occassional Publication Series, 2, 1-158, Reading.

Wright, V.P. & P.L. Smart, 1994: Paleokarst (Dissolution Diageneis): Its Occurrence and Hydrocarbon Exploration Significance. - In: Wolf, K.H. & G.V. Chilingarian, Eds., Diagenesis, IV, Developments in Sedimentology, 51, 489-502, Elsevier, Amsterdam.

Wyszoczański-Minkowicz, T., 1969: An attempt at relative age determination of fossil bones by fluorine-chlorine-apatite method. - Studia Geologica Polonica, XXVIII, 1-79, Warszawa.

Zhang Shouyue, 1989: Paleokarst of China. - In: Bosák, P., D.C. Ford, J. Głazek & I. Horáček, Eds.: Paleokarst. A Systematic and Regional Review, 297-311, Elsevier-Academia, Amsterdam-Praha.

Zhu, R.X. & K.K. Tschu K.K., Eds., 2001: Studies in Paleomagnetism and Reversals of Geomagnetic Field in China. - Sciences Press, 168 pp., Beijing.

Address
Institute of Geology, Academy of Sciences of the Czech Republic
Rozvojová 135, 165 02 PRAHA 6, CZECH REPUBLIC
E-mail: Bosak@gli.cas.cz

THE EVOLUTION OF THE KARST VERSUS THE DISTRIBUTION AND DIVERSITY OF THE HYPOGEAN FAUNA

BORIS SKET

Abstract
*Within the biogeographical merodinaric karst areas, ranges of some stygobiotic species are in discord with actual drainage patterns. Some cases in Gastropoda and Crustacea are presented. Sometimes their ranges resemble the areas of hypothetical prekarstic paleodrainages. It has been supposed that after transition underground some species reside in those areas which they occupied before the advanced karstification. It has been shown that the interspecific competition may force a species to stay in the area of its origin. At least some rearrangments in their headwaters has to have occurred in the past if one such animal taxon is present in two actual drainages. A case (*Monolistra caeca *in southern Slovenia) is presented, where the species distribution and racial diversity could give a hint for paleohydrographical assumptions.*
Key words*: biogeography, cave fauna, Dinaric karst, Isopoda, paleohydrography*

INTRODUCTION; THE DINARIC CAVE FAUNA AND ITS DISTRIBUTION PATTERNS

The Dinaric karst is inhabited by the richest obligate subterranean fauna in the World. While the richest in the terrestrial cave fauna is the SE part of the Dinaric region (compare Gueorguiev 1977), the richest in the aquatic (stygobiotic) fauna is surprisingly its NW part in Slovenia (Sket 1999). Different entities, taxa (systematic units/groups), show different patterns of geographical ("biogeographical") distribution, which must mirror the development of the territory, including its karstification as well as the ecological, genetic, and other peculiarities of an individual animal taxon itself. It is the aim of this contribution to provoke karst geomorphologists to define some paleogeographical situations, which could explain different biogeographical patterns, i.e. different kinds of distribution areas of animal species in the karst underground. Or, to provoke them to use some biogeographical patterns as cues for their paleogeophysiographical reconstructions.

Very few comprehensive reviews about the distribution of cavernicolous species in the Dinaric region exist. However, we are preparing to produce a complete enumeration of the known fauna including its taxonomic composition as well as distribution of species. The following biogeographical patterns could have been established mainly on parts of the aquatic, i.e. stygobiotic fauna (Sket, 1994).

(**1**) The taxa with **broad distribution ranges**, approximately with European (i.e. western Palearctic) distribution, are mainly very successful, ecologically generalist species, inhabiting different epigean habitats and penetrating also underground. In caves they may develop troglomorphies (the characteristic morphological characters of troglobionts/stygobionts) and thus they produce stygobiotic races. In the case that a natural catastrophe extinguishes all epigean populations, such a taxon would result in a series of disconnected cave populations of one species. This is a very instructive case that can help to explain some other discontinuous distribution areas. The best-known taxa of such a kind are some crustacean species, like the isopod *Asellus aquaticus* (Linne) and the amphipod *Synurella ambulans* (O.F. Mueller).

(**2**) Stygobiotic **Dinaric taxa with members further west and east** are probably relicts of the fauna which developed on the newly emerged Adriatic microplate which established temporary land bridges with continental masses, alternately towards the West and East during the Oligocene and lower Miocene (Roegl & Steininger, 1983). Hardly any detailed paleogeographical situation could explain to us the presence of the European cave shrimp (genus *Troglocaris*) in France, the Dinarides and below the Caucasus or of the large isopods of the genus *Sphaeromides* in France, along the Adriatic coast (in the Dinarides) and in Carpathian Bulgaria and Serbia.

(**3**) Similarly limited to their place of origin seem to be the **holodinaric taxa**. Most of them should have been inhabitants of the prekarstic continental waters of the region (Chappuis, 1926; Sket, 1986), although some authors consider them to be direct immigrants from the sea. One has to consider that the finer distribution pattern of the holodinaric cave tube worm (*Marifugia cavatica* Absolon & Hrabe, Polychaeta: Serpulidae) fits very well with that of the unambiguously continental cave salamander *Proteus anguinus* Laurenti (Amphibia: Proteidae). It is very likely that such animals inhabited the regional surface waters, probably mainly the lakes, and invaded cave waters in a number of places and during a long span of time (Sket, 1997).

(**4**) The merodinaric **distribution pattern** of subterranean taxa also seems to be determined by the distribution of surface fauna in prekarstic ages. The **NW Dinaric**, the **SE Dinaric** and the **paralittoral** regions are not contiguous karst areas, which could allow their inhabitants to master them by a subterranean spreading. The exclusion of the Kvarner (Quarnero gulf) from the paralittoral region (Sket, 1988), shows clearly that it is not defined by its actual ecological conditions; this type of distribution must have evolved prior the sinking of the gulf which was a Pleistocene event (Prelogović et al., 1975).

(**5**) The most likely to be influenced by the karst development, mainly by changes of the river systems, seem to be distribution areas and distribution patterns of some taxa in smaller **areas within the merodinaric regions**. Two formal types of distribution patterns will be discussed here: (1) the "Dinaric directed" distribution areas and (2) distribution areas along hypothesised prekarstic rivers in Slovenia.

The point in both cases is the **disagreement of species distribution ranges with recent drainages** and river flow directions, either on the surface or subterranean ones (Sket,

1970; Sket & Bole, 1982; Bole, 1985). I will not discuss here the feasibility of particular paleohydrographical hypotheses. I will only try to find (or repeat) some cases of accordance of species distribution areas with possible (and more or less probable) hydrographical situations in the past.

2 DISCUSSION - PALEOGEOGRAPHY AND SMALL-SCALE BIOGEOGRAPHICAL PATTERNS

2.1 THE CASE OF "DINARIC-DIRECTED" DISTRIBUTION AREAS

(1) Distribution ranges along the Dinaric faults may cross the actual surface and undersurface streams which mainly cross the Dinaric ridges (Sket, 1970). According to Melik (1963: 62) the previous (paleo-)drainages should have been more strongly structurally conditioned. Therefore we can suppose that the flow directions of a number of streams as well as the length axes of lakes, used to be parallel with the direction of Dinaric faulting, at least for a shorter period during the karstification of the Dinarides or prior to it. This is also a likely explanation for the above mentioned distribution patterns. Some cases of such elements will be presented:

The gastropod *Lanzaia vjetrenicae* Kuščer was found in resurgences of Popovo Polje waters in the Neretva valley, in the cave Vjetrenica in Popovo Polje, both in Hercegovina, and in springs near Podgorica in Montenegro. Its distribution area consequently belongs at least to two independent (detached) influents into the Adriatic.

The amphipod *Gammarus (Metohia) carinatus* (Absolon) inhabits the headwaters of the Trebišnjica river (between Gacko and Bileća) and the Obodska pećina at Rijeka Crnojevića in Montenegro. More in the NW, *Niphargus trullipes* Sket, a specialised and therefore rare amphipod species, has only been found in the caves Vjetrenica in Popovo Polje and Gospodska Špilja in the headwaters of the Cetina.

The isopod taxon *Monolistra (Pseudomonolistra) hercegoviniensis brevipes* Sket exhibits a more than 150 km long distribution area along the line Medak - Gračac - Knin - Cetina in Croatian Lika and Dalmacija (Dalmatia; Sket, 1965)), thus crossing a number of actually separate affluents of the Adriatic. Its relative *Monolistra (Microlistra) pretneri spinulosa* Sket is also present in two separate river systems, that of Krka and Zrmanja, as well as on the actually offshore southern tip of the Cres Island in the Kvarner (Quarnero) Gulf.

Monolistra (Typhlosphaeroma) bericum hadzii Sket and an undescribed *M. (T.) bericum* ssp. (however, their relation with the north-Italian species *M. bericum* (Fabiani) is questionable) inhabit two parallel areas crossing the Istra (Istria) Peninsula, each one including affluents to both sides of the peninsula (Sket, new data).

The case (Bole, 1985) of the gastropod species *Hadziella sketi* Bole exceeds somehow the scope of the Dinaric direction discussion. It is present underground along the Zrmanja river and the middle reaches of the Krka river in northern Dalmacija (Dalmatia). The comparatively recent (in the Pleistocene) flow changes as supposed by Fritz (1972) can hardly directly explain this distribution area. His hypothesis, however, indicates the perpetual changes of river systems in the area which can consecutively also explain the presence of this species in two major drainage systems: the same species is also present in the headwaters of Una in the Danube catchment. This is not the unique case of such a distribution type. In the actually Danubian headwaters of the Una river, the epigean gastropod species *Orientalina bosniaca* (Radoman) is present, whose provenience is also the Adriatic area; the genus is represented in the Zrmanja, Krka and Cetina catchments by another species (*O. curta germari* (Frauenfeld)). Further, such a redirection of headwaters can explain the occurrence of species of the Danube-alien amphipod genus *Echinogammarus* along catchments of the Kupa (Karaman, 1931), Una (Sket, unpublished), Vrbas (Pljakić, 1962), and Bosna (Karaman, 1934).

2.2 THE CASE OF COINCIDENCE WITH HYPOTHETICAL "PALEO-STREAMS"

(2) Better known and therefore apparently more complex is the situation in Slovenia, for which some "paleohydrographical speculations" have been done. Modern views (e.g. Šušteršič, 1996) do not always support the classical genealogical interpretation of "dry valleys" in karst; nevertheless, a certain number of paleohydrographical hypotheses is seducingly congruent with distribution patterns of some cave species.

(2a) It has been supposed (Melik, 1931, 1952) either that the today's headwaters of the Slovenian Krka catchment flew in the past towards the Ljubljanica/Pivka river or that Ljubljanica continued its flow into the actual area of these waters (Gams, 1987: 93). In both cases a connection of the upper reaches of the Krka with Ljubljanica catchment is supposed. Any of these suppositions can very easily explain the presence of at least one stygobiotic gastropod species, *Acroloxus tetensi* (Kuščer) in cave waters of both systems. Both systems are also inhabited by very close pairs of monolistrine crustaceans: *Monolistra (Typhlosphaeroma) racovitzai racovitzai* Strouhal and *M. (Microlistra) spinosissima* (Racovitza) along the underground Pivka while their vicariants *M. (T.) racovitzai karamani* Sket and *M. (M.) spinosa* (Racovitza) along the Krka.

(2b) The valley (polje) of Ribnica and Kočevje drains with a number of parallel or crossing subterranean corridors mainly perpendicularly to their own (and the Dinaric) direction towards the valley of Krka, crossing underground the polje Dobrepolje. Nevertheless, cave waters in the borders of Dobrepolje and close to Kočevje are inhabited by one monolistrine species, *Monolistra (Monolistra) caeca* Gerstaecker, while in caves and springs along the Krka only another species, *M. (T.) r. karamani* (and the very different *M. (M.) spinosa*) can be found. Biologically, the absence of *M. caeca* in parts of these streams can only be explained by interspecific competition.

In only two caves in Bela Krajina - by way of exception - similar pairs of Monolistrini co-occur. In both, *M. caeca* and *M. racovitzai conopyge* Sket, live in the same small cave stream, but they are separated in the lentic and lotic parts of it, respectively (Sket,

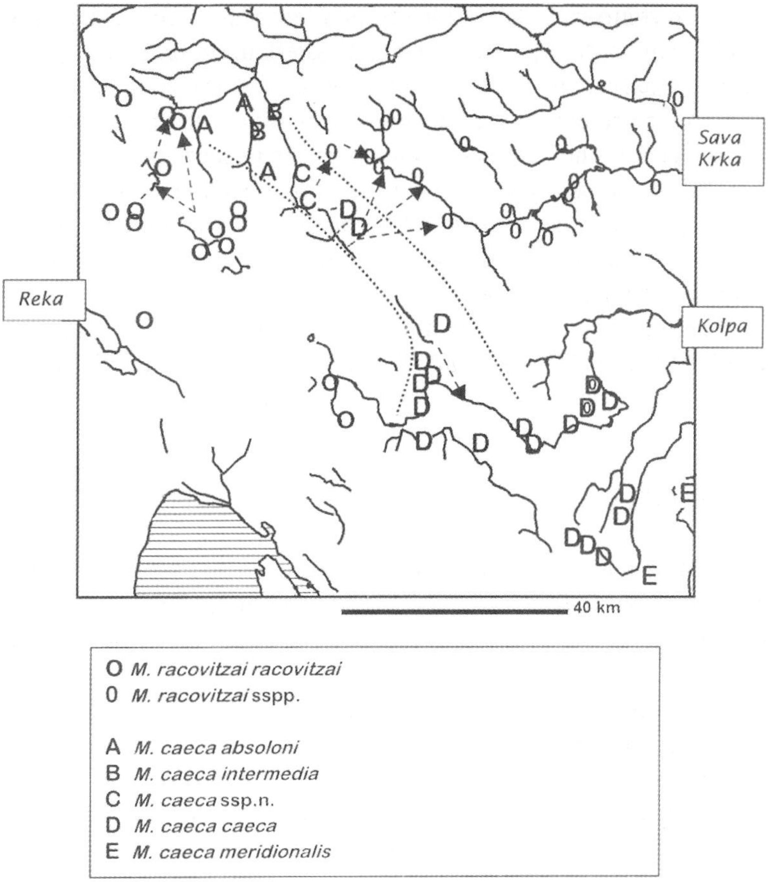

Fig. 1. Distribution of some Monolistra *species in SE Slovenia and in the adjacent area of Croatia. Dashed lines are proven flow directions underground. Dotted lines border the* Monolistra caeca *area and the hypothetical area of a paleo-drainage.*

1964). If the competition between related species is strong enough to keep these otherwise not very specialised cave species apart, we can imagine that under some circumstances it could also prevent species from colonising parts of the younger drainage systems.

The bulk of the *M. caeca* area is along the Kolpa/Kupa river and its tributaries in the Croatian Kordun. It has been speculated that before the karstification progressed, apparently in Pliocene, the waters from the Ribnica-Kočevje valley flew superficially in a SE direction towards the Kolpa (Melik, 1928: 79; Jenko, 1959). This fits very well with the idea that an epigean predecessor inhabited this part of the Kolpa catchment and colonised later its subterranean derivatives, most probably independently in some locations and through the time. Similar ecological conditions caused a parallel evolution of those separate populations and kept them similar in spite of changes.

2.3 WHAT CAN THE BIOGEOGRAPHIC PATTERNS SUGGEST TO A PALEOGEOGRAPHER?

One could expect that the upper reaches of the above mentioned past tributary of the Kolpa diverted the first. One could also expect that the populations of *M. caeca* which were first isolated from the rest of the species had the highest chance to be different. In fact, from the Kordun and Kolpa towards Videm-Dobrepolje (i.e. Podpeška jama) in the NW direction, all populations of this crustacean are morphologically nearly identical, therefore are considered as one subspecies, *M. caeca caeca*. From Podpeška jama further NW, however, very similar but nevertheless distinct races occur, namely: *M. c. intermedia* Sket, *M. c.* ssp. nova, *M. c. absoloni* Racovitza. In this order, they are more and more distant from the ancient confluence with the Kolpa river and they more and more morphologically differ from *M. c. caeca* (compare Sket, 1986). If we accept the other cases of accordance of distribution areas with hypothesised prekarstic river systems as sufficient to recognise this interrelation (which might for some still not be the case), the complex situation with the *M. caeca* subspecies may have a certain degree of a predictive value. *Mutatis mutandis* this would mean that, in this special case, this Kolpa's paleotributary had its headwaters at the southern borders of today's depression of the Ljubljansko Barje, which was supposed to have become a depression only during the Pleistocene (Gams, 1987: 92). The SE direction of outflow from these latitudes would contradict the modern geophysiographical and hydrographical setting. It is also adverse to Melik's (1928) suppositions that the actual confluents of the Ljubljanica in the Ljubljansko Barje (Iška, Želimeljščica) had the same flow direction before the karstification and that they even received a confluent from the polje Dobrepolje. On the other hand, such a biogeographically based supposition would be logically closer to Radinja's (1972) explanation of the presence of siliceous sands (quartz sands) in the western Dolenjsko region; they should have been brought by waters flowing in the opposite direction. Šifrer (1970) also supposes recurrent changes of the outflow directions in the area.

In this context, one could shed some doubts to the supposition of Melik (1952) that the prekarstic divide between the Kolpa/Kupa and Ljubljanica drainages was the same as it is now. Without any small changes or a subterranean bifurcation we could hardly explain the presence of *M. racovitzai racovitzai* at the Kolpa springs; this taxon is widely distributed in the Ljubljanica waters. In the extreme case, this could even suggest that the very headwaters of the Kolpa river were previously a part of the Ljubljanica drainage.

CONCLUSIONS

If the distribution area of a species recently bound to a subterranean habitat, terrestrial or aquatic, is in opposition with the actual drainage system area, two conditions had to coincide in its history:

(1) The population must have been isolated in a drainage system with a different

flow direction, and (2) the ecological mechanisms, most probably interspecific competition, must prevent spreading of species along the actual subterranean streams. However, we can not be certain that the faunistic situation was always preventing a species to spread; normally, species are able to change their distribution areas if this is physically possible. Therefore, the presence of a subterranean species in two actual drainages can only testify that some rearrangement of their upper parts occurred in the past.

In particularly felicitous situations, the distribution of animal taxa can suggest us the gradual changes in a drainage area; such is the case of *Monolistra caeca* subspecies in the western Dolenjsko area in Slovenia.

ACKNOWLEDGEMENT

I thank F. Šušteršič (Ljubljana) for some terminological remarks as well as for his commentary about possible flaws of paleogeographical hypotheses in karstology.

REFERENCES

Bole, J., 1985: Recentni podzemeljski polži in razvoj nekaterih porečij na dinarskem krasu.- Razprave (Dissertationes), classis IV, SAZU 24, 315-328

Chappuis, P.A., 1926: Die Tierwelt der unterirdischen Gewaesser.- Die Binnengewaesser, III, 175 pp, Stuttgart

Fritz, F., 1972: Razvitak gornjeg toka rijeke Zrmanje.- Krš Jugoslavije, 8(1), 1-16

Gams, I., 1987: Razvoj reliefa na zahodnem Dolenjskem (s posebnim ozirom na poplave).- Geografski zbornik 26(2), 64-96,

Gueorguiev, V.B., 1977: La faune troglobie terrestre de la Peninsule Balkanique. Origine, formation et zoogeographie.- Ed. Acad. bulgare Sci., 182 pp, Sofia

Jenko, F., 1959: Hidrogeologija in vodno gospodarstvo krasa.- Državna Založba Slovenije, 237 pp, Ljubljana

Karaman, S., 1931: Gammarus cari, n.sp. aus Jugoslavien.- Zoologischer Anzeiger, 94(9-10), 265-268.

Karaman, S., 1934: VI. Beitrag zur Kenntnis jugoslavischer Suesswasseramphipoden.- Zoologischer Anzeiger, 107(11-12), 325-333

Melik, A., 1929: Pliocensko porečje Ljubljanice.- Geografski vestnik, 1-4 (1928), 69-88

Melik, A., 1931: Hidrografski in morfološki razvoj na srednjem Dolenjskem.- Geografski vestnik, 7, 66-100

Melik, A., 1952: Zasnove Ljubljaničinega porečja.- Geografski zbornik, 1, 5-31

Melik, A.,1963: Slovenija. Geografski opis, I.- Slovenska matica, 617 pp, Ljubljana

Pljakić, M., 1962: Ein Beitrag zur Kenntnis der Taxonomie, Verbreitung und Migration des Gammarus pungens M. Edw.- Izdanija, Zavod za Ribarstvo NR Makedonije (Skopje), 3(2), 15-26

Prelogović, E., M. Arsovski, V. Kranjec, V. Radulović, B. Sikošek & S. Soklić, 1975: Paleogeografska evolucija teritorije Jugoslavije od tercijera do danas.- Acta seismologica jugoslavica, 2-3, 7-11

Radinja, D., 1972: Zakrasevanje v Sloveniji v luči celotnega morfogenetskega razvoja.- Geografski zbornik, 13, 197-243

Roegl, F. & F. F. Steininger, 1983: Vom Zerfall der Tethys zu Mediterran and Paratethys.- Annalen des naturhistorischen Museum Wien, 85/A, 135-163

Sket, B., 1964: Ostliche Gruppe der Monolistrini. I. Systematischer Teil.- International Journal of Speleology, 1(1-2), 163-189, tab. 22-44

Sket, B., 1965: Oestliche Gruppe der Monolistrini. II. Biologischer Teil.- International Journal of Speleology, 1(3), 249-267, tab. 60-66

Sket, B., 1970: Presenetljive novosti v jamski favni Bosanske Krajine (Uberraschende Novitaten der Hohlenfauna in der Bosanska Krajina).- Naše jame, 11, 193-100

Sket, B., 1970: Ueber Struktur und Herkunft der unterirdischen Fauna Jugoslawiens.- Biološki vestnik, 18, 69-78

Sket, B., 1986: Evaluation of some taxonomically, zoogeographically, or ecologically interesting finds in the hypogean waters of Yugoslavia (in the last decades).- Comunicacions, 9. Congreso Internacional de Espeleologia, 1, 126-128

Sket, B., 1988: Zoogeografija sladkovodnih in somornih rakov (Crustacea) v kvarnerskovelebitskem območju (Zoogeography of the freshwater and brackish Crustacea in the Kvarner-Velebit islands (NW Adriatic,Yugoslavia).- Biološki vestnik, 36(2), 63-76

Sket, B., 1994: Distribution patterns of some subterranean Crustacea in the territory of the former Yugoslavia.- Hydrobiologia, 287, 65-75

Sket, B., 1997: Distribution of Proteus (Amphibia: Urodela: Proteidae) and its possible explanation.- J. Biogeogr., 24, 263-280

Sket, B., 1999: High biodiversity in hypogean waters and its endangerment - the situation in Slovenia, Dinaric karst, and Europe.- Crustaceana, 72(8), 767-779

Sket, B. & J. Bole, 1982: Organisms as indicators of hypogean water connections (summary).- Naš krš (Sarajevo), 6(12-13), 115-117

Šifrer, M., 1970: Nekateri geomorfološki problemi Dolenjskega krasa (Quelques problemes geomorphologiques du Karst de Dolenjsko (SE Slovenie).- Naše jame, 11, 7-15

Šušteršič, F., 1996: Poljes and caves of Notranjska. - Acta carsologica, 25, 251-289

Address
Department of Biology, Biotechnical Faculty, University of Ljubljana
p.p. 2995, 1101 Ljubljana, Slovenia
E-mail: B.Sket@Uni-Lj.si

KARST GEOMORPHOLOGY

Evolution of Karst: From Prekarst to Cessation, 235-241, Ljubljana-Postojna 2002

THE ROLE OF VALLEY SYSTEMS IN THE EVOLUTION OF TROPICAL KARSTLANDS

MICHAEL DAY

Abstract
There are compelling a priori *and* a posteriori *reasons to regard fluvial valley systems as integral functional components in the evolution of tropical karstlands. Beyond consideration of valley systems initiated by allogenic surface drainage into karstlands or superimposed from overlying non carbonate strata, there is a rigorous theoretical model, elucidated by Smith (1975) but not widely cited, that demonstrates how autogenic surface drainage, which may well develop initially in karst landscapes, becomes increasingly subterranean as a consequence of increasing secondary permeability. There are also numerous studies, including detailed field investigations, which reveal the continuing existence or inheritance of such valley systems in existing tropical karstlands.*
Valley systems remain prominent where karstification is inhibited by lithological or structural factors and where rainfall is seasonal and intense. Even where valleys have been dismembered or destroyed by subsequent karstification they play a continuing role in influencing the distribution of closed depressions, corridors, saddles and residual hills.
Key words: *valleys, tropical karstlands, evolution.*

INTRODUCTION

Karstlands in the tropics cover over a million square kilometers, including 750,000km^2 in the humid tropics. Major tropical karstlands include those in southern China, Southeast Asia, northern Australia, the Middle East, South America, Central America and the Caribbean (Sweeting, 1972; Ford & Williams, 1989; Day, 2000).

Tropical karstlands are developed in carbonate rocks that are highly variable, and range from Holocene to Paleozoic in age (0-570m years BP). Their dissolution has produced a wide range of karst landscapes, including dry valley networks, dolines (sinkholes), polygonal karst depressions (cockpits), residual hills (cones and towers), and extensive cave systems. Tropical karstlands have been influenced markedly by a wide array of tectonic, eustatic and climatic changes (Day, 2000).

THEORETICAL MODEL

There have been a number of theoretical considerations of the role of valley systems in karst landscapes. Following the ideas of Cvijic (1893), Penck (1900) considered that a fluvial phase generally preceded karstification, a view that was incorporated into the general model of karst evolution developed by Grund (1914).

The most explicit general model of surface valley development and subsequent abandonment is that provided by Smith (1975). In this model, which regards valleys as an essential element of karst landscape, initial drainage on a limestone surface lacking high primary permeability commences in a similar manner to that on non-limestone strata, with fundamentally similar integrated drainage nets and drainage basin morphologies. Partial or complete abandonment of the surface drainage system, at which time the valleys become dry or underdrained, occurs subsequently when, as a result of epikarstic and deeper dissolution, secondary permeability develops to the threshold at which potential surface drainage is "pirated" underground. White (1988, 11) expresses it thus: "The transition from a fluvial valley to a karst valley takes place as the valley becomes underdrained because both trunk and tributaries lose their flow to the developing underground drainage system."

Smith explicitly considers this model in the context of tropical cockpit karst, which "...is invariably developed on massive limestone with low primary permeability but nevertheless displays no evidence of an integrated surface network of streams." (Smith, 1975, 143). This may be because "...enclosed depression drainage can extend to a situation where no signs of an original integrated valley network remain." (ibid, 143). Likewise, White (1988, 13) acknowledges that "If the soluble rocks are thick and their areal extent large, all traces of valley morphology could disappear, to be replaced with an undulating surface of sinkholes."

A similar sequence may pertain where allogenic discharge into a karst area becomes increasingly diverted underground through time. Ford & Williams (1989, 426) express this as follows: "As hydraulic gradient steepens and the average flows of incoming allogenic streams reduce, sink points become more localized and morphologically more distinct."

A not dissimilar situation pertains where inheritance exerts a major influence on karstic evolution following uplift of a previously karstified surface (Ford & Williams, 1989). Here "...inherited topography will guide runoff underground and hence guide solution in the epikarst. Residual hills become incorporated into the topographic divides of the emerging, rejuvenated karst." (Ford & Williams, 1989, 458). This pattern of development chartacterises the margins of the Guizhou Plateau karst, in China (Smart et al. 1986).

In explaining non-random dispersion patterns of enclosed depressions Williams (1972a) invoked the role of topographic slope, regional dip and fissure patterns that orient corrosion by directing runoff and infiltration. Moreover, it is evident from morphometric studies that "...karstification does not disorganize the stream pattern as has commonly been assumed. It reorganizes it." (Ford & Williams, 1989, 423).

FIELD AND OTHER EVIDENCE

Clearly there are tropical karstlands in which pre-existing drainage patterns have been superimposed from overlying impermeable covers onto underlying carbonate rocks. This is almost certainly the case in Papua New Guinea (Williams, 1972) and it may also have occurred elsewhere, for example in Belize and Guatemala (Miller, 1987), and in Puerto Rico (Monroe, 1974, 1976, 1979).

Lehmann (1936) postulated that a fluvial phase had preceded the development of kegelkarst in the Gunung Sewu of Java, although there it transpires that the valley system there developed as consequent drainage on an uplifted erosion surface (Ford & Williams, 1989). Lehman considered the conspicuous orientations of depressions and residual hills, the *gerichteter* karst in the Gunung Sewu, to have developed from a series of valleys, but he also stressed the importance of structural controls in controlling these orientations. Quinif & Dupois (1985) also stressed the influence of this valley network on the evolution of the Gunung Sewu.

There are numerous tropical karstlands in which valley systems dominate the landscape, with dolines being of secondary importance. One well-documented case is in Barbados (Fermor, 1972; Day, 1983), where there are extensive and imposing valley systems developed in a pinnate pattern on a series of raised reef terraces. Fermor (1972) attributed these valley systems to development under previously wetter climates, but subsequent karstification has played an equally, if not more significant role, as valleys and dolines are, in a sense, competitive (Day, 1983). Similar valley systems are developed in Guadeloupe (Lasserre, 1954, Blume, 1974; Day 1978).

Another example is in northern Jamaica, where sub-parallel limestone valley systems developed primarily on the Montpelier Formation characterize a 200km^2 area between Montego Bay and Oracabessa (Day, 1985). Some of these valleys exhibit spring fed perennial flow, but in most the flow is ephemeral. Although still essentially intact, portions of some valleys are beginning to be dismembered by the development of karstic depressions (Day, 1978).

With respect to Jamaica, there has long been discussion about the strength of evidence for dendritic drainage systems in the karst of areas such as the Cockpit Country (Sweeting, 1958; Versey, 1959, 1972; Aub, 1969a,b; Smith, 1975; Day, 1978).

Here, subsequent karstification has been extreme, but clearly there are still the vestiges of valley systems, particularly in peripheral zones, and where "...extensive areas...possess elongate depressions which appear en masse, as sinuous, steep-sided corridors winding between residual hills." (Day, 178, 154). Depressions along the Cockpit Country margins particularly are notably elongated, contain extensive fluvial sediments, and flood regularly. Elongated, compound depressions, locally known as glades, are common and, although it is not evident from a distance, virtually every cockpit depression has at least one associated corridor - a relatively low elevation entrance from an adjacent depression - and strings of depressions at increasing elevation are encountered as one penetrates into the Cockpit Country from its edges. These corridors are important routeways within the landscape, and their persistence and integration hints at a fluvial inheritance. Moreover, the existence of active drainage systems within cockpits, not only where there is a superficial sediment cover, indicates that surface drainage still occurs even after extreme karstification.

Monroe (1974) provided a striking example of valley systems in the karstlands of northern Puerto Rico. Here, dendritic valley systems developed on the Lares limestone west of Ciales probably were superimposed from an overlying Tertiary clastic cover. Depressions have since developed in the valleys and most of the drainage is now underground. Similar systems occur elsewhere in northern Puerto Rico (Monroe, 1976, 1979).

Miller (1987) has provided clear evidence of the inheritance of fluvial paleodrainage patterns in the karstlands of Belize and Guatemala, and has demonstrated how their legacy is imprinted on the polygonal karst that has developed subsequently. Much of the karst landscape contains "...through-flowing rivers, dry and hanging valleys, and topographically-descending doline corridors, all prima-facie evidence for fluvio-karst development." (Miller, 1987, 53). Moreover, morphometric analysis of cockpit karst in the area reveals a non-random pattern associated with photo-lineations, and cockpit soils show a clear affinity with soils developed on non-carbonate rocks. "Fully-integrated streams from non-carbonate highlands appear to have been the primary factor in developing the surface karst of the area; disaggregation of a fluvio-karst surface has produced classic cockpit karst..." (Miller, 1987, 53).

In the same area there is a particularly well-developed system of dry valleys tributary to valleys with intermittent flow just to the north of Flores, in the Peten. Here a series of intact valley systems with intermittent flow become dismembered headward by valley floor depressions, initially giving way to interrupted dry valleys with ephemeral flow, and eventually disintegrating entirely into polygonal cockpit karst (Day, 1978).

A very similar situation pertains throughout much of Belize, where there is clear evidence of dismembered valley systems throughout the karst, for example in the Yalbac Hills of the Cayo District, in the Hummingbird and Sibun-Manatee areas of the Northern Boundary Fault karst and in the northern part of the Vaca Plateau (Day, 1986; Miller, 1986; Reeder et al, 1996)

In the Kimberley District of Western Australia there exist a wide array of valley systems to which dolines and other characteristic karst landforms are subsidiary (Jennings & Sweeting, 1963; Goudie et al., 1990). Seven main types of valley have been identified by Goudie et al (1990): through-cutting allogenic river valleys such as Windjana Gorge; major flank embayments; pediment passes such as Wombarella Gap; pocket valleys such as Barnet Gorge; broad amphitheatres fronted by narrow reef edge gaps; valleys in the interior of the reef with internal drainage; and valleys paralleling the ancient reef edge behind ramparts such as the Chedda blind valley.

DISCUSSION AND CONCLUSION

There is no fundamental reason why surface fluvial valley systems should not be regarded as an integral evolutionary component of tropical, and indeed other karst landscapes, particularly where primary permeability is low, where drainage systems are superimposed from overlying strata, or where allogenic drainage intrudes upon the carbonate area. Moreover, there exists a clearly elucidated theoretical model of such evolution in which surface drainage and valley systems become subsumed by underground drainage and enclosed depressions as secondary permeability increases through time, perhaps ultimately becoming indistinguishable, although not inconsequential.

Individual field and other studies reveal a wide spectrum of instances in which valley systems have left a clear legacy in tropical karstlands. In some areas valley systems remain essentially intact; in others they have undergone varying degrees of decay, ranging almost to destruction, but their imprint is in many cases still decipherable in the palimpsest that is the average tropical karst landscape. Clearly, in many tropical karstlands surface fluvial processes feature prominently in the past, the present and the future of landscape development.

To date, the facility with which valley legacies in tropical karstlands may be revealed has been constrained by the limitations of investigative techniques. Morphometric analysis has been of considerable utility, and is clear that additional light may be shed on the matter by current studies, such as that ongoing in the Jamaican Cockpit Country (Chenoweth & Day, 2001) involving the use of digital elevation models to delineate the landscape in a geographic information system (GIS).

REFERENCES

Aub, C.F.T., 1969a: The nature of cockpits and other depressions in the karst of Jamaica. Proceedings, 5th International Congress of Speleology, Paper M15.

Aub, C.F.T., 1969b: Some observations of the karst morphology of Jamaica. Proceedings, 5th International Congress of Speleology, Paper M16.

Blume, H., 1974: The Caribbean Islands. - London: Longman.

Chenoweth, M.S. & M.J. Day, 2001: Developing a GIS for the Jamaican Cockpit Country. In: Geotechnical and Environmental Applications of Karst Geology and Hydrology, ed. B.F. Beck & J.G. Herring.- Lisse: Swets & Zeitlinger.

Cvijic, J., 1893: Das Karstphaenomen. Versuch einer morphologischen Monographie.- Geographische Abhandlungen Wien, 5, 3, 218-329.

Day, M.J., 1978: The morphology of tropical humid karst with particular reference to the Caribbean and Central America.- DPhil Thesis, University of Oxford.

Day, M.J., 1983: Doline morphology and development in Barbados.- Annals of the Association of American Geographers, 73, 2, 206-219.

Day, M.J., 1985: Limestone valley systems in north central Jamaica.- Caribbean Geography, 2, 1, 16-33.

Day, M.J., 1996: Conservation of karst in Belize.- Journal of Cave and Karst Studies, 58, 2, 139-144.
Day, M.J., 2000: Tropical Karst.- In: The Oxford Companion to the Earth, ed. P.L. Hancock & B.J. Skinner. Oxford: Oxford University Press: 1057-1058.
Fermor, J., 1972: The dry valleys of Barbados: A critical review of their pattern and origin.- Transactions of the Institute of British Geographers, 57, 153-165.
Ford, D.C. & P.W. Williams, 1989: Karst Geomorpohology and Hydrology.- London: Unwin Hyman.
Gillieson, D., 1996: Caves: Processes, Development, Management.- Cambridge MA: Blackwell.
Goudie, A.S., Viles, H., Allison, R., Day, M.J., Livingstone, I. & P.A. Bull, 1990: The geomorphology of the Napier Range, Western Australia.- Transactions of the Institute of British Geographers, 15, 308-322.
Grund, A., 1914: The Geographical Cycle in the Karst. Reprinted in translation in: Karst Geomorphology, ed. M.M. Sweeting. Stroudsburg: Hutchinson Ross, 54-59.
Jennings, J.N. & Sweeting, M.M., 1963: The limestone ranges of the Fitzroy Basin, Western Australia: a tropical semi-arid karst.- Bonner Geographische Abhandlungen 32, 1-60.
Lehmann, H., 1936: Morphologische studien auf Java.- Geographische Abhandlungen III, Stuttgart.
Lasserre, G., 1954: Notes sur le karst de Guadeloupe.- Erdkunde, 8, 115-118.
Miller, T.E., 1987: Fluvial and collapse influences on cockpit karst of Belize and eastern Guatemala.- In: Karst Hydrogeology: Engineering and Environmental Applications, ed. B.F. Beck. Rotterdam: AA Balkema: 53-63.
Miller, T.E., 1996: Geologic and hydrologic controls on karst and cave development in Belize.- Journal of Cave and Karst Studies, 58, 2, 100-120.
Monroe, W.H., 1974: Dendritic dry valleys in the cone karst of Puerto Rico.- U.S. Geological Survey Journal of Research, 2, 2, 159-163.
Monroe, W.H., 1976: The karst landforms of Puerto Rico.- US Geological Survey Professional Paper 899.
Monroe, W.H., 1979: Caves and canyons in the karst belt of northern Puerto Rico.- Zeitschrift fur Geomorphologie, Supplementbande 32, 21-24.
Penck, A., 1900: Geomorphologische Studien aus der Hercegovina.- Zeitschrift Deutsche Osterreich Alpenver, 31, 25-41.
Quinif, Y. & C. Dupuis, 1985: Un karst en zone intertropicale: Le Gunung Sewu a Java: Aspects morphologiques et concepts evolutifs.- Revue de Geomorphologie Dynamique, 34, 1, 1-16.
Reeder, P.P., Brinkman, R. and Alt, E., 1996: Karstification of the northern Vaca Plateau, Belize.- Journal of Cave and Karst Studies, 58, 2, 121-130.
Smart, P.L., Waltham, A.C., Yang, M. & Y. Zhang, 1986: Karst geomorphology of western Guizhou, China.- Transactions of the British Cave Research Asociation 13, 3, 89-103.
Smith, D.I., 1975: The problem of limestone dry valleys – implications of recent work in limestone hydrology. – In: Processes in Physical and Human Geography, ed. R.F.Peel, M. Chisholom & P. Haggett.- London: Heinemann, 130-147.

Sweeting, M.M., 1958: The karstlands of Jamaica. Geographical Journal, 124, 2, 184-199.

Sweeting, M.M., 1972: Karst Landforms.- London: Macmillan.

Versey, H.R., 1959: The hydrological character of the White Limestone formation of Jamaica. Transactions of the 2nd Caribbean Geological Congress, Kingston: 59-68.

Versey, H.R., 1972: Karst of Jamaica.- In: Karst: Important Karst Regions of the Northern Hemisphere, ed. M. Herak & V.T. Stringfield.- Amsterdam: Elsevier: 445-466.

White, W.B., 1988: Geomorphology and Hydrology of Karst Terrains.- New York: Oxford University Press.

Williams, P.W., 1972: Morphometric analysis of polygonal karst in New Guinea.- Bulletin of the Geological Society of America, 83, 761-796.

Address
Department of Geography, University of Wisconsin-Milwaukee, P.O. Box 413
Milwaukee, Wisconsin, USA
E-mail: mickday@uwm.edu

ıops and
ess world-
rt advice.

ent
ilize
evaluate
l mutual

Evolution of Karst: From Prekarst to Cessation, 243-258, Ljubljana-Postojna 2002

KARST LANDSCAPE EVOLUTION

GEORG KUFMANN

Abstract
We present results of a numerical study of karst denudation on limestone plateaux. The landscape evolution model used incorporates not only long-range fluvial processes and short-range hill-slope processes, but also large-scale chemical dissolution of limestone surfaces. The relative efficiencies of fluvial and chemical processes are of equal importance to the landscape evolution of a plateau dropping to sea level along an escarpment. While fluvial processes have an impact confined to river channels, the karst denudation process is more uniform, removing material also from the plateau surface. The combined effect of both processes results in a landscape evolution almost twice as effective as the purely erosional evolution of an insoluble landscape.
Keywords: *Landscape evolution, dissolution kinetics, denudation, karst.*

INTRODUCTION

Landscape evolution is governed by a balance of forces; on the one hand, vertical tectonic movements resulting from the interaction between lithospheric plates, and on the other, erosion and deposition controlled by a range of processes whose relative importance depend on local climatic conditions, vegetation, and rock type. During the last decade, numerical models simulating landscape evolution from a large-scale, long-term perspective have become increasingly sophisticated. Most surface process models incorporate the effects of short-range processes such as local hillslope diffusion and long-range processes such as fluvial transport (Willgoose et al. 1991, Beaumont et al. 1992, Chase 1992, Howard et al. 1994, Tucker et al. 1994, Kooi et al. 1994, Braun et al. 1997), and they have been applied to the evolution of rifted margins, regions of continental convergence and mountain building. While these models describe landscape evolution satisfactorily in temperate climates and insoluble geological settings, other surface processes of regional importance have so far been largely neglected. For example, glacial erosion has been regarded as an important process in mid- to high-latitude active orogenic regions, which have experienced repeated large-scale glaciations during the last two million years. Recently, Braun et al. (1999) have incorporated a first-order parameterization of ice-bedrock interaction into a large-scale fluvial erosion model. They showed how the interplay between the two processes leads to enhanced rates of surface erosion in mountaineous areas affected by periodic climatic fluctuations.

In the present paper, another process governing landscape evolution in soluble rocks is considered. As surface runoff enriched in carbon dioxide becomes weakly agressive and is able to remove calcite by chemical dissolution, typical karst landscapes evolve, forming steep-walled valleys, enclosed depressions, and, finally, subsurface drainage through caves (e.g. Jennings 1985). While the evolution of subsurface drainage in a karst landscape had been successfully modeled in the past (e.g. Groves et al. 1994, Howard et al. 1995, Clemens et al. 1997, Siemers et al. 1998, Kaufmann et al. 1999, Kaufmann et al. 2000), no attempt has been made so far to parameterize chemical dissolution on the surface of a karst landscape, which is termed karst denudation (e.g. Jennings 1985). These two processes, subsurface drainage through evolving cave systems and surficial karst denudation, are coupled in that the surface discharge on a mature karst landscape quickly disappears underground and drainage is dominated by subsurface flow. As a consequence, valleys become dry, streams disappear at sinks and closed depressions, and surface processes driven by surface flow become less efficient. Herein, attention is focussed on the karst denudation process, while the effect of subsurface drainage and chemical enlargement of fractures within the rock is disregarded. Such a simplified model can thus be regarded as a first step in quantifying the evolution of a soluble landscape.

A karst landscape is often characterized by steep and prominent gorges, which separate limestone plateaux. Compared to insoluble landscapes, gorges occur more frequently and are more rugged. Examples include the Vicos Gorge in Greece, the Verdon Gorge in southern France, the Strickland Gorge in New Guinea, which are very deep and steep and all formed in relatively young mountain ranges, but also the Geikie, Windjana, and Galeru Gorges in Western Australia and the Tarn, Lot, and Dourbie Gorges in the Grandes Causses of southern France, which are prominent features in lower relief landscapes. In all cases, the plateaux dissected by these steep-walled gorges are denudated more evenly.

Measurements of long-term denudation rates on soluble landscapes are often based on the height of pedestals above the surrounding limestone surface. These pedestals are remnants of an older surface, protected by erratic boulders from the last glaciation. It is commonly assumed that the height of the pedestals is a measure of surface lowering since the retreat of the ice at the end of the last glaciation. Jennings (1985) has reviewed literature data on pedestals, and reports denudation rates between 15 and 40 mm/kyr. Short-term denudation rates can be measured by micro-erosion meters (Trudgill et al. 1981). Forti (1984) reports denudation rates from the Triestine karst in Italy, ranging from 20 mm/kyr in regions of relatively low (1442 mm/yr) precipitation, to 30 mm/kyr near Mount Canin characterized by a much higher (2800 mm/yr) precipitation rate. Additional short-term denudation rates reported by Jennings (1985) are around 5-17 mm/kyr on bare rock surfaces.

In the present paper, a simple parameterization of solutional processes is developed and incorporated into an existing surface process model (CASCADE). A series of numerical experiments is then performed in which an originally steep escarpment flanking a flat, high-elevation plateau is allowed to evolve through time. In these experiments, the parameters controlling the efficiency of each process (fluvial incision, hillslope diffusion, and chemical dissolution) are varied to investigate their relative influence on the form of the landscape and the rate at which it evolves.

Table 1: *Reference model parameters.*

Parameter	Decription	Unit	Value
v_i	Net precipitation	[mm yr^{-1}]	400
κ_D	Diffusion constant	[m^2 yr^{-1}]	0.2
$\kappa_R v_i$	Erosion constant	[m yr^{-1}]	0.01
L_S	Alluvium length scale	[km]	10
L_B	Bedrock length scale	[km]	100
ρ	Calcite density	[kg m^{-3}]	2700
T_C	Temperature	[$^{\circ}$C]	10
p_{CO_2}	CO_2 pressure	[atm]	$10^{-3.5}/10^{-2.5}$
$\kappa_C v_i$	Dissolution constant	[m yr^{-1}]	0.007/0.014

GEOMORPHIC MODEL

Large-scale landscape evolution on tectonic timescales is controlled by a number of processes. *Short-range* hillslope processes, such as weathering, slope wash, mass wasting, and soil creep, redistribute mass over short distances, while *long-range* flow processes, such as fluvial erosion and sedimentation, and karst denudation, control landscape evolution over long distances. Other processes such as glacial erosion and landsliding are not discussed in the present formulation. The mathematical approach for both short- and long-range processes used in model simulations is outlined below.

HILLSLOPE PROCESSES

Hillslope processes are modelled by means of linear downslope diffusion (e.g. Kooi et al. 1994, Braun et al. 1997),

$$\left(\frac{dh_i}{dt}\right)_{diffusion} = \kappa_D \nabla^2 h_i \qquad (1)$$

which assumes that the rate of change of topography h_i at node i is proportional to the second spatial derivative of h_i, κ_D is assumed constant and is termed diffusivity. The topography h_i is the sum of bedrock height and sediment cover. Following Beaumont et al. (1992), the diffusivity can be expressed as $\kappa_D=\boldsymbol{u}_D\boldsymbol{h}_D$, where $\boldsymbol{h}_D$ is the thickness of a regolith layer and u_D is the transport velocity of the eroded material. This implies that κ_D is a function of both the lithology (small κ_D for resistant bedrock, larger κ_D for detachable sediments) and climate (increased weathering increases the thickness of the regolith layer). Thus, short-range processes are important on steep landscapes with strong curvature; they reduce the high-frequency content of the topography spectrum. As a consequence, topography is smoothed, slopes decline, drainage divides are eroded and move towards the area of lower slope gradients (Kooi et al. 1994).

FLUVIAL PROCESSES

Erosion and deposition of sediments and bedrock is modeled as a channel-flow process. The discharge q_i (in m^3 s^{-1}) at node $\boldsymbol{i}$ is defined as the sum of upstream discharge q_i^u and local discharge $q_i^l = v_i A_i$,

$$q_i^u = q_i^u + v_i A_i, \tag{2}$$

where $v_i = p_i - e_i$ is the net precipitation (precipitation p_i minus evapotranspiration e_i, in m s^{-1}), A_i is the surface area around node $\boldsymbol{i}$, and q_i^u is the amount of surface runoff already collected in the upstream catchment of node $\boldsymbol{i}$. The maximum carrying capacity of the channel between node $\boldsymbol{i}$ and lower neighbour $\boldsymbol{j}$ is given as (e.g. Beaumont et al. 1992, Kooi et al. 1994)

$$Q_i^e = \kappa_R s_i q_i, \tag{3}$$

where κ_R is a dimensionless river erosion constant. Note that the maximum carrying capacity (in m^3 s^{-1}) depends both on local slope s_i and discharge q_i, but a river must not necessarily be at maximum carrying capacity. Sediment flux Q (including suspended sediment and bedload) is calculated as the cumulative sum of sediment transported from the upstream nodes. Q_i is compared to the maximum carrying capacity, Q_i^e. In cases where $Q_i \geq Q_i^e$, the river deposits sediments; in cases where $Q_i \leq Q_i^e$, the river incises. The *fluvial erosion rate* (in m s^{-1}) is given by

$$\begin{aligned} \left(\frac{dh_i}{dt}\right)_{fluvial} &= \frac{Q_i - Q_i^e}{A_i}, Q_i \geq Q_i^e, \\ \left(\frac{dh_i}{dt}\right)_{fluvial} &= -\frac{Q_i^e}{w_i L_e}, Q_i < Q_i^e. \end{aligned} \tag{4}$$

In (4), L_e is a characteristic length scale for erosion, which is defined differently for erosion in alluvials ($L_e = L_s$) or in bedrock ($L_e = L_b$), $w_i = w_r \sqrt{q_i}$ is the channel width, with $w_r = 0.1$ (in $\sqrt{ms^{-1}}$), and l_i as the channel length. For $L_e << l_i$, material is easily eroded, as it is highly detachable. In this situation, the downstream graded river section of the river rapidly propagates upstream towards the headwater of the river, and the ungraded river section rapidly steepens. River profiles are characterized by a short steep upper section and a long low-gradient downstream section. In contrast, $L_e >> l_i$ characterizes more resistant bedrock and longer erosion timescales. In these situations, grading is inefficient and river profiles are characterized by a more uniform gradient.

In summary, long-range fluvial transport processes result in landscapes in which drainage divides are not eroded and remain stationary, while river profiles steepen in the upstream part of the ungraded section, and slope gradients decline in the downstream graded section.

Table 2: *Karst denudation parameters.*

Parameter	Description	Unit	Value
T	Absolute temperature	[°K]	$T_C + 273.16$
I	Ion activity	[-]	0.1
A	Debye-Hückel coefficient	[-]	$0.4883 + 8.074x10^{-4} T_C$
B	Debye-Hückel coefficient	[-]	$0.3241 + 1.600x10^{-4} T_C$
$\log \gamma_{Ca}$	Activity coefficient	[-]	$\frac{-4A\sqrt{I}}{1 + 5.0x10^{-8} B\sqrt{I}}$
$\log \gamma_{HCO_3}$	Activity coefficient	[-]	$\frac{-1A\sqrt{I}}{1 + 5.4x10^{-8} B\sqrt{I}}$
K_1	Mass-balance coefficient	[mol l^{-1}]	$-356.3094 - 0.06091964T + 21834.37/T + 126.8339\log T - 1684915/T^2$
K_2	Mass-balance coefficient	[mol l^{-1}]	$-107.8871 - 0.03252849T + 5151.79/T + 38.92561\log T - 563713.9/T^2$
K_C	Mass-balance coefficient	[mol^2 l^{-2}]	$-171.9065 - 0.077993T + 2839.319/T + 71.595\log T$
K_H	Mass-balance coefficient	[mol l^{-1} atm^{-1}]	$108.3865 + 0.01985076T - 6919.53/T - 40.45154\log T + 669365/T^2$

CHEMICAL PROCESSES

On soluble landscapes such as limestone plateaux, the landscape is also altered by chemical dissolution, as surface water enriched in carbon dioxide is weakly aggressive and is able to dissolve the limestone surface. The *denudation rate* (in m s^{-1}) can be defined as (e.g. Dreybrodt1988)

$$\left(\frac{dh_i}{dt}\right)_{chemical} = 10^{-3} \kappa_C \frac{q_i}{A_i}, \tag{5}$$

where κ_C is a dimensionless dissolution constant given by

$$\kappa_C = 40x10^3 \frac{[Ca^{2+}]_{eq}}{\rho}. \tag{6}$$

Here, ρ is the density of calcite (in kg m^{-3}), and $[Ca^{2+}]_{eq}$ the equilibrium concentration of calcium (in mol l^{-1}), given as (Dreybrodt, 1988, pp. 27.

$$[Ca^{2+}]_{eq} = \left(p_{CO_2} \frac{K_1 K_C K_H}{4K_2 \gamma_{Ca} \gamma_{HCO_3}^2} \right)^{1/3} \tag{7}$$

The coefficients K_1, K_2, K_C and K_H are experimentally derived mass balance coefficients (e.g. Plummer et al. 1982), which depend on temperature (Table 2). The dimensionless ion activities of calcium and bicarbonate, γ_{Ca} and γ_{HCO3}, can be derived from the extended Debye-Hückel equation (e.g. Truesdell et al. 1974, Robinson et al. 1955). The carbon dioxide pressure P_{CO2} (in atm) may vary over several orders of magnitude in nature, from $10^{-3.5}$ atm over bare rock, $10^{-2.5}$ atm in temperate climate soils, to $10^{-1.5}$ atm in tropical soils (e.g. White, 1984). Hence, κ_C depends on climate (temperature), and strongly on lithology (CO_2-pressure in atmosphere and soil).

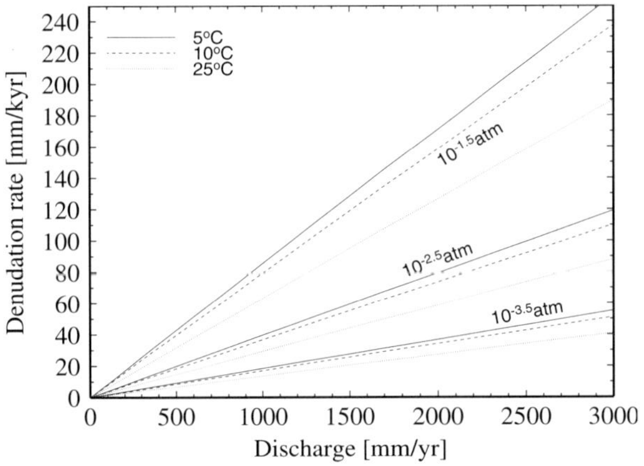

Fig 1. Denudation rate as a function of discharge for different partial carbon dioxide pressures (in atm) and water temperatures (in °C).

Note that (5) depends on discharge only. The factor 40 is necessary to transform $[Ca^{2+}]_{eq}$ from mol l^{-1} to kg m^{-3}. In Fig. 1, denudation rates as a function of discharge are shown for three different temperatures and carbon dioxide pressures. It is observed that the carbon dioxide pressure is the dominant factor controlling denudation, while changes in temperature are less important.

RESULTS

All numerical experiments start with identical initial topographies. The model domain is a rectangular area of 100-km side length, discretized into an irregular grid of 2500 nodal points, with an average nodal spacing of 2 km. An initial topography is chosen resembling a high plateau with an average height of 1000 m, and dropping to sea level (0 m) along its southern boundary over a distance of 10 km. This drop in topography simulates an escarpment created by a recent continental rifting event. The plateau itself rises slightly towards the northern boundary to ensure that initial drainage is towards the south and all surface runoff drains through the escarpment. Both northern and southern boundaries have fixed elevation, but sediment is allowed to exit across these boundaries.

REFERENCE EXPERIMENTS

Two reference runs based on fluvial erosion and diffusion alone where initiated to establish reference landforms to which soluble landscapes can be compared. Both the modelled topography after 1 Myr of evolution and a characteristic example of a river profile through time were examined in order to better define differences in morphology between the evolving landscapes. Model parameters are listed in Table 1 for reference run 1 shown in Fig. 2. To characterize each experiment, following Kooi et al. (1994), the ratio of diffusive to fluvial efficiency is given as

$$R_1 = \frac{\kappa_D}{\kappa_R v_i}. \qquad (8)$$

For run 1, R_1 = 20 m; this low value of R_1 indicates that long-range fluvial processes dominate the landscape evolution, which can be seen in the modeled topography after 1 Myr (Fig. 2a), dominated by eight steep rivers draining the plateau. All rivers follow fairly linear courses, and the valleys are characterized by steep sidewalls and are relatively narrow. The initial escarpment is left unchanged except where it has been incised by the rivers. A typical river profile is shown in Fig. 2b and is characterized by a convex shape near the escarpment edge and a relatively linear, less steep section near the base. This indicates that diffusive processes control the evolution in the ungraded river section. Fluvial erosion is responsible for the efficient removal of sediments, and the resulting graded river section is less steep and more linear. The escarpment retreats fast along the main rivers, but the headwaters of the rivers on the plateau remain at a constant height.

Results of the reference run 2 are shown in Fig. 3. Here, the diffusion constant is increased by a factor of 100 to $\kappa_D = 20$ m^2 yr^{-1} to simulate a wetter climate. With a diffusive to fluvial efficiency ratio of R_1=2000 m, diffusion is much more efficient in this run. As a consequence, the simulated topography is much smoother after 1 Myr. The short-range diffusional processes have filtered out the high-frequency components of the topography, especially across the escarpment. Rivers flow in wide valleys with gentle sidewalls. The ungraded river section extends much further downstream, as can be seen in the typical river profiles redrawn (Fig. 3b). The convex shape of the ungraded river section extents halfway down the escarpment, and the shorter graded river section is characterized by a steep gradient. Escarpment retreat is less effective, when compared to reference run 1.

Notably, the river erosion on the plateau itself is not very effective for both reference runs, as the erosion rate (4) depends on the product of channel slope and discharge. Hence, the lack of relief on the top of the plateau inhibits erosion.

KARST DENUDATION EXPERIMENTS

Next, the additional effect on landscape evolution introduced by chemical dissolution of limestone is examined. According to (5), removal of material by chemical dissolution only depends on discharge, not on slope gradient (as for fluvial erosion), nor on

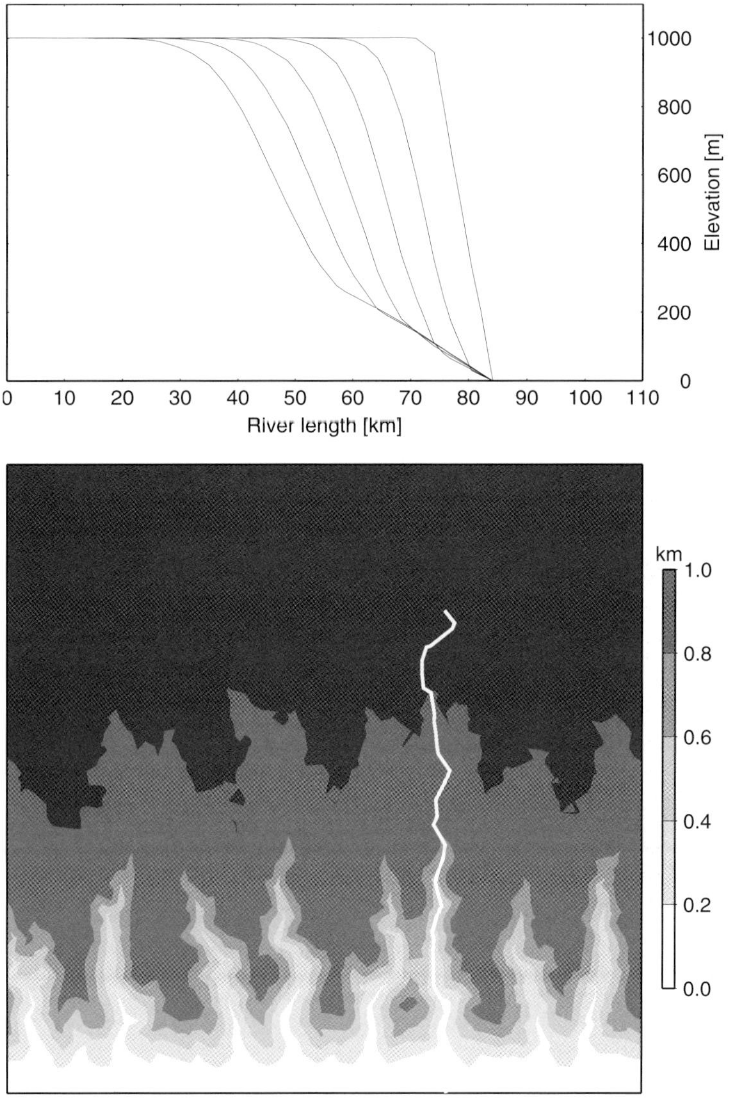

Fig 2. Modeled topography after 1 Myr. The evolution is based of fluvial erosion and diffusion, parameters are given in table 1. The thick line on top of the topography represents the course of the river, whose profile is shown in the top panel as a function of time, for subsequent time steps 0.2, 0.4, 0.6, 0.8, and 1 Ma.

curvature (as for hillslope processes). Therefore, karst denudation is also an efficient process on the gently sloping plateau area, where surface runoff increases in downstream direction to the south, and along the base of the escarpment. However, drainage divides cannot be eroded away by fluvial processes, or any process that is dependent on discharge. As a consequence, a different landform evolution is expected on a soluble landscape. A second ratio is introduced, relating diffusive efficiency to the sum of fluvial and chemical efficiency,

$$R_2 = \frac{\kappa_D}{(\kappa_R + \kappa_C)\nu_i}. \tag{9}$$

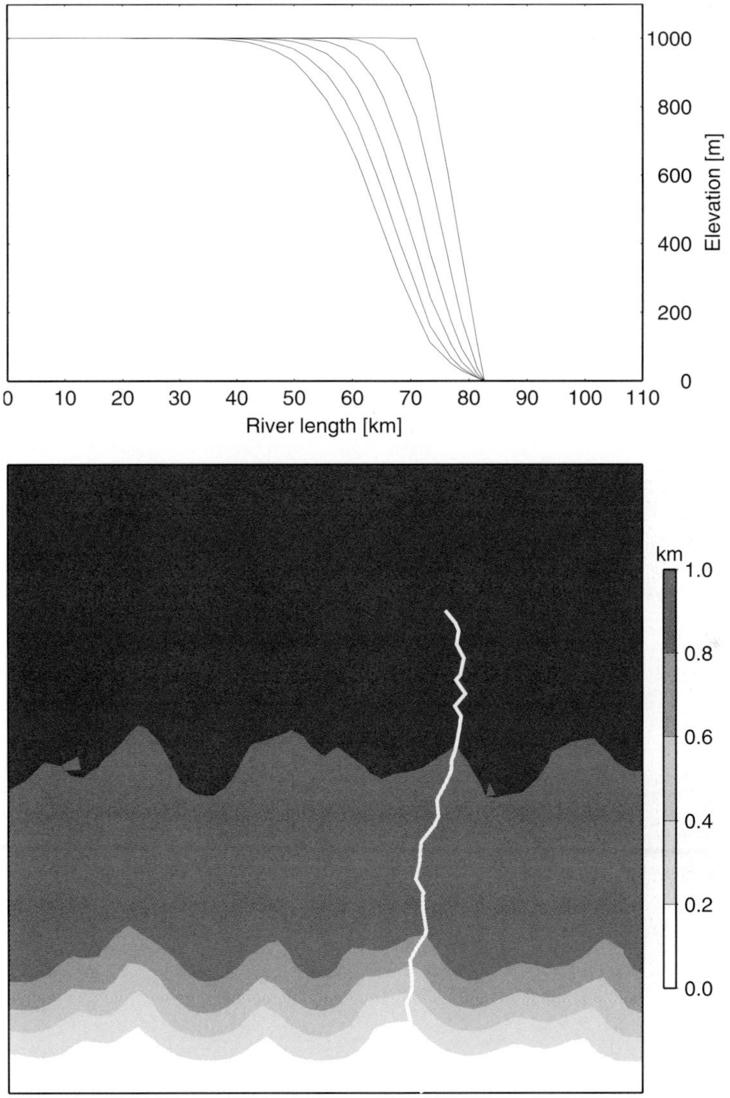

Fig 3. Same as Fig. 2, but based on fluvial erosion and increased hillslope diffusion.

Results from the first of the two model runs are shown in Fig. 4. A low value of carbon dioxide pressure of $P_{CO2}=10^{-3.5}$ atm is assumed that is characteristic of barren karst surfaces. All other parameter values are as defined in Tables 1 and 2. For the given parameters, the dissolution constant $\kappa_C v_l$ is comparable to the fluvial constant $\kappa_R v_i$; therefore both processes are similarly effective. Hence, the efficiency ratio is reduced to R_2=12 m (compared to R_1=20 m for the reference run 1). Long-range processes are therefore more effective. This can be seen after 1 Myr of landscape evolution, by which time the plateau is deeply dissected by eight major rivers (Fig. 4b). Most of the rivers

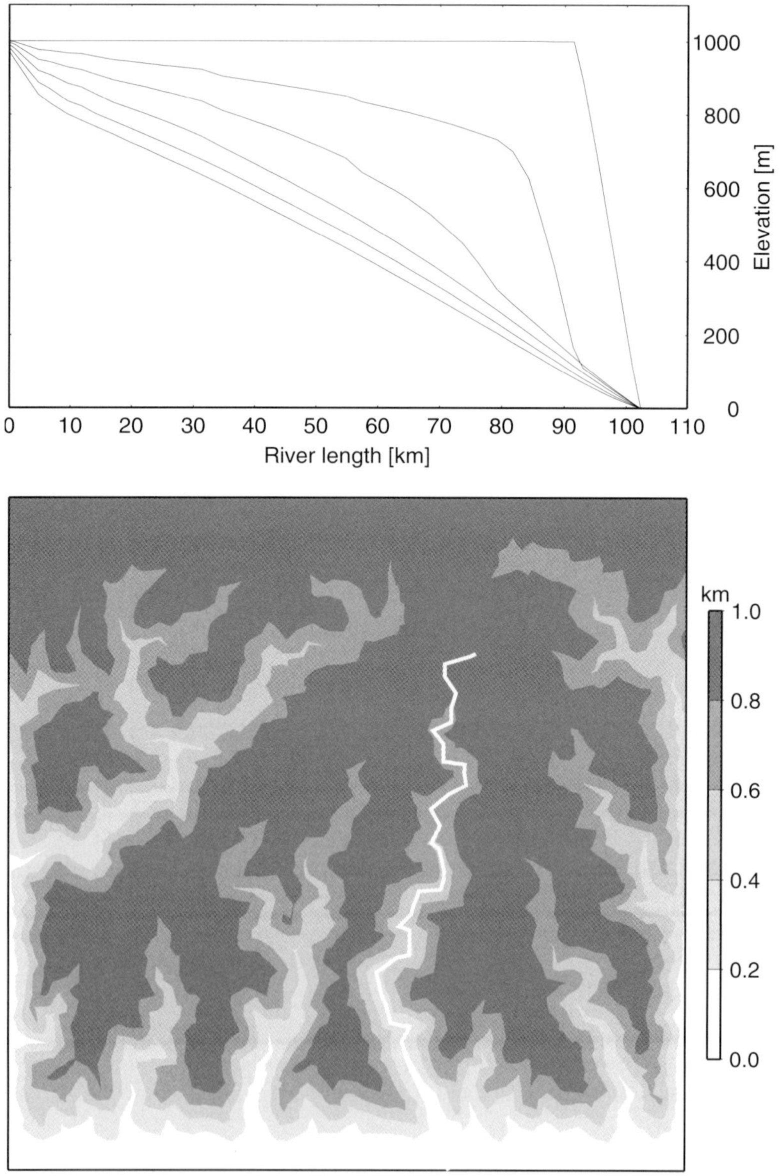

Fig 4. Same as Fig. 2, but based on karst denudation, fluvial erosion and diffusion. The partial carbon dioxide pressure is $10^{-3.5}$ atm.

have wide flat-bottomed valleys in their downstream graded section, whose sidewalls are generally steeper than in the reference run 1. In parts, the old plateau surface is reduced to narrow necks between deep river gorges. Major differences in river profile geometry can be observed (Fig. 4a).

In contrast to the reference runs on insoluble landscapes, the ungraded upstream river section now is significantly eroded. Valley incision starts close to the headwaters along the northern end of the plateau. The ungraded river section is characterized by a concave gradient similar to gradients resulting from diffusion processes. Gradients in

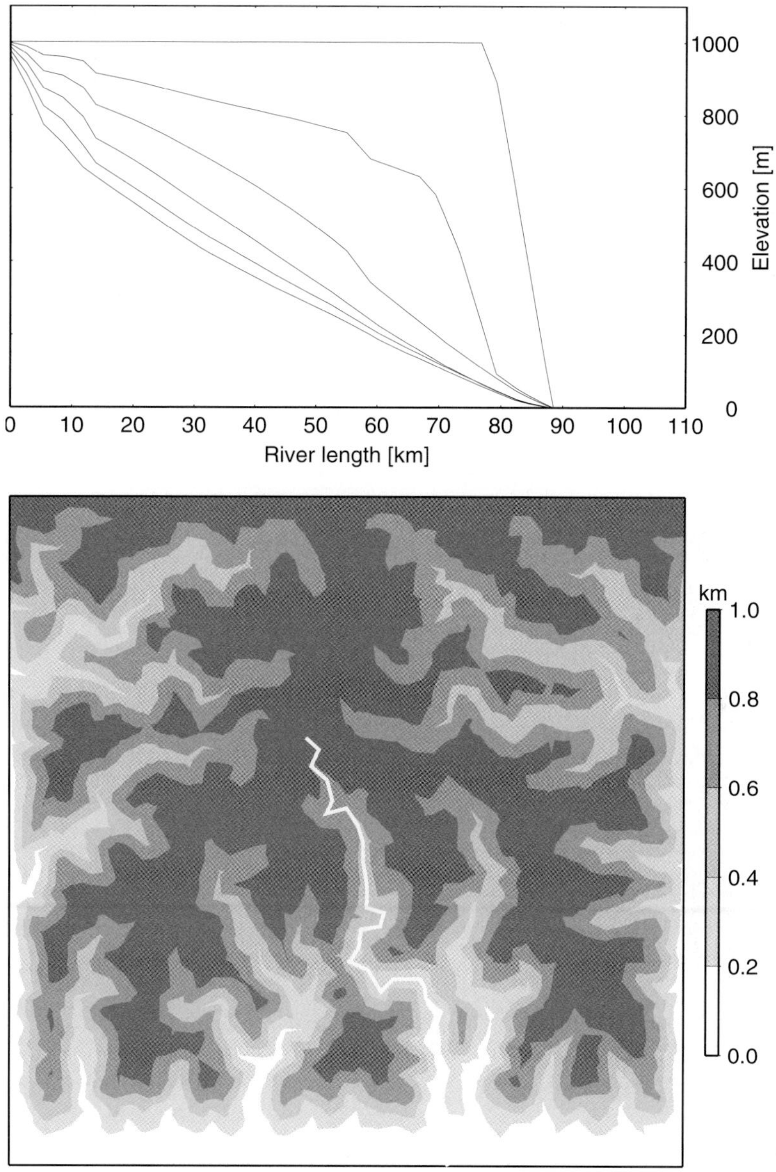

Fig 5. Same as Fig. 2, but based on karst denudation, fluvial erosion and diffusion. The partial carbon dioxide pressure is $10^{-2.5}$ atm.

the downstream graded river sections are low and convex to linear in shape, and thus dominated by fluvial processes. With time, the graded river section is cutting back into the plateau and gradients decline, while the ungraded river section is steepening. However, in contrast to reference run 1, incision is significant also on the plateau itself; thus, the total vertical elevation drop across the escarpment is reduced with time.

In the next run (Fig. 5), the carbon dioxide pressure is increased to $P_{CO2}=10^{-2.5}$ atm, simulating a temperate climate soil cover. Surface runoff now percolates slowly through the soil and is enriched in carbon dioxide, thus becoming more aggressive. Consequently, chemical dissolution is enhanced, as can be seen in the larger value of $\kappa_C = 0.037$. The efficiency ratio is further reduced to R_2=8 m; thus, diffusion is even less efficient. Surface morphology after 1 Myr is similar to the previous run, with eight major rivers draining the plateau to the south (Fig. 5a). However, river valleys are much more incised, resulting in deep narrow gorges reaching far upstream. The effect of an increased carbon dioxide pressure can be seen more clearly in the chosen set of river profiles (Fig. 5a). While the general characteristics – concave steepening gradients in the ungraded section and flat convex to linear gradients in the graded section - are similar to the previous run, valley incision has progressed much more. In fact, after 1 Myr the graded low-gradient river section occupies more than 80 percent of the river, leaving only a short but very steep ungraded river section close to the main drainage divide in the north.

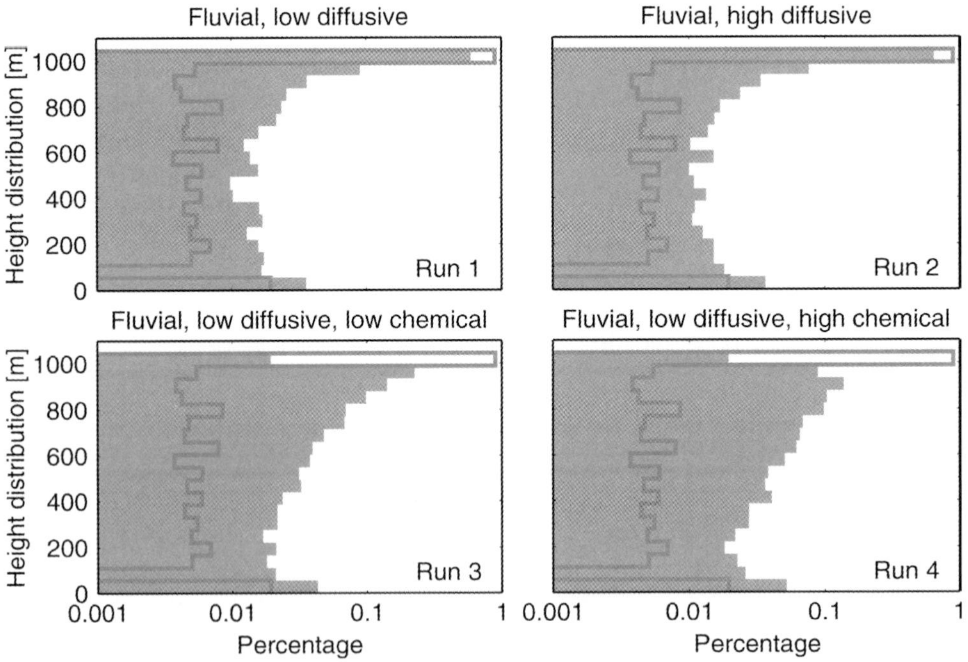

Fig 6. Hypsometric curves for the initial (solid line) and the final (grey areas) models.

HYPSOMETRIC CURVES

The effect of denudation on landscape evolution can also be seen in a statistical quantity, the hypsometric curve (Fig. 6). This quantity is derived from the topographical elevations of the model domain by summing up the elevations for a particular elevation range and relating it to the total elevation. As it can be seen in Fig. 6a, the initial topography for all models is characterized by a peak in the hypsometric curve around the 1000 m elevation, which represents the initial plateau topography. As the escarpment is fairly steep, the initial hypsometric curve for elevations between sea level and 1000 m is almost uniform and orders of magnitude lower than the peak at 1000 m altitude. At sea level, a second peak in the hypsometric curve represents the outwash plain of the plateau.

For the reference models shown in Figs. 2 and 3, the final hypsometric curves are characterized by a uniform increase of elevation between sea level and 1000 m elevation, which represents the incised river sections. The plateau surface itself has been reduced in size, as the peak is slightly smaller, but the elevation has been kept, as no erosion is possible on the plateau. No significant differences between the low and high diffusion landscapes is visible.

However, for the two models with karst denudation shown in Figs. 4 and 5, the final hypsometric curves are different: The peaks for the plateaux has moved downward and decreased significantly, as the denudation is able to lower the plateaux height itself. For

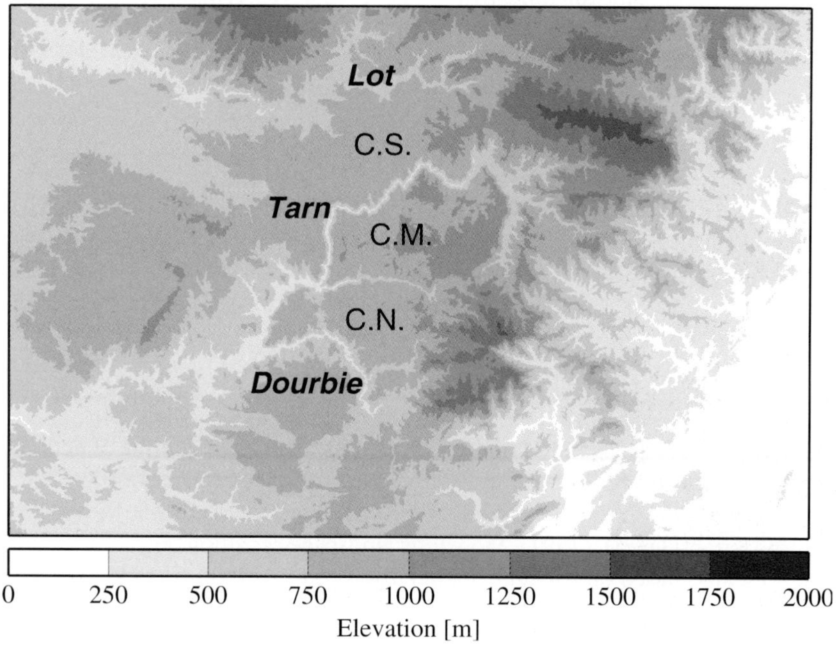

Fig 7. Topography of the Grandes Causses in southern France, with the deep, narrow gorges of the rivers Lot, Tarn and Dourbie, and the Causse de Sauveterre (CS), Causse Mejean (CM), and Causse Noir (CN).

larger effects of karst denudation (higher partial carbon dioxide pressure), the peak has moved further downwards and the hypsometric curve has become more uniform.

DISCUSSION

The numerical models presented herein are a first attempt to incorporate chemical processes into landscape models. Thus, only a qualitative comparison with topographical data can be made without statistical testing.

The modeled topography of the runs including karst denudation is similar to a low-relief plateau dissected by narrow river gorges such as the Grandes Causses in southern France, where the deep, steeply incised gorges of the Tarn, Lot, and Dourbie contrast with the relatively flat segments of the plateau of the Causses in between (Fig. 7). The evolving river valleys can have a significant sinuosity, and often only small remnants of the original plateau surface separate two gorges as narrow necks. As the karst denudation process is as effective as fluvial river erosion in eroding a landscape, evolution on a limestone plateau will downgrade the landscape surface twice as fast as on a similar sandstone plateau. The major difference in the karst denudation and the fluvial erosion processes are visible on the plateau itself: while fluvial erosion is less effective on the flat plateau, as fluvial erosion rate depends on the product of channel slope and river discharge, karst denudation can effectively remove material on the plateau itself, as denudation rate depends only on river discharge. Hence, karst denudation is an efficient process for surface lowering on plateau landscapes.

ACKNOWLEDGEMENTS

The DEM data have been kindly provided by Francis Lucazeau from Universite de Montpellier II. The figures in this paper are drawn using the GMT graphics package (Wessel et al. 1991, Wessel et al. 1998).

REFERENCES

Beaumont, C., Fullsack, P., and Hamilton, J. (1992). Erosional control of active compressional orogens. In: K. R. McClay, editor, *Thrust Tectonics*, pages 1-18. Chapman and Hall, New York.

Braun, J. and Sambridge, M. (1997). Modelling landscape evolution on geological time scales: a new method based on irregular spatial discretisation. *Basin Res.,* **9**, 27-52.

Braun, J., Zwartz, D., and Tomkin, J. H. (1999). A new surface processes model combining glacial and fluvial erosion. *Ann. Glaciol.*, **28**, 282-290.

Chase, C. G. (1992). Fluvial landsculpturing and the fractal dimension of topography. *Geomorphology*, **5**, 39-57.

Clemens, T., Hückinghaus, D., Sauter, M., Liedl, R., and Teutsch, G. (1997). Modelling the genesis of karst aquifer systems using a coupled reactive network model. In: *Hard Rock Hydrosciences*, IAHS Publ., volume 241, pages 3-10, Colorado. Proceedings of Rabat Sym. S2.

Dreybrodt, W. (1988). *Processes in Karst Systems*. Springer, Berlin.

Forti, F. (1984). Messungen des Karstabtrages in der Region Friaul-Julisch-Venetien (Italien). *Die Höhle*, **35**, 135-139.

Groves, C. G. and Howard, A. D. (1994). Early development of karst systems 1. Preferential flow path enlargement under laminar flow. *Water Resour. Res.*, **30 (10)**, 2837-2846.

Howard, A. D. and Groves, C. G. (1995). Early development of karst systems 2. Turbulent flow. *Water Resour. Res.*, **31 (1)**, 19-26.

Howard, A. D., Dietrich, W. E., and Seidl, M. A. (1994). Modeling fluvial erosion on regional continental scales. *J. Geophys. Res.*, **99 (B7)**, 13971-13986.

Jennings, J. N. (1985). *Karst geomorphology*. Blackwell, Oxford.

Kaufmann, G. and Braun, J. (1999). Karst aquifer evolution in fractured rocks. *Water Resources Res.*, **35 (11)**, 3223-3238.

Kaufmann, G. and Braun, J. (2000). Karst aquifer evolution in fractured, porous rocks. *Water Resources Res.*, **36 (6)**, 1381-1392.

Kooi, H. and Beaumont, C. (1994). Escarpment evolution on high-elevation rifted margins: Insights derived from a surface processes model that combines diffusion, advection, and reaction. *J. Geophys. Res.*, **99 (B6)**, 12191-12209.

Plummer, L. N. and Busenberg, E. (1982). The solubilities of calcite, aragonite and vaterite in CO_2-H_2O solutions between 0 and 90°C, and an evaluation of the aqueous model of the system $CaCO_3$-CO_2-H_2O. *Geochim. Cosmochim. Acta*, **46**, 1011-1040.

Robinson, R. A. and Stokes, R. H. (1955). *Electrolyte solutions*. Butterworths Sci. Publ., London.

Siemers, J. and Dreybrodt, W. (1998). Early development of karst aquifers on percolation networks of fractures in limestone. *Water Resour. Res.*, **34 (3)**, 409-419.

Trudgill, S. T., High, C. J., and Hana, F. K. (1981). Improvements in the micro-erosion meter. *Brit. Cave Res. Group Tech. Bull.*, **29**, 3-17.

Truesdell, A. H. and Jones, B. F. (1974). WATEQ, a computer program for calculating chemical equilibria of natural waters. *U.S. Geol. Surv. J. Res.*, **2 (2)**, 233-248.

Tucker, G. E. and Slingerland, R. L. (1994). Erosional dynamics, flexural isostasy, and long-lived escarpments: A numerical modeling study. *J. Geophys. Res.*, **99**, 12229-12243.

Wessel, P. and Smith, W. H. F. (1991). Free software helps map and display data. *EOS*, **72**, 441-446.

Wessel, P. and Smith, W. H. F. (1998). New, improved version of generic mapping tools released. *EOS*, **79**, 579.

White, W. B. (1984). Rate processes: chemical kinetics and karst landform development. In: R. G. La Fleur, editor, *Groundwater as a geomorphic agent*, pages 227-248. Allen and Unwin, London, Boston, Sydney.

Willgoose, G., Bras, R. L., and Rodriguez-Iturbe, I. (1991). A physically based coupled channel network growth and hillslope evolution model. 2. Applications. *Water Resour. Res.*, **27 (7)**, 1671-1684.

Address
Institute of Geophysics, University of Göttingen, Herzberger Landstrasse 180, 37075 Göttingen, Germany.
E-mail: gkaufman@uni-geophys.gwdg.de

Evolution of Karst: From Prekarst to Cessation, 259-266, Ljubljana-Postojna 2002

LITHOLOGIC AND MORPHOLOGICAL PROPERTIES AND ROCK RELIEF OF THE LUNAN STONE FORESTS

MARTIN KNEZ & TADEJ SLABE

Abstract
Stone forests emerged when carbonate rock previously covered with sediment and soil became exposed. Along with subcutaneous factors, rain, their topographical position and karst perforation, their shape and size were primarily determined by the rock itself. The forests developed in horizontal or gently sloping rock strata cleft by vertical joints and fissures. Diverse examples of stone forests that formed in almost identical conditions show that the shape of the pillars is mainly the consequence of the distribution and density of fissures in the rock, its stratification, and different rock strata composition. The rock forms on the pillars are divided into subcutaneous forms, composed rock forms, and forms shaped by rainwater. The composition of the rock enables their creation and influences their shape and distribution.
Key words: *Lunan stone forests, lithology, morphogenesis, rock relief*

1. INTRODUCTION

Stone forests emerged from subcutaneous karst karren since the limestone was covered with thick layers of sediment and soil. They consist of stone pillars and teeth (Song 1986). Stone teeth are smaller protuberances less than five meters tall. Pillars, however, are from five to fifty meters tall and of various shapes. They developed in diverse horizontal or gently sloping rock strata (5^0-15^0) cleft by vertical faults, joints, and fissures (Ford, Salomon, & Williams 1996). The Lunan stone forests are considered a form of covered karst.

The central part of the Lunan stone forests spreads over eighty hectares; larger and smaller stone forests, however, cover as much as 350 km^2.

Under the forests there are various karst cave networks.

We presented recent research on the Lunan stone forests in detail, described them, and assembled material on them in the book *South China Karst 1* (Chen et al. 1998) and elsewhere (e.g., Knez & Slabe 2001a, 2001b); this paper adds the results of the comparison of different types of stone forests as shown in the Fig.1.

2. LITHOLOGIC PROPERTIES OF STONE FORESTS

The stone forest area consists of early Permian carbonates of the Qixia and Maokou formation. These are two of the most important basalt formations from which numerous

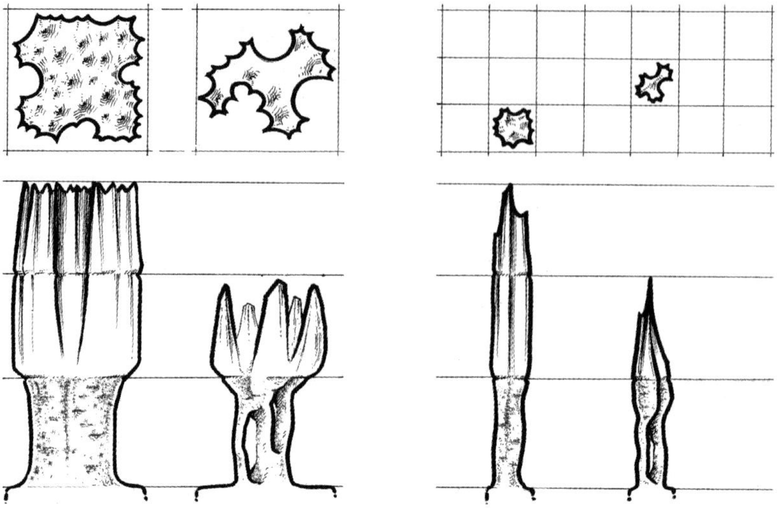

stone forests emerged in the southern Yunnan province of Lunan. Typical for Qixia formations are micrite limestone with intercalated dolomite and dolomitized limestone with intervening layers of slate. In the lower part of Maokou formations, limestone alternates with dolomite and dolomitized limestone. In the upper part we find a succession of limestone layers that in some places are thin and in others several meters thick as well as solid limestone that contains several-decimeter large nodules of chert in individual horizons. The main lithologic properties of Maokou formations are roughly similar to those of Qixia formations, except that in Maokou carbonates we do not find a major influence of late diagenetic dolomitization and in some places a considerable secondary porosity. However, both show a strong diagenetic alteration of the basic rock, which is undoubtedly also a consequence of intensive volcanic (basalt lava) activity during the transition from the Paleozoic era to the Mesozoic era. The rock contains an extremely high percentage of carbonate.

In the area studied we find considerable variations in thickness, porosity, and degree and type of dolomitization, in the components of inclusions, and in the colour of individual layers that are reflected in the formation of the stone forests (Knez 1998).

What is macroscopically most noticeable in the geological profiles is the different thickness of layers, which varies from ten centimeters to many meters, according to some data even more than thirty meters (Song 1986). In the stone forests we encounter rock sequences composed of several meter thick homogeneous and compact layers where karstification is advancing considerably faster on the tops, along bedding planes and individual fissures, and below the surface (Shilin Central Forest, Naigu) as well as sequences of thin-layered (10 cm and more) limestone (Pu Chao Chun) where already intensive karstification is accelerating along numerous lithologic junctions. In the geological profiles we find an alternation of thickly-stratified and thinly-stratified carbonate as well (Naigu, Pu Chao Chun). Where the layers are thinner, the pillars can be much thinner due to more rapid corrosion (Naigu, Pu Chao Chun).

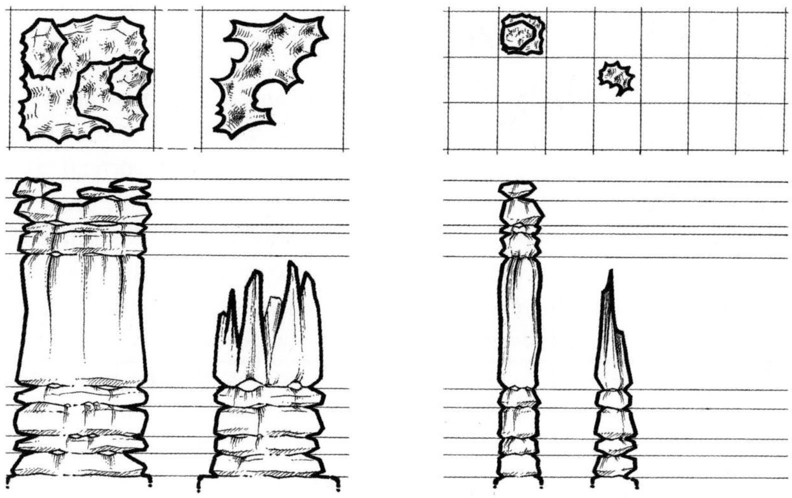

Fig.1. Typical shapes of pillars in Lunnan stone forests.

In some places we encounter thicker segments of very porous layers (Lao Hei Gin) where the intercrystal porosity exceeds 20% in most cases. Typical for these are dolosparite and dolomicrosparite of the grainstone type. Diameters of light brown and in some places extremely pure and almost completely transparent dolomite grains reach one millimeter while their average diameter is one third of a millimeter. In contrast to the homogeneous and compact rock, a segment of the porous layers does not karstify merely along the lithotectonic junctions but across the whole profile in accordance with the stage of porosity. The rate of karstification of such rock is substantially greater and additionally accelerated locally below the surface.

Late diagenetic dolomitization is also typical of some layers. Where increased porosity and dolomitization appear in the same layers (Lao Hei Gin), more intensive karstification is found as well. A special example is the dolomitization of only individual smaller fields in such a way that otherwise homogeneous, compact, and impermeable rock becomes freckled (Naigu). Dolomitized limestone is therefore less influenced by karstification than pure thickly-stratified limestone (Shilin Central Forest). To a lesser degree, we see that dolomite fields, usually with a diameter of a few centimeters, protrude from the rock.

Layers with inclusions more resistant to karstification protrude from the profiles as well. One example is the chert that is the result of allochemical early diagenetic processes (Shilin Central Forest, Naigu). Less soluble inclusions macroscopically influence slower karstification only locally while microscopically corrosion is substantially more intensive at the junctions between the inclusions and limestone.

Due to volcanic activity at the time of sedimentation and after it, the colour of the rock changes from light grey to yellow-brown.

3. THE SHAPING OF STONE FORESTS

a. Influence of fissuring of rock on the shape of the forest and size of stone pillars

The networks of distribution of the pillars, that is, the ground plans of the stone forests, are congruent with the fracturing of the rock, in this case largely vertical, and take various shapes. The pillars can be linked in rows between distinct fault areas or close together, or the stone forest or parts of it can consist of individual wide or narrow pillars. Cracks between the pillars have thus been corroded to various widths ranging from a few dozen centimeters to ten meters and more. This diversity in the network of pillars can occur in the same forest, as for example in the Naigu forest.

As a rule, pillars with smaller cross sections occur with a dense network of fissures (provided, of course, they are not diminished primarily by corrosion) and larger pillars occur with a sparser network. The latter, which can often be described as larger rock masses as well, have broader tops dissected into several points on thickly-stratified rock.

b. Influence of rock strata on the shape of stone pillars

The rock from which the stone forests developed consists of strata of different thickness and composition. This is reflected in the shape of the stone pillars, particularly in their cross sections, the shape of their tops, and their rock relief.

The shape of pillars that develop on thick and uniformly composed rock strata shows hardly any influences but rather reflects a more or less uniform development from subcutaneous karren to stone forest. The central part of the Lunan stone forests is an example. Narrower pillars have pointed or blade-like tops and relatively flat or subcutaneously undercut walls. Wider stone pillars, however, often have broad tops dissected into many points with notches between them.

Longitudinal sections of pillars on thin rock strata (Pu Chao Chun) are often jagged since they are dissected by wall notches occurring along the bedding planes, or their shapes reflect the uneven resistance of the different rock strata to the factors of their formation. Cross sections of the pillars are of various sizes and shapes. Thinner strata disintegrate faster and therefore the pillar tops are relatively flat and have a typical rock relief (Pu Chao Chun). Where the strata are thinner, as a rule the pillars are narrow. Subcutaneous tubes occurring along bedding planes can develop into subcutaneous channels when they occur on the top of a stone pillar or be reshaped by rainwater.

c. Influence of rock composition on the shaping of stone pillars

Rock composition, particularly if it is diverse, may decisively influence the shape of the stone pillars, as much their longitudinal sections as the size of the cross sections.

Porous strata are often subcutaneously perforated and disintegrate more rapidly on the surface (Naigu, Lao Hei Gin). Pillars are most narrow at the level of porous strata. Above them occur forms typical of overhanging walls and below them of gently sloping wall sections. The pillars break fastest along them. The tops of pillars occurring on such rock are most often of ununiform shapes.

Rock strata with less soluble components usually protrude from the walls, and if they are at the top, the tops are broader than the lower parts of the pillar and the pillars therefore acquire characteristic mushroom shapes. These are particularly distinct if the pillars occur on rock whose lower strata are relatively more soluble, porous, or disintegrate rapidly (Naigu).

d. Influence of subcutaneous factors on the shape of the stone forests

Subcutaneous factors created the pointed tops of subcutaneous teeth and caused the undercutting of pillars. At levels where sediment and soil surrounded the stone pillars for a long period, larger notches or half-bells developed. Below the surface, pillars were most often hollowed out along bedding planes and more porous rock strata. The narrowest stone pillars can also be subcutaneously hollowed. Subcutaneous factors working only on individual parts of the stone pillars, as in cases when their tops are covered with soil and vegetation, most distinctly dissect them vertically when water trickles through the soil and corrodes the rock or when the water flows from the soil down the pillars. Rainwater sharpens the pillar tops, reshapes the traces of their original subcutaneous formation, and with time also carves unique shapes distinctly reflected in the rock relief.

4. ROCK RELIEF OF STONE FORESTS

a. Subcutaneous rock forms

Subcutaneous rock forms are divided into rock forms that developed under sediment and soil due to water flowing along the contact between the sediment and the rock, rock forms that developed due to the percolation of water through soil that only partly covered the rock, and rock forms that developed at the top level of soil or sediment surrounding the rock (Slabe 1999). The first group of subcutaneous forms includes subcutaneous scallops that developed on a relatively permeable contact between the rock and the sediment and subcutaneous channels of various sizes that developed due to water flowing concentrated along the contact between the wall and the sediment that covered the rock and filled the cracks along vertical fissures. The diameter of the largest channels can reach several meters. Many reach from the top to the bottom of the pillars and are therefore several dozen meters long.

The broader tops of pillars and teeth are dissected by medium-sized and smaller subcutaneous channels and cups that developed under soil which only partly covered the rock due to water percolating through the soil and flowing along the contact with the rock. The subcutaneous channels (Slabe 1999, 259) have characteristic semicircular cross sections or cross sections like an inverted omega wider at the bottom and have diameters reaching one meter. At joints, particularly on the rim of the tops, they are narrower and deeper. Most frequently they are linked in a branching dissected network. The multiple levels of subcutaneous channels bear witness to the progressive exposure of the stone teeth. Subcutaneous cups (Slabe 1999, 263) are semicircular cups of various sizes with diameters ranging from a few centimeters to a meter and more. They are found on the tops of broader stone pillars and at the bottom of funnel-shaped notches on the walls beneath them.

The most porous largely dolomite strata in the Naigu and Lao Hei Gin forests are relatively densely perforated with subcutaneous tubes with diameters ranging from several centimeters to a meter or two. On their circumferences we can find rock forms as well. Above-sediment channels are the result of water flowing over the sediment when the cavities were filled with sediment; floor channels developed when the cavities emptied as the level of sediment surrounding the pillars dropped.

b. Composed rock forms

Composed rock forms are also distinctive. These are larger channels on the lower parts of the pillar walls. They developed due to water flowing from the subcutaneous channels on the broader pillar tops or leading from funnel-shaped notches. At the bottom of these there are or once were subcutaneous cups. The rims of the tops therefore have larger or smaller funnel-shaped outlets (Naigu), most often reshaped by rainwater. Smaller but of similar origin are the vertical channels that lead from subcutaneous tubes. Rainwater has reshaped these, particularly deepening the former subcutaneous channels that crisscrossed the broader tops (Pu Chao Chun). The channels are therefore the trace of subcutaneous dissolving of the rock and rainwater that may gradually completely dominate when the rock is exposed.

Notches and half-bells occur where long-lasting levels of soil and sediment surrounded the pillars (central part of the stone forest, Lao Hei Gin; Slabe 1999).

c. Rock forms shaped by rainwater

Rock forms shaped by rainwater are naturally most distinct on the tops and upper parts of the walls of stone pillars; they include flutes, channels, rain pits, and solution pans. They often develop on old subcutaneous rock forms, reshaping them or in combination with the factors shaping subcutaneous rock forms creating composed rock forms.

Flutes are found usually on broader and dissected tops; on pointed tops they are rare, which is primarily the consequence of their steep walls. They occur on protuberances where they are arranged like rays around the highest point and on the walls of subcutaneous channels and exposed solution pans. Channels on steep walls dissect the stone pillar tops more distinctly. They have diameters of up to half a meter and measure up to five meters in length. They are relatively shallow, especially if compared to those linked to the subcutaneous shaping of the rock, and must be distinguished from the previously described channels linked to the development of subcutaneous rock forms. They are the trace of rainwater activity and frequently start on relatively sharp tops. In time, these channels also acquire a funnel-like outlet, even if less distinct at first.

Solution pans are found on broader stone pillar tops. Larger ones that developed from subcutaneous cups are often open, semicircular, and have drain channels and flutes at their circumference. Their diameters can exceed one meter. They are also found at the bottoms of the funnel-like notches that developed from subcutaneous cups.

5. CONCLUSION

Numerous examples of stone forests that developed in almost identical conditions show that the diverse shape of the pillars is primarily a consequence of the properties of the rock, from the distribution and density of joints and fissures in the rock and its stratification to its composition. However, we must also consider the significance of the effect on their shaping by subcutaneous factors and transformation by rainwater, that is, the course of their development in various periods.

The Lunan stone forests formed in early Permian carbonates of the Qixia and Maokou formation. They are characterized by a diverse alternation of very pure limestone, dolomitized limestone, and dolomite, by alternating thin and thick layers, in some places by distinct late diagenetic dolomitization, and by secondary porosity. The strata are mostly horizontal or inclined by five to ten degrees. Due to vigorous tectonic action, they are fractured by numerous vertical and subvertical joints and fissures.

The diverse fracturing, stratification, and rock composition are reflected in the shapes of the stone forests and their stone pillars. In the same stone forest, which developed on diversely composed rock, pillars may be of various but typical shapes, the consequence of their development on different levels of a diverse rock column.

The shape of stone pillars occurring on thicker and uniformly composed rock strata reflects primarily the development from subcutaneous karren into a stone forest, and the traces of subcutaneous factors are gradually reshaped by rainwater. Cross sections of stone pillars occurring on thin rock strata are often jagged, and their tops (even of thinner pillars), which as a rule are pointed, are often flat, the consequence of the rapid disintegration of thin strata. Porous rock strata are most often subcutaneously perforated and disintegrate faster on the surface; the pillars are therefore narrower and the tops on such rock have no characteristic shapes. More resistant rock strata protrude from the cross section. The tops of the narrower pillars are sharp, sharpened as much by subcutaneous factors as by rainwater. The broader tops, however, are dissected by points and funnel-like cups.

The unique development of the stone forests is also reflected in their rock relief. Rainwater gradually reshapes the subcutaneous rock relief. The most distinct and particularly the largest rock forms are subcutaneous and composed rock forms. Subcutaneous rock forms include scallops, large channels, notches, half-bells, and subcutaneous channels and cups on broader tops. Composed rock forms include the channels that lead from the subcutaneous channels or subcutaneous cups and dissect pillar walls. Many pillars are subcutaneously undercut, while their tops have been reshaped by secondary subcutaneous rock forms and forms carved by rainwater. The rock relief of broader stone pillars is unique as well, particularly those with broader tops, either on thick rock strata where secondary subcutaneous forms occur or on tops that developed due to the disintegration of thin rock strata when subcutaneous tubes occurring along bedding planes developed into subcutaneous forms or large channels that were reshaped by rainwater. Both forms indirectly influence the shape of the pillar walls due to water flowing from them and carving channels. As a rule, smaller rock forms do not occur on dolomite rock, on very porous rock, or rock filled with larger inclusions.

The development of stone forests and their rate of growth in a particular period are also influenced by the position and development of karst caves below them, that is, by the manner the water–and the sediment and soil with it–flows from the karst surface. Various periods can also be determined from the karst caves. In the Baiyun Cave below the Naigu stone forest we can identify periods characteristics of cave development in epiphreatic conditions when water flowed rapidly through the cave and deposited gravel, periods of the cave flooding and being filled with fine-grained sediment, and followed by a period of the rapid deepening of the central tunnel by a water current that swept away most of the sediment from the cave. This last event, which was a consequence of the rapid intermittent lowering of the water table below the stone forest, made possible its faster growth as well (Šebela et al. 2001).

REFERENCES

Chen, X. et al., 1998: South China Karst I, Zbirka ZRC 19, 247p.

Ford, D., J.N. Salomon, P. Williams, 1996: Les "Forets de Pierre" ou "Stone forests" de Lunan.- Karstologia 28, 28/2, 25-40

Knez, M., 1998: Lithologic Properties of the Three Lunan Stone Forests (Shilin, Naigu and Lao Hei Gin).- In: South China Karst I, Chen X. et al., Zbirka ZRC, 19, 30-43

Knez, M. & T. Slabe, 2001a: Oblika in skalni relief stebrov v Naigu kamnitem gozdu (JZ Kitajska).- Acta carsologica 30/1, 13-24

Knez, M. & T. Slabe, 2001b: The Lithology, Shape and Rock Relief of the Pillars in the Pu Chao Chun Stone Forest (Lunan Stone Forests, NW China).- Acta carsologica 30/2, 129-139

Slabe, T., 1999: Subcutaneous rock forms.- Acta carsologica 28/2, 255-271, Ljubljana.

Song Lin Hua, 1986: Origination of stone forest in China.- International Journal of Speleology 15 (1-4), 3-33

Šebela, S., Slabe, T., Kogovšek, J., Liu, Hong, Pruner, P., 2001: Baiyun Cave in Naigu Shilin, Yunnan Karst, China.- Acta geologica sinica. (Engl. ed.). 75/3, 279-287

Address
Karst Research Institute ZRC SAZU, Titov trg 2, 6230 Postojna, Slovenia
e-mail: knez@zrc-sazu.si, slabe@zrc-sazu.si

Evolution of Karst: From Prekarst to Cessation, 267-273, Ljubljana-Postojna 2002

RIVERS IN KARST GEOMORPHOLOGY

ROY McDONALD

Abstract
This paper offers two suggestions. First, the importance of rivers should be explored more widely in interpreting karst landscape development, within and beyond the tropics, including the classical karst areas. Second, the solutional evolutionary model needs to be more rigorously field tested, including using geological and sedimentological evidence to substantiate conclusions about the processes that create specific landforms.

INTRODUCTION

Geological and sedimentological evidence showed the important role of rivers in forming tower karst landscapes in Belize (McDonald 1979a), Indonesia (McDonald 1976), and Malaysian Borneo (McDonald 1979b, McDonald and Ley 1985). This work disproved the theoretical models of solutional karst landscape evolution promulgated by Grund (1914) and Lehmann (1953), at least for these tower karst regions. The findings were presented cautiously at the time because they were different from the prevailing view, and possibly represented exceptional circumstances rather than the norm. Since then, however, there have been other challenges to the theoretical models of solutional karst evolution and additional examples of river action as a dominating process in karst geomorphology.

EVIDENCE OF RIVER ACTION

Perennial, intermittent, and ephemeral rivers are everywhere in karst regions around the World, just as they are found everywhere in landscapes formed in noncalcareous rocks. The presence of rivers in karst landscapes seems particularly apparent in areas of heavy rainfall, where large perennial rivers are commonplace, such as in Belize, Indonesia, West Malaysia, Malaysian Borneo, southern China, Madagascar, Jamaica, Puerto Rico, South Africa, and New Guinea. Rivers are also prominent features of karst landscapes in the more temperate and drier regions. For example, the Rivers Cherwell, Dorn, Glyme, Evenlode, and Windrush are prominent features of the karst of the Oxfordshire Scarplands in central England. Other examples include the rivers Obrh and Strzen in the Losko and Cerknisko poljes, Slovenia.

Many of the landforms produced by rivers in karst regions are similar to the landforms produced by rivers in noncalcareous rocks, and some are different. The similar forms include terraces, floodplain depositional and erosional features, and incised meandering channels. The different landforms include blind- and half-blind valleys, pocket valleys, dry valleys, cliff-foot caves (fussholen or footcaves), and subterranean river segments.

River valley development dominates the geomorphology of the karst region near Gales Point, Belize (McDonald 1979). Quamina Creek, Big Creek, Soldier Creek, Cornhouse Creek, Jenkins Creek, Manatee River, and Sibun River are amongst the rivers that have cut valleys through the limestone, trimmed back the limestone hillsides, and in some places created wide valley floors with scattered tower outliers. The power of the rivers as geomorphic agents is striking in the field. There are cliffs and cliff-foot caves where the rivers flow along the bases of the limestone hills and tower outliers. Massive blocks of limestone talus from adjacent cliffs can be observed in the riverbeds of Quamina Creek and Soldier Creek, both about 12 km southwest of Gales Point. A talus block measuring 4 m x 8 m x 15 m in Soldier Creek documents a sudden 4 m retreat in an adjacent 20 m high cliff. The wide valley floors or plains between the limestone hills are underlain by limestone, but are covered by about 6 m of alluvium. The lower 3 m to 4.5 m consists of fluvial gravels typically not larger than 5 cm x 10 cm x 15 cm, within a matrix of sand. The upper 1.5 m to 3 m of the alluvium consists of sand, silt, and clay. The fluvial gravels are distinctive in this area because they are predominantly composed of dark-colored non-calcareous rocks, including slate, shale, and sandstone, clearly brought in by the rivers from the adjacent Maya Mountains.

The formation of valley floors in the Gales Point karst region by lateral fluvial erosion is demonstrated by geologic and sedimentary evidence. The same rounded fluvial gravels found in the rivers can be observed in cliff-foot caves now located well away from the active river channels. These cliff-foot caves were formed by lateral river erosion, and then were abandoned as the positions of the rivers shifted. The presence of the rounded fluvial gravels in these caves demonstrates their origin by lateral river erosion. Surface erosion by overland runoff around the bases of the limestone outliers, and elsewhere on the valley floors, also commonly exposes the same fluvial gravels as are found in the active river channels, further confirming the fluvial origin of the broad valley floors.

Similarly, in northern Borneo, geological and sedimentary evidence demonstrates river action is responsible for the development of broad valley floors, cliff-foot caves, and karst towers along the Melinau River and its tributaries near Gunung Mulu (McDonald and Ley 1985). For example, footcaves at the base of Bukit Lobang Kelawar, a tower located along the Melinau River near its confluence with the Pala River, contain cemented deposits of the same well-rounded sandstone gravel that is found in the bed of the nearby river channel.

The karst landscape in Sulawesi, Indonesia (McDonald 1976, 1979b), shows a history of river incision, valley formation, lateral erosion, aggradation, and reincision in its dissected plateaus, raised terraces, gravel-filled cliff-foot caves, river valleys, broad fluvial plains, and tower karst outliers. Geologic and sedimentary evidence of the work of rivers in creating the broad valley floors and plains is widespread, and is striking because of the texture and color contrast between the white, crystalline limestone bedrock and the mottled, dark, and rounded volcanic gravel transported into the karst landscape by rivers such as the Lealleang, Patunuang, and Pangkadjene.

The cliff-foot caves at the edges of the present valley floors in Sulawesi show a history of being: 1) created by lateral river erosion; 2) filled in by fluvial gravels; and 3) in some instances partly exhumed by erosion by local surface runoff. The identification of the infill of fluvial gravels was critical to the interpretation of these features as being the result of river action. There are also combinations of sheer cliffs and cliff-foot caves that are "stranded" high above the present valley floors. The river-borne gravels found in these high cliff-foot caves, and on the slopes below the caves, explain the origin of the cliffs and caves. They were formed by lateral river erosion, and then were abandoned as the rivers shifted laterally and became more deeply incised. These stranded cliff-foot caves tend to be concentrated at levels about 4.5 m, 18 m, and 100 m above the present valley floors (McDonald, 1979b). The gravels in the highest terraces can be deeply weathered, in some cases appearing only as oval-shaped ghosts within a clay or fine-silt weathering profile.

This Sulawesi karst area is especially interesting in considering the evolution of the science of karst geomorphology, since Sunartadirdja and Lehmann (1960) offered the landforms there as examples of the solutional evolutionary model of tropical karst development. Not only does the geological and sedimentological evidence refute this assertion, but also shows a complex history of starts, stops, reversals, and restarts of geomorphic processes that are not consistent with the solutional evolutionary theory.

DEVELOPMENT OF POLJES IN SULAWESI

Sunartadirdja and Lehmann (1960) recognized a range of karst depression morphology in the Sulawesi karst area, and considered the various depressions to comprise stages in an evolutionary scheme of solutional karst landform development. The solution of the limestone along structural weaknesses was thought to produce linear depressions or karst streets ("Karstgassen"). The wider openings at the intersections of the karst streets were considered small poljes ("Kleine Poljen"). Lateral solutional undermining by overland runoff or flood wash (Losungsunterschneidung) was believed responsible for expanding the small poljes into "Embryonal Poljen," and then expanding these embryonic poljes into true poljes. Sunartadirdja and Lehmann (1960) believed the floors of the embryonic and true poljes were sealed by insoluble weathering residue derived from the solution of the limestone during the vertical solutional incision of the relief. They also noted the sediments contain volcanic material, but did not pursue the questions that might have been raised by this evidence. The final stage in the evolution, the development of karst margin plains ("Karstrandebenen"), was believed to result from the coalescence of the ever-expanding poljes.

Sunartadirdja and Lehmann (1960) provided visual evidence to support their hypotheses. They described an embryonic polje near the village of Lealleang, as translated: *The formation of such small poljes by karst corrosive expansion can be observed well in the vicinity of Lealleang. Parallel to a deep intervening break of the karst margin plain passes a fracture line in a northeasterly direction. It forms a wide karst street, which in places has expanded to form a small polje plain with vertical walls.* Furthermore, the appearance of the edges of the poljes in the vicinity of the villages of Daimanggala and Bontobonto seemed to Sunartadirdja and Lehmann (1960) to support their theory. As translated, they wrote: *Next to the steep tower slopes are diagonal slopes; they are likely made of debris fallen as a result of solutional undermining.* However, Sunartadirdja and Lehmann (1960) did not provide detailed field evidence to verify their conclusions. In fact, subsequent detailed field studies carried out by the writer within these poljes (McDonald 1979b) showed a more complex geomorphology than envisioned by Sunartadirdja and Lehmann (1960), as discussed in the following.

The embryonic polje at Lealleang is a linear feature that trends southwest to northeast and varies in width from about 20 m to 400 m. It is cut into the *Tonasa Limestones* (Sukamto 1975), which include massive coral limestone, bioclastic limestone interbedded with tuffaceous Globigerina marl and bituminous limestone, and local intercalations of limestone breccia and sandy limestone. The *Tonasa Limestones* were laid down during the Eocene to Middle Miocene, and are at least 560 m thick, although their exact thickness is not known. The massive coral limestone is at least 150 m thick, is unbedded, well jointed, and overlies mainly thin-bedded, sometimes impure limestones that dip to the southwest at about four degrees. The top of the coral limestone dips along with the underlying beds, and declines in elevation toward the southwest from a maximum of 564 m to about 250 m above sea level.

The floor of the embryonic polje is far different from the nearly level, thinly mantled polje floor envisioned by Sunartadirdja and Lehmann (1960). The floor of the polje is composed of thick deposits of noncalcareous rocks of the *Walanae Formation*. These beds, although much dissected, are undisturbed, and are up to 100 m thick in places. Especially noteworthy is the presence of blue clay, which according to Bartstra (1976) contain the gastropods, *Globigerinoides obliquus* and *Globigerinoides extremus* that indicate a Late Miocene to Pliocene age for the lower marine portion of the *Walanae Formation*. This blue clay occurs in the polje in association with underlying unconsolidated marls and overlying thin-bedded tuffs. This embryonic polje, therefore, appears to have been deeply incised by the end of the Pliocene, and then filled by about 100 m of rocks of the *Walanae Formation*.

The *Walanae Formation* consists of clayey, sandy, gravelly, and partly tuffaceous material. It is marine in the lower portion and terrestrial in the upper portion. According to Bartstra (1976), the upper portion may be Pleistocene in age. The undisturbed beds of marl, blue clay, and thin-bedded tuffs make up the lower 60 m of the deposit in the embryonal polje. These beds are overlain by about 40 m of coarse fluvial gravels. The gravel contains well-rounded boulders and cobbles of volcanic rock, derived from the mountains to the east and brought into the polje by rivers. Therefore, the polje was in existence by the Late Miocene to Pliocene, and was first filled by marine sediments of that age, and later by terrestrial, river-borne sediments. This phase of valley filling and river aggradation appears to have been completed during the Pleistocene.

Subsequent to their deposition in the Lealleang polje, the rocks of the *Walanae Formation* were dissected, and may have been subject to alternating periods of incision and aggradation, as suggested by terrace remnants commonly about 4.5 m and 18 m above the present valley floors. The floor of the polje is very uneven and varies in elevation from 25 m to 125 m above sea level. While at one time the polje contained a river, as evidenced by the fluvial gravel, it is now characterized by karstic drainage into sinks that occur along the valley sides, and the gravel floor has been eroded into a series of closed depressions, each drained to one side or the other by sinks. The limestone walls of the polje show little evidence of modern corrosion by rain or by solutional undermining by overland runoff. Instead, the walls are coated by thick deposits of reprecipitated calcite, in which are sometimes cemented fine alluvium and rounded cobbles of volcanic rock, up to about 125 m above sea level, the maximum height of the *Walanae Formation* gravels in this area.

Similarly, the poljes at Diamanggala and Bontobonto contain thick deposits of noncalcareous *Walanae Formation* rocks, which have been much dissected by several active rivers. The Daimanggala polje covers about 6 sq km, and is drained by the rivers Balleangintoa, Pakallampek, and Buakmata, which sink at the base of a limestone cliff on the west side of the polje. The Bontobonto polje, to the north, is smaller, and probably should be regarded as a part of the larger Daimanggala polje because it is only the uneven relief of dissected *Walanae Formation* rocks that separates the two poljes. This smaller polje is drained by the Tammale River, which flows into Daimanggala polje and joins with the Buakmata River.

High limestone cliffs, and a line of high-level cliff-foot caves occur along the limestone hillsides on the edges of the poljes. The cliff-foot caves lie about 100 m above the lowest points on the polje floors. Below these caves are more moderately sloping (about 60 degrees) hillside segments. A more or less continuous line of cliff-foot caves can be traced along the sides of the two poljes, and into the adjacent Panagi River Valley. Field inspection revealed the presence of rounded volcanic gravel of the *Walanae Formation* in the 100 m high cliff-foot caves, and as colluvial deposits on the moderate slopes below the caves. Shallow excavations revealed the moderate slopes to be composed of undisturbed beds of the *Tonasa Limestones*, and not the talus supposed by Sunartadirdja and Lehmann (1960). In further contrast to Sunartadirdja and Lehmann's interpretation, the floors of the poljes are composed of thick deposits of *Walanae Formation* rocks, dissected into individual watersheds by the several rivers. They are not composed of thinly mantled limestone bedrock.

In addition, the rock outcrop separating the two poljes from the adjacent Panagi

River Valley was determined through field study to be a ridge composed of crystalline shists. These noncalcareous basement rocks underlie the Tonasa Limestones, and are known only to be pre-Tertiary in age (Bartstra 1976). The Panagi River is fed by limestone springs to the west of this ridge, and then flows westward, eventually to the South China Sea.

The line of high cliffs and cliff-foot caves, along with the sedimentary evidence show the Diamanggala polje, Bontobonto polje, and adjacent Panagi River Valley were joined together as one continuous river valley at about the end of the Pleistocene, having been filled by about 100 m of noncalcareous rocks of the *Walanae Formation* during the Late Miocene/Pliocene to Pleistocene. Since the Pleistocene, the valley fill was incised to its present level by several active rivers. Crystalline shist basement rocks were exposed by the incision, and this resulted in the separation of the two poljes from the Panagi River Valley. A remaining ridge of *Walanae Formation* rocks between the Buakmata River and Tammale River creates an additional topographic divide between the Diamanggala and Bontobonto poljes, and the impression they are separate karst depressions.

Clearly, the geomorphology of the Diamanggala and Bontobonto poljes is not consistent with the explanations offered by Sunartadirdja and Lehmann (1960). The polje floors are not nearly level, and are not thinly mantled by sediments. They are not expanding to form a larger polje, and they will not eventually coalesce by Losungsunterschneidung to form a karst margin plan. In fact, the Pleistocene history of the poljes shows the disintegration of a once larger valley into smaller depressions, now separated from one another by ridges of noncalcareous rocks. The moderate valley slide slopes are not composed of talus, but consist of *in situ* limestone that was exposed by the partial removal of the Late-Miocene/Pliocene to Pleistocene valley fill deposits by rivers.

DISCUSSION

The importance of rivers should be explored more widely in interpreting karst landscape development, within and beyond the tropics, including the classical karst areas. Rivers are important agents of geomorphic change, but are sometimes either not recognized or appear to be underestimated in many karst landscapes. Where rivers are present, their potential role in the geomorphic development of the karst landforms should be thoroughly evaluated, including detailed field studies and the consideration of geological and sedimentological evidence.

The solutional evolutionary model needs to be more rigorously field tested, including using geological and sedimentological evidence to substantiate conclusions about the processes that create specific landforms. Evidence from Belize, northern Borneo, and particularly Sulawesi, Indonesia, shows the general appearance of particular karst landforms, such as poljes, cannot be used to draw conclusions about the geomorphic processes or evolutionary sequences of landform development. Geological and sedimentological evidence should be described and evaluated to support process-related conclusions in karst geomorphology.

REFERENCES

Bartstra, G.-J., 1976: Walanae Formation and Walanae Terraces in the Stratigraphy of South Sulawesi (Celebes, Indonesia). - Quartar, v. 27.

Grund, A., 1914: Der geographische Zyklus im Karst. - Z. Ges. Erdk., Berl. 52: 621-640.

Lehmann, H., 1953: Karstenwicklung in den Tropen. - Die Umschau in Wissenschaft und Technik 18: 559-562.

McDonald, R., 1976: Limestone Morphology in South Sulawesi, Indonesia. - Z. Geomorph. Supple. 26: 79-91.

McDonald,R., 1979a: Tower Karst Geomorphology in Belize. - Z. Geomorph. Supple. 32: 35-45.

McDonald, R.,, 1979b: Tower Karst Geomorphology, with Special Reference to Belize, Indonesia, and Malaysia. - D.Phil. Thesis, University of Oxford, 317 p.

McDonald, R. and Ley, R. (1985): Tower Karst Geomorphology in Northern Borneo. - Zeit.f.Geom. 29: 483-495.

Sukamto, R. (1975): Reconnaissance Geologic Map of Ujung Pandang Area, Sulawesi Selatan (1:250,000): Geological Survey of Indonesia, Bandung, Java.

Sunartadirdja, M. A., & H. Lehmann (1960): Der tropische Karst von Maros und Nord-Bone in SW-Celebes (Sulawesi). - Z. Geomorph. Suppl., 2: 49-65.

Address
2743 14th Street, Sacramento, California 95818, U.S.A.
E-mail: roy.mcdonald@mwhglobal.com

Evolution of Karst: From Prekarst to Cessation, 275-281, Ljubljana-Postojna 2002

THE CONTACT KARST LANDSCAPE OF SALENTO PENINSULA (APULIA, SOUTHEN ITALY)

GINALUCA SELLERI, PAOLO SANSÒ & NICOLA WALSH

Abstract
A contact karst landscape has been investigated in the Salento penisula (Apulia, southern Italy). The geological, hydrogeological and morphological conditions allow the development of a drainage network flowing towards the North. It bring allogenic waters to marginal depressions whose bottom is studded by a number of cave collapse sinkholes. Sinkholes development broke the drainage network in smalles basins. Landscape evolution has been strongly influenced by recent tectonics as it determined the formation of the endorheic area, the general flow of allogenic waters toward the North and the position of cave collapse sinkholes.
Keywords: *contact karst, cave collapse sinkholes, tectonics*

INTRODUCTION

Research about the karst landscape evolution of the mid-southern part of Salento penisula (Apulia, southern Italy) has been stimulated by the necessity to assess the hazard related to the development of cave collapse sinkholes in the area. In fact, the 13 March 1996 a cave collapse sinkhole, up to 20 m deep and wide, formed in an area marked by a number of older similar forms, posing a relevant threat to the close urbanized area.

In this paper, the first data about the geological, hydrogeological and morphological conditions which influenced the landscape evolution are reported along with processes which are responsible for sinkholes development.

Photo 1. A view of cave collapse sinkhole at Torre Mozza.

GEOLOGICAL AND HYDROGEOLOGICAL SETTING

The Salento peninsula is the southernmost part of the Apulia region (southern Italy). Apulia is the emerged part of a plate stretching between the Ionian Sea and the Adriatic Sea which constitutes the foreland of both Apenninic and Dinaric orogens. It comprises a Variscan basement covered by a 3-5 km thick Mesozoic carbonate sequence - the Calcari delle Murge unit -, and overlain by thin deposits of Neogene and Quaternary age (Ciaranfi et al., 1992).

The mid-southern part of Salento peninsula is marked by a wide endorheic area, bordered both toward the East and the West by degradated fault scarps which are the flanks of two narrow ridges lengthened in NNW-SSE direction. Marls, calcareous marls and calcarenites belonging to several Pleistocene sedimentary cycles extensively crop out in the endorheic area. These deposits cover a stratigraphic sequence compound by

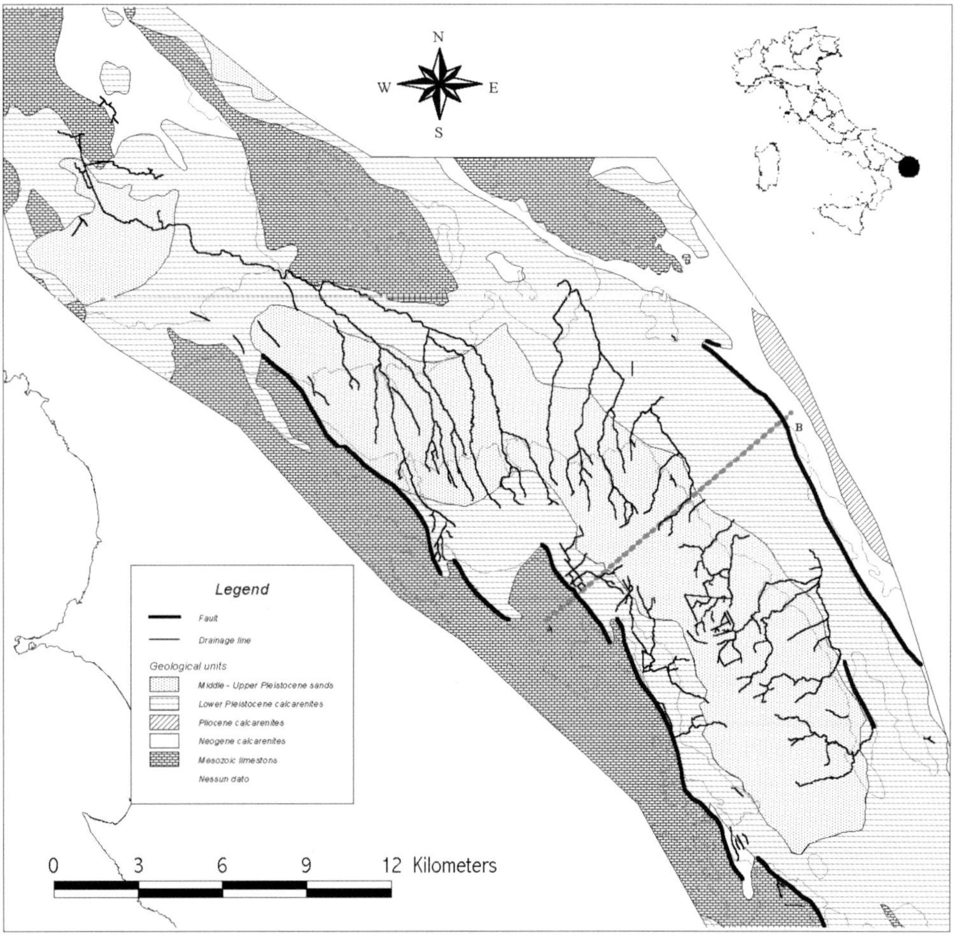

Fig. 1. Geological map of mid-southern area of Salento peninsula

five calcareous units whose age is comprised between the Upper Cretaceous and the Upper Pliocene.

Two elongated depressions characterized the margins of the endorheic area. They are shaped on Lowest Pleistocene deposits (Bossio et al., 1987), up to 70 m thick, made by calcareous, bioclastic sandstones, locally clinostratified; they shade into bluish clayey marls toward the centre of the area. The bottom of depressions is covered by thick, sandy colluvial deposits.

The most part of endorheic area is constituted by a flat surface, gently sloping northeastward, reaching 120 m of altitude at its SE part. The surface is shaped on white quartz sands that can be most likely referred to the Middle Pleistocene. To the northwest, a low relict cliff joins this surface to a wide marine terrace placed between 40-80 m of altitude whose deposits, made by coarse calcareous sandstones, lie transgressively on Lower Pleistocene sandy and clayey deposits (D'Alessandro et al., 1994).

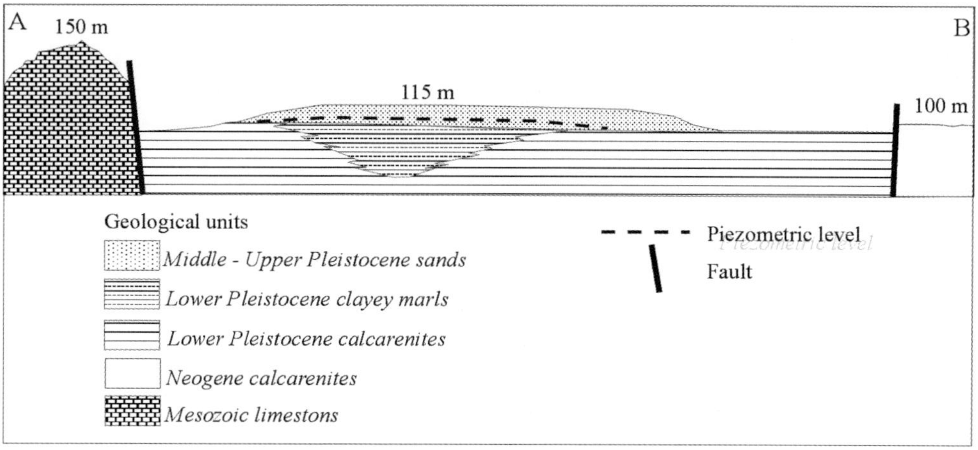

Fig. 2. Schematic cross-section of mid-southern area of Salento peninsula

The Salento peninsula is marked by a wide, deep aquifer flowing into the Mesozoic limestones which rests on sea-water intruded from the nearby coastal area (Ghyben-Herzberg principle). However, a number of shallow water tables are host in the more recent deposits. In particular, in the endorheic area several water tables can be found within the Lower Pleistocene calcareous sandstones and in the Middle Pleistocene sands even if their characteristics are not well-known. However, a significative drainage from shallow water tables to the deep aquifer is most likely to occur along subvertical planes of greater hydraulic conductivity.

GEOMORPHOLOGICAL SETTING

An hydrographic network flowing from the marine terraces top surfaces to the bottom of marginal depressions. Three areas with uniform drainage network direction (NW, NE and SW) are separated by two main divides. The former runs in NNW-SSE direction for about 25 km, close to the western border of the endorheic area. It is placed along the prolongation of the axis of morphostructural high which borders to the North the area. The second divide is shorter and E-W oriented.

Short, straight valleys incise the border fault scarps. Longer, meander-like valleys developed on unpervious, sandy deposits; valleys follow a sub-angular pattern with straight streams flowing in NNW-SSE and NW-SE directions in area where Lower Pleistocene calcareous sandstones crop out. Valleys end at a number of cave collapse sinkholes aligned in NNW-SSE and NW-SE directions.

Cave collapse sinkholes show sub-cilindric shape, up to 30 m deep and up to 20 m wide, often linked to karstic caves. The process of sinkhole activity is presently active as suggested by the recent development of a new cave collapse sinkhole in area marked by the presence of three older similar forms. Sinkholes formation has been responsible for

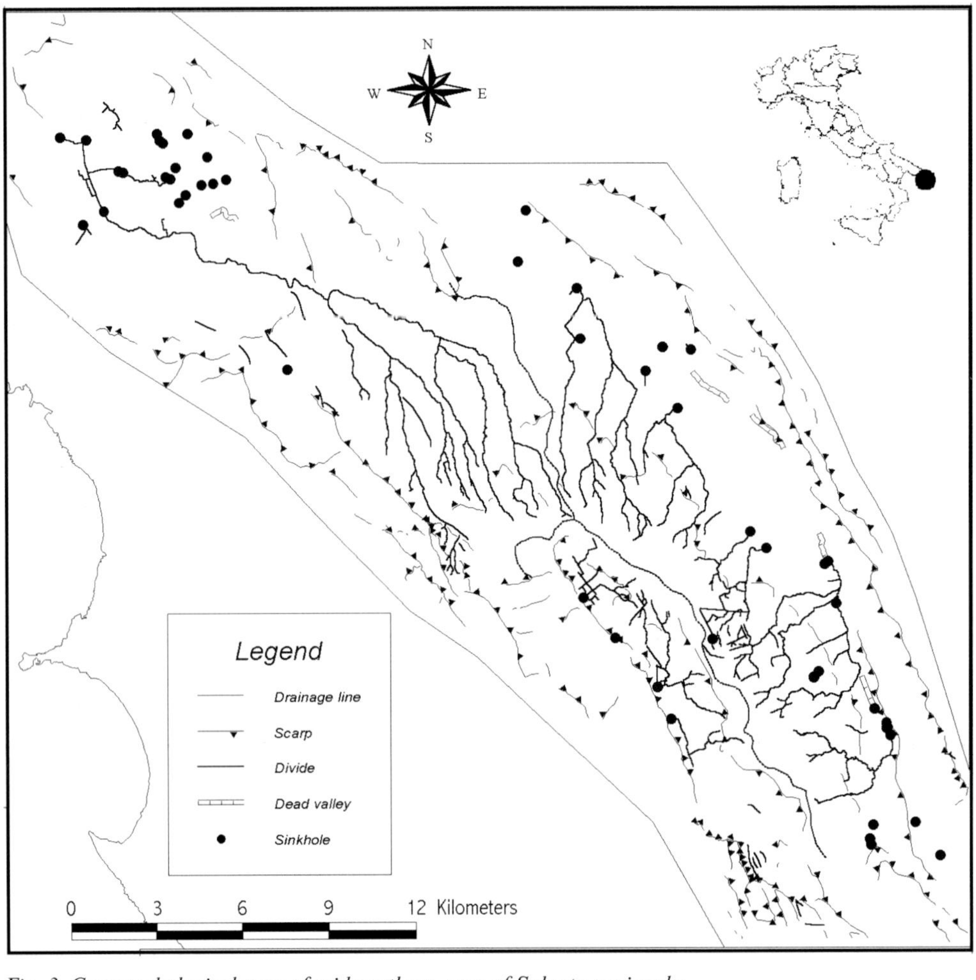

Fig. 3. Geomorphological map of mid-southern area of Salento peninsula

the breaking out of the hydrographical network and for the genesis of a number of dead valleys which can be recognized at the northeastern border of the area.

Cover sinkholes, up to 20 meters wide, are located at the border of marine terraced surfaces. Several cover sinkholes formed recently in the southernmost part of the endorheic area.

DISCUSSION

The landscape shown by the midsouthern Salento area is an example of contact karst whose genesis and evolution is linked to the occurrence of a contact between unpervious, non-karstic rocks and pervious, karstic rocks.

According to Gams (1994) the main factors influencing the geomorphological evolution of these particular areas are the discharge and the chemical characteristics of allogenic waters, the quantity and grain size of material transported by the allogenic river, the permeability of karstic rocks, the relief amplitude, the depth of the piezometic level, the relation between the size of outcropping area of impermeable and permeable sediments, and, finally, the age of karstic landscape.

In particular, the landscape of the midsouthern Salento area can be seen as a particular type of border karst due to the presence of the sub-horizontal contact between the Middle-Upper Pleistocene unpervious deposits and the Lower Pleistocene karstic terrains. The impermeable cover allowed the development of a drainage network responsible for the flow of allogenic waters to the marginal depressions. A number of cave collapse sinkholes bring allogenic water into underground circulation along subvertical planes of major hydraulic conductivity, generally corresponding to main joints or fault planes.

The geomorphological analysis shows that the evolution of this karstic landscape has been strongly controlled by a very recent, even if not intense, tectonic activity. The tilting on the area towards NE which interested the entire Salento region (Palmentola, 1987) induced the general northward flowing of the upper portion of the drainage network, shaped on the Middle Pleistocene sandy cover. On the contrary, the lower part of it, flowing on Lower Pleistocene calcarenites, is strongly controlled by the geological structure so that streams flow in the same directions of main tectonic alignments. The small uplift of the morphostructural high which borders to the North the area should be responsible for the development of main divide which run across the endorheic area in NNW-SSE direction.

A relict drainage network flowing into some sinkholes placed in the northen part of the area can be reconstructed. It has been broken by the development a number of cave collapse sinkholes into smaller basins, causing in same cases the formation of short dead valleys.

The development of the cave collapse sinkholes is linked to the particular lithological sequence of Lower Pleistocene calcarenites, made up by well-cemented calcareous sandstones in the uppermost levels shading downward to sands and silts interbedded with calcareous- marly layers, to the relatively abundant quantity of allogenic waters and to the occurrence of planes of major hydraulic conductivity. Caves widen in the lower levels made by sands and silts and assume shapes according to the joints pattern and the occurrence of unpervious layers. The increasing volume of caves and the intersection between strata planes and joints are the main factors inducing the fall of cave ceiling.

Cover sinkholes have been detected near the borders of Middle Pleistocene sands outcropping, which host a surficial water table. The genesis of these landforms would be linked to soffusion process produced by the vertical drainage of the water table into the lower aquifers.

CONCLUSIONS

The geomorphological analysis of endorheic area of Salento peninsula suggests that the landscape can be seen as a particular type of border karst due to the presence of the sub-horizontal contact between the Middle-Upper Pleistocene unpervious, non-karstic deposits and the Lower Pleistocene karstic terrains. Allogenic waters are drained by a hydrographic network toward the margin of the endorheic area where a number of cave collapse sinkholes can be found. Their development has been promoted by the peculiar litho-stratigraphic characters of Lower Pleistocene calcarenites. Sinkholes broke the drainage network in smaller basins, forming a number of dead valleys.

Recent tectonics strongly influenced landscape evolution as it determined the formation of the endorheic area, the general flow of allogenic waters toward the North and the position of cave collapse sinkholes.

REFERENCES

Bossio, A., Guelfi, F., Mazzei, R., Monteforti, B., Salvatorini, G., Varola, A. 1987: Precisazioni sull'etŕ dei sedimenti pleistocenici di due cave del leccese (San Pietro in Lama e Cutrofiano). Atti del Convegno sulle conoscenze geologiche del territorio salentino. Lecce 12 dicembre 1987. Quaderni di Ricerche del Centro Studi Geotecnica e di Ingegneria Lecce, 11, 147-174, Lecce

Ciaranfi, N., Pieri, P., Ricchetti, G. 1992: Note alla carta geologica delle Murge e del Salento (Puglia centro-meridionale). Mem. Soc. Geol. It., 106, 449-460, Roma.

Colombi, A., Di Loreto, A., Nolasco, F., Capelli, G., Salvati, R. 2001: The purposes of the main sinkhole project in the Latium Region of central Italy. Geotecnical and Environmental Application of Karst Geology and Hidrology, 73-76, Beck and Herring Eds.

D'Alessandro, A., Mastronuzzi, G., Palmentola, G. & Sansň, P. 1994: Pleistocene deposits of Salento leccese (Southern Italy): Problematic relationships. Boll. Soc. Paleontol.It., 33(2), 257-263.

Gams, I., 1994: Types of contact karst. Geogr. Fis. Dinam. Quat., 17, 37-46.

Palmentola, G. 1987: Geological and geomorphological outlines of the Salento leccese region (Southern Italy). Atti del Convegno sulle conoscenze geologiche del territorio salentino. Lecce 12 dicembre 1987. Quaderni di Ricerche del Centro Studi Geotecnica e di Ingegneria Lecce, 11, 7-23, Lecce.

Address
Ginaluca Salleri
Dipartimento di Geologia e Geofisica, Universitá di Bari, Italy
Paolo Sanso
Osservatorio di Chimica, Fisica e Geologia ambientale, Dipartimento di Scienza dei Materiali, Universitá di Lecce, Italy
Nicola Walsh
Dipartimento di Geologia e Geofisica, Universitá di Bari, Italy

LATE PLEISTOCENE REDIRECTION OF THE CERKNIŠČICA RIVER: EFFECT ON THE NEIGHBOURING KARST

FRANCE ŠUŠTERŠIČ, SIMONA ŠUŠTERŠIČ & UROŠ STEPIŠNIK

Abstract
Detailed study of the Cerkniščica's sediments in Cerkniško polje revealed that the river turned this direction relatively late, presumably in the middle Würm. Its alluvial fan choked the main vertical ponors, and deflected the river westwards, i.e. into Rakov Škocjan valley, and further on, into Planinska jama. Increased quantity of water that entered the East branch of the cave redirected the flow of the Pivka river into the North branch, and reactivated since long time ago, choked (present) entrance to the cave. Retransported sediment from Planinska jama can be traced across Planinsko polje into the ponor caves on the North.
Keywords: *Classical Karst, Planinska jama, Pleistocene, cave sediments, cave dynamism, karst hydrology*

INTRODUCTION

The paper discusses the late Quaternary dynamics of the Cerkniščica river, which lies within the Ljubjanica River catchment. The latter, also known as "The River of Seven Names", is the best-known sinking river in the Classical Karst of Slovenia. Figure 1 shows the locations and relationships of significant features discussed in the text.

The Cerkniščica River is the only predominantly non-karstic tributary to Cerkniško Polje. Whereas the Cerkniščica enters the polje through a canyon-like valley, most of its upper catchment area appears to be a relatively equilibrated fluvio-denudational surface, adapted to a base-level about 40m higher than the present main stream (S. Šušteršič, 2002). Modern incision within the upper Cerkniščica basin, triggered by reversal (Fig. 1) of the Cerkniščica River into the Cekniško Polje, and consequently driven by a lowering of the outlet by about 40m, has influenced only the main streams, to form deep, narrow valleys. Based on a detailed geomorphological study of the reversal area, S. Šušteršič (o.c.) demonstrated that it was a relatively fast, catastrophic, event.

This paper investigates the direct downstream consequences for this part of the Ljubljanica River catchment, especially for Planinska jama.

EVOLUTION OF THE CERKNIŠČICA RIVER[1]

Other than the non-karstic Cerkniščica River, the tributaries feeding Cerkniško Polje are completely karstic. It is extremely difficult to estimate the inflow and outflow of the polje, and figures are difficult to find in the literature. Combined data from Žibrik & Pičinin (1973, 5) and Gospodarič & Habič (1979, 103)[2] provide the following yearly average input. Note that the proportions are crucial:

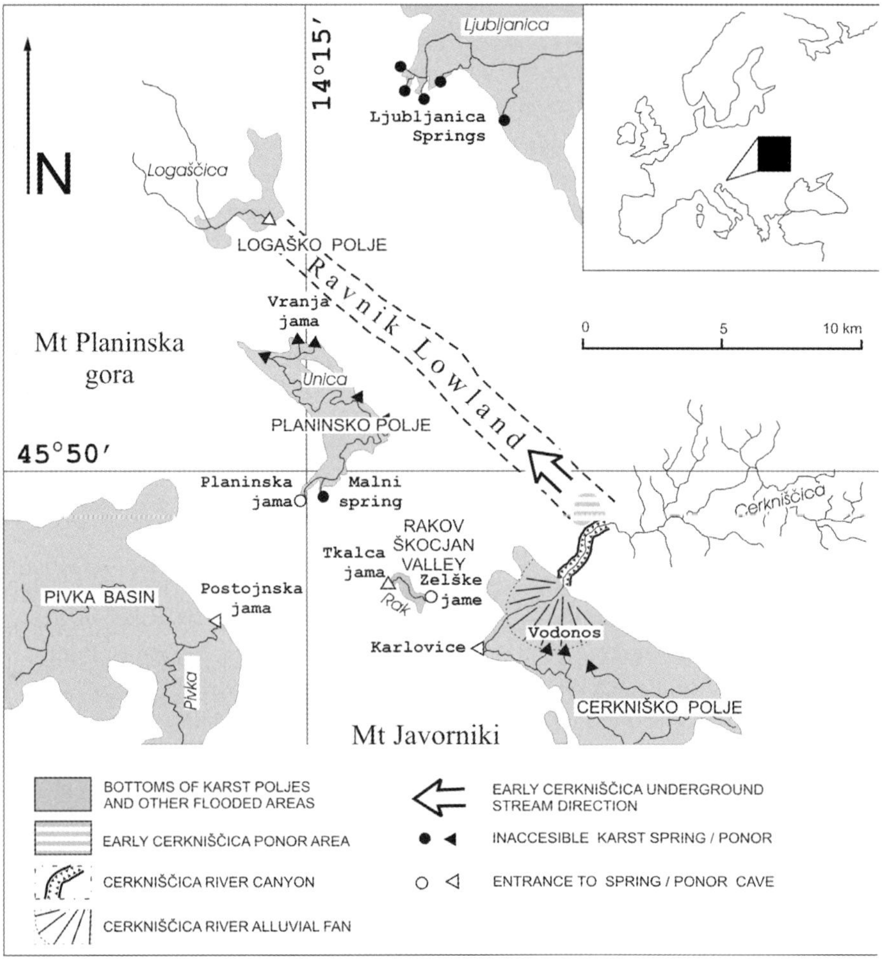

Fig. 1. Location map of part of the Ljubljanica River catchment, showing the locations of features discussed in the text.

[1] In this paper, only information directly concerning its topic is given. For more exhaustive data about the wider area the reader is referred to Gospodarič & Habič, 1979 and F. Šušteršič, 1996.

[2] Relatively uncertain absolute data reflect the difficult and unreliable field measurements, so that the authors prefer to give just data for particular observations. Consequently, the final results must be viewed with some reservation, though the basic proportions remain constant with different observers.

Cerkniščica	$1.23 m^3 s^{-1}$	8.54%
Other	$13.17 m^3 s^{-1}$	91.46%
Total	$14.40 m^3 s^{-1}$	100.00%

Presently, most of Cerkniško Polje drains through ponor caves (Fig. 1) in its north-western-most embayment. It is confirmed that the cave ponors direct water through the Rakov Škocjan valley (Fig 1) and further, into the springs at Planinsko polje (Fig. 1).

The entire low flow (plus some excess normal and high flow) sinks into vertical ponors (plus estavelles) in the polje floor. Unlike large ponor caves, these are narrow openings in the bedrock beneath sediments, and are inaccessible to humans. Only a few of these sinks, including Vodonos, the most efficient (Gospodarič & Habič, 1976, 116-120), have been dye traced, but it is generally accepted that they drain directly to the Ljubljanica springs at Vrhnika.

Outputs through the two main ponor types, as well as the general water level in the polje, depend essentially upon the contemporary inflow pattern. Gospodarič & Habič (o.c., 120) estimate the total capacity of the vertical ponors as $<6 m^3 s^{-1}$, whereas the capacity of the cave ponors is $>>20 m^3 s^{-1}$ (o.c., 124). These rough estimates differ from less consistent estimates by earlier workers (o.c., 96-103), but the basic proportions seem reasonable. So, about 20% of the present average output from Cerkniško polje drains directly to the Ljubljanica springs, whereas about 80% ($11 m^3 s^{-1}$) flows in the direction of Rakov Škocjan, and on to Planinsko polje. These waters first reappear in the Rakov Škocjan valley, as the Rak River.

When the discharge in the Rak is low, its water sinks into Tkalca jama[3] (cave) and flows to boulder-choked springs in the Malni pocket valley on the southern margin of Planinsko polje. When the Rak water levels are higher, surplus water flows through completely water-filled, only partly explored, passages into the East Branch[4] of Planinska Jama (Morel, 2000,2001). After leaving the North Branch, the river (now the Unica) flows across Planinsko polje, where it is joined by the only important tributary appaerig from the Malni spring.

Planinsko polje has no large, direct ponor caves. However, as well as in the main ponors, underground water is seen in some large caves, among which Vranja jama is of particular interest. The Unica gradually sinks, eventually to reappear from the Ljubljani-

[3] The most direct stream towards Planinsko polje is not significant, and it is omitted from further discussion.

[4] Planinska jama consists of three main branches. The eastern one brings water from Cerkniško polje (plus Mt Javorniki in the South, which is outside present interest). At the Confluence, it joins the West Branch where the river Pivka, after having passed through a huge, incompletely explored siphon, arrives from Postojnska jama. The united rivers obtain a new name, i.e. the Unica. It leaves the cave through the North Branch and enters Planinsko polje in its southwestern-most corner. The East and West branches are each more than 2km long, whereas the North Branch is less than one kilometre long. It must be noted that this terminology is not completely unknown, but not widely used. In order to avoid confusion when discussing changes in the stream direction, it is used strictly throughout this paper. The identities are:

Name used here:	Alternative/former name:
East Branch	Rak Branch
West Branch	Pivka Branch
North Branch	Entrance Branch

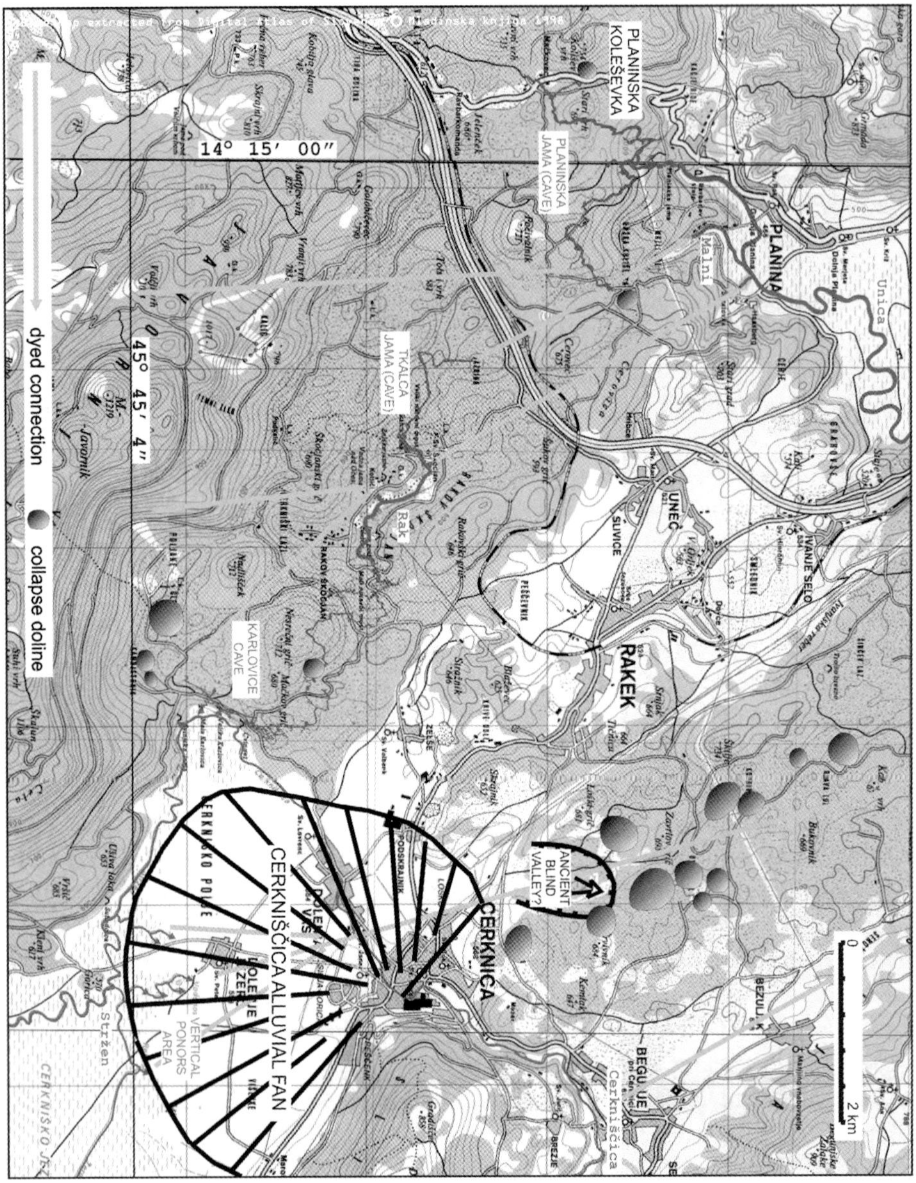

Fig. 2. General hydrogeological conditions in the central area of the karstic-Ljubljanica catchment.

ca springs at Vrhnika, where waters from various sources, including discharge from the vertical ponors in the Cerkniško Polje, are mixed together.

The literature (see F. Šušteršič 1996, 256) agrees that, in the not too distant past, the Cerkniščica River turned northwestward near the present village of Begunje. Early authors assumed that it flowed on the surface through the present Ravnik lowland (o.c., 257, Fig. 2), towards the present Logaško Polje. During systematic mapping of unroofed caves in the central part of Ravnik, about 10km northwest from the present river, F. Šušteršič (1998) revealed an abandoned, completely in-filled cave system.

At the top of the sediment fill is a dolomite conglomerate, lithologically identical to the present Cerkniščica River sediment load. Based on general appearance and characteristic grain-size profile, F. Šušteršič (o.c.) argued that the conglomerate is a Pleistocene cold stage deposit. In most outcrops flowstone occurs sandwiched between the conglomerate layers. The flowstone is too old to be dated by the U-Th series method, i.e. older than 350ka. The presence of pebbles derived from local rocks within the cave sediments confirmed the anticipated - but underground - flow direction (o.c., 128).

The same material as the Ravnik conglomerate, i.e. Norian and Rhaetian dolomite pebbles plus some bauxite and chert, is in the uppermost sediment in the present Cerkniščica alluvial cone (Pleničar, 1953 and Gospodarič & Habič, 1979). In the lower part of the cone Gospodarič & Habič (o.c., 43) found a spruce cone. C^{14} analysis revealed its age at about 55ka. The same authors quote Šercelj (1974), who found pollen, testifying stadial vegetation, in the same layer. So, the lower sediment package must date from the Würm I era, whereas the gravel must be younger.

Formation of the Cerkniščica cone perhaps occurred on the first occasion that fluvial sediment entered the polje in significant amounts (F. & S. Šušteršič, in preparation), as there is no evidence that anything similar happened earlier. Pleničar (1953) notes that many boreholes into the underlying bedrock found even sediment filled caverns He reports (o.c., 112-113) that they are filled with loam and sand, but his cross-sections stress the presence of flowstone (o.c., Prof. 3-5). Despite this equivocal information, it is questionable whether the earlier relative water table elevation was comparable with the present one, and whether the polje held surface water at all.

After the river crosses the alluvial cone it flows about 1km over the flat, loamy sediment in the extreme northwestern corner of the polje, and disappears into the main (Karlovice) ponor caves. Insignificant riverbed sandbanks indicate that the present river can transport minor quantities of coarse sediment from the cone, or even from more distant parts of the catchment, but the present sedimentary input into the Karlovice ponor caves is minute. First impressions are that the system's main channels are epiphreatic, whereas other explored channels, i.e. older, fragmentary, passages up to about 60m above the present water table, are mostly phreatic. This implies that in the more remote past the input to the caves (and to the polje) was completely karstic.

Fresh sinks in the polje's alluvial cone (Jenko, 1959, 214; Gospodarič & Habič, 95) indicate that fluvial sediment has buried an active ponor area. This is clearly evident at the toe of the cone, where, at several locations, especially at the Vodonos ponor complex, recent sapping is so active that local inhabitants must fill in the holes. It implies that the present (post-Würmian) situation is unstable, and the sinking river is re-establishing its former conditions.

A number of large, but relatively mature[5] collapse dolines have long been known all

[5] In the sense that no perpendicular walls are preserved, and the slopes are generally gentle.

along Ravnik, north of Cerkniško Polje (F. Šušteršič, 1973). Without receiving deeper consideration they were attributed to former outflow from Cerkniško Polje. More recently, outcrops of the conglomerate mentioned above were found in some of the doline slopes. Seemingly recent subsidence cones in the floors of other dolines indicate that, after a time gap, underground flow is resuming its activity. Complex water tracing experiments (Gospodarič & Habič, 1976, 199) revealed relatively fast (7.4cm s^{-1}) underground flow between the Vodonos (vertical) ponor and Velika Ljubljanica spring, confirming that highly transmissive karst channels lie in between.

Close inspection of a detailed map of the area between the present vertical ponors and the collapse dolines (Fig.2) reveals a relief feature resembling a partly disintegrated blind valley[6]. Its present floor is between 601m and 615m, which is almost the same elevation as that of the ancient Cerkniščica valley at the point where it meets Ravnik. If this interpretation is valid, it would mean that at some stage - certainly before the Cerkniščica's flow reversal - the entire polje could have drained in this direction and the present cave ponors were bandoned.

All this indicates that in the not too distant past much more water could have drained from Cerkniško polje directly to the Ljubljanica springs at Vrhnika than drains today. Concurrently a smaller quantity should have supplied the ponor caves and thence the Malni pocket valley at Planinsko Polje. In the extreme, the input into Malni from the southeast would be reduced to an insignificant contribution of direct drainage from Mt Javorniki intercepted by the Rakov Škocjan valley[7].

Recharge from the Cerkniščica River alone would not directly influence drainage from the polje significantly. A 1.23m s^{-1} increase in input meant only a c.10% increase of the total, which the existing ponors could cope with without a major problem. However, the indirect influence was dramatic. After breakthrough, large amounts of cryoclastic gravel reached the Cerkniško Polje at almost the exact location of the ponors, causing the water to go directly to the Vrhnika springs. Gravel deposition was so concentrated that it cut off, and eventually completely eliminated the whole ponor area. The presently inactive collapse dolines in Ravnik (mentioned above), north from the most northeastern corner of Cerkniško Polje, indicate the existence of a large cave system that was suddenly abandoned.

It is impossible to estimate directly how much water was deflected towards the present cave ponors. The extent of the presently inactive collapse dolines supports an earlier idea that, at least for a certain period, most of Cerkniško polje might have drained northwards (towards the Vrhnika springs). In the extreme, it means that, after the de-

---

[6] No detailed study of this embayment has yet been carried out, so that other interpretations are possible.

[7] This raises the question of the former role, or even existence. of the main ponor caves, i.e. the Karlovice system and its direct continuation (Žalec et al., 1997) Zelške jame, the main spring cave in the Rakov Škocjan valley. Statistical study of cave distribution led F. Šušteršič (1996, 2000) to conclude that this is just a rejuvenated part of a larger system, formed essentially in phreatic conditions, before strike-slip movement along the Idria Fault (according to F. Šušteršič, 1996, 270, Fig.5, No.4) Putting aside still-disputed questions of the strike-slip timing, formation of such a cave system probably preceded polje development. Mišič (1998) found flysch-derived sand in Zelške jame, which is surprising on consideration of present flow conditions.

flection, a stream of up to 14m^{3}s^{-1} might have surged into the Rakov Škocjan valley, and further on, to Planinsko Polje. If even half of this quantity entered Planinska jama, the Pivka (present average discharge 4.84m^{3}s^{-1}; Žibrik, Lewicki & Pičinin, 1976, 49, Tab.2) could not have coped with it, and the consequences should be observable.

LATE QUATERNARY DYNAMICS OF PLANINSKA JAMA

In his comprehensive treatise Gospodarič (1976) gives extensive information about late Quaternary development in Planinska and Postojnska jama caves. His main goal was, however, to extract general data about both caves, and to make regional generalizations. His work is based fundamentally on study of sediments in both caves, and the factual data he presented fit the purposes of the present paper exactly.

Gospodarič (o.c.) stated that, at the time of deposition of the oldest detected sediment (i.e. coloured chert), most of the present cave (considering it as voids in the bedrock) must have existed, though some passages had not yet achieved their ultimate dimensions. From Plate 3A (o.c., 128-129) it is clear that the original, large elliptical phreatic passages are so well preserved that significant mechanical erosion before deposition of the coloured chert cannot be hypothesised.

Gospodarič (o.c., 134, Tab. 3) provides a clear view of general sedimentary events in Planinska jama. Applying his basically stratigraphical findings to the plan of the cave (Fig. 3), and omitting less significant details, the following late Quaternary history can be extracted:

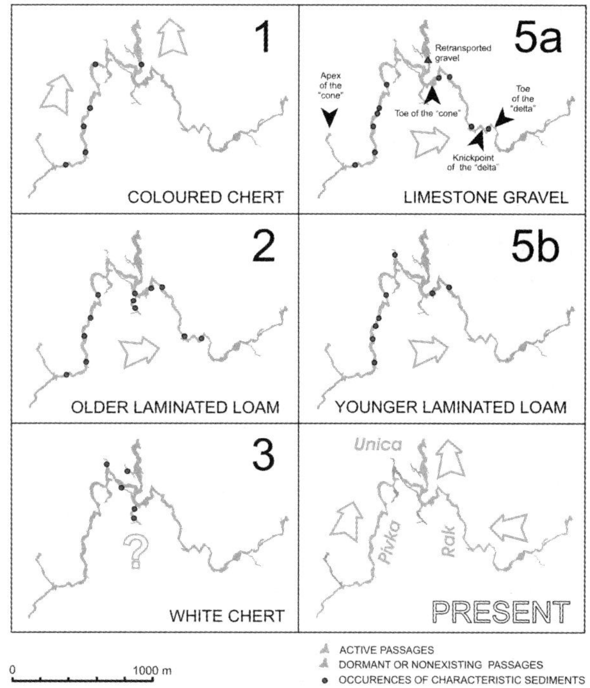

Fig. 3. Location of the main sediments in Planinska jama during the sedimentary events outlined in Table 1.

Table 1 Main sedimentary events in Planinska jama(extracted and rearranged after Gospodarič, 1976, Tabs 1 and 3)

1	Middle Quarternary	Sedimentation of coloured chert	the West and the North branches active; the East Branch dormant	input close to the present inlet to the West Branch; output through the North Branch towards the present "cave entrance" (i.e. outlet)
2	before approx. 78 ± 8.4 ka b.p.	Sedimentation of "older laminated loam"	flooding of the West and the East branches to the elevation about 475m a.s.l.; the North Branch dormant	Stream direction unknown: the most likely input close to the present "inlet" to the West Branch; output through the East Branch towards the present Malni spring
3	Riss	Sedimentation of white chert	Only relatively small passages close to the Confluence; the rest of the cave dormant	Stream direction equivocal; in both possible cases inlets and outlets away from the present main conduits
4	Riss-Würm	Flowstone growth, dated 80 ka b.p.	general data about the location of the stalagmite insufficient, perhaps too high to be related to "fluvial" phases	
5a	before approx. 30 ka b.p.	Deposition of limestone gravel	The West and the East branches active; the North Branch dormant	input through "Paradise" near the present "inlet" to the West Branch; output through the East Branch towards the present Malni spring

5b	Lower Würm	The West and the East branch evacuated from limestone gravel; sedimentation of "younger laminated loam" in the West Branch	All three main branches active; the West Branch flooded	Stream direction comparable to the present; input through the West and the North branches; output through the North Branch

Note: The events are numbered according to Gospodarič (o.c.), except event No.5 is split in two sub-events (a, b), to distinguish between deposition of limestone gravel and "younger laminated loam". The table is inverted compared to the original, which followed standard geological rules of superposition.

To make the developments in Planinska jama more readily comparable with the events in Cerkniško polje, more comments on particular details are needed.

1. Coloured chert fragments are deposited throughout the cave in a layer no thicker than 1m (Gospodarič, o.c., 58). This indicates that the Pivka flowed without great obstacles through the West and North branches, in the general direction of the present outlet (cave entrance). The East Branch, which presently carries high waters from Rakov Škocjan, and indirectly, from the Cerkniško Polje, appears to have been inactive at this time - but not choked. Otherwise it could not have become sediment-filled during the next event.

2. Impressed by the existence of visually comparable sediments in many caves and even on the surface in the vicinity, Gospodarič considered deposition of the "older laminated loam" as a paramount regional event (o.c., 61). However, there was no conclusive proof that all loams were the same age or at least had the same mineralogy. He viewed it as an outcome of a general "sedimentation phase", following an "erosion phase". This terminology is purely Davisian, and raises doubts. In principle, increased production of loamy material is possibly a regional event, triggered, say, by climate change (o.c., 60). On the other hand, the actual deposition is an immediate consequence of a decrease in the water's transport capacity, which primarily reflects a local change in stream velocity. Similar elevations of the highest known laminated loam deposits taken over as wide an area as possible in Planinska jama, indicate that a uniform water body once existed in the cave. Failure to match each lamination in the loam between locations, according to de Geer's varve method (o.c., 60-61), indicates either that deposition was not fully contemporaneous at different locations, or that local influences prevailed. So, it seems more feasible to interpret deposition of the "older laminated loam" as a local event.

The absence of "older laminated loam" in the dormant North Branch is somewhat surprising. Extensive collapse near the outlet, or choking by materials produced by slope processes on the facing Mt Planinska gora could explain this. Yet, in either case, loam-laden water could penetrate into the North Branch and some traces of "older laminated loam" should exist in remote corners. Gospodarič's explanation that the loam was totally removed during subsequent extensive widening of the passage is not convincing.

The break between deposition of coloured gravel and of "older laminated loam" was caused by the cessation of flow in the general direction of the present cave outlet, and the Pivka's reversal towards the Malni spring. Whereas the existence of waters from Rakov Škocjan in the East Branch in the previous phase (**1**) cannot be confirmed, in the present phase (**2**) it is actually excluded.

3. Gospodarič (o.c., 61) noted: "Sinking (i.e. underground[8]) river deposited the sediment (i.e. white chert gravel) into the (nearly completely) in-filled Planinska jama, into the upper third of its (main) branches, under the ceiling, or into independent, higher lying channels, which had been formed around the Confluence above the elevation of 475m a.s.l." The highest known location is 490m a.s.l. At just one location (480m a.s.l.) the white chert lies on the "older laminated loam", whereas elsewhere small quantities appear in "pockets" in the cave walls. The vertical range of 15m within an approximate distance of 500m is large, and the vertical distribution reveals no spatial pattern. Both raise the question of whether the deposits are in their primary position.

Putting this doubt aside, only one explanation, offered by Gospodarič (o.c., 46-47), is possible. During white chert deposition, most of the cave's main branches were completely sediment filled (perhaps choked with coloured chert and "older laminated loam") and water had to re-use "parallel" passages that had become inactive a long time before. Gospodarič (o.c., 62) stated that the presence of the white chert gravel is an indicator of an increase in the velocity of the river to at least 0.5m s^{-1} and its ability to carry a heavier load. The present authors accept the latter idea as a fair statement only for very local conditions. Gospodarič's more general conclusion (o.c., 62) that "the river could flow faster towards Planinsko polje" is just one less feasible possible interpretation.

Gospodarič (o.c., 62) confirmed the source of the white chert gravel as the southern part of the Pivka basin. Hypothetically, when the river began to carry it into the cave, Pivka's catchment area had expanded dramatically. Assuming channel sections were not adapted to larger discharge, increased velocity would inevitably result in increased gravel entrainment, which apparently supports Gospodarič's statement. However, the question of the coloured chert gravel remains. Thus, the present authors prefer the view that the white chert gravel indicates a less important episode, when the main channels were nearly totally inactive. The river must predominantly have by-passed the presently known cave passages, and the stream direction remains uncertain.

4. Due to lack of data this episode remains unclear. Whereas flowstone growth in higher, dry parts was inevitable, the more important question involves what was happen-

[8] Due to subtle undertones in the particular words used by Gospodarič, "one-to-one" translation from Slovene into English is not appropriate. Expressions in brackets are added by F. Šušteršič to give readers a more accurate impression of the original idea.

ing at lower elevations. During the subsequent **(5a)** episode, the West and East branches were initially sediment free. So, a major erosional event must have taken place after deposition of the white chert gravel. Gospodarič (o.c., Table 1, 69 [126]) believed that erosion and sedimentation went hand-in-hand. However, it is difficult to recognize a direct logical connection between white chert gravel in some high, remote, smaller, passages, and the massive scouring that swept the main passages clear of about 1 Mm^3 of material. Considering the flow pattern indicated by white chert gravel distribution, the erosional mechanism would require a radical change of general circumstances, just to make it operate. So, the effects should not be considered contemporaneous without strong material proof.

The flow direction cannot be determined directly. As during the next phase (**5a**) the river followed a highly transmissive route towards the Malni spring. Flow from the Pivka inlet through the West Branch and further eastwards through the East Branch is probable. If so, after some tens (or even hundreds[9]) of thousands of years, the general hydrogeological regime of the "older laminated loam" deposition was restored. In other words, the obstacle in the Malni spring area vanished. Evacuation did not include the North Branch, which remained inactive, and the present (cave entrance) outlet remained blocked. In this paper the erosional event is termed **pre-5a**.

5a. Emplacement of limestone gravel in the West and East branches appears to be one of the most dramatic events in Planinska jama's known history. Gospodarič (o.c., 62-65) gives well-supported information about the geometry and formation of the cone-like[10] pile in the cave. Micropalaeontological study by Pavlovec (cit. Gospodarič, o.c., 64) confirmed that the gravel originates from the Planinska koliševka collapse doline. The length of the longitudinal section of the gravel pile totals about 3.5km. In the whole of the West Branch, plus about 100m farther into the East Branch, the profile of the gravel bank decreases exponentially, which is characteristic of high flow velocities, indicating a free water surface. Its apex at almost 495m elevation and its toe at about 470m remain virtually constant for the next kilometre and a quarter, before suddenly dropping down and wedging out after another 100m. This is typical of deltaic sedimentation[11], implying that the East Branch water level was more or less stable at 470m. Input through "Paradise" (Fig. 3, bottom, right) near the present "inlet" to the West Branch, and output through the East Branch towards the Malni spring is evident.

So, the West and East branches were not only active, but they even permitted unimpeded coarse sediment transport. Possible North Branch activity, indicated by Gospodarič (o.c., 62) - discussed below - remains, at best, questionable.

---

[9] This follows from Gospodarič's (o.c., Table 3, 112 [134]) estimation that sedimentation of "older laminated loam" is Rissian, and sedimentation of coloured chert gravel pre-Rissian. However, this is just a subjective opinion, based on apparent analogy. The present authors believe that, due to the lack of material data for more remote events, Gospodarič's time estimation is "logarithmically biased".

[10] It is difficult to speak about a true "cone" if sedimentation is confined within a cave channel.

[11] Unfortunately, the presently known occurrences of the gravel are not large enough to make it possible to prove the existence of expected dipping layers, characteristic of deltaic sedimentation.

5b. "younger laminated loam" appears in the West Branch and in adjacent parts of the East Branch. Gospodarič (o.c., 65) noted that "it must have been eroded from the other parts of the East Branch". It has not been detected in other parts of the cave, including the North Branch. The sediments reach elevations of about 480m, which yields some important information:

- the water still flowed eastward, i.e. towards the Malni pocket valley;
- the cave outlet was impeded, but not blocked;
- flow through the cave was relatively free;
- the North Branch was still inactive.

Evidently limestone gravel emplacement had ceased. As the dynamics of the collapse doline do not imply any intrinsic cause[12], the most feasible explanation is that the Pivka found a by-pass to Planinska koliševka. There is little doubt that this was the present inflow siphon, which has been dived (430m-long, 54m-deep; Vrhovec, 2000, 177) without reaching open cave on the other side. Relatively rapid by-pass formation corresponds to the theoretical expectations of Dreybrodt (2000) and his team.

post-5b Gopodarič based his work primarily on sedimentation within the cave, so the importance of the extensive erosion following the **5**th episode is generally underestimated. The most important in context was a reversal of flow in the East Branch. Before the reversal the Pivka flowed from west to east from the West Branch and then along the East Branch, by-passing the North Branch. Subsequently, the flow of the Rak (currently > 10 m^3s^{-1}) entering the cave from the east became significantly stronger than that of the Pivka (4.8 m3s-1). A probably relatively short period of back-up and flooding is assumed, following which the combined waters of the two streams re-opened the North Branch and flowed northwards together towards the present entrance (Fig. 3).

Discussing episode **5a**, Gospodarič (o.c., 62) wrote: "The (i.e. limestone)[13] gravel layer shows most evidence of erosional rounding between the Confluence and the cave entrance (i.e. in the North Branch)". He wondered (o.c., 56) why - in the only occurrence he found - "the pebbles are the most rounded among all of the studied samples in the cave". The location in question is about half way from the "cone" apex to the "deltaic" toe, still within the torrent's "area of influence". An obvious explanation is that these more-rounded pebbles are now in a secondary position. Having its source to the east of the cave, the gravel was first deposited far up the East Branch. This primary gravel deposit was subsequently reworked, and the limestone clasts suffered additional rounding during transport from the East Branch to their present position in the North Branch.

[12] Gospodarič (o.c., 64) opines that the massive gravel production was a result of the cold Pleistocene climate (Lower Würm [Tab.3]). Photographs (Plates 4B, 7A and 7B) and sieving diagram (Fig.24, 63), however, do not support this idea. The gravel contains a relatively small share of pebbles of dimensions, characteristic of Pleistocene gelifractional products, and too many very coarse particles. So it appears closer to normal fluvial sediment. This implies that the gravel was washed out from the base of the collapsed pile in the cave, without direct control from the surface. It does not preclude the process culminating during a cold period, but it would be mere coincidence.

[13] Expressions in brackets are added by the authors to give a more accurate impression of the original ideas.

Redeposition even reached the northern side of Planinsko Polje, where Gospodarič (1982, 181-183, Fig.2) found material derived from Planinska jama in Vranja jama. He wrote: "Pebbles of coloured and white chert, deposited together and simultaneously, are of special stratigraphical interest." ... "In the sedimentary fill of Vranja jama they appear mixed, so that it (i.e. gravel) had been eroded and transported in hydrological and geomorphic conditions which permitted such transport. ... it could take place in humid and relatively cold climate of the younger Pleistocene, probably at the beginning of the Würm". As might be expected he related the gravel to the evacuation of Planinska jama (Gospodarič, 1976). His unusual proposition that the cold period was humid becomes understandable considering his view that sudden entrainment of the gravel (as a fraction of the more massive outwash of nearly all of Planinska jama) should be driven by recognizable increase of discharge. The only explanation he could imagine was increased precipitation.

A few years ago a new excavation appeared within the same profile. In the gravel of local material covering the Planinska jama derived material, splinters of large fossil mammal bones (indeterminate to the naked eye) were found. Clearly, fossil collectors did the digging. Normally they collect only remnants of the *Ursus speleaus*, and it is quite likely that the animal in question really was a cave bear[14]. As this became extinct before Würm III, this hints that outwash of Planinska jama occurred during Würm II, or earlier.

DISCUSSION AND CONCLUSIONS

Before the deposition of limestone gravel, derived from the Planinska koliševka basement, the West and East branches of Planinska jama had been cleared of almost all sediment. This development does not appear to be logically connected with the subsequent sedimentation of the gravel "cone", which grew only due to the doline's underground dynamics. By the end of this development, the water level in the East Branch rose to the relatively stable elevation of 470m, which is some metres higher than present (when the outlet in the Malni direction is choked). So, at this time some back-up must have occurred behind the area of the Malni springs, either due to collapse near the outlet, or due to increased recharge from elsewhere, i.e. from the east.

This backing-up became more and more pronounced, so that:

- the Pivka was forced to reopen a blocked, early, outlet in the area of the present cave entrance (outlet);
- the input pressure from the East increased further, and waters from Cerkniško Polje (the present Rak River) penetrated into the East Branch.

Assuming that coarse gravel is more difficult to erode than loam, the reversal happened at the time that was least suitable for it. Steady increase of input pressure is more likely a consequence of gradual elimination of the vertical ponors in the Cerkniško Polje

[14] It must be noted that an indisputable skeleton of ursus speleauswas found in Najdena jama, only 100m away, (Gospodarič, 1982, 180).

floor, due to alluvial fan growth, than of rather random collapse of the (Malni) pocket valley slopes.

The reversal can be dated by coarse material within the Cerkniščica alluvial cone, which must have been deposited after 55ka b.p., as this is the age of the spruce cone near its base. On the other hand, Planinska jama was finally washed clear of most of its gravel (originating from Planinska koliševka) before the end of Würm II, as *Ursus spelaeus* bones lie above the re-transported gravel in Vranja jama. So, some conclusions can be drawn:

- in general, the present passage layout in Planinska jama existed before the late Pleistocene (statement by Gospodarič, o.c.);
- at that time, only the Pivka can be proven to have flowed through the cave;
- the outlet position switched between the present cave "entrance" and the Malni valley, perhaps due to random choking of the springs;
- after Würm I the Cerkniščica inundated Cerkniško polje. Gradual elimination of the main vertical ponors deflected the main stream westwards, into the present cave ponors;
- this water found its outlet (to Planinsko polje) in the Malni valley, and blocked the outflow of the Pivka;
- the Pivka reopened a long-choked outlet in the area of the present cave "entrance";
- before the end of Würm II the East Branch of Planinska jama was washed clear of older sediments. Redeposition reached right across Planinsko polje, i.e. into Vranja jama.

And more generally:

- the development in Planinska jama during the last 100ka was very "vigorous", but it did not essentially affect the layout of pre-existing bedrock channels;
- catastrophic events in cave history are more common than generally expected, and ongoing effects can be very far reaching.

The main points are clear, though available data do not cover all of the details, and some of them may require revision. Events in Cerkniško Polje directly influenced the development of Planinska jama. An apparently independent inundation of Cerkniško polje by the Cerkniščica and an until now rather enigmatic flow reversal in the East Branch of Planinska jama are related.

ACKNOWLEDGEMENTS

The final draft of this paper was much improved by the constructive suggestions of Margaret and Arthur Palmer, whose obviously detailed reading, underlying knowledge, and understanding of the topic presented, are acknowledged with thanks. Throughout the development of the paper, the authors have greatly appreciated queries and suggestions from David Lowe. We thank him for his insights and for his efforts in "smoothing" the English translation.

REFERENCES

Central cave register of Slovenia, maintained by the Karst Research Institute ZRC SAZU and the Speleological Association of Slovenia.

Digital Atlas of Slovenia, 1:50000. Mladinska knjiga, Ljubljana (1990).

Dreybrodt, W., & Eisenlohr, L., 2000: Limestone dissolution rates in krast environments. In A.B. Klimchouk, D.C.Ford, A.N. Palmer, W. Dreybrodt (Eds.): Speleogenesis, Evolution of Karst Aquifers, National speleological society, 136-148, Huntsville.

Ford, D. C., Williams, P.W., 1989: Karst geomorphology and hydrology. Unwin Hyman, 1 - 601, London.

Gospodarič, R., 1976: The Quaternary caves development between the Pivka basin and Polje of Planina (Summary[1515] The titles of summaries/abstracts (if they exist) are given just to show the foreign reader the contentsof the original texts, which are, however, considered in the whole. Acta carsologica, **7,** 8-135, Ljubljana.

Gospodarič, R., 1982: Stratigraphy of cave sediments in the Najdena jama at Planinsko polje. Acta carsologica, 10**,** 173-193, Ljubljana.

Gospodarič, R., and Habič, P, 1976, Underground water tracing, Institute for the Karst Research SAZU, Postojna, 1-309, Postojna.

Gospodarič, R., and Habič, P., 1979: Karst phenomena of Cerkniško polje (Summary), Acta carsologica, 8**,** 7-162, Ljubljana.

Jenko, F., 1959: Recherches récentes sur les cours d'eau souterrains du karst Slovčne (Réssumé). Acta carsologica, 2**,** 209-227, Ljubljana.

Mišič, M., 1998: X-ray diffraction analysis of Palaeozoic and Mesozoic carbonate formations in Slovenia (in Slovenian). Unpublished doctorial thesis, University of Ljubljana, NTF, Dept. of geology, 1-164, Ljubljana.

Morel, S., 2000: Behind the Mysterious lake (in Slovenian). Naše jame, 42, 135-147, Ljubljana.

Morel, S., 2001: Behind the Mysterious lake - addition (in Slovenian). Naše jame, 43, 184, Ljubljana.

Pleničar, M., 1953: Contribution to the geology of Cerkniško polje (Summary). Geologija, 1, 111- 119, Ljubljana.

Stepišnik, U., 2001: Collapse dolines in the Postojna karst (in Slovenian). Unpublished diploma thesis, University of Ljubljana, FF, Dept. of geography, 1-99, Ljubljana.

Šušteršič, F., 1973: On the problems of collapse dolinas and allied forms of high Notranjsko / Southcentral Slovenia (Summary). Geografski vestnik, 45, 71-86, Ljubljana.

Šušteršič, F., 1996, Poljes and caves of Notranjska, Acta carsologica, 25, 251-289, Ljubljana.

Šušteršič, F., 1998: Interaction between tha cave system and the lowering karst surface. Case study: Laški Ravnik. Acta carsologica, 27 (2), 115-138, Ljubljana.

Šušteršič, F., 2000: Speleogenesis in the Ljubljanica river drainage basin, Slovenia. In A.B. Klimchouk, D.C.Ford, A.N. Palmer, W. Dreybrodt (Eds.): Speleogenesis, Evolution of Karst Aquifers, National speleological society, 397-406, Huntsville.

Šušteršič, F., Čar, J., & Šebela, S., 2001: Collector channels and deflector faults (Summary). Naše jame, 43, 8-22, Ljubljana.

Šušteršič., F. & Šušteršič, S., in preparation: The Cerkniščica alluvial fan.

Šušteršič, S., 2002: Geographical characteristics and development of the Cerkniščica catchment area. (in Slovenian). Unpublished diploma thesis, University of Ljubljana, FF, Dept. of geography, 1-96, Ljubljana.

Vrhovec, T., 2000: Diary of diving in Pivka and Planinska jama (in Slovenian). Naše jame, 42, 162-163, Ljubljana.

Žalec, P., Vrhovec, T., Mihailovski, M., Zwölf, D., Drole, F., 1997: Cave system Zelške jame-Karlovica (in Slovenian). Naše jame, 39, 87-94, Ljubljana.

Žibrik, K. & Pičinin, A., 1973: A contribution to the knowledge about the Ljubljanica karst catchment area (in Slovenian). 3th international symposium of underground water tracing, Reports 1, 3-7, Ljubljana.

Žibrik, K., Lewicki, F. & Pičinin, A., 1976: Hydrologic investigations. In: Gospodarič, R., and Habič, P., Underground water tracing. Institute for the Karst Research SAZU, Postojna, 43-55, Postojna.

Address
France Šušteršič
University of Ljubljana, Dept. of Geology, Aškerčeva 12, SI-1000 Ljubljana, Slovenia
E-mail: france.sustersic@ntfgeo.uni-lj.si
Uroš Stepišnik
University of Ljubljana, Dept. of Geography, Aškerčeva 2, SI-1000 Ljubljana, Slovenia
E-mail: urosstepisnik@slo.net
Simona Šušteršič
University of Ljubljana, Dept. of Geography, Aškerčeva 2, SI-1000 Ljubljana, Slovenia
E-mail: simona_sustersic@hotmail.com

Evolution of Karst: From Prekarst to Cessation, 299-306, Ljubljana-Postojna 2002

THE ROLE OF SOIL COVER IN THE EVOLUTION OF KARRENFELDS

ANIKÓ ZSENI

Abstract
Soil samples were collected on limestone pavement areas of North England and on Karrenfelds of Aggtelek Karst and Villányi Mountain, Hungary. Samples are from different solutional and tectonical features of limestone. During the examination the pH and carbonate content of soils were measured. The comparison of the Hungarian and English soils results in the following: (i): Great differences can be found in soil pH according to the different karstic features in the case of the English samples. In spite of the similarly rich variety of karstic features and forms in short distances in the Hungarian Karrenfelds the results show only minor differences in soil pH. (ii): The results of the English measurements verify that the soils with lower pH are related to deeper solution features. (iii):The neutral and weakly basic pH-values of Hungarian soil samples came from deep and well-developed solutional forms suggest the protection of the underlying limestone almost completely from dissolution (although the carbonate contents are low). (iv): Comparisons between soils, which connect directly and do not connect directly with limestone verify that proximity to limestone causes a higher soil-pH, while soils, which do not have direct contact with limestone have a lower, acid pH.
Key words: *limestone pavements, karrenfelds, karren-forms, dissolution of karren, soil-filling, soil-pH*

I. INTRODUCTION

To understand the evolution of different karstic features, especially types of karren, the investigation of soils on karst landforms are very important. There are some interesting questions e.g.: are there any connections between solutional power of soil (so pH and carbonate content) and the deepness, smoothness, roundness of limestone forms; and has the proximity to limestone an effect on the soils? To answer these questions soil samples were collected on limestone pavement areas of North England (Fig. 1.) and on Karrenfelds of Aggtelek Karst and Villányi Mountain, Hungary (Fig. 2.). Human influences have played an important role in the evolution of both Hungarian Karrenfelds. Previously the slopes were covered by sediment (on Szársomlyó Hill: loess). Intensive cultivation (viniculture) caused soil erosion, and greater and greater parts of limestone blocks have loose their soil-cover. On the bare and thin-covered surfaces of limestone different solutional forms can be seen.

Soil has an important role in the evolution of different karstic features, such as types of karren. The role of a soil cover in the evolution of different karren forms depends on the pH of soil. In general, calcareous soils with high pH (pH of 7 to 9, calcium

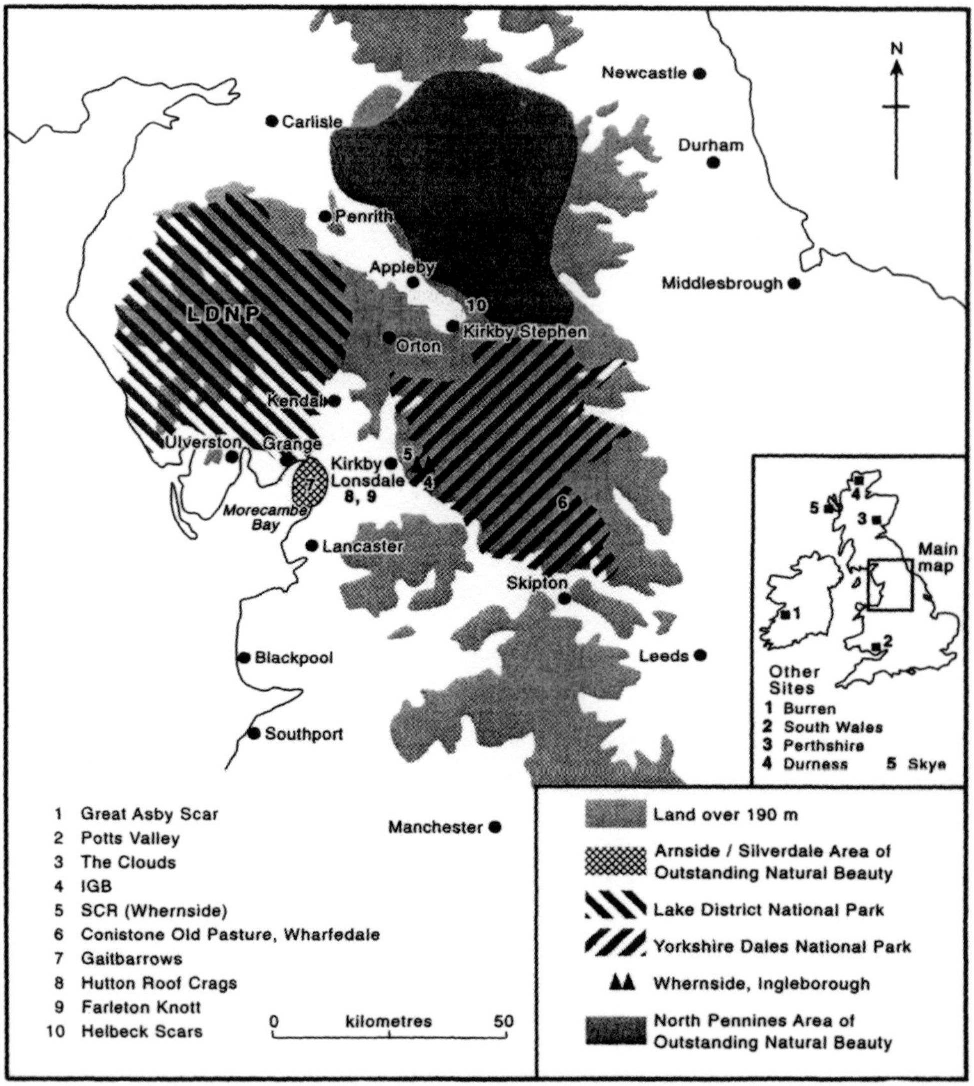

Fig. 1. Limestone pavement areas in Great Britain

carbonate content is higher than 10 %) protect the underlying limestone almost completely from erosion, because water becomes saturated with bicarbonate on passing through the soil profile. So the soil water arriving at soil-bedrock interface is incapable of dissolving the bedrock. (TRUDGILL, S. 1985). If the percolating water is not saturated, then solution will take place. Under acid soil limestone is extensively weathered. Erosion of limestone is most severe beneath deposits supporting acid vegetation and with a pH between 4 and 7 and a calcium carbonate content of 0 to 1 %. (TRUDGILL, S. 1985).

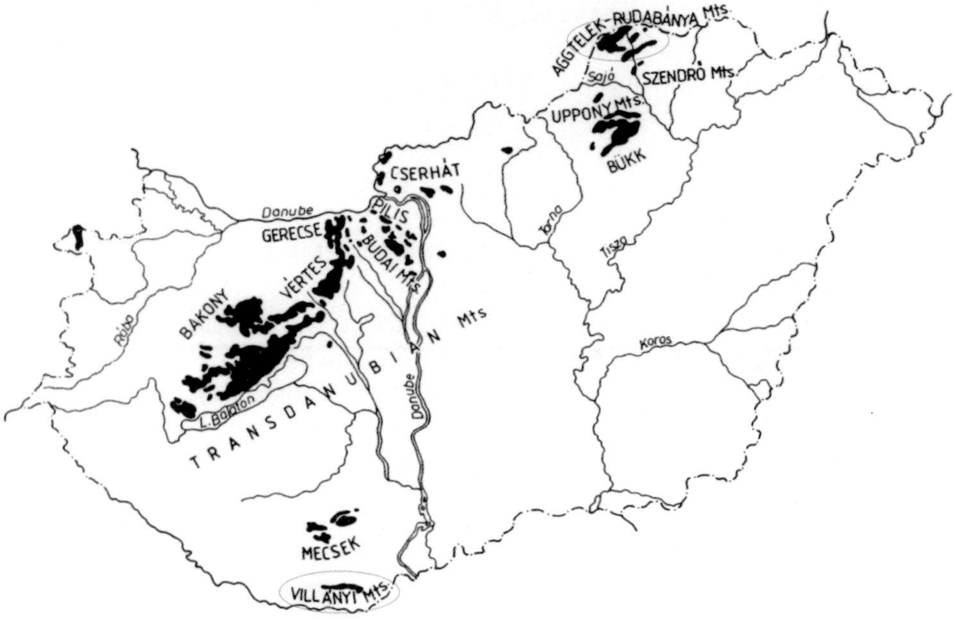

Fig. 2. Geographical distribution of the karst areas in Hungary (HEVESI, A. 1989.)

II. SAMPLING AND MEASURING

60 soil samples were collected from limestone pavement areas of North England, 50 samples (Ö 1-50) on Ördögszántás (Aggtelek Karst) and 41 (SZ 1-41) on Szársomlyó Hill (Villányi Mountain). The samples are from different solutional karren-forms (runnels, root-karrens), tectonic fissures (grikes), foot of limestone blocks, top of limestone and grass patches. The so-called root-karren is a special type of karrens and it is very common on Ördögszántás. It is a typical solutional form: the roots of plants dissolve limestone by the emitted root-acids. So they developed former by the dissolution power of roots and after soils filled in them.

The aim of the investigations is to clear up the followings: are there any connections between present solutional power of soil (so pH and carbonate content) and the deepness, smoothness, roundness of limestone forms; and whether has the proximity to limestone an effect on the soil pH and carbonate content. From the literature the answers can be expected, but different results were found in the case of the English and the Hungarian samples.

During the examination the pH was measured in distilled water and in 1 M KCl solution by digital pH-meter. The soil: water ratio is 1:2,5 (6 g soil and 15 cm^3 water or KCl solution). The pH(H_2O) shows actual soil reaction, while pH(KCl) gives information about potential soil reaction. The ΔpH (=pH(H_2O) - pH(KCl)) of soils was calculated as well. The ΔpH value gives us an important information about the acidification tendency of soils: if the value is about 1 or more, than the soil tends to acidify. Scheibler-calcimeter was used to determine the carbonate content of soils.

III. RESULTS

1. SOILS OF LIMESTONE PAVEMENTS

Soil samples are grouped according to whether they came from flat limestone surface, shallow runnel (depths of a few cm) or deeper runnel, to investigate the role of the soil pH in the solution of limestone (Fig. 3.). The pH values of the 3 soils from flat surfaces (HRC1, ASC2, COP1) are between 6,91-7,8. The carbonate content of one soil is 6 %, but it is below 0,5 % in the case of the two other soil samples. The pH values of the soil samples, which came from shallow runnels (HRC8, UBP1, GAS7, GAS8, ASC3, ASC5) are about 6,06-7,67. The carbonate content of these soils is less than 0,5 %. The pH values of the soils of the deep runnels (NBC1, HRC7, HRC10, UBP6, GAS3, ASC4, ASC6, ASC7, COP2) are always less than 7 (4,33-6,93). The lowest pH values are in this latter category when comparing these 3 groups of soils. The carbonate content is usually 0 %, except in a few cases, but it is always below 0,8 %. (ZSENI, A. - KEVEINÉ BÁRÁNY, I., 2000.)

The results of the measurements verify that the soils with lower pH are related to

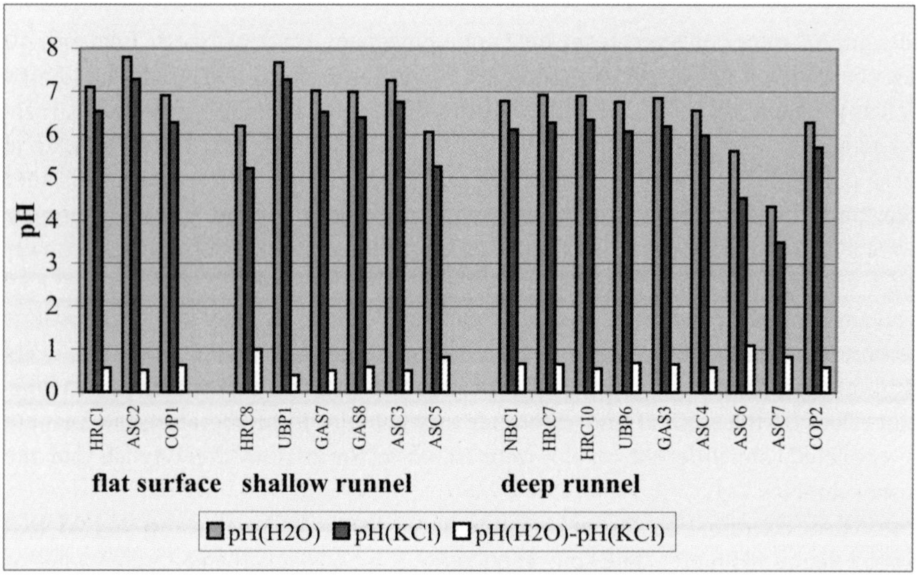

Fig. 3. pH of soils, which were collected from flat surfaces, shallow runnels and deep runnels, limestone pavements, North England

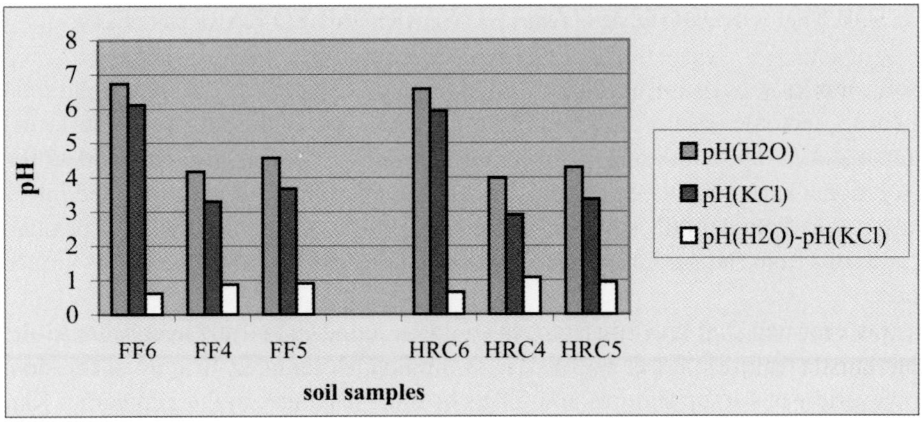

Fig. 4. Connection between pH of soils and proximity to limestone, limestone pavements, North-England

deeper solution features, not surprisingly as their solvent power is greater than that of the soils with higher pH.

Other soil samples are grouped according to whether they are at the foot of pavements where they are in direct contact with the limestone surface or in a few metres away from the limestone: in grass patches or in dolines. The soils far away from limestone can be a few decimetres in depth. From the measured data it can be seen that the pH is higher in soils in directly contact with the limestone (ZSENI, A. - KEVEINÉ BÁRÁNY, I., 2000.). The pH values of these soils are about 6,0-6,7 and the carbonate contents are 0 %. The soils of grass patches and dolines (which are a few metres away from the limestone) have acid pH (around 4-5) and the carbonate content is 0 %. The ΔpH is always high, around 1. (ZSENI, A. - KEVEINÉ BÁRÁNY, I., 2000.).

Soil samples close to each other were collected to examine the differences of the soils, which connect directly and do not connect directly with limestone. These series are the FF4-5-6 and the HRC4-5-6 samples. The FF4-5 and HRC4-5 samples are from grass patches a few metres away from limestone outcrop. The FF4 and HRC4 are from the upper 10 cm of the soils. The FF5 and HRC5 are from below the former. The FF6 sample is 5 metres away from the FF4-5 samples, directly at foot of runnels. The HRC6 sample is a few metres away from the HRC4-5 samples and directly connects with the limestone outcrop. The pH is much higher in the soils which connect directly with limestone, pH=6,6-6,7 (Fig. 4.). They have no carbonate content. The soils of the grass patches are very acid. The pH is about 4 and it increases downwards in the soil profile (Fig. 4). The ΔpH-values are higher (around 1) than those in the soils, which have direct contact with limestone. They have no carbonate content of course. So not only does the soil have an effect on the limestone, the limestone also has an effect on the soils. Proximity to limestone causes a higher soil-pH, while the soils, which do not have direct contact with limestone have a lower, acid pH.

2. SOILS OF ÖRDÖGSZÁNTÁS AND SZÁRSOMLYÓ KARRENFELDS

Soil samples grouped according to whether they came from different solutional karren-forms, tectonic fissures, foot of limestone blocks, top of limestone (flat surfaces) and grass patches. The solutional forms are divided into 2 parts: root-karren and all the other solutional karren-forms. Soil samples from the top of limestone are divided into 2 parts also: soils from a totally smooth flat limestone surface (dissolution is not presumable), and soils from flat surfaces where minor solutional forms can be seen: the surface is etched.

It was expected that great differences could be found in soil pH according to the different karstic features, just as in the case of the English samples. In spite of the similarly rich variety of karstic features and forms in short distances in the Hungarian Karrenfelds, the results show only minor differences in soil pH. Soils on both Hungarian Karrenfelds seem to be rather homogeneous, while on the English limestone pavements not only the appearance of limestone surface but even the soil pH can vary in short distances. In Ördögszántás the smallest pH(H_2O) value is 6,50, the highest is 7,95, while in Szársomlyó these values are 6,33 and 7,66. (In the case of English limestone pavements: 3,73 and 7,67.) The carbonate contents of soils is lower than expected in the case of these neutral soils, most of them is lower than 0,5 % and the highest value is only 2,15 %. The low calcium carbonate content may not able to protect satisfactorily the underlying limestone from erosion. Table 1. contains the mean of pH, ΔpH and carbonate content of the soil-groups.

***Table 1.**: Means of pH and carbonate content*

sample sites	pH(H_2O)		pH(KCl)		ΔpH		carb. Cont. %	
	Ördögszántás	Szársomlyó	Ördögszántás	Szársomlyó	Ördögszántás	Szársomlyó	Ördögszántás	Szársomlyó
R	7,40	7,43	6,67	6,67	0,72	0,77	0,4	0,8
S	7,36	6,96	6,63	6,38	0,73	0,57	0,3	0,5
R+S	7,38	7,20	6,65	6,53	0,73	0,67	0,3	0,6
T	7,41	7,00	6,68	6,32	0,73	0,68	0,3	0,3
Fe	6,84	7,10	6,20	6,49	0,65	0,61	0,2	0,7
Fs	7,35	6,98	6,50	6,41	0,85	0,57	0,2	0,3
C	7,02	6,85	6,30	6,17	0,72	0,68	0,1	0,1
GP	6,85	6,75	6,30	6,01	0,56	0,74	0,2	0,1

Legend: **R**: soils from root-karren, **S**: soils from other solutional forms, **T**: soils from tectonical fissures, **Fe**: soils from "etched" flat surfaces, **Fs**: soils from "smooth" flat surfaces, **C**: soils at foot of limestone outcrop, **GP**: soils from grass patches

If we make a comparison between the soils of all the solutional forms (root-karren and the others) in the Hungarian Karrenfelds and the soils of solutional forms in the English limestone pavements, the difference is striking. In the case of the English soils the lower pH-values (mean pH(H_2O) = 6,61) show present dissolutional processes, while the Hungarian soil samples suggest the protection of the underlying limestone almost completely from dissolution (although the carbonate contents are low). By reason of the present soil pH, these solutional forms in the Hungarian Karrenfelds either had to develop former or there is (are) process(es), which can cause the lowering of pH occasional (?), seasonal (?), so solution can take place. (The soil samples of Szársomlyó were collected in April, 2001, the samples of Ördögszántás in September, 2001; but for an other investigation one soil sample was collected in Ördögszántás in July, 1998, and this sample shows no difference (neutral pH) compared to the latter samples.) So the soil conditions point to the fact that only earlier processes are responsible for the evolution and formation of the root-karrens and the present soil-filling helps to preserve the forms.

An other interesting question is whether there is a difference between the soils which are from a totally smooth flat limestone surface (dissolution is not presumable) and the other soils which are from flat surfaces where minor solutional forms can be seen: the surface is etched. In the case of soil samples from Ördögszántás the differences in pH verify that soils with lower pH are related to deeper solution features (etched surface), not surprisingly as their solvent power is greater than that of the soils with higher pH (totally smooth, flat surface) (Table 1.). In the case of the soil samples from Szársomlyó these differences can not be seen, moreover, the soils on totally smooth surfaces have a bit lower pH and carbonate content than the soils on etched surface have (Table 1.). The ΔpH is lower in the samples of Szársomlyó than samples of Ördögszántás, which means smaller acidification tendency in the soils of Szársomlyó. The English soils collected from flat surfaces have similar pH as soils of Ördögszántás, but the ΔpH-values resemble the soils of Szársomlyó.

Just in England, soil samples close to each other were collected to examine the differences of soils, which connect directly and do not connect directly with limestone. These series are the Ö 7-8-9, SZ 5-6-7, SZ 12-13 and the SZ 34-35-36 samples. The Ö 7, SZ 5, 12, 34 are from directly at foot of limestone outcrop while the others are from grass patches a few metres away from the limestone outcrop. The soil depth was about 10 cm at sample site SZ 13, and about 15-20 cm at sample sites Ö8-9, SZ 6-7 and SZ 35-36. The Ö 8, SZ 6, SZ13, SZ35 are from the upper 10 cm of the soils, while the Ö9, SZ7 and SZ36 are from below the former. The result show not so great differences than in the case of English samples (Fig. 4.,5.). There is no difference at all in soil pH and carbonate content in the case of the Ö 7-8-9 samples. The pH of SZ 5-6-7 and SZ 34-35-36 samples show a little difference between soils which connect directly and do not connect directly with limestone, but the pH of grass patches are not so low than that in the soils of English grass patches. The main reason for this is the great difference between the landforms: deep soils can be found not at all in the Hungarian Karrenfelds. The soils are so shallow here, that proximity to limestone causes high soil-pH in the case of grass patches as well.

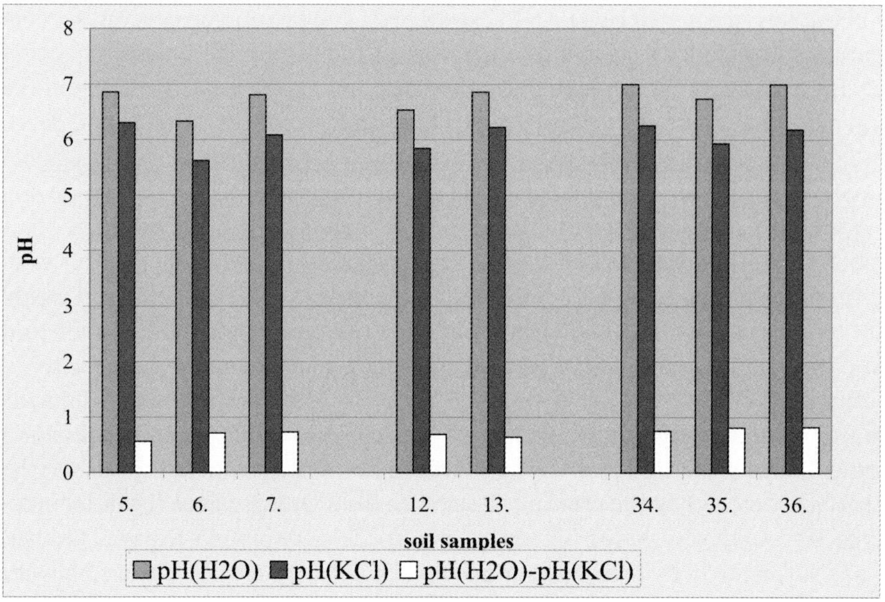

Fig. 5. Connection between pH of soils and proximity to limestone, Szársomlyó, Villányi Mountain

REFERENCES

Hevesi, A. 1989: Development and evolution of karst regions in Hungary. - Karszt és Barlang, Special Issue, Budapest, pp. 3-16.

Trudgill, S. 1985: Limestone geomorphology. In: Geomorphology Texts 8. (edited by K. M. Clayton), Longman, pp. 53-70.

Zseni, A. - Keveiné Bárány, I. 2000.: Nagy-Britannia mészkőjárdái és a talaj hatása azok fejlődésében (Limestone pavements of Great Britain and the influence of soil in the evolution of them). - Karsztfejlődés V., Szombathely, pp. 181-194.

Széchenyi István University,
Department of Environmental Engineering, Hungary, H-9026 Győr, Egyetem tér 1.
E-mail: zseniani@sze.hu

SPELEOLOGY AND SPELEOGENESIS

Evolution of Karst: From Prekarst to Cessation, 309-318, Ljubljana-Postojna 2002

THE ROLE OF THE EPIPHREATIC ZONE AND THE SURROUNDING ENVIRONMENT IN CAVE GENESIS:

THE SIEBENHENGSTE EXAMPLE

PHILIPP HÄUSELMANN, PIERRE-YVES JEANNIN, STEIN-ERIK LAURITZEN & MICHEL MONBARON

Abstract
Observations of the speleogenetic phases of Bärenschacht, as well as the actual flooding beaviour, allow to draw a new, comprehensive model linking the two existing speleogenetic theories by Ford & Ewers (1978) and Audra (1994). The initial galleries form below the watertable, whereas the mature phreatic tubes are reshaped in the epiphreatic zone. Linking the speleogenetic phases and the sediment successions, a relative chronological table can be dressed. This table, combined with absolute datings, then can be used for paleoclimatological and paleomorphological information that is no more available at the surface.
Keywords: *speleogenesis, epiphreatic zone, Siebenhengste*

INTRODUCTION

Cave genesis, as a process of dissolution and transport, is linked with stratigraphy and tectonics, as well as with waterflow and climate. Many models have been developed to describe cave formation processes. In the classical model of cave genesis by Ford & Ewers (1978), looping passages are attributed to the phreatic realm, whereas the theory of Audra (1994) suggests that they form in epiphreatic conditions. The first part of the present contribution aims to link those theories. We concentrate on the genesis of penetrable cave systems. We don't take into consideration the very beginning of cave formation, but instead try to explain how the "mature" cave forms.

In the second part, the link of speleogenesis with the surrounding environment is demonstrated with some illustrative examples. We deliberately concentrate on morphology and sediments and let aside the widely known analyses of stable isotopes. With those observations alone, a reconstruction of paleogeography and paleoclimate is already possible.

LOCATION

The cave system north of Lake Thun is situated in the north-western Alps, adjacent to the Molasse basin (Fig. 1). From Lake Thun, the system extends to the Schrattenfluh, a

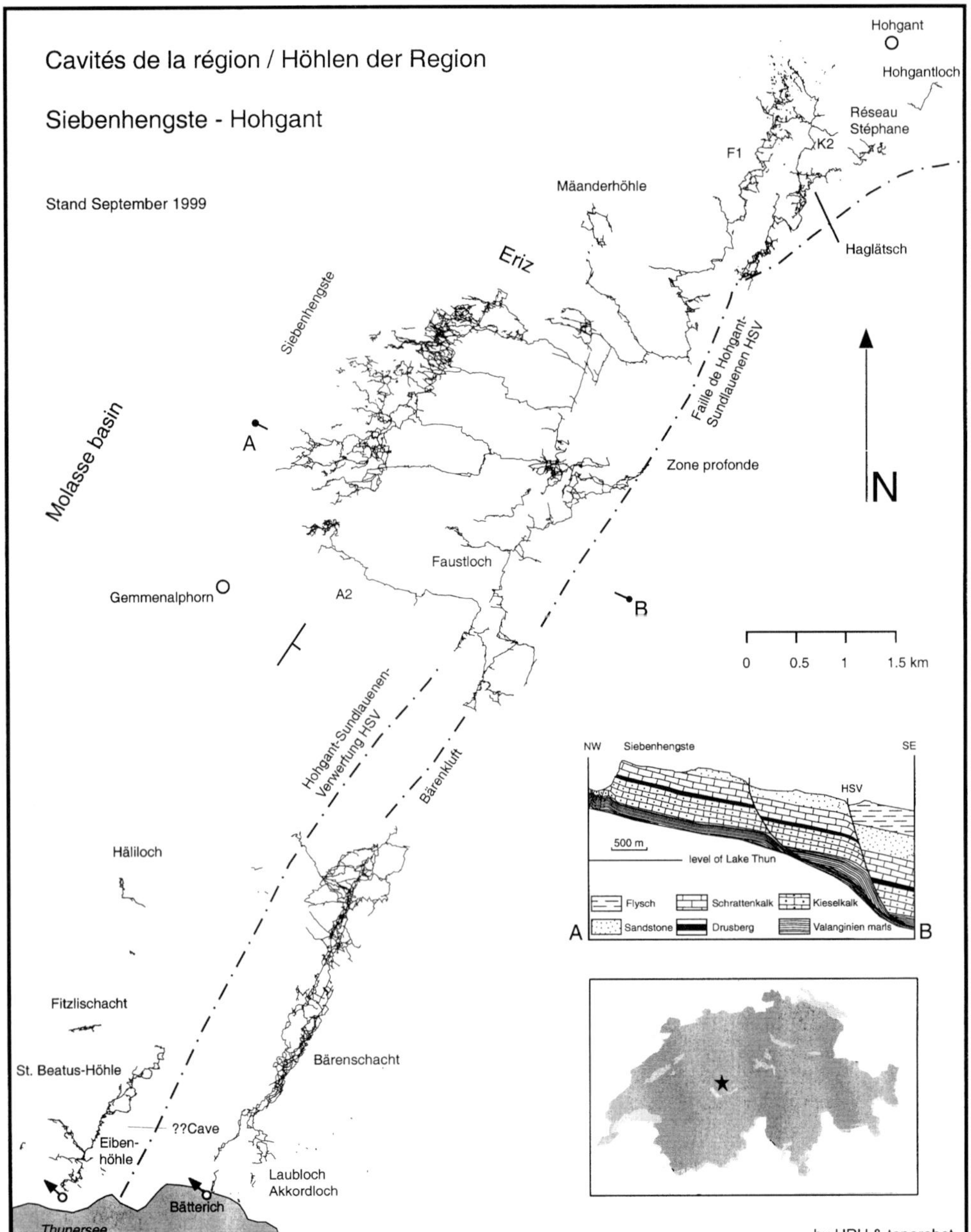

Fig. 1. The cave region of Siebenhengste-Hohgant

massif that lies north of the deeply incised valley of the Emme. The entire ridge forms a southeast-dipping slope, cut in the northwest by steep cliffs. The highest parts, between 1700 m and 2000 m a.s.l., are largely denuded and composed of limestone pavement. At lower altitudes, firs grow on swampy ground. Precipitation ranges between 1500 and 2000 mm/year.

GEOLOGY

The Helvetic domain consists of the following strata of interest: On top of the siliceous limestone) lie the Drusberg marls which normally form the impermeable bottom of the karstic system. The Schrattenkalk, above the Drusberg marls, has a thickness of 150 - 200 m. It is the main karstic aquifer. From Kieselkalk to Schrattenkalk the stratigraphic sequence was deposited during the Lower Cretaceous. The overlying Hohgant series (Eocene) consists of a complicated sequence of alternating quartzitic and calcareous sandstones and reaches up to 200 m thickness.

The general geological features include a monoclinal slope, dipping to the southeast at 15-30^0, which is interrupted by several longitudinal normal faults that extend from Lake Thun north to the Schrattenfluh. The biggest fault is the Hohgant-Sundlauenen fault HSV, where th offset is around 150 m in the Hohgant region and increases to more than 650 m in Sundlauenen near Lake Thun. The monoclinal slope is further disrupted by dextral strike-slips.

GENESIS OF THE KARSTIC SYSTEM

The current knowledge of the genesis of the multi-phase system is described by Jeannin, Bitterli & Häuselmann (2000). A broad overview is given here. The twelve phases indicating former estimated spring levels are labelled according to the present-day altitude of the corresponding karst springs.

The first four phases (1950, 1720, 1585, and 1505 m a.s.l.) of the karst system show a flow direction from Sieben Hengste and Hohgant towards the valley of Eriz. At this time, the Aar valley may not have existed. A dramatic change in both hydrologic and tectonic settings induced a 180° change of flow direction, such that, from this time on, the waters were directed towards the Aar valley. Seven additional phases (1440, 1120, 890, 805, 760, 700 and 660 m a.s.l.) were identified. The last and present phase corresponds with the altitude of Lake Thun, 558 m a.s.l. Today, the region is divided into two water catchment areas (Häuselmann & Otz, 1997), one in the southwest draining towards St. Beatus cave, and the other comprising the BŠrenschacht, Sieben Hengste, Hohgant and the Schrattenfluh, draining towards Bätterich.

PART I: THE ROLE OF THE EPIPHREATIC REALM

THE TWO PRESENT MODELS OF PASSAGE FORMATION

The classical model of passage formation is the most widely accepted "four state model" (Ford & Ewers, 1978) The four state model puts the characteristics of the passage (loops in the phreatic realm, depth of karstification below the karst water table) in relation to the fissure frequency of the karstic massif. Therefore, this model predicts deep phreatic karstification and huge loops only in thickly bedded limestone wich has small fractures, and an "ideal" water table cave in karst massifs that are thoroughly fractured and highly permeable.

Another more recent model is Audra's (1994). He puts a main question mark behind the notion of "phreatic passages", saying that most of the well-known, rounded passages that generally are attributed to having been created below the water table, are in fact produced in the epiphreatic zone. His reasoning is that only in the epiphreatic zone is corrosion sufficiently strong to provide effective solubility. Audra (1994) infers that virtually all cave passages are created in the epiphreatic zone.

THE OBSERVATIONS IN BÄRENSCHACHT

Three superimposed, now inactive, phases of cave genesis are identified in this large cave system. For each phase, the loops of the phreatic passages become higher with increasing distance from the spring. The height of the watertable given by canyon-tube transitions correlates well with the height inferred from the top of the loops as described above. The canyon transitions show a steep inclination in the water table (1.3 to 2.1 degrees). The definition of the corresponding height is attributed to the presumed spring level because of the watertable inclination: Phases at 700, 760, and 890 m asl are recognised.

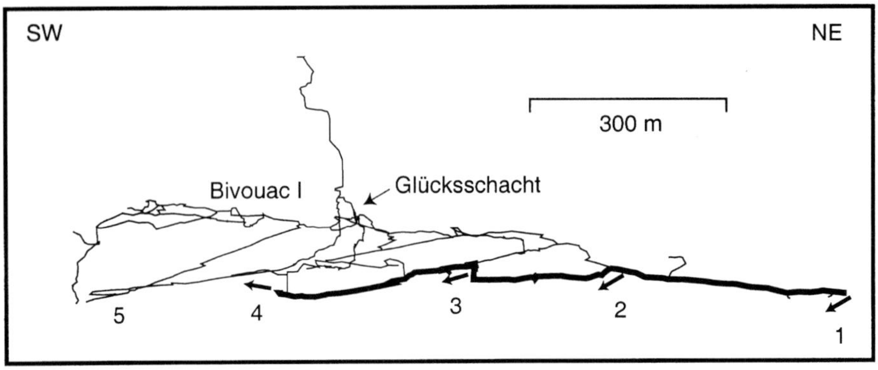

Fig. 2. Schematical sketch of the northern part of Bärenschacht. This illustrates the flooding mechanism. The water rises from the North sump (1) and overflows into Zone nord basse (2), fills the shaft (3) from below before filling the Longs couteaux (4). Eventually it overflows and fills the Karstwaserlabyrinth (5).

The observations further showed that the watertable inclination is not due to structural and/or tectonic effects: there are no limiting factors such as impervious layers or faults.

Observations in today's active phase allow to describe the flooding mechanism as well as the passage formation: when flooding occurs, the water is not rising uniformly from the lower, permanently flooded galleries, but instead the system functions in the "filling-overflow" manner (Fig. 2). Sediments remaining only at the rims of the vadose riverbed and elongated high-velocity scallops at the gallery's base prove that there are huge vadose flows. The whole passage morphology, however, is phreatic, in spite of the sometimes considerable vadose flow prevailing. Therefore, it seems that phreatic corrosion is dominant although vadose conditions are often present.

Observations in conduits of phase 700 have shown that the same filling-overflow mechanism was most likely working during this older phase.

THE SOUTIRAGES

During flood events, the conduits are filled with water to the top of the loops. At low water stages, the loops become empty, therefore an outflow must exist at the bottom of the loops. These outflow passages are well known and have been called "soutirages". The soutirages are small galleries that go down in the direction of the present water table. Soutirages occur in the present epiphreatic zone as well as in fossil loops. They always have a phreatic morphology and are much smaller than the main conduits which form the loops.

Soutirages are only formed in the epiphreatic zone. Observations in Bärenschacht show (Fig. 3) that, especially in the downstream section, the main tubes experience perennial phreatic conditions and the epiphreatic flooding occurs only in the upstream section. This is confirmed by the fact that soutirages do not exist in the downstream tubes.

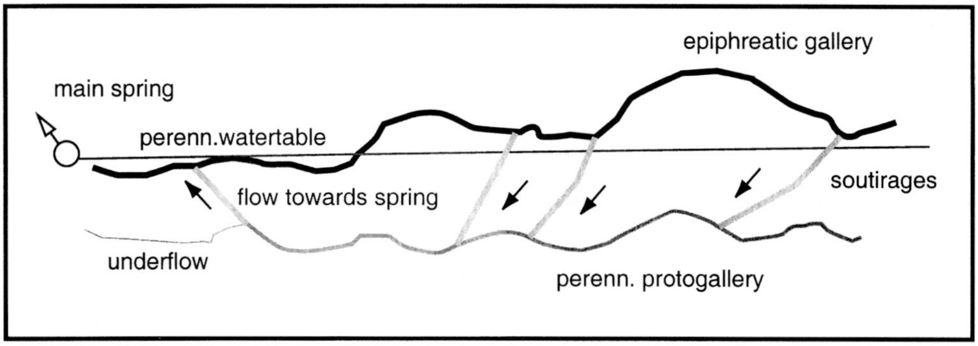

Fig. 3. The galleries of the Bärenschacht in phase 760. Light grey, thin: galleries that are not active; black: main epiphreatic gallery; light grey: soutirages; dark grey: perennially flooded gallery; arrows: upflow galleries.

CONCLUSION

Observations of the cave genesis phases and of the flooding behaviour led us to postulate a new model of cave genesis that links both models of Ford & Ewers (1978) an (Audra, 1994):

1. Initial passages form below the water table The mature cave passages of phreatic morphology form below and above the perennial water table.
2. The definition of a cave phase is given by its spring and the height of the epiphreatic zone.
3. This height is given by "normal" high-water events such as spring snowmelt and heavy summer rain.
4. Soutirages drain the water from the epiphreatic zone towards the perennial flooded zone, in which new galleries form.

PART II: THE INFLUENCE OF THE SURROUNDING LANDSCAPE AND CLIMATE

CONNECTION TO THE VALLEY

If there is no evidence that the karst water level is controlled by geologic structure, it has to be connected with the elevation of the spring. This elevation itself is usually determined by the regional water level related to the valley floor.

Assuming that valley deepening would be caused by continuous fluvial erosion, it would reflect progressive spring deepening and gradual (mainly vadose) deepening of the corresponding speleogenetic phase. If there is no such sign, the valley deepening must have happened by a rapid process. It was followed by a time of long relative stability, in which the next speleogenetic phase developed. In the present alpine valleys, the most probable agents of a quick valley deepening are the quarternary glaciers.

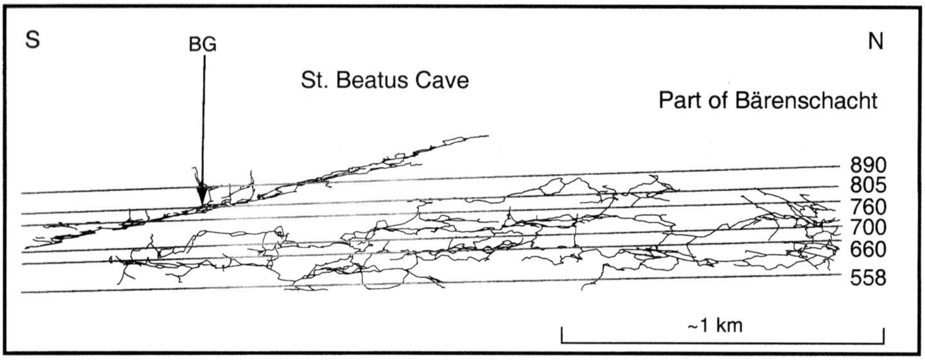

Fig. 4: N-S-projection of Bärenschacht and St. Beatus Cave with the recognised phases.

We conclude that the speleogenetic phases reflect the deepening of the valleys in time. Therefore, observations of the speleogenetic phases give information about both the relative elevations of the valley bottom as well as their succession in time and provide an effective tool for the reconstruction of paleorelief. Equivalent information at the surface is usually no more present, due to the abrasive effects of the youngest glaciations.

Inclined cave levels with spring elevations at 558, 660, 700, 760, 805, and 890 m a.s.l. are identified in Bärenschacht and St. Beatus Cave (Fig. 4).

DATING OF THE PHASES AND CLIMATIC EVENTS

When did this valley deepening happen? Caves, like most erosional forms, cannot be dated directly. This has to be done with the help of the sediments within the cave. Since speleothemes usually deposited in vadose conditions, the first appearance of it in a phreatic gallery tends to reflect the first drying up of this gallery. Therefore this gives a minimal age of the next lower phase observed, and a maximal age for the phase that created the gallery where the speleothemes were found.

Thus it is necessary to place the various sediment profiles within the frame of the phases, and to correlate the overall morphology of the gallery with the sedimentary succession. Like this, a relative chronological order is made. On this base, the dating of some speleothemes results in a chronological table that indicates phase transitions (and therefore valley deepenings), sedimentation and erosion events and related absolute ages. In the following part, a sedimentary profile of St. Beatus Cave is used as an example for dating the morphologic and climatic changes.

BIWAKGÄNGE UNTEN (BG, FIG. 5)

The initial phreatic genesis of an elliptic conduit is followed by a deposition of gravel (BG31, not visible on Figure). The gravel is cemented. A vadose entrenchment of the bottom follows. A dropstone (BG23) grows near the bottom of the entrenchment. A sandy deposition is partially eroded and followed by another gravel and sand succession (BG1-6, BG24, 22). A next, bigger erosion precedes the sediments BG7-9, which are followed by the sands BG11-BG13. The next silt deposition (BG15) is contemporaneous with the sand deposition BG14, that falls down from the ellipse shoulder. The whole silt period is interrupted at least once, when the sinter BG20 is deposited in vadose conditions. The last silt deposition (BG17) concludes the succession.

Dating of the dropstone BG23 gave ages of 236 (+15/-13) ka at the top and 238 (+19/-16) ka at the base. Sinter BG20 gave 161 ka (+14/-13), corrected for detritic Th), Sinter BG25 had 170 (+14/-13), and sinter BG27 had 85 (±5, corrected) ka.

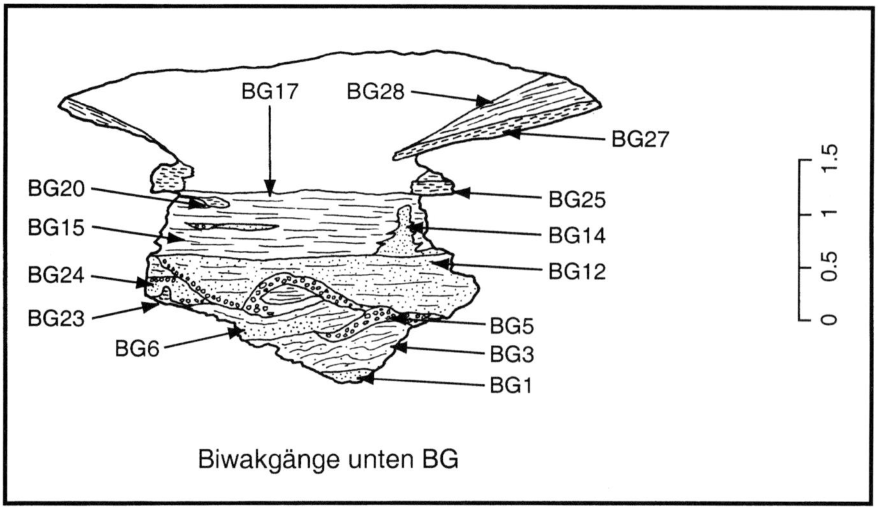

Fig. 5. The sediment profile in Biwakgänge of St. Beatus Cave.

INTERPRETATION OF THE PROFILE

While phase 760 was active, gravel was deposited in the galleries belonging to phase 805. After a change towards warmer climate, a thick sinter (FG, KOH, cementing BG31) was deposited in the ellipse downstream of Biwakgänge. Both sinters are older than 350 ka. Another change in climate, probably towards a slightly wetter one than our climate today, induced an huge flow rate and therefore the re-erosion of both sinter and bedrock to a depth of about two meters. A next, drier phase was responsible for the deposition of the dropstone BG23 that has an age of 237 ka.

A next deterioration of climate led to the deposition of a sand-gravel succession which is truncated at least two times by other (eventually minor) erosions. This succession is then capped by another varved silt deposit that indicates the onset of the next glaciation.

During phase 700, most of the St. Beatus Cave was already in vadose conditions, due to the geological perching of this cave. However, several sedimentation/erosion events of St. Beatus Cave can also be attributed to this timespan. After the deglaciation and some erosion, a warm period was responsible for the deposition of sinter BG20 and BG25 in Biwakgänge (161-170 ka). A next erosional event, followed by a deposition of varved silt, marks the onset of the next glaciation.

The following silt deposition is thought to be due to the next glaciation which also was responsible for the deepening of the valley to 660 m. This assumption is based on a "best fit" idea, that has no direct evidence available in the field. However, a comparison of morphology and datings indicate that this change has to have happened between 160 and 100 ka in any way.

CONCLUSION

The above example has shown that an elaboration of a relative timeframe that is then dated absolutely, gives precious information both for the speleogenetic phases as well as for the climatic and morphologic events outside the cave. We think that many paleoclimatic investigations in caves are too much focussed on stable isotope studies, and a significant potential for maleoclimatical and paleomorphological interpretation is still not exploited. It is our wish that more such studies will be undertaken, not only in the Alps, but anywhere in the world.

ACKNOWLEDGEMENTS

Our first and biggest thanks go to the many cavers, whose interminable mapping made it possible to explore the secrets of Bärenschacht and many caves in the region. Especially the work of Luc Funcken and, more recently, Rolf Kummer permitted to have new and important insight into this fascinating world. Without the work of Thomas Bitterli, one of the leaders of the scientific exploration of Siebenhengste, this paper would not be complete. His premature death is a big loss. Peter Pfister dug the profile in St. Beatus Cave: thanks a lot. The elaboration was financially helped by the Swiss Nationalfonds for Scientific Research (grant no. 2100-053990.98/1). We warmly acknowledge the discussions and comments of Art and Peggy Palmer as well as Philippe Audra. A review of Meredith Kelly considerably improved the English.

REFERENCES

Audra, Ph., 1994: Karst alpins - Genése de grands réseaux souterrains. - Karstologia Mémoires, 5, 280 p.

Ford, D.C. & R.O. Ewers, 1978: The development of limestone cave systems in the dimensions of length and depth. - Can J Earth Sci, 15, 1783-1798.

Häuselmann, Ph. & M. Otz, 1997: Wasserfärbung im Gebiet Gemmenalp-Sieben Hengste: Ziele und Resultate. - Proceedings of the 12th International Congress of Speleology, La Chaux-de-Fonds (Switzerland), 2, 31-34.

Jeannin, P.-Y., T. Bitterli, & Ph. Häuselmann, 2000: Genesis of a large cave system: the case study of the North of Lake Thun system (Canton Bern, Switzerland). - In A. Klimchouk, D. C. Ford, A. N. Palmer, & W. Dreybrodt (Eds.), Speleogenesis: Evolution of Karst Aquifers (pp. 338-347). NSS.

Address
Philipp Häuselmann
Geographical Institute, University of Fribourg, Perolles, 1700 Fribourg, Switzerland
E-mail: praezis@geo.unibe.ch
Pierre-Yves Jeannin
Swiss Institute of Speleology and Karst Studies SISKA, c.p.818, 2300 La Chaux-de-Fonds, Switzerland
Stein Erik Lauritzen
Geologisk Institutt, Universitetet i Bergen, Allegaten 41, 5007 Bergen, Norge
Michel Manbaron
Geographical Institute, University of Fribourg, Perolles, 1700 Fribourg, Switzerland

Evolution of Karst: From Prekarst to Cessation, 319-326, Ljubljana-Postojna 2002

CESSATION OF KARSTIFICATION DUE TO THE SEA-LEVEL RISE?

CASE STUDY OF THE Y-CAVE, DUGI OTOK, CROATIA

MLADEN JURAČIĆ, TATJANA BAKRAN-PETRICIOLI,
DONAT PETRICIOLI

Abstract
Along the eastern Adriatic coast a number of submerged karst phenomena are found (caves, submarine springs, poljes...) due to the recent (Late Pleistocene-Holocene) sea level rise of the order of 120 m. Formation of a submarine cave (Y-cave, 86 m long, entrance 6 - 12 m below sea level, with an air pocket above sea level) is discussed. Special attention was given to speleothems and recent corrosion in the remote shallow part of the cave. The role of endolithic and biomineralizing organisms is stressed.
Key words: *erosion/corrosion, accumulation, submerged karst, endolithic and epilithic fauna, Adriatic Sea*

INTRODUCTION

The investigated submarine cave is located on the SW coast of the Dugi Otok Island near the Brbinjšćica (Brbišćica) Cove, Croatia (Fig. 1). It was visited, photographed and a topographically measured.

Most of the Croatian Adriatic coast is formed in karstified limestones and belongs to the Dalmatian-type coast (defined after Von Richthofen as *drowned mountainous coast consisting of parallel fold ranges, resulting in zigzag channels parallel and normal to the general coastal trend*, Fairbridge, 1968). Caves and sinkholes (along with other karst features such as dolinas) are common below the sea level. Most of them were formed under subaeral conditions during periods of lowered sea level (Corregari et al, 1996; Benac & Juračić, 1998; Vaniček et al., 2000). However, in the coastal zone a distinction must be made between those features formed below and at the sea level at the coast by recent processes, and those that land-sea interface changes have by chance located there. In view that most of the caves are polygenetic, the aim of this investigation was to bring up dilemmas of development of karstification in drowned cave located near the sea level. One would expect the cessation of karstification process (corrosion) below the sea level, but evidence is presented on biocorrosion and an indication that some secondary corrosion is occurring in the zone where presumably there is mixing of the ground(fresh)water and seawater.

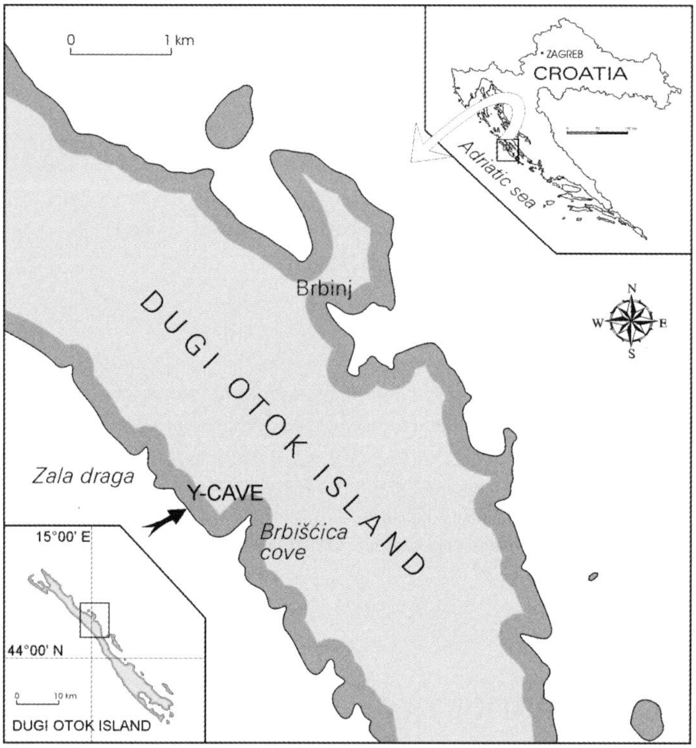

Fig. 1. Location of the Y-cave at Dugi Otok Island, Croatia.

RESULTS

The coast where Y-cave is located is built of bedded Turonian limestones (Fuček et al., 1991). In the same area there are few other submarine and coastal caves. The location is 14° 59' 04,8"E and 44° 03' 27,3"N (Fig.1).

The topographic sketch of the cave plan, with longitudinal and characteristic transversal profiles (cross-sections) is given in Fig. 2. Cave entrance is 12 m below actual sea level and 6 m high (Fig. 3). The entrance part is 6-7 m large with flattened floor covered with coarse to fine loose sediment (Fig. 3; possible archaeological site!). The remaining part is much narrower, except of the widening (small hall) at the turn of the main channel. The hall is positioned higher than the rest of the cave and there is an air pocket in it. Moreover, in the hall, speleothems above and below the water level are found (Fig. 4). Total length of the cave is 87 m. A very rugged appearance of the flanks of the channel is found in the deeper part of the cave (Fig. 5).

In the entrance part of the cave, where there is still enough light for sciaphilic algae, a precoralligenous aspect of coralligenous biocenosis was noted. In shaded parts of the entrance this biocenosis is replaced by biocenosis of semi-dark caves where sponges like *Agelas oroides* (Schmidt), *Axinella damicornis* (Esper), *Dictyonella incisa* (Schmidt), *Pet-*

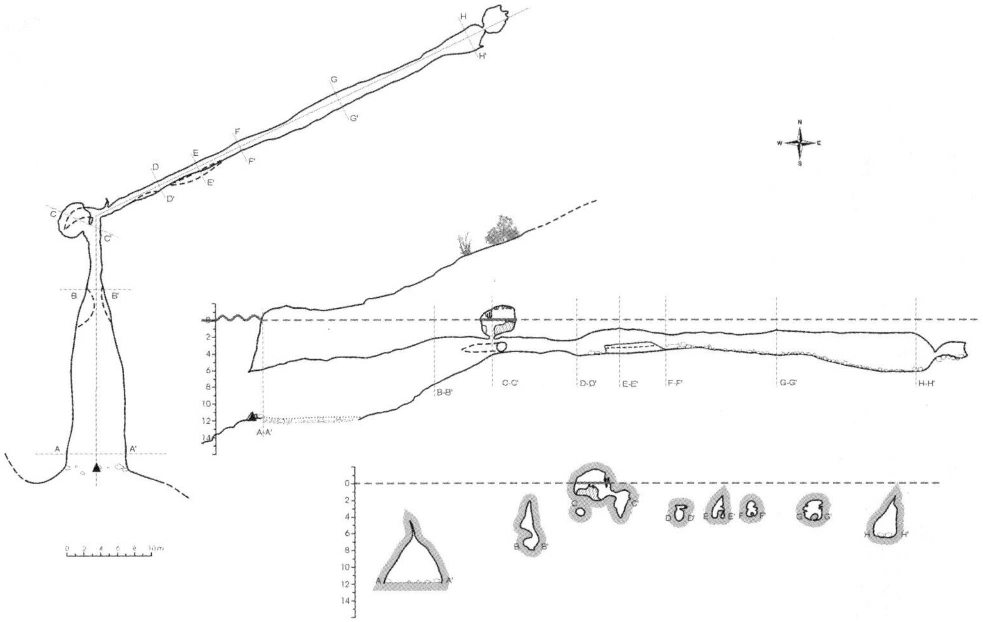

Fig. 2. Plan of the Y-cave with longitudinal profile and characteristic sections.

Fig. 3. Cave entrance at 12 m depth.

Fig. 4. Partially submerged speleothems in the small hall, approximately at section C-C'.

Fig. 5. Corrosionally sculptured channel in remote part of the cave, approximately at section F-F'.

rosia ficifomis (Poiret), *Reniera sarai* Pulitzer, *R. fulva* Topsent, *R. cratera* Schmidt, *Cliona schmidtii* (Ridley) and *Plakina bowerbanki* Sarŕ dominated. Very well developed biocenosis of semi-dark caves is present all the way to the turn of the main channel (Fig. 2, section C-C'). Towards the end of the cave biocenosis of semi-dark caves is replaced with biocenosis of caves and ducts in complete darkness. Behind the turn of main channel, towards the section F-F', sponges still prevail. We noted there *Chondrosia reniformis* Nardo, *Spirastrella cunctatrix* (Schmidt), *Tethya aurantium* (Pallas), *Corticium candelabrum* Schmidt, *Plakina bowerbanki* Sarŕ and *Isops intuta* (Topsent). Very abundant population of gastropod *Homalopoma sanguineum* (Linnaeus) was also noted there as well as presence of rare fish *Oligopus ater* Risso. At the end of the cave organisms were present in very low abundance. Besides sponges noted for middle part of the cave the following species were also found: *Sycon elegans* (Bowerbank), *Geodia conchilega* Schmidt, *Diplastrella bistellata* (Schmidt), *Petrosia ficifomis* (Poiret), *Discodermia polydiscus* Bocage, *Spongia virgultosa* Schmidt and *Myrmekioderma* sp. Also some polychetes and bryozoans of not yet determined species were noted in the deepest and darkest part of Y-cave. However, on the ceiling and in the upper part of flanks of channel in this part of the cave no organisms were recorded (Fig. 5).

Numerous organisms that live in the biocenosis of semi-dark caves are limestone-eroding organisms. They can burrow (Clionid sponges), bore (bivalves) and scrap (mollusks and echinoids) the substrate (Rützler, 1975). These processes are evident in the Y-cave: in the Fig. 6. a part of wall located between sections B-B' and C-C' is shown with

Fig. 6. Part of the cave wall with pronounced bivalve corrosion located between sections B-B' and C-C'.

Fig. 7. Traces of bioerosion (possibly by Clionid sponges) on the limestone protrusion in the main channel between sections C-C' and D-D'.

pronounced bivalve corrosion (*Lithophaga* ?), whereas in the Fig. 7. traces of bioerosion (*Cliona* ?) in the main channel between sections C-C' and D-D' is shown.

DISCUSSION

The investigated cave was formed under subaeral conditions in Turonian limestones most probably during Pleistocene, when the sea level was lowered and oscillated between present and -120 m (Fairbanks, 1989; Lowe & Walker, 1997). Moreover, partially submerged speleothems (Fig. 4) have obviously been deposited also during lowered sea level. One could presume that they were deposited during last glacial age, the Würm.

A very regular shape of the cave suggests the tectonic predisposition of its formation along fault fissures stretching 0-180° and 64-244°. The water flow enlarged the channel, and what is interesting, it seems that the cave is episodically still hydrologically active. A visit to the cave location during the rainy period (February 2001) revealed brackish water pouring from the cave entrance.

It is commonly accepted that sea flooding leads to the cessation of the karstification process (Ford & Williams, 1992), at least to the water depth of 500 m where the seawater is saturated on $CaCO_3$ (Seibold & Berger, 1996). However in the Y-cave there are indications of recent corrosion process (appearance of solution sculptures in the remote part of the cave just below the sea level (Fig. 5). Corrosion process could presumably continue due to episodic freshwater occurrence and mixing with seawater near the sea level in the remote part of the cave.

Distribution of biocenoses in Y-cave is similar to the cave at Krk Island (North Adriatic, Arko-Pijevac et al. 2001). The other corrosion (karstification) processes that must be taken into account, and were documented in the biocenosis of semi-dark caves (in the entrance and middle part of the cave), are biocorrosion and bioerosion (Figs. 6 and 7).

CONCLUSION

Although seawater flooding normally leads to the cessation of the karstification process and its fossilization, the presented example from the Y-cave confirms that karstification occurs in the zone of mixing of freshwater and seawater. However, the biocorrosion and bioerosion must be also taken in account while discussing the shaping of submerged caves.

REFERENCES

Arko-Pijevac, M., Benac, Č., Kovačić, M., & Kirinčić, M., 2001: A submarine cave at the island of Krk (north Adriatic Sea).- Natura Croatica, 10, 163-184.

Benac, Č. & Juračić, M. ,1998: Geomorphological indicators of the sea level changes during Upper Pleistocene (Würm) and Holocene in the Kvarner region.- Acta Geographica Croatica, 33, 27-45.

Correggiari, A., Roveri, M., & Trincardi, F. ,1996: Late Pleistocene and Holocene evolution of the north Adriatic Sea.- Il Quaternario - Italian Journal of Quaternary Science, 9/2, 697-704.

Fairbridge, R.W. (ed): The Encyclopaedia of Geomorphology.- Reinhold Book Corp., New York, 942-947.

Ford, D. & Williams, P., 1992: Karst Geomorphology and Hydrology.- Chapman & Hall, London, 601 p.

Fuček, L., Jelaska, V., Gušić, I., Prtoljan, B., & Oštrić, N., 1991: Padinski turonski sedimenti uvale Brbišnica na Dugom Otoku.- Geol. vjesnik, 44, 55-67.

Lowe, l.l. & Walker, M.J.C., 1997: Reconstructing Quaternary environments.- Longman, London, 446 p.

Rützler, K., 1975: The role of burrowing sponges in bioerosion. - Oceanologia (Berlin), 19, 203-216.

Seibold, E. & Berger, W.H., 1996: The Sea Floor. An Introduction to Marine Geology (third edition).- Springer Verlag, Berlin, 356 p.

Vaniček, V., Juračić, M., Bajraktarević, Z., & Ćosović, V., 2000: Benthic foraminiferal assemblages in a restricted environment - An example from the Mljet Lakes (Adriatic Sea, Croatia).- Geologia Croatica, 53, 269-279.

Address
Mladen Juračić
Department of Geology, Faculty of Science, Zvonimirova 8, HR-10000 Zagreb, Croatia
E-mail: mjuracic@chem.pmf.hr

Tatjana Bakran-Petricioli
Department of Biology, Faculty of Science, Rooseveltov trg 6, HR-10000 Zagreb, Croatia

Donat Petricioli
OIKON d.o.o., Vlade Prekrata 20, HR-10000 Zagreb, Croatia

Evolution of Karst: From Prekarst to Cessation, 327-337, Ljubljana-Postojna 2002

KARST CONDUIT EVOLUTION

GEORG KAUFMANN

Abstract
We derive the equations governing flow and evolution of single karst conduits, which are enlarged by chemical dissolution in the ternary system water-carbon dioxide-calcite. Two conduit geometries are compared, a circular conduit and a rectangular conduit. Flow in the evolving conduits can be laminar or turbulent, depending on the flow velocity in the conduit. We discuss the limiting effect of turbulence on the flow rates, and show that both geometries result in similarly enlarged karst conduits.
Keywords: *Dissolution kinetics, conduit, karst.*

INTRODUCTION

A first step in numerically modeling the evolution of a karst aquifer is always the model of a single fracture, representing an initial channel in the rock penetrable by aggressive water, enriched in carbon dioxide. The solution is undersaturated with calcium, and the fracture can be enlarged by chemical dissolution. While flowing through the fracture, calcium is dissolved and the solution becomes saturated.

Since the work of White (1977), it became apparent that the calcium dissolution rate drops by several orders of magnitude close to the saturation of the solution with respect to calcium, thus allowing for much larger penetration length of undersaturated, aggressive solution within the proto-conduits. In fact, this drop in dissolution rate, termed *kinetic trigger* by White, initiates the solutional widening far from recharge locations at the surface.

Several numerical models on single fracture growth have been published (Dreybrodt 1990, Palmer 1991, Groves et al. 1994a, Dreybrodt 1996, Kaufmann et al. 1999, Dreybrodt et al. 1999, Palmer 1999). These models simulate the evolution of a single fracture as a simple analog of flow along a fracture or a bedding plane, and the evolution of the fracture width is controlled by the dissolution rate. At the exit of the fracture, slow dissolution rates are responsible for the slow growth of the exit diameter, while the entrance of the fracture grows faster during this initial phase. As time proceeds, the solution at the exit becomes sufficiently undersaturated to increase the dissolution rate by several orders of magnitude, and a breakthrough is achieved. From then on, the entire fracture grows at a constant pace. Dreybrodt (1996) derived an analytical relation for this *breakthrough time* as a function of fracture geometry, hydrostatic pressure drop, and dissolution chemistry for a single fracture. In this relation, the breakthrough time is inversely proportional to the cube of the initial fracture width, and the geometry of the preexisting fractures largely controls the speed of the karstification process.

GEOMETRY OF CONDUIT

We assume that flow in a limestone aquifer can be modeled using the concept of flow in fractured rocks. Therefore, we regard the most probable flow path as given along the junctions of small fissures with bedding planes (Fig. 1). We adopt two geometrical models to simulate flow along the intersection. The first model is a circular conduit model, simulating a conduit along the intersection of the fissure and the bedding plane (Fig. 1a). The conduit is characterized by its length l and ist diameter d, the cross-sectional area is $A = \pi d^2/4$. The second model is a rectangular conduit and adopts a rectangular cross-section along the fissure (Fig. 1b), which is characterized by its length l, the width a and the height b. The cross-sectional area is $A = ab$.

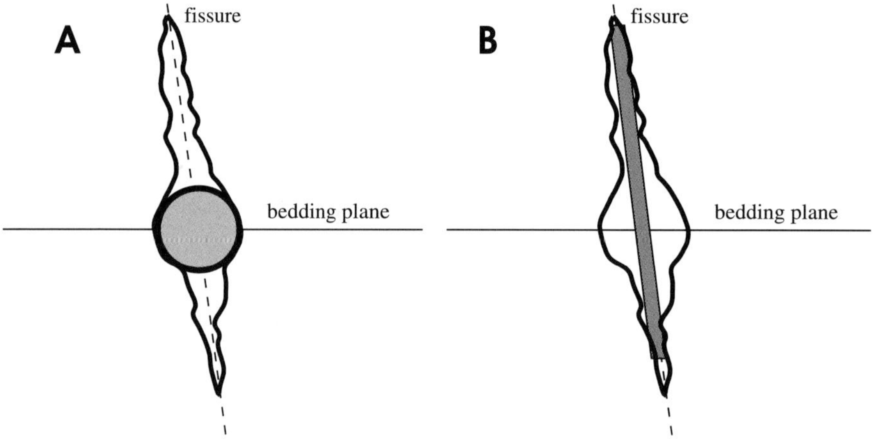

Fig 1. Geometrical models for the flow path along the intersection of a fissure and a bedding plane. Left: circular conduit, right: rectangular conduit.

FLOW IN CONDUIT

Flow in the conduit is modeled as fully developed, incompressible Poiseuille flow with no buoyancy forces (e.g. Turcotte et al. 1982, pp.237ff). The flow is driven by the hydrostatic pressure difference Δp across the conduit, which can also be expressed as head loss (in m), $\Delta h = \Delta p/\rho g + \Delta z$, with ρ the density of water, g the gravitational acceleration, and Δz the change in elevation between upstream and downstream ends of the conduit, assumed to be zero in our models. Alternatively, we introduce the hydraulic gradient, $i = \Delta h/l$.

For a given head loss Δh, we calculate the flow rate Q (in m^3 s^{-1}) in the conduit. A general form relating head loss and flow rate is given by a power-law equation of the form

$$\Delta h = RQ^n, \tag{1}$$

with R a coefficient for the conduit geometry and flow properties, called resistivity.

LAMINAR FLOW

We first assume that flow is laminar. Then the linear Hagen-Poiseuille flow law applies, which reads (e.g. Beek et al. 1975)

$$n = 1, \quad R = \frac{12\eta}{\rho g}\int_0^l \frac{dx}{a^3 b M_0}, \tag{2}$$

with η the viscosity of water, ρ the density of water, g the gravitational acceleration, and M_0 a factor depending on the fracture geometry,

$$M_0 = 0.6 - 0.3\ a/b, \text{ ellipsoidal}$$

$$M_0 = 1.0 - 0.6\ a/b, \text{ rectangular} \tag{3}$$

In (2), the geometrical properties $a=a(x,t)$, $b=b(x,t)$, and $M_0=M_0(x,t)$ are all functions of the distance along the fracture, x, and the time t, as they can be enlarged by chemical dissolution. However, we first consider the initial case, in which the fracture geometry is uniform along its length. For large rectangular conduits ($b>>a$) and for circular conduits ($a=b=d$), we then find

$$R = \frac{40\eta}{\rho g}\frac{1}{d^4}, \text{ circular conduit}$$

$$R = \frac{12\eta}{\rho g}\frac{1}{a^3 b}, \text{ rectangular conduit} \tag{4}$$

We compare the inverse of the resistivity R, called the conductivity $K=1/R$, for a circular conduit and a rectangular fracture with a fixed height of $b=1$ m (Fig. 2). For the circular conduit, conductivities decrease over several orders of magnitude from $K=10^{-4}$ to 10^{-13} m^2 s^{-1} with decreasing conduit diameter. The conduit length is less important, as for the range of values considered, conductivities decrease only by less than one order of magnitude with conduit length. For a rectangular conduit, in order to obtain similar values for the conductivities, we need to decrease the fracture width by one order of magnitude, when compared to the conduit diameter. The variation of conductivities with fracture width is less pronounced than for conduit diameter. However, it still decreases from $K=10^{-5}$ to 10^{-12} m^2 s^{-1}.

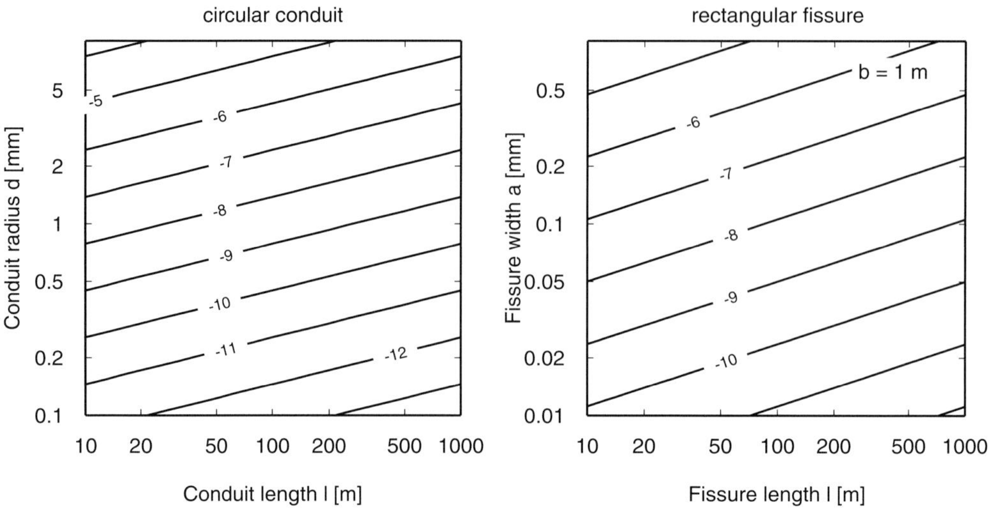

Fig 2. Conductivities K *as a function of length and width. The conductivities are shown as* log K *(in* $m^2 s^{-1}$*) for (left) a circular conduit and (right) a rectangular conduit with constant height of 1 m.*

Two special cases can be discussed.

EQUAL RESISTIVITIES

Firstly, we compare a conduit and a fracture having the same resistivity, $R_{\text{conduit}} = R_{\text{fracture}}$. Equating (4)a and b results in a relation between conduit diameter and fracture width:

$$a = \left[\frac{12d^4}{40b}\right]^{1/3}.$$

For a nominal fracture height of *b=1* m, resistivities are equal, if $a \cong 0.7d^{4/3}$ holds. Thus, the fracture width has to be about one order of magnitude smaller than the the conduit diameter. Note that in this case the cross-sectional area of the fracture is about 100 times larger than for the conduit!

EQUAL CROSS SECTIONS

Secondly, if the cross-sectional area of the conduit is equal to the cross-sectional area of the fracture, $\pi d^4 / 4 = ab$, the resistivities are related by

$$R_{conduit} \cong 7.4\frac{a}{b}R_{fracture}.$$

Again, for a nominal fracture height of $b=1$ m the relation reduces to $R_{\text{conduit}}=7.4\ a\ R_{\text{fracture}}$. Hence, for equal cross sections, the fracture conductivity is several order of magnitude larger than the conduit conductivity!

TURBULENT FLOW

If turbulent flow is allowed, we can use the non-linear Darcy-Weissbach flow law (e.g. Jeppson 1976),

$$
\begin{aligned}
& n = 2, \\
& R = f \frac{8}{\pi^2 g} \frac{l}{d^5}, \text{ circular conduit,} \\
& R = f \frac{8}{\pi^2 g} \frac{l}{a^3 b}, \text{ rectangular conduit.}
\end{aligned}
\qquad (5)
$$

In (5), f is the dimensionless *friction factor*, characterizing the flow regime in the conduit. With $u = q/A$ the mean velocity in the fracture, the dimensionless *Reynolds number* is defined as

$$\text{Re} = \frac{ud}{\eta} \qquad (6)$$

Flow can be either laminar or turbulent, depending on the flow velocity in the fracture. The transition between laminar and turbulent flow occurs around $\text{Re} \cong 2200$. For small flow velocities, flow is unidirectional and termed *laminar*. Then,

$$f = f_l = \frac{64}{\text{Re}}, \ \text{Re} \leq 2200 \qquad (7)$$

holds. For laminar flow, inserting (6) and (7) in (5)a and the result in (1) reduces the flow relation to a linear relation, with $n=1$, $R_l = 128\eta l/(\pi \rho g d^4)$. Hence, R_l is equivalent to the one derived above (4).

For larger velocities, eddies develop along the conduit walls, and flow becomes *turbulent*. Depending on Re and the *wall roughness*, w, the friction factor is taken as the maximum of

$$
\begin{aligned}
& f_s = 0.3164\ \text{Re}^{-0.25}, \\
& f_t^{-0.5} = 1.14 - 2\log\left[\frac{w}{d} + \frac{9.35}{\text{Re}} f_t^{-0.5}\right], \\
& f_r^{-0.5} = 1.14 - 2\log\left[\frac{w}{d}\right],
\end{aligned}
\qquad (8)
$$

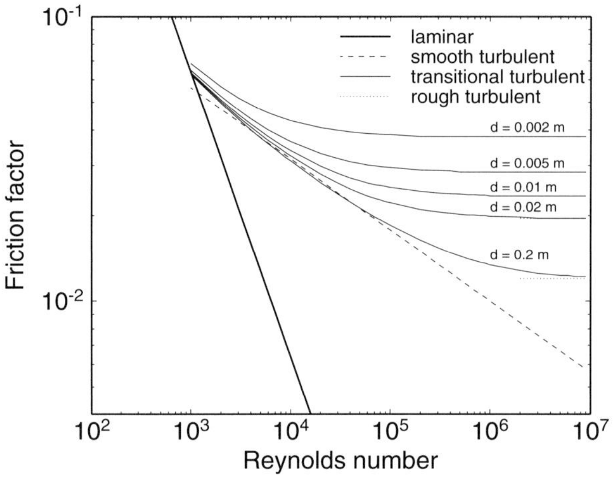

Fig 3. Friction factor as a function of Reynolds number, in the case of transitional and rough turbulence for different diameter d.

with f_s smooth turbulence, f_r rough turbulence, and f_t the transition between smooth and rough turbulence. Note that for rough turbulence, the friction factor becomes independent from *Re*. Note also that the friction factor for the transitional regime is given by an implicit equation, which has to be solved iteratively.

A comparison between friction factors depending on *Re* is shown in Fig. 3. For small *Re*, the laminar friction factor is one order of magnitude larger than all turbulent friction factors. In the turbulent flow regime, the implicit equation for the transition between smooth and rough turbulence, f_t, can be approximated by f_s for small *Re* and large *d*, and by f_r for large *Re*.

The Reynolds number (6) explicitly depends on the flow rate *Q*. Thus, a distinction between laminar and turbulent flow can only be made *a posteriori*. We start calculating a laminar flow rate, and then derive *Re*. For *Re>2200*, flow is turbulent and has to be recalculated using a turbulent friction factor, which is taken as the maximum from (8). Note that for a given conduit the turbulent flow rate is smaller than the laminar flow rate, thus, turbulence is limiting the flow in a conduit.

EVOLUTION OF CONDUIT

The enlargement of a conduit can be derived from the conduit geometry (*a*, *b*, *d*, *l*), and the Ca^{2+}-flux rate, $F_{Ca}{}^{2+}$. We start with a circular conduit of length *l* and uniform diameter $d(x)=d$. The conduit is subdivided into *n* elements of length Δl_j, and radius $\Delta r_j = d / 2$. The length increments are following a logarithmic distribution (e.g. Groves et al. 1994b) to ensure that the steep gradient in calcium concentration in the entrance section of the conduit are properly resolved. Dissolution in the conduit and subsequent enlargement is then modeled in several steps:

1. Calculate flow rate *Q* from conduit geometry, *l*, *d*, hydrostatic pressure difference, Δh, and flow regime, *f*, using (1) and (5).

2. Assign $[Ca^{2+}]_j$ at the upstream end of element j and calculate the Ca^{2+}-flux rate $F^j_{Ca^{2+}}$ in the element, using a relation of the form

$$F_{Ca^{2+}} = k_i \left(1 - \frac{[Ca^{2+}]}{[Ca^{2+}]_{eq}}\right)^{n_i}, i = 1,2, \tag{9}$$

where $[Ca^{2+}]_{eq}$ is the equilibrium value of $[Ca^{2+}]$ (in mol cm^{-3}), at which the solution is saturated with calcium. Eq. (9) accounts for both the higher flux rate (low-order kinetics) for $[Ca^{2+}] < [Ca^{2+}]_s$ and the several orders of magnitude lower flux rate (high-order kinetics) for $[Ca^{2+}] > [Ca^{2+}]_s$. Here, $[Ca^{2+}]_s$ is the calcium threshold concentration, at which the flux rate changes from low to high-order kinetics; it is generally between 60-90 percent of $[Ca^{2+}]_{eq}$. The flux rate in (9) is given in mol cm^{-2} s^{-1}.
For low-order kinetics, both CO_2-hydration and mass transport through diffusion are rate-limiting, and the flux rate can be approximated by a linear relation,

$$n = 1. \tag{10}$$

The rate coefficient k_1 has been determined by several authors. From analytical analysis of the rate equations (Buhmann et al. 1985a, Buhmann et al. 1985b), Dreybrodt (1996) has derived the value

$$k_1 = 4x10^{-11}\ mol\ cm^{-2}\ s^{-1}. \tag{11}$$

Palmer (1991) has derived rate coefficients k_1 from the experiments on calcite dissolution performed by Plummer et al. (1978). His coefficients depend on temperature T and CO_2-pressure p, $k_1=k_1(T,p)$, and the exponent is a function of CO_2-pressure p, $n_1=n_1(p)$, and varies between 1.5 and 2.2. Note that the coefficients k_1 tabulated in Palmer (1991) must be normalized by the atomic mass of calcite, m_r, to fit (9).
For high-order kinetics, the dissolution of calcite along the interface solution-rock is rate-limiting, and we find (e.g. Palmer, 1991):

$$n_2 = 4, \tag{12}$$

$$k_2 = k_1 \left(1 - [Ca^{2+}]_s\right)^{(n_1 - n_2)}. \tag{13}$$

The rate coefficient k_2 is several orders of magnitude larger than k_1.

3. Calculate additionally dissolved calcium in length element j, using

$$d[Ca^{2+}] = \frac{F^j_{Ca^{2+}}}{Q} \Delta A_j, \tag{14}$$

with $\Delta A_j = 2\pi\ \Delta r_j \Delta l_j$ the surface area of the conduit element.

4. Calculate calcium concentration at downstream end of length element j,

$$[Ca^{2+}]_{j+1} = [Ca^{2+}]_j + d[Ca^{2+}], \qquad (15)$$

and handle new calcium concentration farther down.

5. Calculate wall retreat within length element *j*, using

$$\frac{dr_j}{dt} = \frac{F^j_{Ca^{2+}} m_r}{\rho_c}, \qquad (16)$$

with ρ_c the density of calcite.

6. Update the radius of length element *j* for time step Δt,

$$\Delta r_j = \Delta r_j + \frac{dr_j}{dt} \Delta t \qquad (17)$$

7. Repeat (2)-(6) for all length elements, then calculate a new effective diameter (Groves et al. 1994b), using

$$d_e^4 = \frac{l}{\sum_{j=1}^{n} \frac{\Delta l_j}{(2\Delta r_j)^4}} \qquad (18)$$

The effective diameter corresponds to a conduit, which experiences the same head loss as the conduit with the variable radius.

8. Update the flow rate Q using the new effective diameter d_e and proceed with (1), until the desired evolution time is reached. The analysis for a rectangular conduit is similar and therefore not discussed.

An example of the evolution of a circular conduit is shown in Fig. 4. Here, the solution enters the conduit from the left side. As dissolution proceeds in the early phase, only the entrance section is sufficiently enlarged, the downstream section grows only slowly (dashed lines). This is a result of the slow high-order kinetics, as the Ca^{2+}-concentration quickly reaches levels close to saturation further downstream. Thus, sufficient dissolution only occurs within the entrance section. When enlargement proceeds, more highly undersaturated solution is carried further downstream, and the conduit finally grows at a relatively constant pace (solid lines).

The importance of high-order kinetics close to the saturation of the solution, $[Ca^{2+}]_{eq}$, becomes obvious, when we discuss the Ca^{2+}-concentration along the conduit (Fig. 4). At the onset of evolution, low-order kinetics in the entrance section results in solution close to saturation within a few centimeters. As a consequence, modeling only low-order kinetics would result in no significant conduit growth, and enlargement would be limited to a few centimeters to meters from the entrance, depending on conduit geometry and film

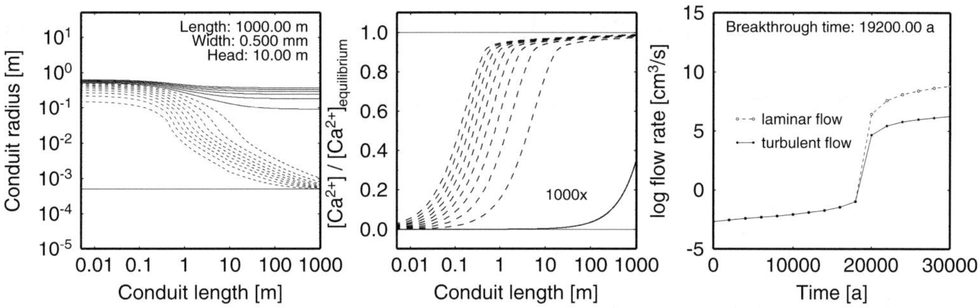

Fig 4. Left: Evolution of conduit radius. Flow is driven from left to right. The thin line indicates the initial conduit width, dashed lines are enlarged conduit widths before, solid lines after low-order kinetics is established. Lines are plotted at time steps of 2000 years. Middle: Profiles of calcium concentration in karst conduit for different times. The time step is 2000 years. Dashed lines indicate concentrations before, the solid line after low-order kinetics is established. Note that the solid line is scaled by a factor of 1000. Right: Flow rate in a karst conduit. The dashed line represents an evolution, where only laminar flow is considered, for the solid line flow can switch into the turbulent flow regime, if the Reynolds number is large enough.

thickness. By taking high-order kinetics into account, when the solution is close to saturation, the Ca^{2+}-flux rate is reduced by several orders of magnitude, and now slightly undersaturated solution can be carried much farther downstream. Dissolution is now occurring several kilometers within a conduit. This mechanism, termed kinetic trigger by White (1977), is largely responsible for enlarging fracture in limestone during the early phase of karstification.

The flow rate at the exit of the conduit resembles the two-stage evolution. During the first stage, high-order kinetics controls the conduit growth, the flow rate increases slowly with time. When the more effective low-order kinetics is established within the entire conduit, the flow rate increases over several orders of magnitude within a very short time interval. This time interval is called breakthrough time by Dreybrodt (1990), it is a characteristic parameter for conduit growth and depends on conduit diameter d, length l, and head loss Δh. Note that flow in the conduit also becomes turbulent, and neglecting turbulence would result in an overestimation of the flow rate.

The evolution of a rectangular conduit is shown in Fig. 5. While the general charac-

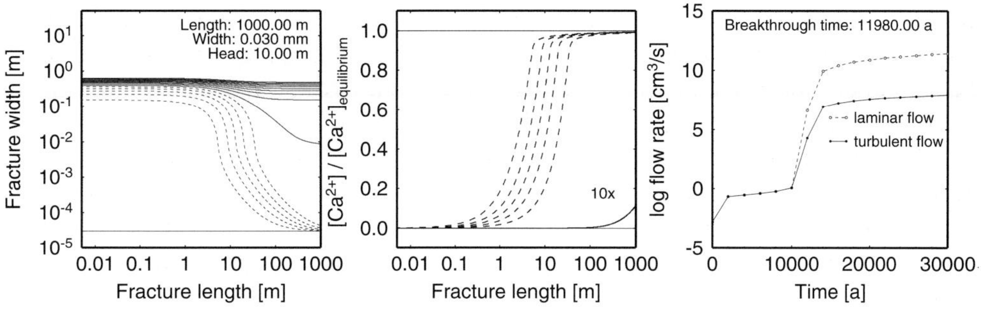

Fig. 5. As Fig. 4, but for a rectangular fracture of 1 m height.

teristics are similar to the growth of a circular conduit, differences occur in the entrance section during the early phase. For the rectangular conduit, the entrance part is enlarged more uniformly, but after the breakthrough occurred, the rectangular conduit growth resembles the evolution of the circular conduit well. Flow rates again increase by several orders of magnitude at breakthrough time.

DISCUSSION

We have discussed flow and evolution of proto-conduits in limestone, which are enlarged by chemical dissolution. Two typical conduit geometries, a circular pipe and a rectangular fracture, have been compared. While the enlargement exhibits differences in the early stage of evolution, after breakthrough time both geometries experience similar enlargement. As in our model flow can become turbulent, the flow rates in the enlarged conduits is significantly lower than for conduits, which experience laminar flow conditions only.

ACKNOWLEDGEMENTS

The figures in this paper are drawn using the GMT graphics package (Wessel et al. 1991, 1998).

REFERENCES

Beek, W. J. and Muttzall, K. M. K., 1975: *Transport Phenomena*. John Wiley, London.

Buhmann, D. and Dreybrodt, W., 1985a: The kinetics of calcite dissolution and precipitation in geologically relevant situations of karst areas. 1. Open system. *Chem. Geol.*, **48**, 189-211.

Buhmann, D. and Dreybrodt, W., 1985b: The kinetics of calcite dissolution and precipitation in geologically relevant situations of karst areas. 2. Closed system. *Chem. Geol.*, **53**, 109-124.

Dreybrodt, W., 1990: The role of dissolution kinetics in the development of karst aquifers in limestone: a model simulation of karst evolution. *J. Geol.*, **98 (5)**, 639-655.

Dreybrodt, W., 1996: Principles of early development of karst conduits under natural and man-made conditions revealed by mathematical analysis of numerical models. *Water Resour. Res.*, **32 (9)**, 2923-2935.

Dreybrodt, W. and Gabrovsek, F., 1999: Dynamics of the evolution of single karst conduits.

In: A. B. Klimchouk, D. C. Ford, A. N. Palmer, and W. Dreybrodt, editors, *Speleogenesis: Evolution of Karst Aquifers*, pages 184-193. National Speleological Society, New York.

Groves, C. G. and Howard, A. D., 1994a: Minimum hydrochemical conditions allowing limestone cave development. *Water Resour. Res.*, **30 (3)**, 607-615.

Groves, C. G. and Howard, A. D., 1994b: Early development of karst systems 1. {P}referential flow path enlargement under laminar flow. *Water Resour. Res.*, **30 (10)**, 2837-2846.

Jeppson, R. W., 1976: *Analysis of flow in pipe networks*. Ann Arbor Sci. Pub., Ann Arbor.

Kaufmann, G. and Braun, J., 1999: Karst aquifer evolution in fractured rocks. *Water Resour. Res.*, **35 (11)**, 3223-3238.

Palmer, A. N., 1991: Origin and morphology of limestone caves. *Geol. Soc. Am. Bull.*, **103**, 1-21.

Palmer, A. N., 1999: Digital modeling of individual solution conduits. In: A. B. Klimchouk, D. C. Ford, A. N. Palmer, and W. Dreybrodt,(editors), *Speleogenesis: Evolution of Karst Aquifers*, pages 194-200. ational Speleological Society, New York.

Plummer, L. N., Wigley, T. M. L., and Parkhurst, D. L., 1978: The kinetics of calcite dissolution in CO_2-water systems at 5°C to 60°C and 0.0 to 1.0 atm CO_2. *Am. J. Sci.*, **278**, 179-216.

Turcotte, D. L. and Schubert, G., 1982: *Geodynamics*. John Wiley and Sons, New York.

Wessel, P. and Smith, W. H. F., 1991: Free software helps map and display data. *EOS*, **72**, 441-446.

Wessel, P. and Smith, W. H. F., 1998: New, improved version of generic mapping tools released. *EOS*, **79**, 579.

White, W. B., 1977: The role of solution kinetics in the development of karst aquifers. *Mem. Int. Assoc. Hydrogeol.*, **12**, 503-517.

Address
Institute of Geophysics, University of Göttingen
Herzberger Landstrasse 180, 7075 Göttingen, Germany
E-mail: gkaufman@uni-geophys.gwdg.de

Evolution of Karst: From Prekarst to Cessation, 339-344, Ljubljana-Postojna 2002

CARBONATE KARST CAVES IN IRAN

EZZAT RAEISI

Abstract
Iran is divided into the five structural zones of Zagros, Sanandaj-Sirjan, Central Iran, East and South-East Iran, and Alborz and Kopet-Dagh. Karstic carbonate formations cover about 11 % of Iran's land area, mostly in the Zagros (55.2 %) and Central Iran (24.3 %). A complete inventory of the caves has not been published so far. Marefat (1994) reported 258 caves, but this does not cover all the caves of Iran. The karst caves in Iran are mainly small. The longest length in 57 % of the caves is less than 100 meters and only 5 caves are found with lengths larger than 1000 m. In spite of the large extent of karstified land in Iran, the number of caves and their lengths are less than expected. The small number of caves is due to the fact that many cave entrances have been filled by talus or transported sediments on the steep slopes of high mountains or closed off by entrance breakdown in the high risk earthquake zone of Iran. The short lengths of caves is also explainable because the thickness of the karst formations is mainly small and the rapid rate of uplifting and local base of erosion reduce the time of cave development in one level.
***Keywords**: Karst, Cave, Iran*

GEOLOGICAL SETTING

Iran is geologically a part of the Alpine-Himalayan orogenic belt. Five major structural zones different in structural history and tectonic style can be distinguished in Iran (Stocklin, 1968). These five zones consisting of a) Zagros Range; b) Sanandaj-Sirjan Range; c) Central Iran; d) East and South-East Iran; e) Alborz and Kopet-Dagh Ranges are shown in Figure 1. The Zagros Range is the result of the opening and closure of the Neo-Tethys oceanic realm. Deformation began in the Zagros orogenic belt since the Mesozoic age. The Zagros is divided into the three structural zones of Khozestan Plain, Simply Folded Zone (ZSFZ) and Thrust Zone (Stocklin, 1968). The ZSFZ, with a width ranging from 150 to 250 km, is a sequence of the Late Precambrian to Pliocene shelf sediments about 12 km thick, mainly consisting of limestone, marl, gypsum, sandstone and conglomerate. Since the Miocene Age, it has been folded into a series of huge anticlines and synclines. The ZSFZ passes northeastward into a narrow zone of thrusts bounded on the northeast by the Main Zagros Thrust Line. A wide variety of lithologies including crushed limestone, radiolarite and ultrabasic and metamorphic rocks have been intensively thrust faulted in this zone. The width of the thrust zone varies from 10 to 70 km and makes up

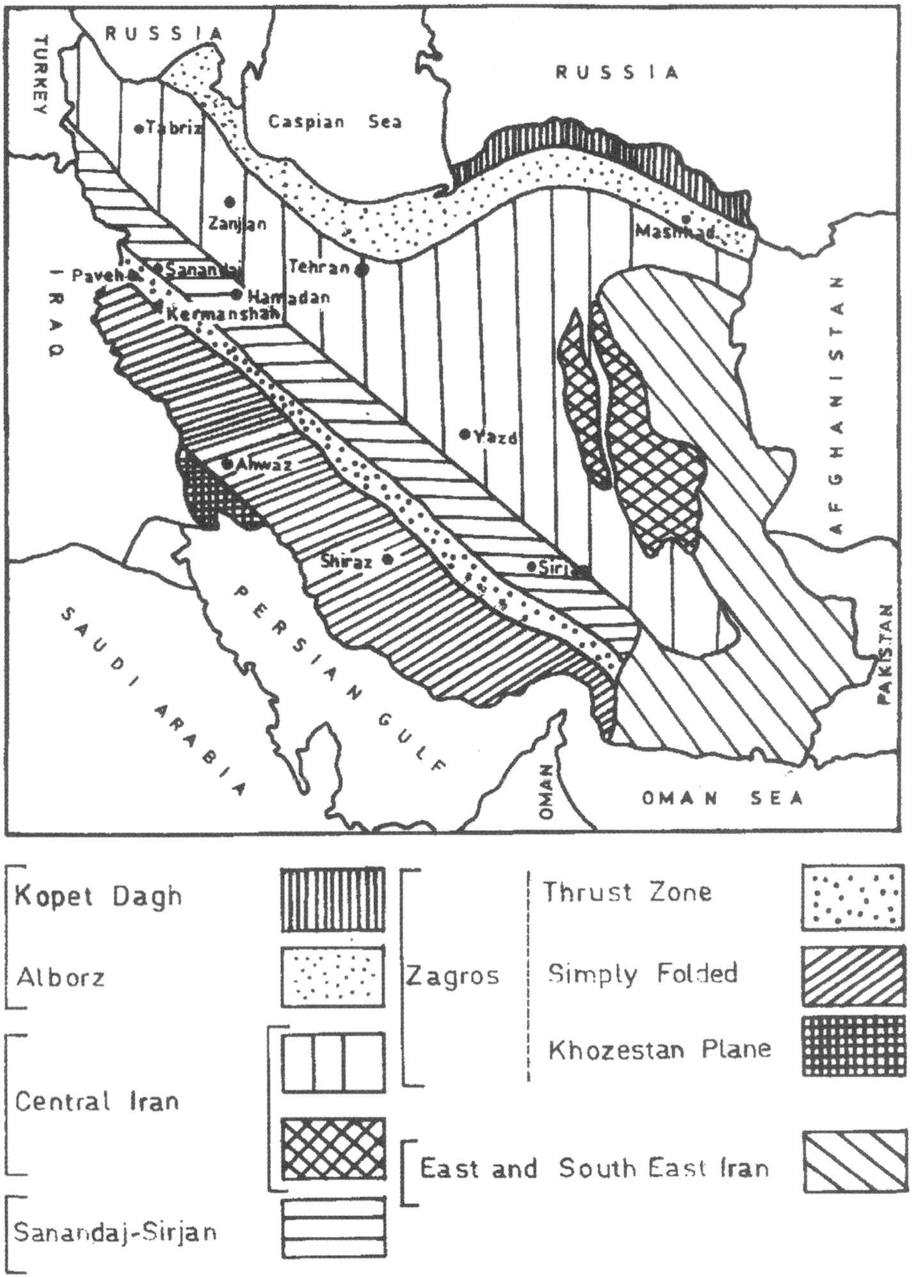

Fig. 1. Structural map of Iran (Stocklin, 1968)

the highest elevations in the Zagros. The Sanandaj-Sirjan Zone is composed mainly of granite, diorite and metamorphic rocks. The Central Zone comprises a roughly triangular area. This zone is separated from the Sanandaj-Sirjan by a continuous zone of depressions. This zone is composed of the Precambrian metamorphic basement of Central Iran, overlain by Paleozoic and Mesozoic shelf sediments and a chain of Cenozoic and possibly Mesozoic volcanoes. The Alborz Range is a marginal anticlinorium of Central Iran and it is composed of volcanics, sandstone, shale, siltstone and limestone. The Kopet Dagh Range consists of a Mesozoic-Tertiary sedimentary sequence mostly composed of limestone, shale and sandstone. It is structurally similar to the Zagros. East and South-East Iran is composed of flysch, tuffs and volcanics and colored melange.

Karstic carbonate formations cover about 11 % of Iran's land area (Figure 2). The total area of the karstified carbonate rocks in Iran is about 185 000 km^2, splitting up to 55.2 % in the Zagros, 24.3 % in Central Iran, 15.2 % in Alborz, 4.7 % in East and East-South ran, and less than 0.5 % in the Sanandaj-Sirjan Range. Iran is composed of 52 % highlands and 38 % deserts and saline lakes. Table 1 represents some of the Karst formations in this country (James & Wynd, 1965 and Falcon, 1974) with extensive outcrops,

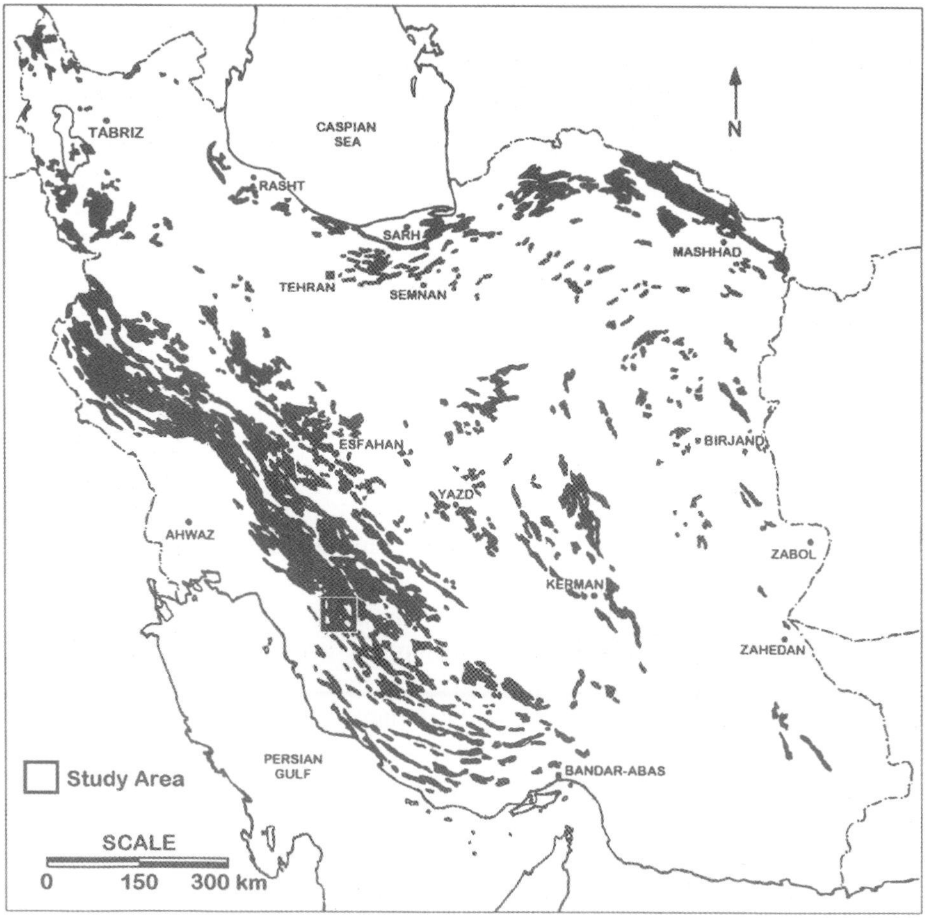

Fig. 2. Distribution map of karstic carbonate formation outcrops in Iran (Raeisi and Kowsar, 1997)

high developments of karst features and high storage capacities. Most of the outcropped carbonate rocks are of the Cretaceous and Tertiary Age.

Table 1. *Some of the karst formations in Iran with extensive outcrops*

Zone	Formation	Age	Lithology	Thickness of type section (m)
Zagros	Surmeh	Early to late Jurassic	Dolomitic limestone and dolomite	672
	Fahliyan	Lower Cretaceous	Limestone	360
	Dariyan	Lower Cretaceous	Limestone	286
	Bistoon	Upper Triassic upper Cretaceous	Limestone	___
	Sarvak	Upper Cretaceous	Limestone	821
	Ilam	Upper Cretaceous	Limestone	190
	Tarbur	Upper Cretaceous	Limestone	527
	Jahrum	Tertiary	Dolomite	467
	Asmari	Tertiary	Limestone	314
	Shahbazan	Tertiary	Dolomite limestone	333
	Guri	Tertiary	Limestone	113
Central Iran	Jamal	Paleozoic	Limestone	473
	Orbitolina	Cretaceous	Limestone	___
Alborz	Lar	Upper Jurassic	Limestone	250 to 350
	Tizkuh	Lower Cretaceous	Limestone	170
Kopet Dagh	Mozduran	Upper Jurassic	Limestone and dolomite	500
	Tirgan	Lower Cretaceous	Limestone	700

CAVES IN IRAN

Though there is an ever increasing interest on caving in Iran, only a few attempts have been made to establish a complete published inventory of the caves that have been explored so far. Most of the cave studies concentrate merely on visiting, photography and/ or mapping the explored caves. Sometimes the complete information about a cave has not been published or it can not easily be found. The speleological committee of Iran has started to collect cave data, but it has not yet been published. Marefat (1994) reported 258 caves, but it does not cover all the caves in Iran. Marefat's inventory comprises partial information about location, altitude, map and length of some of the caves and neither geological settings nor hydrologic features are reported. Table 2 presents the range of lengths of the longest passage of the caves according to this inventory. Length data is not available in 62 % of the caves. These caves are mainly small. The lengths of 57 % of the caves are less than 100 meters and only 5 caves are larger than 1000 m. The largest and best-known caves in Iran are presented in Table 3. The deepest cave is the Parau Cave (751 m depth), located 25 km north of Kermanshah and explored by Judson (1972). This cave has 26 shafts ranging in depth by 5 to 42 m. The Alisadr cave is the most visited cave in Iran. Most of its floors are sumps such that the cave should be visited by boat. The spleothems are lined 3.40 m above the sump surfaces, implying that the water level of the cave was located at a fixed elevation for a long period in the past. In some parts of the cave, the spleothems construct a second level (Iran Karst Research Center,1998). The Katelahkor is located 155 km south of Zanjan. It is an anastomatic multilevel cave (Sivand, 2000). Ghori-Ghaleh, located near Paveh, is formed at the contact of the Jurassic limestone and conglomerate. It is a cave with single passage 1205 m high. An underground stream flows through the whole length of the cave. The Shapour Cave, located 80 Km south of Shiraz, is an archeological and touristic attraction. It is a single anastomatic tiered cave. At the initial stage of subaerial exposure of the karstic Asmari Formation, the Shapour River started entrenching a valley and leakage from the Shapour River through joint and bedding plane fissures enlarged the Shapour Cave (Raeisi & Kowsar, 1997).

Table 2. *Variation of length of the longest passage of the caves in Iran based on Marefat's inventory (1994)*

Length of longest passage	Unmeasured Length	0-100	100-500	500-1000	1000-2000	2000-4000
Number of cave	161	57	30	5	3	2

Table 3. *Some of the characteristics of the largest and / or most visited caves in Iran*

Cave's Name	Length of Longest passage (m)	Depth (m)	Elevation (m)	Litho logy	Hydro geological features
Parau	1365	751	3050	Cretaceous limestone	Shafts
Alisadar	2500	<50	2050	Jurassic limestone and dolomite	Sumps
Katalehkhor	2500		1700	Tertiary limestone	Shafts
Shapour	375	80		Tertiary limestone	Dolines
Nabati	400	50	2625	Cretaceous limestone	
Ghori-ghaleh	3140				Underground Stream

In spite of the large extent of karstified land in Iran, the number and lengths of caves are less than expected. There are many highland karst aquifers without any cave systems at the present time, while big springs are emerging at their bases of erosion. Several levels of caves are expected in the karst sites of Iran, as a result of the rapid rate of uplifting and local base of erosion. There are two main reasons for the small number of caves: a) most of the karst areas are high mountains with steep slopes, therefore many cave entrances have been filled by talus or transported sediments on the steep slopes or closed off by entrance breakdown in the high risk earthquake zone of Iran and b) many springs with high discharge are of the ascending type or closed mouth type without any visible cave systems at the present time, therefore conduit systems of these springs which have developed at the upper level in the past, could not be seen on the surface at the present. The short length of caves is also expectable because: a) the thickness of the karst formations is mainly less than 400 m, b) the rapid rate of uplifting and local base of erosion reduce the time of cave development in one level. The water in the cave conduits leaks to a lower level and prevents further cave development and c) recharges are mainly diffuse flow in the majority of the karst sites, therefore the cave developments initiate where the branches of diffuse flow join each other beneath the surface.

ACKNOWLEDGEMENT

The author thanks the Research council of Shiraz University for financial support.

REFERENCES

Falcon, N.L., 1974: Southern Iran: Zagros Mountains in Mesozoic-Cenozoic orogenic belts, London: Geological Society of London, Special Publication, 4, 199-211,

Iran Karst Research Center. 1998: Field trip guide. 2nd International Symposium on Karst Water Resources. Iran: Ministry of Energy.

James, G.A. & Wynd, J.G., 1965: Stratigraphic nomenclature of Iranian Oil Consortium Agreement area, Bulletin of American Association of Petroleum Geologist, 49(12), 2182-2245

Judson, D., 1972: Ghar Parau. New York: Macmillan

Marefat, A., 1994: Kuhha va Gahrhai Iran [Mountains and Caves of Iran], Tehran: Goli

Raeisi, E. & Kowsar, N., 1997: Development of Shahpour Cave, southern Iran. Cave and Karst Science, 24(1), 27-34

Sivand, S.M., 2001: Geology and study Hydrogeological of the Kataleh-khor Cave (Iran, Zanjan) .- In: Mithevc, A.: Contact karst, Guide booklet for the excursions and Abstracts of the presentations, 9th International Karstological School Classical Karst, Postojna 26-29 june 2001, 32 p, Postojna,

Stocklin, J., 1968: Structural history and tectonics map of Iran: A review. The American Association of Petroleum Geologist Bulletin, 52(7), 1229-1258

Address
Geology Department, College of Science, Shiraz. Iran
E-mail: e_raeisi@yahoo.com

Evolution of Karst: From Prekarst to Cessation, 345-346, Ljubljana-Postojna 2002

THE IMPACT OF HYDROCHEMICAL BOUNDARY CONDITIONS ON THE EVOLUTION OF KARST AQUIFERS IN LIMESTONE TERRAINS

DOUCHKO ROMANOV[1], FRANCI GABROVŠEK[2] & WOLFGANG DREYBRODT[1]

Abstract

The early evolution of karst aquifers depends on a manifold of initial and boundary conditions such as geological setting, hydrologic properties of the initial aquifer, and petrologic properties of the rock. When all water entering at various inputs into the aquifer has equal chemical composition with respect to the system H_2O-CO_2-$CaCO_3$ early evolution under conditions of constant head exhibits breakthrough (BT) behaviour. If the chemical compositions of the input waters are different, deep in the aquifer where the saturated solutions mix renewed aggressiveness occurs, and additional dissolutional widening of fractures by mixing corrosion (MC) changes the hydrologic properties of the aquifer. To study the impact of MC on the evolution of karst we have modelled a simple karst aquifer consisting of a confined limestone bed, 1 m deep, 500 m long, and 251 m wide, with two symmetrically located inputs at a head of 25 m and open flow conditions along the entire widths at base level. To calculate dissolutional widening of the fractures the well known dissolution kinetics of limestone was used, which is linear up to 90% of saturation with respect to calcite and then switches to a non-linear 4th order rate law. First, two extremes are modelled: ***a)*** *Both inputs receive aggressive water of equal chemical composition with $[Ca^{2+}] = 0.75\,[Ca^{2+}]_{eq}$. In this case two channels migrate downstream with that from one input more competitive and reaching base level first, causing breakthrough.* ***b)*** *Water at both inputs is saturated with respect to calcite, but in equilibrium with different partial pressures of CO_2. Therefore dissolution widening can occur only where these waters mix. A central channel starts to grow extending down-head until base level is reached. Flow rates through the aquifer first rise and become constant after the channel has reached base level. In the following runs these two extreme modes of karstification are combined. The waters entering have different chemical compositions and therefore different equilibrium concentrations $[Ca^{2+}]_{eq}$. This allows MC to be active. They are also undersaturated with the inflowing solutions at concentration $[Ca^{2+}]_{in}$ = f $[Ca^{2+}]_{eq}$. . In comparison to the extreme limit a) the action of MC now creates permeability where the solutions mix and diverts the evolution of conduits into this region. Finally one conduit reaches base level and causes breakthrough. This behaviour is found for* f=0.7 ;,0.9 *and* 0.996.

For solutions more close to equilibrium with respect to calcite (f =0.99; 0.9925, and 0.995) BT

[1] *Karst Processes Research Group, Institute of Experimental Physics, University of Bremen, 28334 Bremen, Germany*
E-mail: dromanov@physik.uni-bremen.de, dreybrod@physik.uni-bremen.de

[2] *Karst Research Institute, ZRC SAZU, Postojna, Slovenia*
gabrovsek@zrc-sazu.si

behaviour is replaced by a steady increase in flow rates. In the early state as in the case of MC controlled evolution (case b) a central channel not connected to the input is created by MC and reaches base level. After this event further increase in flow rates is caused by slow dissolutional widening by the slightly undersaturated input solutions flowing towards the central channel. Comparison of the various model aquifers at termination of the computer runs reveals significant differences in their hydrologic properties caused solely by changes of the hydrochemical boundary conditions.
Keywords: *Karst Hydrology, Karstification, Hydrochemistry, Modelling*

Evolution of Karst: From Prekarst to Cessation, 347-356, Ljubljana-Postojna 2002

CHEMICAL WEATHERING OF LIMESTONES AND DOLOMITES IN A CAVE ENVIRONMENT

NADJA ZUPAN HAJNA

Abstract
The weathered parts of carbonate bedrock on cave walls are a consequence of its incomplete chemical dissolution. The phenomenon is expressed in parts of the caves where walls are in contact with clastic fluvial sediments, wetted by percolation water or wetted by condensation water, and not rinsed by flowing or dripping water. The temperature in the cave is not an important parameter of weathered zone formation. Incomplete dissolution is characteristic both of Alpine and of Mediterranean caves. Limestone or dolomite are dissolved by corrosive moisture; the dissolution is distinctly selective and it go as on at intervals depending on inflow of new aggressive water. The weathered zone of limestone or dolomite is almost identical to the parent rocks in its chemical and mineral composition yet it is much more porous. During chemical weathering the amount of Mg, Sr and U is decreased, these components being leached out of limestone and dolomite. The amount of insoluble residue is usually higher in weathered limestones and in some other cases in fresh limestones which is not very common but it may occur.
Key words: *weathering, limestone, dolomite, cave, incomplete dissolution, selective corrosion, soluble residue.*

INTRODUCTION

The appearance of thick, soft zones of an unknown white, silt- or clay-like substance on the walls of cave passages (Fig. 1), looking very much like moon-milk precipitated on cave walls, was the main interest of this research work. Investigated by speleological, geological and chemical research methods, it was realised that these materials are a »soluble« residue of limestone and dolomite solution.

On the cave walls thick zones of weathered limestone or dolomite remain when the solution process ends. This usually happens when there is no more inflow of aggressive water or when flowing water no longer transports the carbonate weathering products.

All of the carbonate rock does not dissolve immediately; and this signifies that it is not carried away from its primary place in its ionic form, but that the disintegrated particles may remain on the cave passage walls. An incomplete dissolution may just prepare the carbonate rock for the mechanical transport of its particles by the flow of water.

Combining the field investigative work with different research methods, I wanted to answer the questions:

Fig. 1. Weathered cave walls in Martinska jama, SW of Slovenia. Cave was formed in Cretaceous limestone.

- are we actually witnessing the carbonate rock weathering or just the precipitation of secondary minerals;
- in what way the carbonate rock structure influences dissolution;
- which factors condition the depth of the weathered zone in carbonate rock;
- in which cases does the weathered rock remain on the channel wall.

A few millimetres thick weathered layer may be noticed very often on cave passage walls. It occurs in fissures, as well as on the rock surface where it is reflected in its roughness. Thicker zones of weathered bedrock, however, are much rarer, especially in larger spaces.

In the cases I have been investigating, dissolution advances well in depth, but it is, however, an incomplete dissolution. Its operation leaves behind a porous sponge-like weathered zone. The dissolution does not favour only the open cracks but also the various structures present in the rock; it dissolves smaller grains, the borders between grains, etc..

The appearance of incomplete dissolution occurs in cave passages, as well as on the earth's surface. Carbonate rock covered by clastic sediments or soil will usually weather under them also. On the surface of a rock covered by alluvium or soil, the so-called subterranean rocky features may get formed due to the flow of water along their contact areas. Their formation as well as the shaping of their surface is, besides the manner of water flow, decided also by the bedrock composition, by the layer graduation structuring and the extent of destruction (Slabe 1999). The processes of chemical reaction between carbonate rock and deposited sediment was described by Renault (1968), who claims that the acid saturated clay in contact with the dolomite absorbs Ca^{2+} from it and that dolomite thus becomes soft.

In the cases I have investigated, the materials which were in contact with each other were carbonate rock and the alluvium of non-carbonate composition and origin. I did not notice any kind of chemical reactions between them (in the sense of data represented by Pezdič *et al.* 1998), at least not on the level of field research as well as when considering their mineral composition.

Sometimes, however, we may come across cases when the carbonate rock in contact with clastic sediments does not display visible signs of being weathered (Mihevc 1996). The author describes scallops on the cave wall which are entirely preserved, although they were in the direct contact with the cave clastic sediments.

Weathered zones of carbonate bedrock may appear in caves of different geographical position and karst type; in Slovenia for example in Alpine and Dinaric karst caves, where different speleogenesis containing limestone and dolomite of different genesis and ages is presented. Research on weathered limestones and dolomites were done in the caves developed in the Upper Triassic limestone and dolomite, Lower Jurassic dolomite and limestone, in different Cretaceous limestones and dolomites and in Paleocene

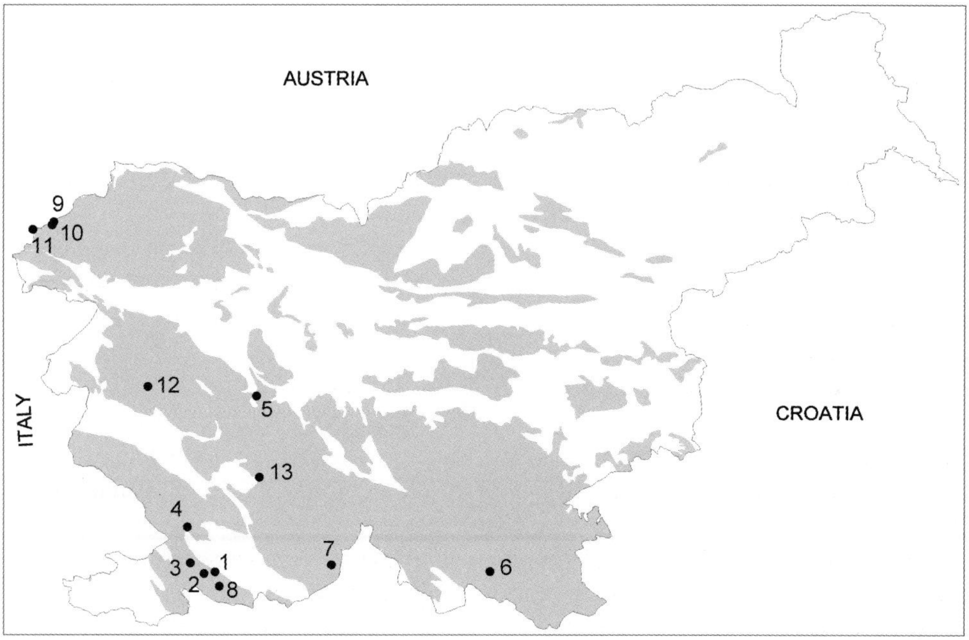

Fig. 2. Location of studied caves in Slovenia. Weathered zones of carbonate rocks may appear in caves of different geographical position, karst type and in limestone and dolomite of different origin and age. Legend: 1 - Pečina v Borštu, 2 - Martinska jama, 3 - Krempljak, 4 - Jama II na Prevali, 5 - Turkova jama, 6 - Remergrund II, 7- Spodmol na Ždroclah, 8 - Polina peč, 9 - Črnelsko brezno, 10 - Cave Čehi 2, 11 - Renejevo brezno, 12 - Velika ledena jama v Paradani, 13 - Jama pod Pečno rebrijo.

limestone of different genesis and textures. Case studies were done in caves Pečina v Borštu, Martinska jama, Krempljak, Jama II na Prevali, Turkova jama, Remergrund II, Spodmol na Ždroclah, Polina peč, Črnelsko Brezno, Čehi II, Renejevo brezno, Velika ledena jama v Paradani and Jama pod Pečno rebrijo (Fig. 2).

Let me emphasise that the cases I am describing, are all examples of *in situ* limestone and dolomite weathering and that phantom rocks with the altered chemical composition were not formed (Vergari & Qinif 1997, Kauffmann *et al.* 1999), but that what appeared as their residue was a porous and discoloured primary rock skeleton.

RESEARCH METHODS AND RESULTS

Different research methods were used to find out what is going on during the weathering of limestone and dolomite in a cave environment. First the field work was done by mapping the passages where weathered cave walls are present. Also the temperature was measured and in one case the *in situ* pH of weathered limestone (in Pečina v Borštu cave). Samples were analysed by chemical methods such as complexometry, EDS analysis on SEM and Ion Beam Analysis, then by x-ray powder diffraction method, in thin-sections, in cross sections of the samples by computer scanner and under the SEM.

The weathered zone of limestone and dolomite is soft when it is wet and solid when dry. The surface of a weathered cave wall retains all the structures and textures of carbonate rock, such as different laminations, fossils (Fig. 3), calcite veins; as micrite or

Fig. 3. Weathered shells in Upper Cretaceous limestone, from Pečina v Borštu, SW Slovenia.

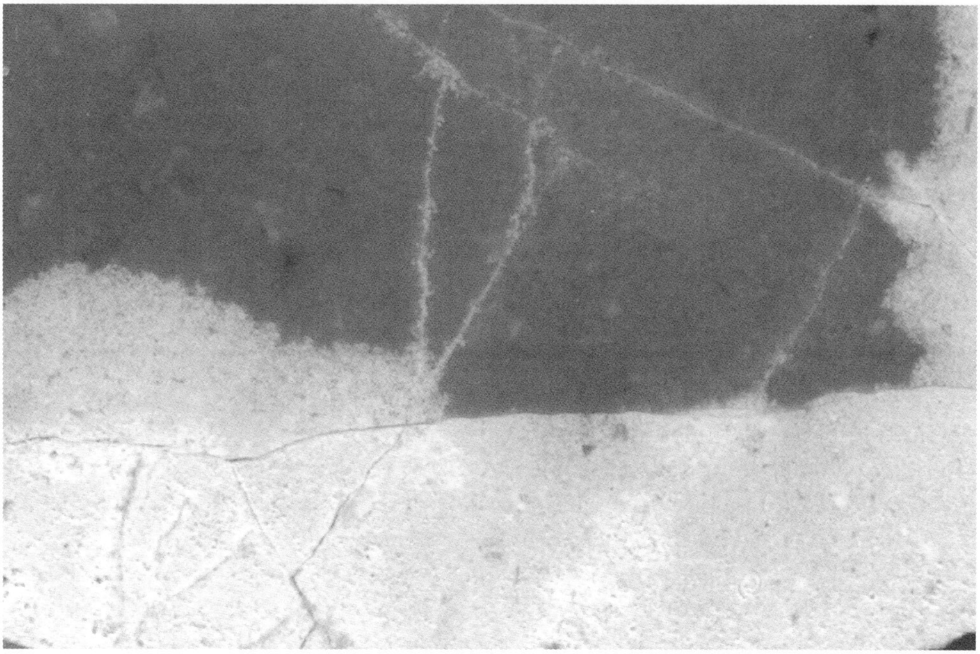

Fig. 4. Progressing of dissolution is faster along open fissures and it is stopped by calcite veins. Paleocene limestone from Jama II na Prevali. Width of the sample is 2,5 cm.

sparite grains which seen as micro-roughness of the wall surface. On some weathered walls the beginning of the boxwork (Palmer 1981) formation is noticed. The thickness of the weathered zone varies from less than a millimetre to several centimetres. Weathered cave walls are usually covered by a brown flowstone crust unless there is direct contact with clastic fine-grained sediments where the weathered surface is uncovered.

It is quite usual to find the thicker parts of the weathered rock predominantly on walls that have been or still are in contact with clastic fluvial sediments. Thicker zones of the weathered rock may come into existence also in cases where percolation water trickles along the wall. In both cases, that is under clastic sediments and when water trickles along the wall, the water is being pulled into the interior by capillary forces and along the interconnected pores and fissures. The same action takes place with condensed moisture.

In cross sections of samples the transition from fresh rock into weathered rock is quite well seen. The dissolution is progressing into the rock along the open fissures (Fig. 4) and along the invisible micro-porosity; we are unable to view the latter, neither in cross sections nor in thin sections. During weathering, the rock first of all loses some of its colour. Then the fading gradually increases, which leads to a state of complete discoloration, at which point the rock's residue becomes white. Through the weathering, that is, through dissolution of individual parts of the rock with carbonic acid, the previously solid compact rock becomes more and more porous. And this does not occur, as we may have expected, only along fissures but also in non-fissured parts (Fig. 4). The dissolution advances into the rock's interior along the chosen structures and leaves in its wake ever larger and more interconnected pores. If the dissolution continues, the sponge-like structure may fall apart and the outer part of what was once a solid rock becomes clay-like and completely soft. The collapsing particles are, with regard to the primary rock structure, of the size order of silt or clay.

Chemical analysis results demonstrated that the amount of Mg, Sr and U in the weathered zone of carbonate rock consistently decreases with weathering. Thus it became evident that during the weathering they are actually disappearing. Mg is leached from the calcite as well as from the dolomite crystal lattice. To where and in what manner remains unknown to me.

The mineral composition of the fresh or weathered parts of carbonate rock does not differ significantly. The amount of insoluble residue is sometimes higher in the weathered and sometimes in the fresh part. The conclusion one may draw from the analyses is that limestones and dolomites in the course of weathering become purer and simultaneously lose their mechanical solidity. By means of mineralogical investigation of the clastic allochthonous sediments I discovered that they do not react chemically with the weathered rock; however they do contribute the moisture required for dissolution. Yet, we do not know whether the deposited sediment might have contained minerals, which would chemically react with the rock on the passage wall and which are not present any more.

DISCUSSION

According to Dreybrodt (1988) the overall dissolution speed is determined by the dissolution on the crystal's surface, by the transportation of ions through the border layer and by the speed of the conversion $CO_2 + H_2O = H^+ + HCO^{3-}$ as well by the lithological parameters of the carbonate rocks. Weathered zones are the result of incomplete carbonate rock dissolution. Thick zones of the weathered bedrock are rare, especially on the larger surfaces. At first sight the most weathered walls appear to be those wetted by percolating water and which are in contact with fluvial sediments, and walls which are subjected to condensation corrosion.

During the selective dissolution of individual parts the once compact carbonate rock becomes more and more porous, not only along the cracks, but also along various structures. From analyses of cross sections under SEM, it is quite evident that what is happening is not a case of secondary minerals' precipitation but of dissolving carbonate rock, which increases the porosity of the rock.

Field investigations, the analysis of cross sections and the moistening of the weathered limestone have led me to a conclusion that the flow of water is, in the case of thick weathered zones on the passage walls, effected molecular diffusion and capillary action, which proves to be the faster. In the cases I am describing, the rock is not only dissolved on the surface, that is frontally, and it does not leave in its wake the smoothed surfaces of the cave walls, as is the case when it is in contact with flowing water where this contact between water and rock lasts sufficiently long to bring about the chemical reaction.

When the inflow or outflow of water stops and the solution which is present in the connected pores gets saturated, or dries up, the rock cease to be dissolved. The weathering of carbonate rocks is usually caused by dissolution, that is, by the transition from rock into solution (Summerfield 1991). The dissolution is distinctly selective. In the first place, smaller grains and the contacts among grains are dissolved. When dealing with clastic sedimentary rocks Skaberne (1980) noted, that they weather chemically and crumble in relation with their structure. I noticed the similar phenomenon also in limestones and dolomites, especially when the dissolution along the edges of mineral granules weakens the mechanical cohesion of the rock. The fact that limestones with sparite and microsparite structure start dissolving along the edges of grains and along the deformities in the crystal surface is already known from the literature (Ford & Williams 1989).

During dissolution pores get larger and become more and more interconnected, so that aggressive water advances more easily and deeper into the rock's interior. With the lapse of time even the more resistant parts of carbonate rock weather as well. Calcite veins and the shell fragments that jut out from the weathered rock surface become porous and soft. During further dissolution the rock gets more porous and fragile until its structure completely collapses. The flow of water in all these cases is not large the actual significance may be ascribed to the moisture, and this moisture is well capable to cause dissolution. The term corrosive moisture used by Davis & Mosch (1988), when they describe the weathering of the clay pebble surfaces, denotes condensed or vadose (percolation) water.

The humidity of weathered walls changed significantly during the course of year. Sometimes the walls were completely wet, at another time entirely dry. The fluctuation of humidity during the year is quite obvious and is related both to the precipitations as well as to the velocity of the trickling along the walls. The penetration of moisture into the weathered part of the wall is very fast. It may stop only at the larger calcite veins, and it may also take some time to cross over open cracks or those partly filled with clay. I attempted to explain the formation of mosaic porosity and the sponge-like rock structure by the model, which is similar to that used by Trudgill (1985), when he tried to determine the formation of porosity in the limestone karst soil (rendzina). Following my own observations, I presume that in cases when the wall dries up, the new moisture penetrates into the rock even faster, because the pores have been emptied. Consequently, I believe that dissolution is going on faster as well, so that water in pores loses its aggressiveness again, the dissolution becomes saturated and pH increases. At every new water wave the water will use the pores and channels which were produced during the previous cycle. It may also widen them a little and the main dissolution front will thus, with each new water wave, move deeper into the rock. Through its contact with carbonate particles in the porous skeleton the aggressive water quickly becomes saturated; so that only a part of its former quantity is still able to interact with the rock. The mechanism is repeated in cycles, so that the rock becomes ever more porous and does not dissolve entirely at first.

This incomplete limestone dissolution is most likely taking place in the vadose zone. The flow of water in the phreatic zone would wash the particles from the wall - if not before, then during its retreat, or the silt would crumble away from the wall of its own accord. The water flow may also simultaneously carry away the ions, and the dissolution would progress into the depth slower, for it would act frontally. There may exist a possibility that the incomplete dissolution is, nevertheless, taking place, yet because of the continuous washing away of the particles we are unable to recognise it. Limestone porosity in the given cases increased because calcite grains that were less resistant to dissolution got dissolved. Dissolved primarily were those grains that were smaller and those whose structure was less well ordered due to the presence of Mg ions in their crystal lattice. Mg ions are, owing to their lower ionic potential, more mobile and are the first to leave their places in the crystal lattice thus they further weaken the interior structure and increase the proneness to dissolution. Theoretically, water in porous media in contact with calcite reach equilibrium immediately it becomes saturated or even supersaturated against $CaCO_3$, but it is not necessary that it is also saturated against Mg^{2+}, so the dissolution of the parts containing Mg ion may go on (Bathurst 1975).

The decrease of the Mg ion share in the weathered parts of limestones and dolomites has already been observed by several authors. The fact that Mg is being extracted from limestone during dissolution was found out also by Kogovšek & Habič (1981) in their measurements of the magnesium hardness. The reason for this is the greater solubility product of $MgCO_3$ when compared to $CaCO_3$. The leaching of Mg during dolomite weathering was stated also by Burger (1989), yet he did not try to explain it. Slabe (1988) interprets the lower share of Mg on the surface of the cave wall which has already been dissolved by corrosion, as the complete dissolution of impure limestone which contains Mg and as the precipitation of pure calcite crystals from the condensed moisture.

Yet, in all the cases, I am describing here, we are actually not witnessing the calcite crystal extraction but the weathering of limestones and dolomites. In cases when the weathered rock is in direct contact with the cave environment, a thin calcite crust is almost always being extracted and deposited on its surface. During the rock's drying, the saturated moisture oozes out of its pores, or it is squeezed towards the weathered rock's surface by the incoming water. However, it still remains somehow unclear, where do the dissolved ions in these cases actually migrate. Especially when we take into account that the weathered rock which is in contact with the alluvium is not even covered with a flowstone layer and that we have not yet found any minerals containing Mg.

The answers to the questions are:

- The zones of carbonate silt or clay and white porous rocks on the cave passage walls are a product of weathering processes and not of secondary minerals precipitation.
- Dissolution penetrates into the rock along various structures, such as cracks, primary porosity, microstructures, crystal's deformities and primary structures covered by micritization or neomorphism, which may also hinder the expansion of dissolution.

- Selective dissolution forms the coarseness on the surface and the sponge-like structure of the weathered rock, which may reach a depth of several centimetres.

My opinion is that the occurrence of the incomplete dissolution of carbonate rocks within speleogenesis may represent an important factor for the formation of initial channels, because carbonate rock porosity increases proportionally with the selective dissolution of calcite and dolomite by carbonic acid and not with dissolution of the more soluble additions (gypsum, anhydrite, etc.) During the weathering, pores in limestone and dolomite augment, they establish connections among them, which leads to increased effective porosity. The enlargement of pores and the expansion of their interconnections is consequently leads to the formation of initial channels. Incomplete dissolution accompanied by the simultaneous washing away of the weathered rock also accelerates the growth of passages. By means of this process the passage's enlargement is faster and more intensive specially during floods or high water splash through the cave channels.

REFERENCES

Bathurst, R. G. C., 1975: Carbonate Sediments and Their Diagenesis.- Second enlarged edition, Elsevier, 658 pp, Amsterdam.

Burger, D., 1989: Dolomite weathering and micromorphology of paleosoils in the Franconian Jura.- Catena Supplement 15, 261 - 267, Cremlingen.

Davis, G. D. & Mosch, C., 1988: Pebble indentations: A New Speleogen from a Colorado Cave.- Bulletin of the national speleological society, 50, 17 - 20, Huntsville.

Dreybrodt, W., 1988: Processes in karst Systems. Springer-Verlag, 288 pp, Berlin, Heidelberg.

Ford, D. C. & Williams, P. W., 1989: Karst Geomorphology and Hydrology.- UnwinHyman, 601 pp, London.

Kaufmann, O., Bini, A., Tognini, P. & Quinif, Y., 1999: Etude Microscopique d'une latérite de type fantôme de roche.- Karst 99 : colloque européen : des paysages du karst au géosystčme karstique : dynamiques, structures et enregistrement karstiques, (Etudes de géographie physique, supplément, 28), 129 - 133, Aix-en-Provence.

Kogovšek, J. & Habič, P., 1981: Preučevanje vertikalnega prenikanja vode na primerih Planinske in Postojnske jame. Acta carsologica, 9 (1980), 129 - 148, Ljubljana.

Mihevc, A., 1996: Brezstropa jama pri Povirju.- Naše jame, 38, 65 - 75, Ljubljana.

Palmer, A. N., 1981: Geology of Wind Cave.- Wind Cave National Park, South Dakota: Hot Springs, South Dakota. Wind Cave Natl. Hist. Assoc., 44 pp.

Pezdič, J., Šušteršič, F. & Mišič, M., 1998: On the role of clay-carbonate reactions in speleoinception; A contribution to the understanding of the earliest stage of karst channel formation.- Acta carsologica 27/1, 187 - 200, Ljubljana.

Renault, P., 1968: Contribution ŕ l'étude des actions mécaniques et sédimentologiques dans la spéléogenčse (Troisičme partie).- Annales de Spéléologie, Centre National de la Recherche Scientifique, 23, 3, 530 - 596, Moulis.

Skaberne, D., 1980: Predlog klasifikacije in nomenklature klastičnih sedimentnih kamnin.-

1.del, Predlog granulometrijske klasifikacije in nomenklature. Rudarsko metalurški zbornik, 27, 1, 21 - 46, Ljubljana.
Slabe, T., 1988: Kondenzna korozija na skalnem obodu Komarjevega rova v Dimnicah.- Acta carsologica, 17, 79 - 92, Ljubljana.
Slabe, T., 1999: Subcutaneous rock forms.- Acta carsologica, 28/2, 255 - 271, Ljubljana.
Summerfield, M.A., 1991: Global geomorphology, an introduction to the study of landforms.- John Wiley & Sons, 537 pp, New York.
Trudgill, S. T., 1985: Limestone Geomorphology.- Longman, 196 pp, London in New York.
Vergari, A. & Quinif, Y., 1997: Les paleokarst du Hainaut.- Geodinamica Acta, 10-4, 175 - 187, Paris.

Address
Karst Research Institute ZRC SAZU, Titov trg 2, 6230 Postojna, Slovenia
E-mail: zupan@zrc-sazu.si

KARST HIDROLOGY

Evolution of Karst: From Prekarst to Cessation, 359-365, Ljubljana-Postojna 2002

DEVELOPMENT OF CATCHMENT AREA IN KARST AS A RESULT OF NATURAL AND ANTHROPOLOGICAL FACTORS

OGNJEN BONACCI

Abstract
The determination of the catchement boundaries and the catchment areas is starting point in all hydrological and hydrogeological analyses. For water circulation in karst, this classical hydrologic problem, represents extremely complex, sometimes not easily solved, task. Physical and chemical processes in karst terrains, accompanied by tectonic movements and strong influence of man's interventions have formed well-linked fissure systems in karst massifs. While considering determination of catchment area in karst one should bear in mind that the karstification process, i.e. the solution and redistribution of surface and subsurface karst features is a continual process which cannot be stopped. Generally, the time unit of these changes is relatively long when compared with the human life, but it is very short when compared with the geological time scale. The catchment areas in karst vary according to the groundwater levels change with time. It should be stressed that human interventions, especially construction of dams and reservoirs, can introduce instantaneous and definite changes in catchment boundaries. In paper some examples are given. The paper researches influence of different factors on the evolution of karst catchment.

INTRODUCTION

A catchment area (drainage basin of watershed) is a topographically defined area drained by spring or open streamflow or system of connecting springs and streamflows such that all outflows is discharged through a single outlet. The determination of the catchment boundary and area is the starting point for all hydrological, hydrogeological and water resources management analyses. In karst terrains this is a difficult and complex task, very often unsolved (Bonacci 1988). Without this data it is not possible properly, efficiently and exactly to make a water budget, to protect water from pollution, to manage the water resources, to use hydrological numerical models for karst regions etc.

The root causes of problems of karst catchments determinations are: 1) heterogeneous and anisotropic surface and underground morphologic karst forms; 2) existence of well developed, complex, deep and unknown underground karst conduits, fissures, joints and cracks; 3) strong interaction between circulation of surface water and groundwater in karst; 4) high and fast oscillations of groundwater in karst (few hundreds of meters); 5) strong connection between inflow (swallow-holes) and outflow (karst springs); 6) small storage capacity of the karst medium and fast groundwater transport through karst conduits; 7) different aspects of duality of water circulation in karst; 8) natural endogenetic and exogenetic processes; 9) influence of man's induced structures and activities (dams, reservoirs, water pumping etc.).

Generally speaking the catchment area defined in karst using surface morphological forms, i.e. orographic or topographic catchment never respond to exact hydrologic or hydrogeologic drainage basin. The differences between orographic and hydrologic or hydrogeologic catchment in karst terrains, as a rule, are so large scale that orographic catchment is not acceptable for any kind of employment. In the same time the situation is complicated by the fact that catchment boundaries and area in karst are changeable in large time scale.

While considering determination of catchment area in karst it should bear in mind that the karstification, i.e. the solution and redistribution of surface and subsurface karst features is a continual process, which cannot be stopped and controlled.

In the same time erosional processes transport of sediments sinkholes development and collapse, landslide and land subsidence, naturally plugging and unclogging of karst conduits, due to tectonic movements, and man's induced influences strongly affect on the changes of the karst catchment areas. The primary objective of this paper was to explain the development of the catchment area in karst as dynamic process, which changes in time due to different natural, and man's induces reasons. An attempt of time and space scale explanation of karst catchment evolution is given.

CATCHMENT IN KARST

Only a few terrains in karst have been studied well enough as to make it possible to define the catchment precisely. In addition to obtaining topographic data on the terrain, it is necessary to carry out measurements, which are used in the determination of the groundwater circulation under the different conditions of the groundwater levels. In order to exactly define the surface and subsurface catchment boundaries it is necessary to conduct detailed geologic investigations and accordingly, extensive hydrogeologic measurements. These measurements primarily include the existence of the links between individual points in the catchment area (connections: ponors-springs, piezometers-piezometers, piezometers-springs etc.) applying one of the tracing methods.

The catchment areas in karst vary according to the groundwater levels, i.e. change with time (Bonacci 1987, 81-97). There is a certain zone within which the watershed limit is moved towards one or the other spring or towards the streamflow. The position of the watershed line depends upon the groundwater levels which change is time. In some situations at very high groundwater levels (after heavy rainfall) fossil and inactive channels and springs are activated in the karst underground, this causing the intercatchment overflow and /or redistribution of the catchment areas (Bonacci 1995; Bonacci 2001).

Only in exceptional cases do the surface (orographic or topographic) and subsurface (hydrogeologic or hydrologic) watershed lines coincide and only in those places were the boundaries between catchments are located in impermeable rocks. The ratio between the orographic or topographic (defined by using surface morphological forms) catchment areas of the springs and the estimated hydrogeologic catchment area in Dinaric karst ranges from 1:2.3 to 1:70 (Čorović et al. 1985).

Determination of the catchment areas of the poljes in karst is extremely complex task due to fact that one polje is only part of a wider system. It represents a subsystem in the process of surface, subsurface and underground water flow through the karst massive. In the same time from the geologic point of wives, the poljes as the largest surface karst form give direct evidence of the karst evolution. Using different approaches (at least geologic, morphologic, speleologic, hydrogeologic and hydrologic) in analyses of water circulation on, bellow and around poljes in karst it is possible to explain connection between karst evolution and development (change) of their catchment areas.

Before approximately 25,000 years ago the level of the Adriatic Sea was 96.4 m lower than at present (Šegota 1968). Than, it represented the erosion basis for the karst area, so that the spring exits appeared at that level. As the sea level was raised new conduits simultaneously formed in the karst, together with the new, higher positions of the coastal spring exits. This process is still going on. The direct consequence is gradual change of the coastal karst springs catchment areas. The change in the position of the coastal karst springs depends upon the local geologic structure. Each actual coastal karst spring has a few conduits. Some of them are active and some are inactive. The main reason for inactivity is existence of clay or any other cork in conduit. This cork can be removed by natural (earthquake) or man's interventions, which can lead to instantaneous change of the spring catchment area (Bonacci 1997).

The existence of a large number of intermittent and permanent springs in the vicinity of the main flow exit of a coastal (Bonacci 1995; Bonacci et al. 1995; Bonacci & Roje-Bonacci 1997) and continental (Bonacci & Magdalenić 1993) karst-aquifer system is common. In these situations after the intensive precipitations the intercatchment overflow and/or overflow from the main spring-flow system to intermittent springs within the same catchment appear. These places could serve for explanation of influence of the karst evolution on the catchment areas development.

NATURAL FACTORS WHICH CONTROL KARST EVOLUTION AND CONNECTS IT WITH CATCHMENT AREA DEVELOPMENT

Tectonic processes which caused formation of faults and folds influenced on separation of karst aquifers and establishment of catchment areas in karst terrains. Choppy (1997) states that faults and folds can play various roles for water circulation in karst: drain, barrier and indifferent. The definite conclusion is that a role of tectonic and its underground and surface karst forms on catchment area formation vary from place to place.

Until now the role of bedding-planes in karst water circulation and catchment area formation has not been understood enough. Knez (1996) gives some promising explanations dealing with the relationship between positions and dimensions of bedding-planes, karst conduit development and groundwater circulation in Škocijanskih jama (Slovenia).

Karst surface and underground forms, which strongly influence on formation of catchment areas, are produced by interaction between rock and erosional environment. Lithological variation is a major factor influencing landform evolution at a number of scales. Trudgill (1985) states that karst hydrology and solution chemistry is still better understood than karst landforms are, however. Very probably this is main reason why link between karst surface and underground phenomena and karst catchment areas development is not explained satisfactory.

The dissolution of rock is the decisive process in the formation of karst (Bögli 1980) and has important role in catchment area formation. Dreybrodt & Siemers (1997) presented a two-dimensional model of the early evolution of karst aquifers for natural and man made conditions. After a long initiation time a sudden and dramatic increase of widening of the fractures and flow through the system ends the initial state. When flow is laminar after this breakthrough event all fractures employed widen at an even pace by several 10^{-2} cm/year. If flow becomes turbulent the widening increases by enhancement of diffusional mass transport up to 10^{-1} cm/year.

Sauter et al. (1997) quote that the understanding of the karstification processes at a catchment scale could be of importance for the quantification of the geometry of karst aquifers as well as their parameter distribution in space. They presented a new modelling approach, integrating the chemical dissolution kinetics of carbonate rocks as well as the special hydraulic characteristic of karst system. The degree of karstification and the variety of different karst features are determined by the interaction between different processes, which are controlled by intrinsic (lithological and petrographic characteristic and the type and geometry of structural elements) and extrinsic (climate, level of discharge, type of vegetation and time period available for karstification) factors. Sensitivity analysis of the duration of karstification to changes in climatic parameters and physic-chemical constants of carbonate dissolution shows that the equilibrium concentration of calcium and initial diameter of the karst conduits are dominant factors (Sauter et al. 1997).

MAN'S INFLUENCE ON THE CHANGE OF CATCHMENT AREA

Human intervention, especially construction of dams and reservoirs as well as interbasin water transfers through long tunnels and pipelines can introduce instantaneous and definite changes in catchment areas and boundaries. In karst terrains those processes very often are uncontrolled. There is huge number of drastic examples. Only a few of them will be shortly described.

The quarrying of limestone from open pits represents the most visually and the most dramatic anthropogenic impact on karst terrains affecting both landforms and geomorphological and hydrogeological processes. For example Gunn & Gagen (1989) estimated that quarrying would have removed more limestone from one karst area in Britain by the end of last century than natural processes over the whole of the Holocene. Overall UK limestone extraction increased from 14 million tonnes in 1895 to 125 million tonnes in 1991.

The strong influence of man's intervention on the water circulation in system of the poljes in karst which causes drastic redistribution of catchment areas can be perfectly illustrated by example of closing estavelle Obod located in the Fatničko polje (Bosnia-Herzegovina). The opening was closed in order to reduce the inflow into the polje and thus to protect it from flooding. After the estavelles opening was closed by concrete, an intensive precipitation caused fast groundwater rising up to 120 m above the opening level. Few abundant temporary springs appeared and sliding were formed at levels higher of the estavelle altitude. Its closing decreased the inflow into the Fatničko polje from 60 m^3/s to 12 m^3/s. The polje was protected from the flood but heavy damages were caused on the horizons high above the poljes where groundwater appeared. This damage called for urgent blowing up of the concrete clog built for closing the opening in order to as soon as establish the previous natural conditions.

The construction of reservoir Salakovac on the Neretva River (Bosnia-Herzegovina) resulted in the flooding of three springs which now function as swallow-holes (Bonacci & Jelin 1989). They discharged 28 m^3/s of water from the full reservoir. All the water that was lost through these ponors appeared some 1 km downstream from the dam in a group of intermittent springs (in natural conditions).

Under the increased water pressure because of a reservoir it is possible to wash out of the clay or sand from clogged karst conditions. Dreybrodt & Siemers (1997) warn that dams and reservoirs in karst accelerate evolution of new karst channels below the dam, which can cause serious water losses within its lifetime.

Drastic changes in groundwater level caused by karstwater withdrawal from the mines in Hungary had led to regional redistribution of karst aquifer. As the water pumping during the last 40 years from the main karst aquifer exceeded the average natural recharge the groundwater level decreased from 30 to 80 m (Csepregi 1997).

CONCLUSION

Water circulation in karst and determination of catchment boundaries and areas are very complex and not easily solved tasks. Natural and man made processes cause changes of catchment area on different time and space scale. An attempt to explain time and space scale effects of different factors, which can cause the changes of the catchment area in karst, is given on Figure 1. The analyses described in this paper stress the need for transdisciplinary approaches incorporating several methods and techniques in the study of development of karst catchment areas.

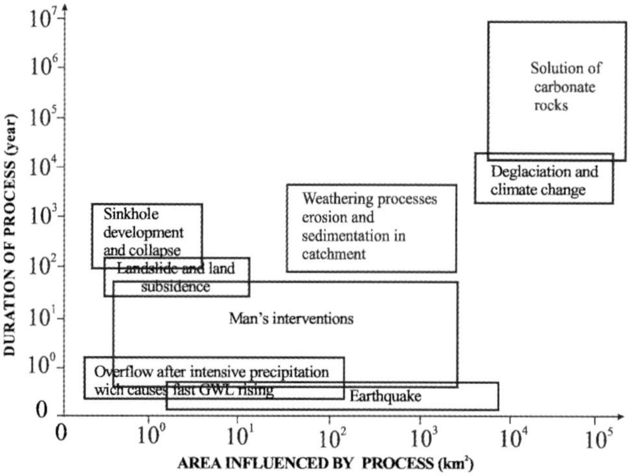

Fig. 1. Time and scale effect of different factors which can cause the changes of the catchment in karst

REFERENCES

Bögli, A., 1980: Karst Hydrology and Physical Speleology. Springer Verlag, p. 284, Berlin

Bonacci, O., 1987: Karst Hydrology. Springer Verlag, p. 194, Berlin

Bonacci, O., 1988: Determination of the catchment areas in karst. IAHS Publ. no. 176, 606-611, Wallingford

Bonacci, O., 1995: Ground water behaviour in karst: example of the Ombla Spring (Croatia). Journal of Hydrology 165, 113-134, Amsterdam

Bonacci, O., 1997: Role of speleology in karst hydrology and hydrogeology. Proceedings of the 12th International Congress of Speleology, Vol. 2, 27-30, La Chaux de Fonds

Bonacci, O., 2001: Analysis of the maximum discharge of the karst springs. Hydrogeology Journal 9, 328-338, Berlin

Bonacci, O., Fritz, F. & Denić, V., 1995: Hydrogeology of Slanac Spring, Croatia. Hydrogeology Journal 3 (3), 31-40, Berlin

Bonacci, O. & Jelin, J., 1989: Identification of a karst hydrological system in the Dinaric karst (Yugoslavia). Hydrological Sciences Journal 33 (5). 483-497, Wallingford

Bonacci, O. & Magdalenić, A., 1993: The catchment area of the Sv. Ivan spring in Istria (Croatia) - Ground Water 31 (5), 767-773,

Bonacci, O. & Roje-Bonacci, T., 1997: Seawater intrusion in coastal karst springs: example of the Blaž Spring (Croatia). Hydrology Sciences Journal 42 (1), 89-100, Walling ford

Choppy, J., 1997: La tectonique et la karst. Proceedings of the 12th International Congress of Speleology, Vol. 1, 367-368, La Chaux de Fonds

Csepregi, A., 1997: Computer simulation of the karstwater table in the Transdanubian Mountain Ranges, Hungary. In: Gunay, G. & Johnsons, I.(eds.) Karst Waters & Environmental Impacts, Balkema, 343-352, Rotterdam

Čorović, A., Cerić, A., Milina, J. & Tomić, M., 1985: Pristup rješavanju zaštite krških vrela (An approach to the protection of karst springs). Vodoprivreda 17 (96-97), 200-205, Beograd

Dreybrodt, W. & Siemers, J., 1997: Early evolution of karst aquifers in limestone: Models on two dimensional percolation clusters. Proceedings of the 12th International Congres of Speleology, Vol. 2, 75-80, La Chaux de Fonds

Knez, M., 1996: Vpliv Lezik na Razvoj Krških Jam (The Bedding - Plane Impact on Development on karst Caves). Znanstvenoraziskovalni center SAZU, p. 186, Ljubljana

Gunn, J. & Gagen, P.J., 1989: Limestone quarrying as an agency of land form change. In: Gillieson, D & Smith, D.I. (eds.) Resource Management in Limestone Landscapes: International Perspectives. Spec. Pub. 2, 173-181, Canberra

Sauter, M., Liedl, R., Clemens, T. & Hückinghaus, D., 1997: Karst aquifer genesis - Modelling approaches and controlling parameters. Proceedings of the 12th International Congress of Speleology, Vol. 2, 107-110, La Chaux de Fonds

Šegota, T., 1968: Morska razina u holocenu i mlađem würmu (sea level in Holocene and Würm). geografski glasnik 30, 15-39, Zagreb

Trudgill, S., 1985: Limestone Geomorfology. Longman, P. 196, London

Address
University of Split
Faculty of Civil Engineering, Matice hrvatske 15, Croatia
E-mail: obonacci@gradst.hr

Evolution of Karst: From Prekarst to Cessation, 367-374, Ljubljana-Postojna 2002

RECESSION CLOUD AS INDICATOR OF KARST AQUIFER DEVELOPMENT

MIHAEL BRENČIČ

Abstract

In the past, on the basis of karst spring hydrogram, extensive theory about groundwater depletion in karst aquifer reflected through spring recesion curves has been developed. To skip theoretical presumptions about the analysis of karst spring recesion, the concept of recession cloud has been intruduced in the paper. The recesion cloud is defined as set of all N_{rec} *recession curves in the spring hydrogram. The cloud could be described with statistical parameter curves (e.g average curve, median curve...). It has been shown that these parameter curves can be modeled with simple exponential or power models. The model curves converge in one point at concentration time* t_c *and concentration discharge* Q_c*. On the basis of extreme value theory has been also shown that it is posible to model return period of the convergence.*

Key words: *karst spring, recession analysis, generalized Pareto distribution, generalized extreme value distribution, return period*

INTRODUCTION

The analysis of a hydrogram and its recession part has long been recognized as an important tool in hydrology and has been the subject of extensive research in the past. With this analysis it is possible to determine various model parameters. Recession analysis is used for solving various water management problems, such as low flow prediction, irrigation analysis, water supply, hydropower plant construction, precipitation run-off modelling etc. (Tallaksen, 1995).

In karst hydrogeology the analysis of a karst spring recession hydrogram represents an important method for the estimation of dynamic reserves, permeability, porosity and transmisivity in karst aquifers (Bonacci, 1993; Ford & Williams, 1989).

In the literature various definitions of recession are given (e.g. Chow, 1988; Linsley et al., 1988). They differ according to the needs and theoretical background and they are sometimes arbitrary and subjective. To avoid theoretical presumptions in the paper only the shape of the total hydrogram and its recession part were experimentally studied. Theoretical background and preliminary results of this study are given.

THEORETICAL BACKGROUND

MONOTONIC RECESSION

In the modelling of hydrogeological phenomenon the system is usually described as a black box, which is defined with the input I(t) variable (e.g. rainfall, infiltration), output variable Q(t) (e.g. discharge) and with the system rules. In classical recession analysis we assume that the recession begins when I(t)=0. The point in time when I(t)=0 is usually chosen on the basis of the conceptual model of a real system or some theoretical suppositions.

In the karst hydrogeological system it is difficult to decide when, if ever, the input variable is zero. In order to avoid subjectivity and arbitrary decision in the determination of time point when I(t)=0, we experimentally studied the shape of the whole recession limb.

Monotonic concentration as a part of the event hydrogram was defined as:

$$\frac{dQ(t)}{dt} > 0 \qquad (1)$$

and monotonic recession as

$$\frac{dQ(t)}{dt} \leq 0 \qquad (2)$$

With this definition we separate the total hydrogram into N_{conc} monotonic concentration curves and N_{rec} monotonic recession curves. In the next step we are dealing with the set of all N_{rec} monotonic recession curves of the total hydrogram. All of the monotonic recession curves are put at the recession time t_i=1 day, regardless of the position of the curve in the total hydrogram. The series of all monotonic recession curves of the same origin are defined as the cloud of monotonic recession.

DESCRIPTION OF RECESSION CLOUD

The cloud of monotonic recession is mathematically described with profile curves based on the calculation of descriptive statistics for every day of particular recession day t_i. For each vertical that belongs to particular recession day t_i with $N(t_i)$ observation discharges $Q(t_i)$ descriptive statistic where calculated. Particular calculated statistics for each t_i connected and treated as profile curves. (Brencic, 2000)

MODEL OF PROFILE CURVES

Profile curves were described with two mathematical models:

a) Power model

$$Q_{P_i} = Q_{0P_i} t^{-\lambda_{P_i}} \qquad (3)$$

b) Exponential model

$$Q_{P_i} = Q_{0P_i} \exp(-\lambda_{P_i} t) \qquad (4)$$

Where λ_{Pi}, Q_{0Pi} are descriptive parameters of the model and index P_i presents the statistical parameter to which the curve is drawn.

CONVERGENCE OF RECESSION CLOUD

For the description of relationship between descriptive parameters Q_{0Pi} and λ_{Pi} from (3) and (4) the following equation is choosen:

$$Q_{0Pi} = A \exp(B\lambda_{Pi}) \qquad (5)$$

The equation (5) represents the model of convergence.

After brief manipulation (Brencic, 2000) it can be shown that time of convergence for power model is t_c=expB. In the similar way we can show that convergence discharge for power model is A= Q_c.

For the exponential model (4) from (5) follows

$$Q_{Pi} = A \exp(\lambda_{Pi} [B - t]) \qquad (6)$$

After brief manipulation (Brencic, 2000) we can show that all modelling curves can converge only at convergence time B=t_c and convergence discharge A=Q_c.

RETURN PERIOD OF THE CONVERGENCE POINT

Empirical data show that Q_c and t_c differ among analysed hydrograms. To compare them in the relative scale, for each hydrogram the return period of recession convergence was estimated. The estimation is based on the recession lengths modelling and on the extreme yearly lengths of recession curves in the set of all recession curves N_{rec}.

Generalized Pareto distribution - GPD has been chosen (Pickands, 1975) for modelling the distribution of recession lengths. Distribution function is defined as:

$$F_t(t; c, k, g) = 1 - \left[1 - \frac{c}{k}(t - g)\right]^{\frac{1}{c}} \quad c \neq 0 \qquad (7)$$

and

$$F_t(t;c,k,g) = 1 - \exp\left(-\frac{1}{k}(t-g)\right) \quad c = 0 \tag{8}$$

With probability density function

$$p_t(t) = \frac{1}{k}\left(1 - \frac{c}{k}(t-g)\right)^{\frac{1}{c}-1} \quad c \neq 0 \tag{9}$$

and

$$p_t(t) = \frac{1}{k}\exp\left(-\frac{1}{k}(t-g)\right) \quad c = 0 \tag{10}$$

Where t is length of particular recession curve N_i and k,c,g are respectively distribution parameters of scale, shape and location of GPD.

GPD is relatively simple distribution. Its parameters can be estimated through probability weighted moments (Wang,1991) derived from Weakby distribution (Greenwood et al., 1979). The fitting of GPD to empirical data based on the estimated parameters can be tested by Kolmogorov Smirnov test of goodness of fit.

It can be shown that GPD is connected with generalized extreme value distribution - GEV. (Davison, 1984, Dargahi-Noubary, 1989) If n is Poisson random variable with intensity ξ and $Y_1, Y_2, .., Y_n$ are independent events with GPD and values of thresholds are $X_1, X_2, ..., X_n$ over u and $X_i > u$ is valid, then distribution function of $T \leq t$ is defined as

$$F(t) = P(T \leq t) = \exp\left[-\xi(1 - \frac{ct}{\theta})^{\frac{1}{c}}\right] \qquad t \geq 0 \tag{11}$$

The equation (11) is special shape of the GEV defined as

$$F(t) = P(T \leq t) = \exp\left[-(1 - \frac{c(t-\gamma)}{\theta})^{\frac{1}{c}}\right] \qquad t \geq 0 \tag{12}$$

and

$$F(t) = P(T \leq t) = \exp\left[-\exp(\frac{(t-\gamma)}{\theta})\right] \qquad t = 0 \tag{13}$$

The fitting of GEV to empirical data based on the estimated parameters of shape c, scale Θ and location γ can be tested by Anderson Darling test (Stephens, 1986). The shape parameter c is the same in GPD and in GEV.

On the basis of GEV parameters the convergence point (t_c, Q_c) of the return period t_{ret} was calculated.

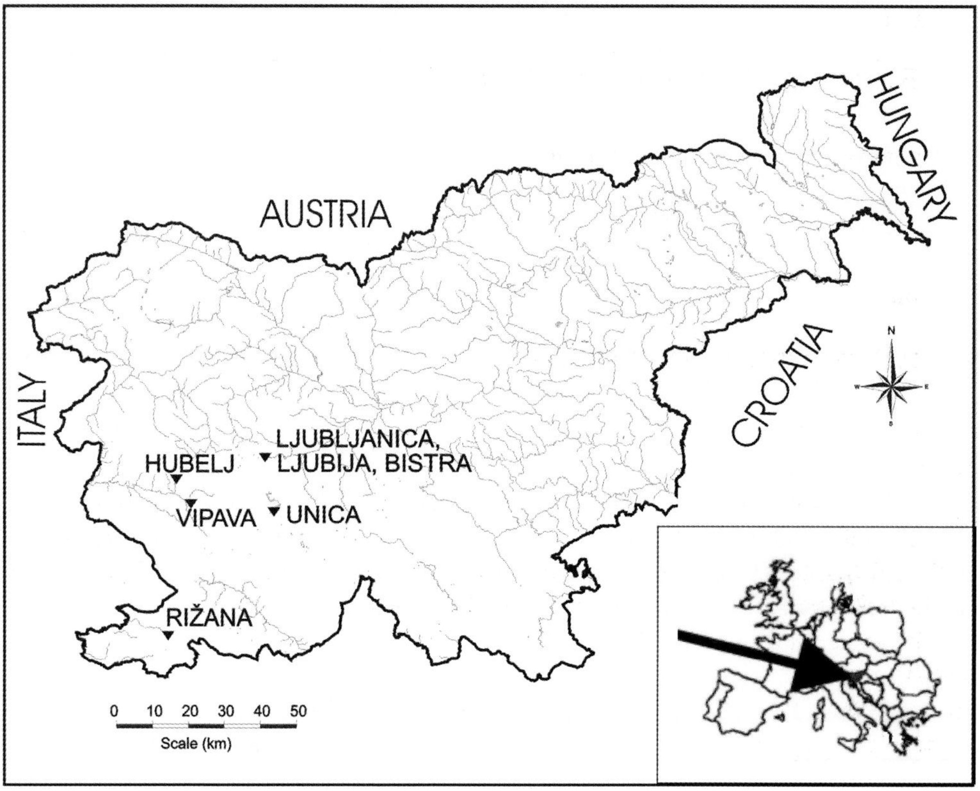

Fig. 1. Position of analyzed springs

RESULTS

Nearly all available hydrograms of big karst rivers and springs in Slovenia were analysed according to the proposed models. The hydrograph data were obtained from the Slovenian Agency for the Environment data bank that is based on their observation network. The lengths of hydrograms are shown in Table 1. The position of rivers and springs are shown in Figure 1.

Table 1 ***Characteristics of analyzed hydrograms***

Spring/River	Period	N of years	N of data points
Bistra	1970 - 1995	26	9496
Unica	1954 - 1994	41	14975
Ljubljanica	1961 - 1994	34	12418
Hubelj	1956 - 1995	40	14610
Ljubija	1952 - 1994	43	15706
Vipava	1960 - 1995	36	13149
Rižana	1965 - 1995	31	11202

The estimated parameters of GPD are given in Table 2 and estimated parameters of GEV are given in Table 3. The shape parameter *c* of GPD is the same as shape parameter *c* of GEV.

Table 2. ***Estimated parameters of Generalized Pareto Distribution***

Spring/River	c	k	g
Bistra	-0,0734	7,108	0,444
Ljubija	-0,0461	7,383	0,484
Ljubljanica	-0,0626	6,412	0,563
Unica	-0,1121	6,262	0,270
Hubelj	-0,1255	5,971	0,444
Vipava	-0,1536	4,861	0,569
Rižana	-0,0627	5,052	0,509

Table 3. ***Estimated parameters of Generalized Extreme Value Distribution***

Spring/River	θ	γ
Ljubija	5,40	30,33
Ljubljanica	5,50	27,07
Unica	5,22	29,02
Hubelj	6,88	27,92
Vipava	6,15	30,43
Rižana	6,29	27,21

Parameters of monotonic recession cloud are given in the Table 4. According to the proposed models from equations (3) and (4) three different types of convergence in hydrograms from Slovenia are determined. The monotonic recession cloud of Bistra spring group does not converge, the percentile model curves are parallel and convergence parameters can not be given.

Table 4. ***Parameters and type of monotonic recession cloud convergence***

Spring/River	t_c [days]	Q_c [m^3/s]	t_{ret} [days]	type of convergence
Bistra	/	/	/	parallel
Ljubija	83	0,19	3053	exponential
Ljubljanica	53	1,40	62	exponential
Unica	59	1,50	85	exponential
Hubelj	246	0,16	>10000	power
Vipava	72	0,77	123	power
Rižana	39	0,70	37	power

DISSCUSSION

The shape of the karst spring total hydrogram and of the particular event hydrograms reflects the properties of the aquifer that drains through the spring. The amplitude of discharges and the shape of the recession limbs are the consequence of fissure to channel ratio in the karst aquifer. Similar properties influence the recession cloud shape and its convergence.

Convergence time t_c and convergence discharge Q_c defines the point after which the depletion of discharges is totally monotonic and without variations. If the ideal recession and base flow is defined as the phenomena where are no influences from recharge are present, then the convergence point (t_c,Q_c) defines the time after which the emptying of the aquifer reservoir is only the consequence of aquifer physical properties. The convergence time t_c defines the beginning of the base flow.

Three types of monotonic recession cloud convergence are defined. In the exponential and power model the convergence exists. In the parallel model of recession cloud the convergence is not present. Among analysed hydrograms only the total hydrogram of Bistra has parallel monotonic recession cloud. The groups of springs that drain out from the same big regional karst aquifer have similar shape of the recession cloud. Vipava and Hubelj rivers that drain out from the aquifer of Trnovsko Banjška plateau have the recession cloud that can be described by power model. The rivers of Ljubljanica aquifer have the recession cloud that can be described by exponential model.

It is believed that differences between convergence times t_c and convergence discharges Q_c among karst springs are the consequence of different fissure to channel ratio in the karst aquifer drained through observed springs. These properties reflect the level of karst aquifer development. Further work in explaining different types of convergence is needed.

REFERENCES

Bonacci, O. 1993. Karst springs hydrographs as indicators of karst aquifers.-Hydrological sciences journal, 36, 51 - 62.

Brencic, 2000: The study of karst spring recession in Slovenia. - in: Sillilo et al. (eds.): Groundwater: Past Achievements and Future Challenges, Balkema, 97-101, Rotterdam.

Chow, V.T., Maidement, D.R., Mays, L.W., 1988. Applied Hydrology.-McGraw Hill Book Company, p. 572, New York.

Dargahi-Noubary, G. R., 1989: On tail estimation: an improved method.-Mathematical geology 21, 829-842.

Davison, A.C., 1984: Modeling excesses over high thresholds with an application.-in: Tiago de Oliviera, J. (ed.): Statistical Extremes and Applications, D.Riedel Publishing Company, 461-482, Dordrecht.

Ford, D. & Williams, P. 1989. Karst Geomorphology and Hydrology.-Chapman & Hall. P. 601, London.

Greenwood, J.A., Landwehr, J.M., Matalas, N.C., Wallis, J.R., 1979: Probability weighted moments: definition and relation to parameters of several distributions expressible in inverse form.-Water resources research 15, 1049-1054.

Linsley, R.K., Kholer, M.A., Paulhus, J.L.H. 1988. Hydrology for Engineers. McGraw Hill Book Company, p. 512, London.

Pickands III, J., 1975: Statistical inference using extreme order statistics. - The annals of statistics 3, 119 - 131.

Stephens, M.A., 1986: Test based on EDF Statistics.-in: D'Agostino, R.B. & Stephens, M.A. (eds.): Goodnes of Fit Techniques, Marcel Dekker, INC., 97 - 193, New York.

Tallaksen, L.M. 1995. A review of baseflow recession analysis. Journal of hydrology 165, 349- 370.

Wang, Q.J., 1991: The POT model described by the generalized Pareto distribution with Poisson arrival rate.-Journal of hydrology 129, 263-280.

Address

Geological Survey of Slovenia, Dimičeva 14, SI-1000 Ljubljana, Slovenia

mbrencic@geo-zs.si

Evolution of Karst: From Prekarst to Cessation, 375-380, Ljubljana-Postojna 2002

GROUNDWATER TRACING IN THE POSHTE - NAZ KARSTIC AREA IN NORTHERN IRAN

NASROLLAH KALANTARI

Abstract
The tracing technique has been recently used in karstified Zagros structural belt in northern Iran. A tracer study (uranine injection) was conducted in Jurassic limestone of the Poshte-Naz area in the Alborz belt to evaluate aquifer parameters and hydraulic relations between a large diameter (about 100 m) sinkhole and springs. A main goal of the project was to find out the source of turbidity of the Emarate drinking water supply spring (SP4) in rainy season. Eight springs, three wells and the Neka River were selected and totally 989 samples in 107 days were collected. In order to select reliable sampling stations, hydrochemical analysis of major ions was carried out and for better interpretation of concentration-time curve, spring discharge was also measured. The results of the tracing by sampling water indicated only a hydraulic connection between Sange- Now spring (SP8) and injection point, while the charcoal packets analysis revealed tracer exits also from spring numbers SP1, SP3, SP4, SP5, SP8, in well s W1 and W2, and in the Neka River. This paper discuses concentration - time curves of charcoal packets for qualitative analysis and exit tracer for quantitative analysis is also assessed.
Key words: *Groundwater, karst, spring, sinkhole, sample, tracer, charcoal packet*

INTRODUCTION

The Jurassic Lar limestone with a total area of about 400 km^2 falls in Alborz chain. Due to tectonics and dissolution processes, this aquifer was karstified and represents a major hydrogeological unit in the north of Iran. The Poshte- Naz (36° 34' to 36 ° 42' N and 53° 16' to 53° 50' E) of mostly mountaneous terrain (elevation 50-1400m) constitute a part of the Lar formation and covers an area of about 80 km^2. The mantled Poshte- Naz karstic terrain (Fig.1) with well developed karstic features (sinkhole, ponor, cave, and dry valley) has a thickness of several hundred meters, receives over 800 mm/y of rainfall and experiences humid climatic condition. Dense vegetation cover and relatively thick soil cover this karst formation on the top. Impermeable shales and schist of Gorgan and Shamshak formations terminate the aquifer at the base. A part from dry valleys, ponors, active and inactive caves, sinkholes appear to be more frequent features on the crest of the Poshte-Naz anticline.

Structural (fractures, faults and Poshte- Naz anticline) and geomorphologic features and dissolution are enhancing fracture porosity which impact karst groundwater potential. In addition, the position of the low and impermeable rocks in the Poshte- Naz

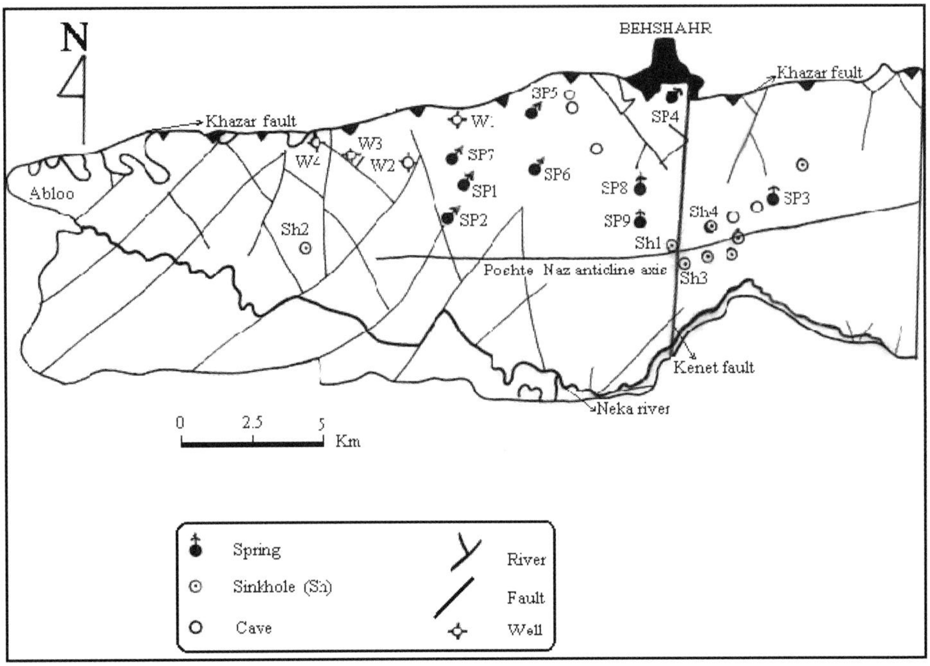

Figure 1. Location map of the study area.

anticline core that hinder downward groundwater movement play a critical role for underground reservoir development. The greater number of springs in the northern part of the Poshte- Naz anticline is the most obvious hydrogeological feature in the area.

Groundwater quality in the Poshte- Naz is generally good and concentration of major ions has evoked significant problems. However, a few good yielding springs- particularly Emarate (SP4), which is used for drinking water supply is turbid in rainy season by surface water input into sinkholes and from pollution point of view this situation is closer to surface than groundwater system. Therefore, a tracing test was proposed in order to find out the exact point of turbidity (sinkhole) and groundwater characteristics.

HYROGEOLOGY AND HYDROCHEMISTRY

The favourable climatic condition, lithological characteristics and intensive tectonics activity generate promising aquifer systems. Diffuse recharge from infiltration through pore space and concentrated recharge through well-developed ponors, sinkholes and shafts recharge the karstic reservoir. Due to topographic gradients, stratum dip, fault behaviour, exposed fracture and coincidence of groundwater with base level erosion, groundwater is emerging in the form of springs with variable discharge in different altitudes (table. 1). The Poshte-Naz karstic aquifers are rich in groundwater and form the principal source of water supply for Behshahr City and surrounding areas. Water supply systems have been mainly based on the intake of natural discharges from karstic aquifers at springs. The main spring in the area is SP4, with an average of 60 L /s and prior to tracing it was believed that its discharge is mainly governed by Sh1 and Kenet fault (Fig. 1).

Table 1. *Represents spring discharge and elevation.*

Spring Nos	Average Spring discharge L/s	Elevation m
SP1	5	150
SP2	25	180
SP3	50	550
SP4	60	50
SP5	20	90
SP6	10	200
SP7	4	140
SP8	7	480

Hydrochemical data is commonly used to depict groundwater flow regime. When detailed analysis of spring water is done, conspicuous differences in water composition indicate catchment area and anomalies in distribution of hydraulic parameters (Zanini et al. 2000). For the same purpose, in the present investigation chemical analysis of springs water was carried out (table.2). The data showed as the chemical parameters are variable and different for all investigated water. On the basis of chemical composition, low SP8 discharge as compare to SP4 and Kenet fault, it was mostly believed that Sh1 is the main recharging source of the SP4 rather than SP8.

Table 2. *Physico - chemical characteristics of water in meq.*

Stations	Sh1	SP4	SP8
Temperature °C	1 2	1 2	1 2
	18 16.5	20 15	18.3 16
Ph	6.7	7.15	7.65
TDS mg/l	312	349	159
Ca^{++}	3.9	3.9	1.5
Mg^{++}	0.33	0.29	0.1
Na^{+}	0.5	0.4	0.2
K^{+}	1.7	2.4	1.2
HCO_3^{-}	2.4	2.6	1.9
SO_4^{--}	0.65	0.7	0.17
Cl^{-}	0.05	0.04	0.02

Temperature in dry (1) and rainy (2) season.

TRACER EXPERIMENT

Prior to the tracer test on the basis of the following it was assumed that water flows from

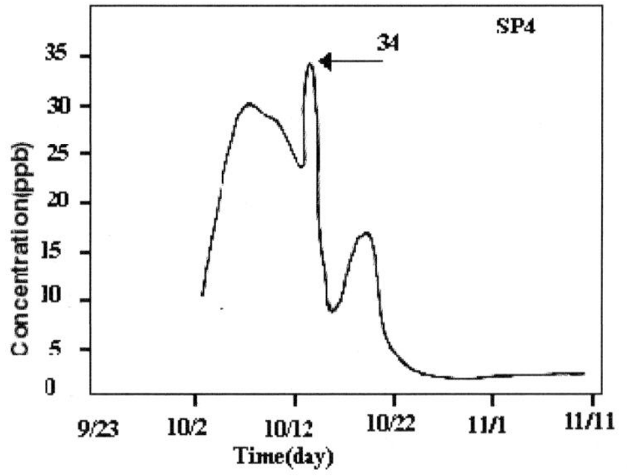

Figure 2. Uranine concentration in packet at spring (SP4).

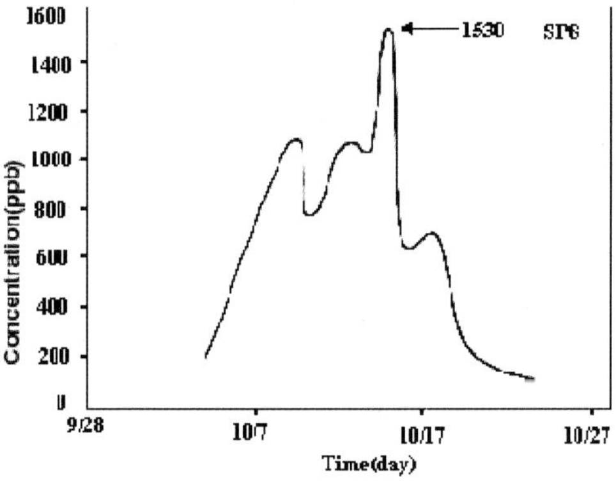

Figure 3. Uranine concentration in Charcoal packet at spring (SP8).

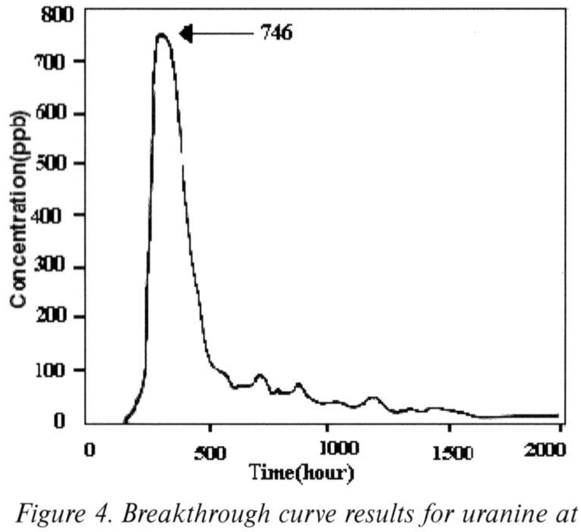

Figure 4. Breakthrough curve results for uranine at spring (SP8).

Sh1 towards SP4. (1) The Kenet fault position which extends N-S and Sh1 and SP4 are positioned on the Kenet fault, (2) distance between Sh1 and SP4 is shortest as compare to other sinkholes, (3) Sh1 is located in SP4 topographic catchment area and elevation difference between Sh1 and SP4 is 750 m, (4) turbidity of SP4 with rainfall. Therefore inspection of the area suggested that the best and most promising point for tracer injection is Sh1 and springs and places where appearance of the tracer would be probable was also determined. A review of literature (Kogovsek et al. 1997), Pavicic & Jvicic (1997), (Stevanovic et al. 1997) and Kass (1998) indicated that uranine tracing has been widely used in karstic terrain. The observation stations were checked for natural or man made background by passive detectors prior to the dye experiment.

On October 18, 1999 at 7 PM 5 kg of uranine in the form of pre-prepared aqueous solution was injected into shaft's sinkhole (Sh1). Then, moreover to rivulet discharge into the shaft, after end of tracer feeding in total 6000 L water was injected into the shaft in order to clean the shaft's wall and to flush the dye tracer. Concerning to sampling, it was done by direct water samples and by bags with activated charcoal. Tracer experiment was monitored in 12 locations including the Neka River, springs and wells around Sh1. The observation period was extended over 107 days and in total, 989 samples were collected while SP4 and SP5 sampled in most detail. Analyses carried out

With spectrofluorometer model AU 10 and accuracy 0.001ppb. Uranine first appearance was 158 hours after injection, and it was only detected at SP8 in water samples during the 107 day test. Since water sample results of injection test demonstrated a connection between Sh1 and Sp8, therefore, probably part of the water sinking at Sh1 emerges to the northeast at SP8. On the other hand activated charcoal results indicated connection between Sh1, SP3, SP4, SP5, SP8, well numbers 1 and 2 and the Neka River. Activated charcoal residence time distribution curves are not commonly in use for qualitative analysis. Lois & Ponta (1999) determined fracture flow path by peak dye concentration of charcoal packets in contaminated karstic terrain. Activated charcoal results (Figs.2,3) depicted tracer appearance time and underground network. Comparison of Figures 3 and 4 depicted that the concentration of SP8 samples is approximately 2 times greater than the water samples concentration. This happen due to continuos absorbance of dye tracers on activated charcoal bags. The concentration of dye in SP4 samplers (Fig. 2) as compare to SP8 samplers indicates reduced concentration to more than 80 times. This might be a result of tracer dilution or low concentration of tracer in SP4 direction and could be also effected by uncontrolled exit of tracer. The difference in arrival date of tracer (charcoal bag results) in SP4 and SP8 with respect to their distance to Sh1 confirm diffuse and conduit flow type for SP8 and SP4. This assumption and samplers result of the other stations support that Sh1 has also a hydraulic connection to the remaining collected sampling points.

The almost unimodal SP8 dye breakthrough curve (Fig. 4) indicated that dye appeared 158 hours after injection. Maximal concentration period was 13 days and about 100 days later on returned back to its initial position. The sharp and unimodal characteristic of curve introduces one main watercourse with no large underground reservoir. The tracer test results in brief is shown in table 3.

Table 3. *Calculated results of tracer test.*

Dominant velocity	0.36 cm/s
Actual distance	4050 m
Mean residence time	465 hour
Skewness	30%
Dispersion coefficient	0.293×10^{-2} km^2/h
Mean basin width	1.72 km
Flow type	Diffuse
Catchment boundary	6.96 km^2

Applying a tortuosity (?) of 1.5 actual distance was obtained. The dominant velocity (v) was computed from actual distance (L) and time with maximal concentration (Tp). Smart (1988) equation was taken to calculate mean residence time (Tr) and skewness (S). Dispersion coefficient (Dd) and the first dye appearance time were used to determine basin width, where this in turn applied to estimate watershed boundary. The distance, velocity and dye appearance determines flow type. On the basis of injected dye mass (kg) and the area under curve (A), maximum SP8 discharge (Qm) was 12.7 L/s which is relatively in accordance with SP8 discharge in high rainfall years.

CONCLUSIONS

In the studied area, well-developed geomorphological features occurrence and spring discharge variation depicted underground karst channels. The injected tracer in Sh1 did not support such channel connections. Even, in spite of tracer appearance (activated charcoal) in SP4 due to absence of dye in SP4 water samples, Sh1 and SP4 interconnection is doubtful to locate the source of SP4 turbidity. The karst underground flows move in privileged directions, most frequently tectonically predisposed. Then, the question is that what is kenet fault role? The low returned quantity of tracer suggested prob able uncontrolled exit. The other possibility for not detecting tracer (water samples) in SP4 and low recovery is considerable SP4 discharge and trace dilution.

Therefore, the water-tracing test at this stage only provided some basic information regarding aquifer characteristics in limited area, and for detail understanding more tracings have to be done in different hydrologic conditions.

REFERENCES

Kass, W. 1999. Dyes. In W. Kass (ed.), tracing technique in geohydrology: 19- 122, Rotherdam: Balkema.

Kogovsek, J., Petric, M. & Liu, H. 1997. Properties of under ground water flow in karst area near Lunan in Yunnan Provi ence. In A. Kranjc (ed.), Tracer hydrology: 255- 261, Rotherdam: Balkema.

Lois, D.G & Ponta,G. 1999. Dye study tracks historical pathway of VOC-bearing industrial waste water from failed pond at metals coating facility: In B. F. Beck., A .J. Pettit & G. Herring (eds), Hydrogeology and engineering geology of sinkholes and karst: 293-299 Rotherdam: Balkema.

Pavicic, A & Jvicic, D. 1997. Drainage basin boundaries of major karst springs in Croatia determined by means of groundwater tracing in their hinterland: In B. F. Beck., A .J.

Pettit & G. Herring (eds), Hydrogeology and engineering geology of sinkholes and karst: 273-278 Rotherdam: Balkema.

Smart, C.C. 1988. Quantitative tracing of the maligne karst system, Albert,Canada. Journal of hydrology, vol 98. pp.185- 205.

Stevanovic, Z., Dragisc, V., Papic, P. & Jemco, I. 1997. Hy drochemical characteristics of karst groundwater in Serbian Carpatho- Balkanides. In G.Gunnay & A.I. Johnson (eds), Karst waters environmental impacts:199-204, Rotherdam:Balkema.

Zanini, L., Novakowski, K.S., Lapcevic, P., Brckerton, G.S., Voralek, J &Talbot, C. 2000. Ground water flow in a fracured carbonate aquifer inferred from combined hydrogeological and geochemical measurements. Groundwater. Vol 38. No 3. pp. 350- 360.

Address
Geology Department, Shahid Chamran University, Ahvaz, Iran
E-mail: nkalantari@hotmail.com

Evolution of Karst: From Prekarst to Cessation, 381, Ljubljana-Postojna 2002

SULFUR, CARBON, OXYGEN, AND HYDROGEN ISOTOPE STUDIES OF FRESHWATER SPRING AND MINERAL SPRING FLOW ON THE KARST MITCHELL PLAIN AND THE CRAWFORD UPLAND OF SOUTHERN INDIANA

NOEL C. KROTHE

Abstract

Water chemistry and stable isotope (oxygen, hydrogen, carbon and sulfur) suggest that two flow systems exist in the karst terrain of Southern Indiana: (1) a shallow flow system, which is dominated by surface water that infiltrates through the soil profile to the epikarst then flows laterally to major vertical joints and fractures to the springs; and (2) a deeper flow system driven by topographic cells forcing water downward where it flows through and dissolve evaporate minerals from the St. Louis limestone. The water then flows upward and discharges at topographic lows. Sulfur isotopic values $\delta^{34}S\ (SO_4)$ for springs in the study area range from +1.1 to +22.1 °/oo. $\delta^{34}S$ of HS^- range from -0.2 to -38.4. The fresh water springs have lighter $\delta^{34}S\ (SO_4)$ values approximately 10 °/oo. The mineral springs are approximately 14 °/oo similar to values of the local St. Louis gypsum (14 to 16 °/oo). Heavier $\delta^{34}S\ (SO_4)$ values (18 to 19 °/oo) in water such as Pluto spring are due to bacterial fractionation. Orangeville rise a major fresh water spring has a low flow $\delta^{34}S\ (SO_4)$ of approximately +16 °/oo and a sulfate concentration of 160 mg/l. The $\delta^{34}S\ (SO_4)$ and sulfate concentration decreases to +9 °/oo and 40 mg/l respectively at high flow. This suggests the mixing of shallow epikarst water and deeper mineral waters. The ranges of $\delta^{18}O$ and $\delta^{2}H$ in the spring waters are -7.0 to -8.0 °/oo and -42 and -49 °/oo respectively. Waters in the study area become enriched in ^{13}C with increased mineral content. Freshwater springs are depleted in ^{13}C ($\delta^{13}C_{DIC}$ = -14 to -12 °/oo). The mineral springs are more enriched in ^{13}C ($\delta^{13}C_{DIC}$ = +1.8 °/oo) near equilibrium with the limestone bedrock.

Evolution of Karst: From Prekarst to Cessation, 383-386, Ljubljana-Postojna 2002

CONCENTRATION OF SELECTED IONS IN WATER PERCOLATING THROUGH JURASSIC CARBONIFEROUS FORMATION

J. MOTYKA, K. RÓŻKOWSKI

Abstract
Within the confines of water migration investigation through a 5 - 15 meters thick aeration zone of fissure-karstic-porous aquifer, the evolution of meteoric water chemical composition for a range of selected minor elements was analysed. Significant increase of strontium and barium concentrations in water drippings within caves was noticed, while concentrations of remaining analysed minor elements: iron, manganese and zinc decreased. Higher ion concentrations were observed mainly in deeper parts of cave system. The only ion not following the pattern was zinc.
***Key words**: fissure-karstic aquifer, zone of aeration, chemical composition modification*

INTRODUCTION

In a year 1996 started an investigation programme of water migration velocity through the aeration zone. For fissure-karstic-porous aquifer test site Zakrzówek horst was selected according to its advantages: small extent and high karstification level making possible water sampling. The idea was to sample two, three selected cave water drippings. With time the programme evolved, range of investigation increased and sampling system developed. Dripping water sampling within cave system turned out to be an effective and practical means of observation of meteoric water chemical composition modification during percolation deep into a massif.

RESULTS AND CONCLUSIONS

Investigations were conducted within cave system consisting of seven caves between April 1996 and December 1997 (Fig. 1). At first three points of drippings were sampled. With time observation network grew up to 33 points. Apart from major elements determination, concentrations of selected minor elements: Ba, Fe, Mn, Sr, Zn were recognised.

Precipitation in the Zakrzówek horst area characterise with quite low pH in range 3,5 -7,0 (mean value 5,5) and electrical conductivity γ changing changing from 12 up to 280 μS/cm (mean value 60 μS/cm). Among minor elements in analysed population of 56 samples predominate iron, reaching mean concentration of 42 ppb, while the meas-

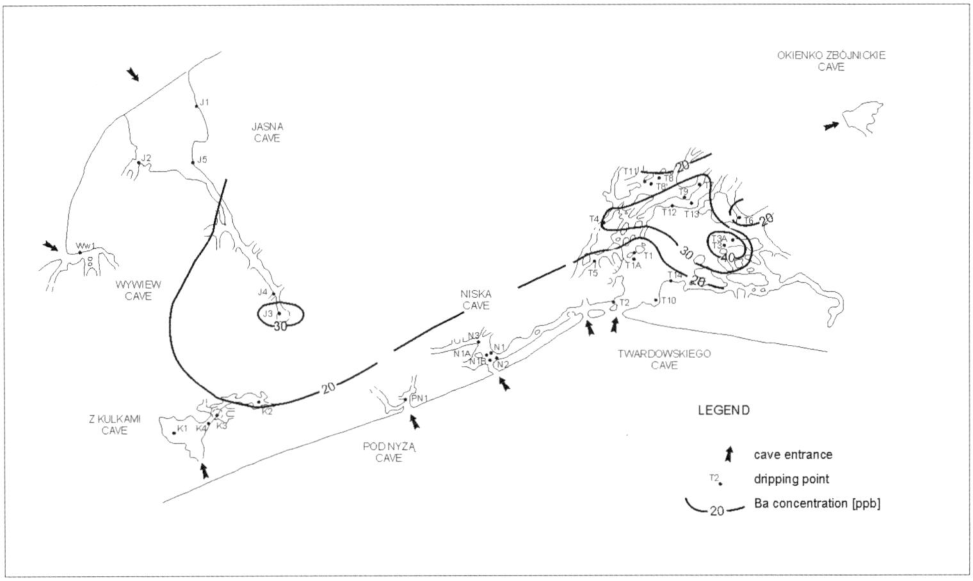

Fig, 1: Contour map of Ba concentration [ppb]

uring range varies from 10 ppb (detection limit, concentrations below the limit included 20 % of population) up to 150 ppb. Mean concentrations of the other minor elements, appropriately Zn, Mn, Sr, Ba amount: 38, 18, 9 and 8 ppb. Maximum, minimum values, medians are compiled in Table 1.

Table 1. *Basic statistics of selected minor elements concentrations in precipitation [ppb]*

	Ba	Fe	Mn	Sr	Zn
Average	8	42	18	9	38
St. Deviation	7	37	17	8	38
Minimum	1	5	1	0,5	1
Maximum	25	150	91	41	168

During precipitation percolation deep into a massif through the overburden of 5 to 15 meters thick, water chemical composition modifies. With the increase of electrical conductivity (from 129 up to 2160 μS/cm, mean 445 μS/cm), selectively increases concentration of individual elements (Table 2). The most significant is the increase of strontium. Precipitation is characterised by mean concentration of that element of 9 ppb, however 14 % of the population were concentrations below the applied measurement technique detection limit (measurements were taken into consideration while counting mean value by taking a half of the detection limit, i.e. 1 ppb). After elimination of indeterminable values, mean concentration rises up to 11 ppb. Among sampled percolating waters no concentrations below 10 ppb were noticed, while maximum determined value was 585 ppb at point T6 in Twardowskiego Cave (Fig. 1). Mean value slightly exceeded 72 ppb.

Table 2. *Basic statistics of selected minor elements concentrations in water drippings [ppb]*

	Ba	Fe	Mn	Sr	Zn
Average	16	65	4	72	6
St. Deviation	10	284	4	52	23
Minimum	1	5	1	10	1
Maximum	48	4319	40	585	313

The second minor element evidently enriching percolating waters is barium. Barium concentration in precipitation averages 8 ppb while after elimination from whole population about 40 % of indeterminable values increases up to almost 13 ppb. Analysing population of cave water drippings chemical composition sporadically can be encountered concentrations below the detection limit (<2 ppb - about 5 % of population), with the maximum of 58 ppb and mean value of 16 ppb. Increase of Ba^{2+} concentration is slight, but evident, what is expressed mainly by a small quantity of values below the detection limit. Barium as the only minor element from the analysed characterises with noticeable spatial distribution (Fig.1). Investigation of Ba^{2+} concentration in individual monitoring points from the second of July 1997 indicates in general concentration increase towards the center of the massif (Jasna Cave, points J3, J4, Twardowskiego Cave, points T3, T4, T7; Fig.1). Lower concentrations at points T6 and T8 (Twardowskiego Cave) can be connected with location at major dislocation zones, additionally strongly karstified thus patent and easily transmitting infiltrating water. Dripping T8 is marked by high efficiency as well as activity practically whole year long.

At the background of Ba^{2+} concentration spatial distribution (Fig. 1), visibly distinguishes the highest concentration at dripping T3 in Twardowskiego Cave, as well as concentrations of Sr^{2+} and Mn^{2+}. At that point were also stated the highest concentrations of major elements, including SO_4^{2-}. Probably the dripping drains fissure-karstic system partly filled with karstic residuum or anthropogenic pollution from surface or subsurface zone.

Remaining analysed minor elements: Fe, Mn and Zn do not determine concentration increase, but in reverse decrease. Average concentrations of Fe, Mn, Zn in precipitation were appropriately: 42, 18, 38 ppb and after elimination of concentrations below the detection limit rose to appropriately: 53, 20, and 41 ppb. Populations of indeterminable concentrations are in comparison with analyses of vadose zone waters slight, appropriately: 22, 11 and 7 % for Fe, Mn, Zn. After migration through regosol and rock formations above drippings increases a percentage of indeterminable with applied measurement technique concentrations. In case of zinc, the percentage exceeds 56 % of population. A bit smaller set form indeterminable concentrations of manganese - 50 % while the biggest of iron - about 62 %. Chemical analysis with concentrations significantly different from the average were observed at the drippings situated in the depth of the massif. Probably water during sampling was contaminated with cave alluvial deposits or fissure-karstic system was flushed with high quantities of meteoric water what at the conditions of higher pressures and increased volumes, flushed additional ion load.

Increased concentrations were observed among the others at July 1997, when heavy rains caused flood in southern Poland. Remaining determinations were mainly done at June and July, months usually rich in precipitation. Average values counted respecting indeterminable and extreme concentrations are compiled in Table 2.

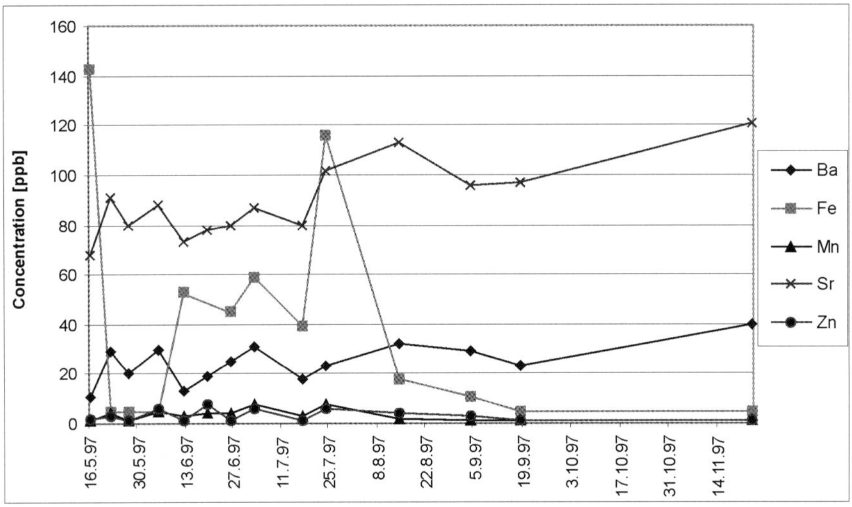

Fig. 2. Selected minor elements concentrations in a T4 dripping (Twardowskiego Cave)

Analyse of concentration variations in time (Fig. 2) shows relative strontium and barium stability with slight amplitude of changes, bigger in case of barium. Iron, manganese and zinc do not follow the pattern. At the whole population mostly predominate indeterminable concentrations, sporadically occur higher, as episodic events. Often increased concentration of iron accompanies slight rise of manganese concentration, seldom increase of zinc concentration.

Another observed regularity is occurrence of increased iron concentrations, rarely manganese, in drippings located deep inside the system, however decreased, often below the detection limit, at the entering cave parts. Zinc do not follow the pattern again.

Acid water infiltrating inside the massif is buffered by dissolving carbonates building the horst. In a neutralisation process pH raises from average 5,5 in precipitation to 7,5 in drippings, with simultaneous increase of electrical conductivity from average 60 μS/cm to 445 μS/cm in caves. Carbonates dissolution process release calcium ions and accompanying similar strontium and barium ions. On the other hand the loss of iron, manganese and zinc ions is connected with sorption of that metals by soil and also within clayey sediments of karstic residuum, as well as creation of sparingly soluble compounds in carboniferous environment.

Address
University of Mining and Metallurgy, Faculty of Mining, Mickiewicza 30, 30-059 Cracow , Poland, e-mails: motyka@uci.agh.edu.pl, kazik@uci.agh.edu.pl

Evolution of Karst: From Prekarst to Cessation, 387-394, Ljubljana-Postojna 2002

THE UPPER UNSATURATED ZONE OF THE KARST AQUIFER IN THE CATCHMENT AREA OF THE HUBELJ SPRING (SW SLOVENIA)

BRANKA TRČEK, MIRAN VESELIČ & JOŽE PEZDIČ

Abstract
The variations of natural tracers in precipitation and in groundwater of a karst aquifer in the catchment area of the Hubelj spring (South-Western Slovenia) enabled us to study the aquifer's behavior. The results provided an insight into the age structure of groundwater and produced data on the aquifer's recharge, storage and discharge processes. The conceptual model of the observed aquifer has been made. It is presumed that its flow and solute transport mechanisms depend on the epikarst zone's behavior.
Keywords: *karst aquifer, conceptual model, epikarst, flow and solute transport, natural tracers*

1 INTRODUCTION

Our research work focusing on behavior of a karst aquifer in the catchment area of the Hubelj spring (South-Western Slovenia) (Figure 1) is presented in this paper. We tried to answer several open questions connected with studies of flow and transport mechanisms in a karst aquifer. The mechanisms that cause flow and solute transport from an upper unsaturated zone were particularly stressed.

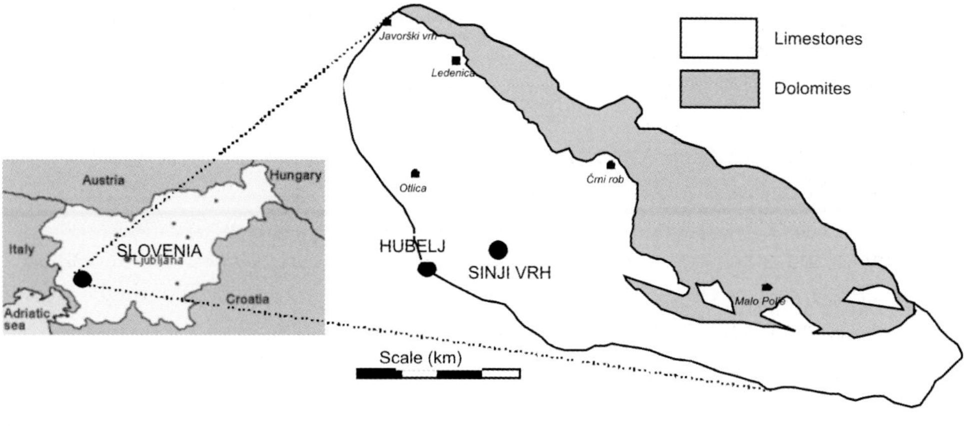

Fig.1. Location of the study area

The research method from a natural tracer and hydrogeochemical field of work was used as the basic one. Its results allowed us to prepare the conceptual model of the observed aquifer.

2 STUDY AREA

The catchment area of the karst spring Hubelj (Figure 1), consisting mostly of Jurassic limestones, is estimated to 50-80 km^2 (Trišič 2001). The study area is a high karst plateau, Trnovski gozd, with the mean altitude of 900 m a.s.l. Shallow soil types (10-50 cm) on limestones are mainly found in this region (Matičič 1997). They have low water holding capacities and high infiltration rates. The average annual precipitation is 2450 mm.

Our research included observations of two aquifer's zones:

- saturated and
- upper unsaturated zone.

The first one was observed in Hubelj that lies at the southern border of Trnovski gozd (Figure 1). Its permanent outflow is at altitudes between 219 and 235 m, its mean discharge is 3 m^3/s, the minimum one is 0.2 m^3/s while the maximum one reaches 59 m^3/s (Janež et al. 1997).

The upper unsaturated zone was investigated in the artificial tunnel, 10-20 m below the surface (Figure 2). The tunnel is located 600 m above the Hubelj spring, near Sinji vrh, at the mean altitude of 825 m a.s.l. (Figure 1).

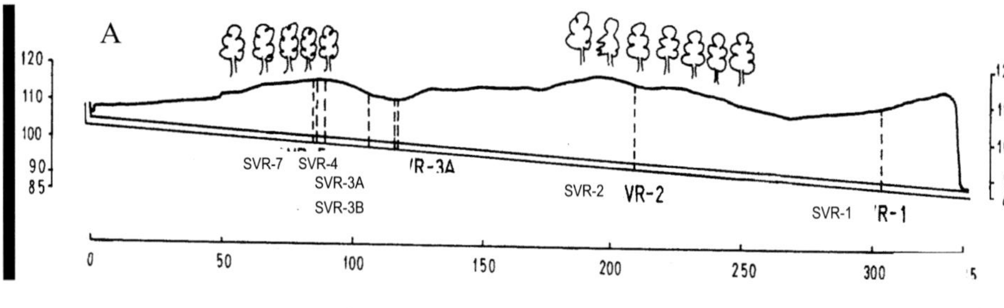

Fig. 2. Longitudinal section of the artificial tunnel with sampling points for isotopic and chemical analyses of groundwater

3 METHODS AND TECHNIQUES

The research's methodological concept included

a) a multiparametric monitoring of precipitation and karst system's waters (seepage water of the artificial tunnel and the aquifer's outflow- Hubelj spring),
   - oxygen, hydrogen and carbon stable isotopes (^{18}O, ^{2}H, ^{13}C),
   - dissolved organic carbon (DOC), alkalinity,

- electroconductivity, temperature, pH,
- discharge, precipitation amount,

that was performed on basis of

b) a two-stage sampling
   - long-term sampling in monthly intervals (1999, 2000),
   - short-term sampling during a storm period in July 2000 that is presented in Figure 3.

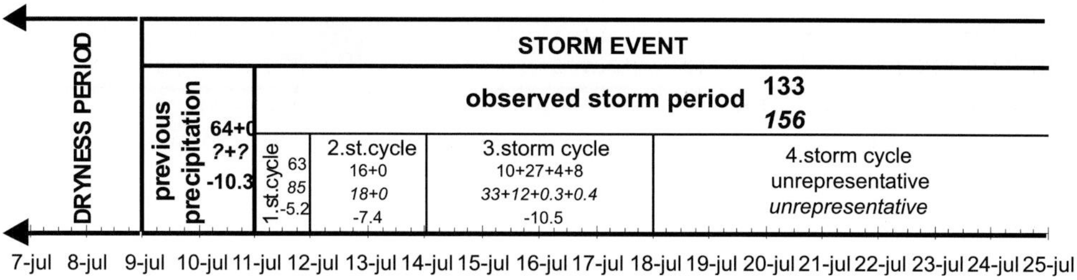

10+ 27 precipitation amount (mm) in the catchment area of the Hubelj spring

33+1 precipirtation amount (mm) at Sinji vrh

-10.5 mean $d^{18}O$ composition of precipitation (‰)

Fig. 3. Presentation of the storm event in July 2000

The storm hydrograph separation techniques were used to determine the contribution of event water to a summer storm flow and the role of the vadose flow component in a summer storm flow generation (Kendall & McDonnell 1998; McDonnell et al. 1990; Sklash & Farvolden 1979; Trček et al. 2001; Trček 2001). They were based on $\delta^{18}O$ and DOC composition of sampled water.

4 RESULTS

The most important results of the long-term sampling are the age estimations of sampled groundwater in the tunnel (Figure 2) and in Hubelj. Differences between the seasonal variation of $\delta^{18}O$ in precipitation and that one in karst system's water were taken into consideration. Because there is just two-year series of data for the study area's precipitation, we used also data of the nearest compatible precipitation station - Ljubljana. Polynomial trends (amplitudes and their phase shifts), linear trends and annual averages of data were compared (Trček 2001). The result is presented in Figure 4. Because of the significant $\delta^{18}O$ seasonal variation and its positive linear trend, the average residence time of water from sampling points SVR-7, SVR-4, Hubelj and SVR-3A is less than five years. It is longer for water from sampling points SVR-3B, SVR-1 and SVR-2. The non-significant $\delta^{18}O$ seasonal variation and its negative linear trend are the reason for that. The estimations of the average residence time for a single sampling point are (Trček 2001):

- 3 months for SVR-7
- 9 months for SVR-4
- 2-3 years for Hubelj
- 4-5 years for SVR-3A
- 5-6 years for SVR-3B,
- at least 10 years for SVR-1 and SVR-2 (it can be one or more decades longer).

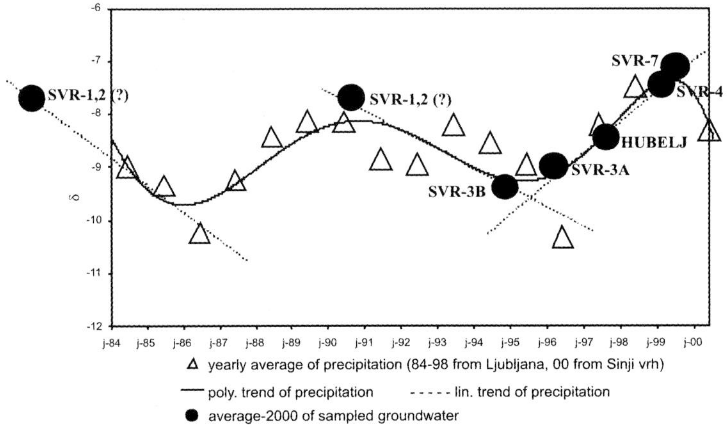

Fig. 4. Annual average composition of karst system's water and precipitation

The short-term sampling's results provide insight into aquifer's recharge, storage and discharge processes. The first storm cycle was the most important part of the event (Figure 3). It caused that the Hubelj's discharge increased from 0.6 to 24 m^3/s (Figure 5). The delay between the start of the first storm cycle and the maximum discharge response in Hubelj was 7 hours, while it was 3 hours in the tunnel respectively (Figure 5). The tunnel's sampling point SVR-3A reacted the first to precipitation (1 hour after the beginning of the first storm cycle), SVR-7 the second (soon after SVR-3A) and SVR-4 the third (4 hours after SVR-7). When the discharge of SVR-3A almost stopped after 1 day, water began to flow to 1 meter apart SVR-3B – the dependence between two kinds of flow (faster and laminar) is expressed. SVR-1 reacted 2 days after the beginning of the first storm cycle, while there was no water in SVR-2 during the storm event. It is obvious that sampling points SVR-1 and SVR-2 are recharged by a laminar flow.

It can be seen in Figure 5a that the amount of the previous precipitation (Figure 3) was somewhat greater from that one of the first storm cycle. Nevertheless, the previous precipitation caused a non-significant Hubelj's discharge increase, from 0.4 to 1.8 m^3/s. The tunnel's upper unsaturated zone also didn't react a lot to this precipitation. There were just slight reactions of sampling points SVR-7 and SVR-1. The previous precipitation thus resulted mainly in aquifer's recharge and storage processes while the precipitation of the observed storm period (Figure 3) resulted also in aquifer's discharge processes.

The $\delta^{18}O$ composition of karst system's groundwater and precipitation (Figures 6, 3) indicated that

- Hubelj contained a significant amount of new water,

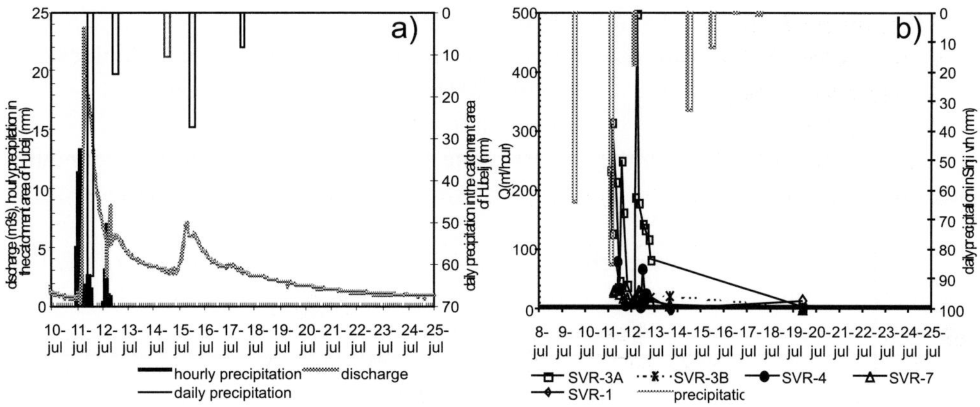

Figure 5. Daily precipitation, hourly precipitation and discharge of a) Hubelj and b) sampling points in the tunnel

- the amount of new water was much lower in tunnel's sampling points (the greatest one is connected with SVR-3A).

The tunnel's data reflected the piston effect

- new water mainly displaced old pre-stored water to the sampling points what was proved also by two-component storm hydrograph separations (Trček 2001).

The role of the upper unsaturated zone on the aquifer's behavior was studied by the Hubelj's storm hydrograph separation. The hydrograph was separated into a base flow, an upper unsaturated zone's water and a new water components (Trček, 2001). The results indicated that the latter two components had to be combined into an epiflow (Kiraly et al. 1995) component.

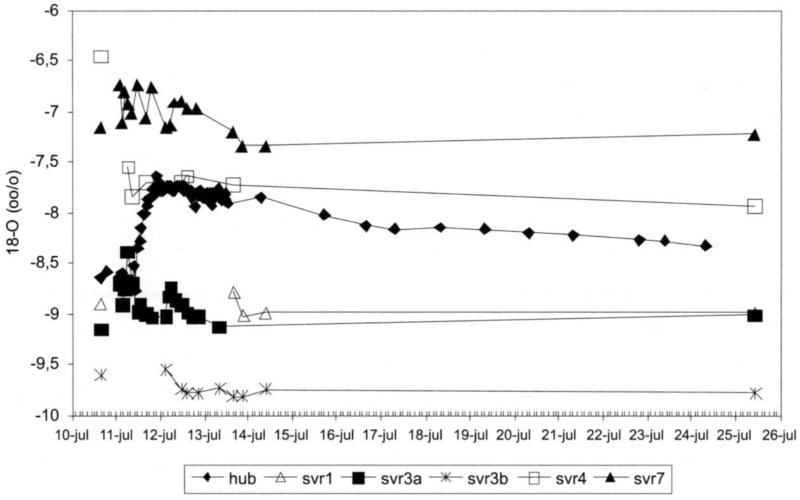

Figure 6. $\delta^{18}O$ composition of sampled groundwater

Consequently, the karst spring's hydrograph was separated into two components:

- base flow - a relatively slow diffuse flow from the low permeable rock blocks,
- epiflow - a fast flow of a) water pre-stored in the epikarst zone, and b) new water

that were accumulated in the epikarst zone's base and drained into karst conduit's network (Figure 7).

The epiflow component reached the maximum value (84%) at the end of the first storm cycle (Figure 7). It mainly decreased afterward and disappeared on 21st when an inversion of hydraulic gradient occurred (since this time its values were even negative). The average epiflow component's part was 41% (containing 54% of new water and 46% of upper unsaturated zone's water) during the observed storm period. It was 48% (containing 31% of new water and 69% of upper unsaturated zone's water) during the period of the first and the second storm cycles respectively.

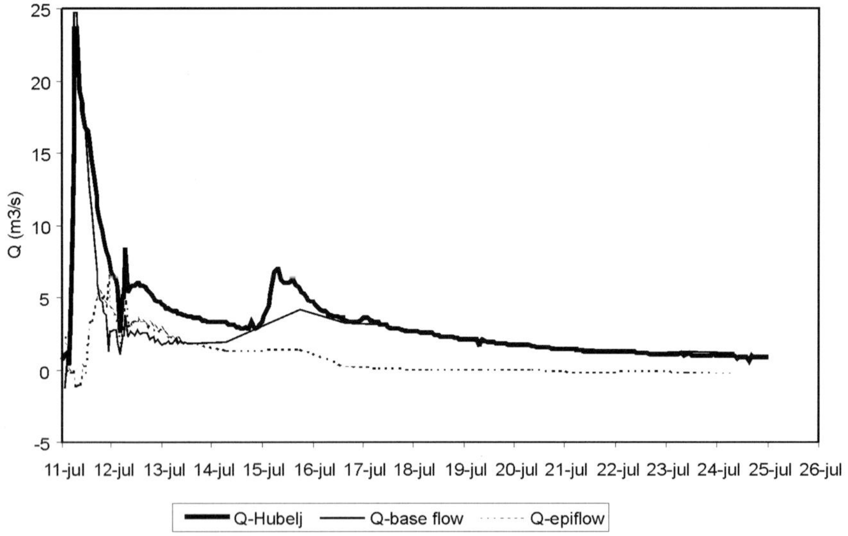

Figure 7. Hydrograph separation of the Hubelj spring

5 DISCUSSION

The results of a single sampling stage are connected and interpreted in the conceptual model of the karst aquifer in the catchment area of the Hubelj spring. The model consists of:

- upper unsaturated zone, including
  a) shallow soils,
  b) epikarst zone,

- lower unsaturated zone, including
  a) storage zone in larger fractures and conduits,
  b) storage zone in low permeable rock blocks,
- saturated zone, including
  a) storage zone in larger fractures and conduits,
  b) storage zone in low permeable rock blocks.

It is presumed that the aquifer's flow and solute transport mechanism depends on the epikarst zone's behavior. The results of the storm event reflect the importance of the epikarst zone's water quantity - the extend of epikarst zone's accumulation and of subsequent discharge to aquifer's lower parts depends on the soil and epikarst zone's water saturation.

6 CONCLUSIONS

Our research indicates the presence of the epikarst zone in the observed karst aquifer and its importance for aquifer's behavior. The results contribute to the knowledge of epikarst zone's properties and functions. It is obvious that this zone should be included in the strategy plans for the karst aquifer's monitoring.

We'll try to further upgrade the here presented results and to compare them with those from other research areas.

REFERENCES

Berg, W.& Čenčur Curk, Barbara & Frank, J., Feichtinger, F.& Nützmann, G.& Papesch, W. & Rajner, V. & Rank, D. & Schneider, S. & Seiler, K. P. & Steiner, K. H. & Stenitzer, E. & Stichler, W. & Trček, Branka & Vargay, Z. & Veselič, Miran & Zojer, H., 2001: Tracers in the unsaturated zone.- Steir. Beitr. Hydrogeol., 2001/52, 1-102.

Janež, J. & Čar, J. & Habič, P. & Podobnik, R., 1997: Vodno bogastvo Visokega krasa. Ranljivost kraške podzemne vode Banjšic, Trnovskega gozda, Nanosa in Hrušice.- Geologija d.o.o., p. 167, Idrija

Kendall, C. & McDonell, J.J., 1998: Isotope tracers in catchment hydrology.- Elsevier, p. 722, Amsterdam

Kiraly, L. & Perrochet, P. & Rossier, Y., 1995: Effect of the epikarst on the hydrograph of karst springs: A numerical approach.- Bulletin d'Hydrogéologie, 14, 199-220

Matičič, B., 1997: Agricultural threats to pollution of water of Trnovsko-Banjška Planota. In Karst hydrogeological investigations in south-western Slovenia (ed. Kranjc, A.).- Acta carsologica, 26/1, 102-113, Ljubljana

McDonnell, J.J. & Bonell, M. & Stewart, M.K. & Pearce, A.J., 1990: Deuterium variations in storm rainfall: Implications for stream hydrograph separation.- Water Resources Research, 26/3, 455-458

Sklash, M.G. & Farvolden, R.N., 1979: The role of grounwater in storm runoff.- Journal of Hydrology, 43, 45-65

Trček, B. & Pezdič, J. & Veselič, M. & Stichler, W., 2001: Changes in $\delta^{18}O$ composition of the Hubelj spring under different hydrogeological conditions. In Proceedings of the Conference on New Approaches Characterizing Groundwater Flow (ed. Seiler, P. & Wohnlich, S.).- Balkema Publishers, 207-211, Lisse

Trček, B. 2001: Solute transport monitoring in the unsaturated zone of the karst aquifer by natural tracers. Doctoral thesis.- University of Ljubljana, p. 125, Ljubljana

Trišič, N., 1997: Hydrology. In Karst hydrogeological investigations in south-western Slovenia (ed. Kranjc, A.).- Acta carsologica, 26/1, 19-30, Ljubljana

Address
Branka Trček, Geological Survey of Slovenia, Dimičeva ulica 14, SI-1000 Ljubljana
E-mail: branka.trcek@geo-zs.si
Miran Veselič, Institute of Mining, Geotechnology and Environment, Slovenčeva 93, SI-1000 Ljubljana
E-mail: miran.veselic@i-rgo.si
Jože Pezdič, Faculty of Natural Science and Technology, Aškerčeva 12, SI-1000 Ljubljana
E-mail: joze.pezdic@ntfgeo.uni-lj.si

Evolution of Karst: From Prekarst to Cessation, 395-401, Ljubljana-Postojna 2002

THE IMPORTANCE OF THREE AND FOUR-COMPONENT STORM HYDROGRAPH SEPARATION TECHNIQUES FOR KARST AQUIFERS

BRANKA TRČEK & NOEL C. KROTHE

Abstract
In Indiana and Slovenia, we have been working in the same research problems, concerning the study of karst aquifer's behavior. We got similar results at different study areas by using an indirect research method: three and four-component storm hydrograph separation techniques basing on natural tracers. The presented techniques are an effective approach for characterizing such heterogeneous aquifers. They produce data on recharge, storage and discharge processes as well as on mechanisms that affect these processes.
Our results are in agreement with actual research hypothesis where it is supposed that an important part of the karst aquifer's recharge arrives (rapidly and in concentrated form) into the conduit network from the epikarst zone. They demonstrate that epikarst's water could occupy up to 50% of spring discharge during precipitation events. This phenomenon could have important consequences on protection and management problems of karst aquifers.
Key words: *karst aquifer, three and four-component hydrograph separation technique, natural tracers, aquifer's (contaminant) behavior*

INTRODUCTION

Karst aquifers are an important source of water supply in Slovenia and Indiana (USA). In order to protect karst aquifers from pollution it is necessary to investigate the behavior of contaminants and understand the natural factors that control this behavior. We have been working in this topic in our countries. The research of flow, storage and solute (contaminant) transport processes in karst aquifers has been particularly stressed. However, this is a difficult task due to karst aquifer's heterogeneity that cause serious problems for normal monitoring and measurement of these processes.

We used an indirect research method, a storm hydrograph separation technique, and studied its effectiveness for characterizing karst aquifer's behavior. Our prior researches (Trček et al. 2001, Lakey & Krothe 1996) demonstrate that the two-component separation technique isn't a suitable research tool. Its results can act just as a first approximation of amounts of pre-storm and new water (rain) that contribute to karst aquifer's storm discharge. Therefore, three and four-component storm hydrograph separation techniques were used in our latter researches. Their results are presented in this manuscript. They are synthesized in the karst aquifer's conceptual model that provide significant data on the recharge, storage and discharge processes as well as on mechanisms that affect these processes.

STUDY AREA

The karst springs

a) Orangeville Rise (its discharge ranges from 0.06 to 5.1 m^3/s), in south central Indiana, and
b) Hubelj (its discharge ranges from 0.2 up to 59 m^3/s), in south-western Slovenia, represent the main discharges of two highly karstified carbonate aquifers (Figure 1).

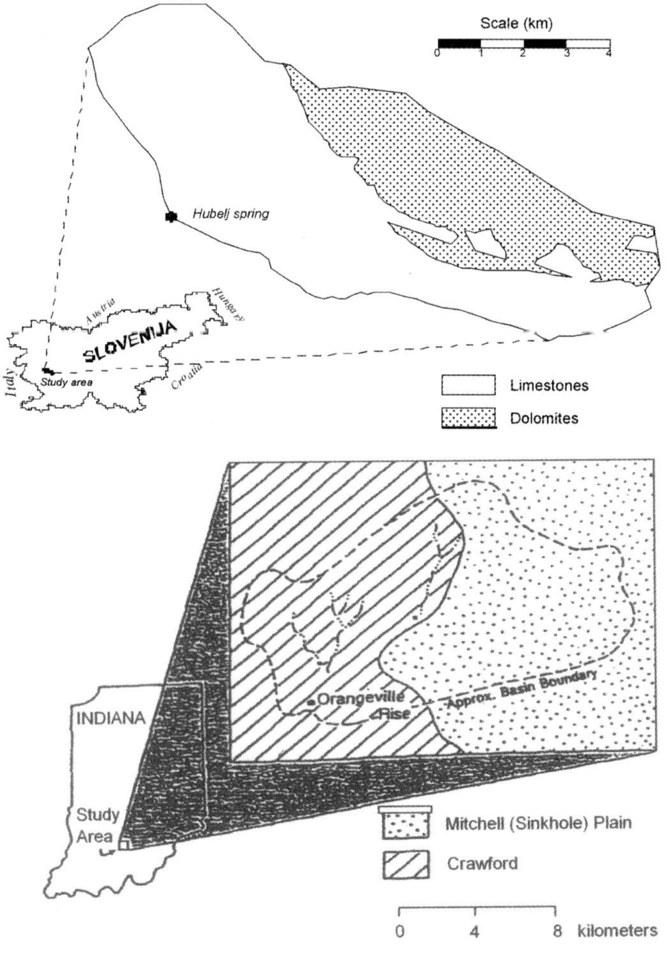

Fig. 1. Location of the study area a) in Slovenia and b) in Indiana

The groundwater basin supplying water to Orangeville Rise has an areal extent of 125 km^2 and lies within two physiografic provinces, the Mitchell Plain and the Crawford Upland (Figure 1b). The Mitchell Plain is a lowland surface developed on middle Missisipian-aged limestones, while the Crawford Upland is a region where formations of sandstone, shale and limestone of West Baden and Stephensport Groups crop out in the surface (Krothe 1998).

The catchment area of the Hubelj spring is a high karst plateau, Trnovski gozd, with the mean altitude of 900 m a.s.l. (Figure 1a). It consists mostly of Jurassic limestons (Janež et al. 1997) and occupies 50-80 km^2 (Trišič 1997).

METHODS AND TECHNIQUES

We used three and four-component storm hydrograph separation techniques in our researches (Kendall & McDonell 1998, Lee & Krothe 2001, Lee & Krothe 2002, Talarovich & Krothe 1998, Trček 2001, Trček et al. 2002).

Storm hydrographs of the Hubelj and Orangeville Rise springs were separated into:

- a new (rain) water,
- an upper unsaturated zone's water (soil +epikarstic water) and
- a base flow water (phreatic + lower unsaturated zone's water) components by three-component technique,

while the second component was subsequently separated into:

- a soil water and
- an epikarstic water components by the four-component technique, respectively.

The hydrograph separation into n components requires the using of (n-1) tracers. We used data on $\delta^{18}O / \delta^{2}H$, $\delta^{13}C$, $\delta^{34}S$, DIC and DOC composition of sampled precipitation and karst system's water (soil, epikarst and base flow water). Incremental weighted means of rain and upper unsaturated zone's water were used to account for their temporal variability (McDonnell et al. 1990).

Our researches included

a) a long-term sampling on a weekly to monthly frame, for establishing base flow characteristics, and
b) a short-term sampling during storm events, for identifying subsurface storage zones and mechanisms of groundwater recharge and discharge.

RESULTS

The four-component separation of the Orangeville Rise discharge over the period of 104 hours after the storm event in 4th of October 1990 is presented in Figure 2 (Lee & Krothe 2001). The proportions of new, soil, epikarstic and base flow water were calculated as 10.6%, 3.1%, 52.3% and 34%, respectively.

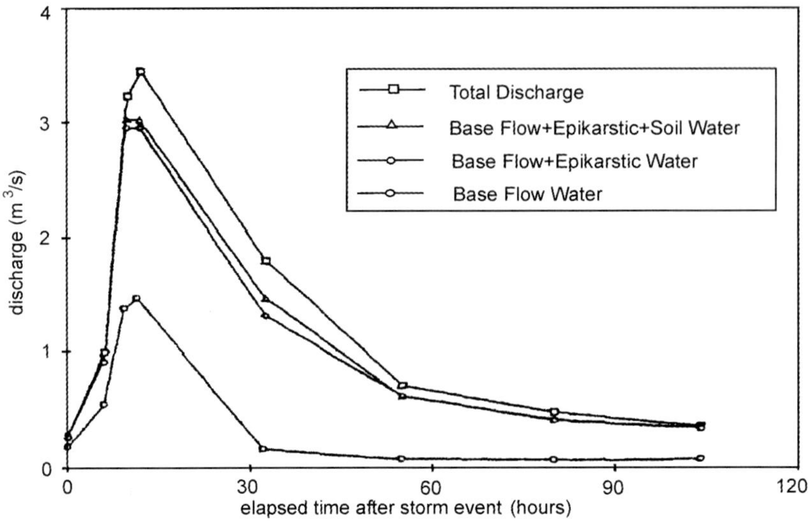

Fig. 2. Four-component hydrograph separation of the Orangeville Rise spring using $\delta^{2}H$, $\delta^{13}C$, $\delta^{34}S$ *and DIC as tracers (after Lee & Krothe 2001)*

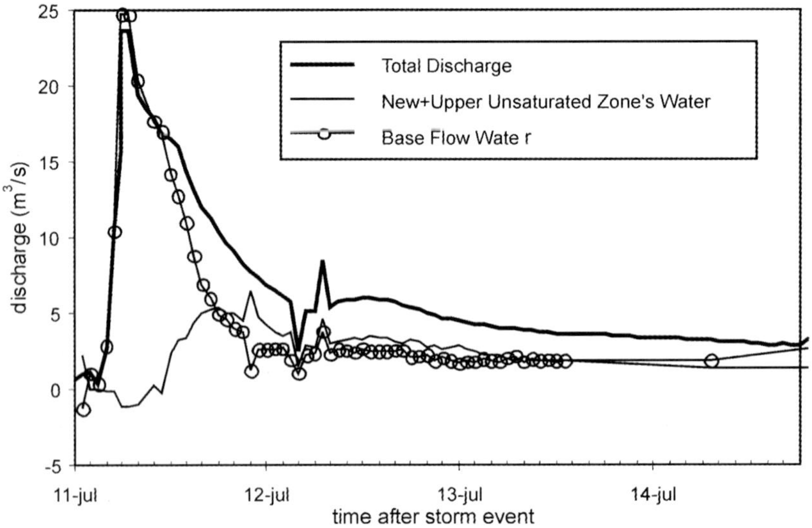

Fig. 3. Three-component hydrograph separation of the Hubelj spring using $\delta^{18}O$ *and DOC as tracers (after Trček 2001)*

The three-component separtion of the Hubelj discharge over the period of 90 hours after the storm event in 11th and 12th of July 2000 is presented in Figure 3 (Trček 2001). The average contributions of new, upper unsaturated zone's and base flow water were 15%, 33% and 52%, respectively. The first two components are combined into one component in Figure 3 to represent the fast concentrated flow through the conduit network that arrives from the epikarst zone.

Our results indicated that the contributions of new and upper unsaturated zone's water (soil and epikarst water) began to increase during the hydrograph recession, while only the base flow component prevailed during the hydrograph concentration.

The results pointed out

- a piston effect (new water displaced pre-stored water in a karst system) and
- a duality of karst aquifer's recharge and discharge processes that is reflected by
  a) the fast concentrated flow through the conduit's network during the hydrograph concentration and initial recession,
  b) the relatively slow diffuse flow from phreatic and vadose zones during the last part of hydrograph recession.

DISCUSSION

We synthesized our results in the conceptual model of karst aquifer's groundwater storage that is presented in Figure 4.

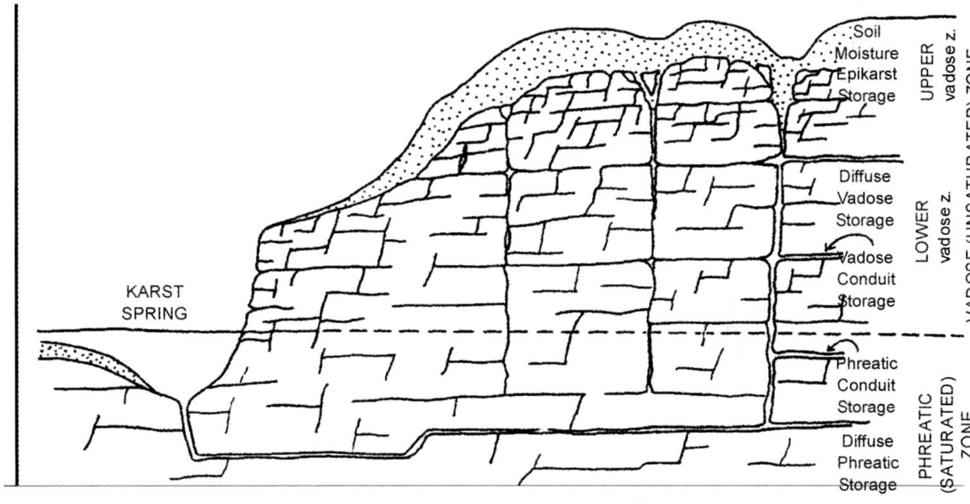

Fig. 4. Conceptual model of karst aquifer's ground water storage (modified from Lakey & Krothe 1996)

The phreatic and lower unsaturated zone conduit storages contribute to discharge during the event hydrograph concentration. New water and the upper unsaturated zone storage (soil moisture and particularly epikarst storage) are together concentrated in a fast conduit flow that arrives from the epikarst zone during the initial event hydrograph recession. The lower unsaturated and phreatic zone diffuse storages prevail during the last part of the event hydrograph recession.

CONCLUSIONS

The presented techniques are an effective approach for characterizing flow and solute (contaminant) transport mechanisms of heterogeneous karst aquifers. Their results are in agreement with actual research hypothesis where it is supposed that an important part of the karst aquifer's recharge arrives (rapidly and in concentrated form) into the conduit network from the epikarst zone. The results demonstrate that epikarst's water could occupy up to 50% of spring discharge during precipitation events. This phenomenon could have important consequences on protection and other management problems, such as base flow characterization, exploitation of groundwater by pumping wells or galleries, etc.

REFERENCES

Berg, W.& Čenčur Curk, Barbara & Frank, J., Feichtinger, F.& Nützmann, G.& Papesch, W. & Rajner, V. & Rank, D. & Schneider, S. & Seiler, K. P. & Steiner, K. H. & Stenitzer, E. & Stichler, W. & Trček, Branka & Vargay, Z. & Veselič, Miran & Zojer, H., 2001: Tracers in the unsaturated zone.- Steir. Beitr. Hydrogeol., 2001/52, 1-102.

Janež, J. & Čar, J. & Habič, P. & Podobnik, R., 1997: Vodno bogastvo Visokega krasa. Ranljivost kraške podzemne vode Banjšic, Trnovskega gozda, Nanosa in Hrušice.- Geologija d.o.o., p. 167, Idrija

Kendall, C. & McDonell, J.J., 1998: Isotope tracers in catchment hydrology.- Elsevier, p. 722, Amsterdam

Krothe, N.C., 1998: Comparison of Oxygen and Hydrogen Isotopes from Two Perrenial Karst Springs, Indiana, USA. In Proceedings of the 9th International Symposium on Water-Rock Interaction (Arehart & Hulston, eds.).- Balkema, 247-250, Rotterdam

Lakey, B. & Krothe, N.C., 1996: Stable Isotopic variation of Storm Discharge from a Perennial Karst Spring.- Water Resources Research, 32/3, 721-731.

Lee, E.S. & Krothe, N.C., 2001: A Four Component Mixing Model for Water in a Karst Terrain in South Central Indiana, USA. Using Solute Concentration and Stable Isotopes as Tracers.- Chemical Geology (Including Isotope Geosciences), 179, 129 - 143.

Lee, E.S. & Krothe, N.C., 2002: Delineating the Karstic Flow System in the Upper Lost River Drainage Basin, South Central Indiana. Using Sulphate and $\delta^{34}S$ Sulphate as Tracers.- Accepted to Applied Geochemistry.

McDonnell, J.J. & Bonell, M. & Stewart, M.K. & Pearce, A.J., 1990: Deuterium variations in storm rainfall: Implications for stream hydrograph separation.- Water Resources Research, 26/3, 455-458

Talarovich, S.G. & Krothe, N.C.,1998: Three Component Storm Hydrograph Separation of a Karst Spring Contaminated by Polychlocinated Biphenyls, Central Indiana.- AAPG, Special Issue: Environmental Geosciences, 5/4, 162-175.

Trček, B. & Pezdič, J. & Veselič, M. & Stichler, W., 2001: Changes in $\delta^{18}O$ composition of the Hubelj spring under different hydrogeological conditions. In Proceedings of the

Conference on New Approaches Characterizing Groundwater Flow (ed. Seiler, P. & Wohnlich, S.).- Balkema Publishers, 207-211, Lisse
Trček, B. 2001: Solute transport monitoring in the unsaturated zone of the karst aquifer by natural tracers. Doctoral thesis.- University of Ljubljana, p. 125, Ljubljana
Trček, B. & Veselič, M. & Pezdič, J., 2002: The upper unsaturated zone of the karst aquifer in the catchment area of the Hubelj spring (SW Slovenia). In Proceedings of the Symposium on Evolution of Karst: Form Prekarst to Cessation (Postojna, 2002).- In print.
Trišič, N., 1997: Hydrology. In Karst hydrogeological investigations in south-western Slovenia (ed. Kranjc, A.).- Acta carsologica, 26/1, 19-30, Ljubljana

Address
Branka Trček, Geological Survey of Slovenia, Dimičeva 14, SI-1000 Ljubljana,
E-mail: branka.trcek@geo-zs.si
Noel C. Krothe, Indiana University, Department of Geological Sciences, 1001 East Tenth Street, Bloomington, IN 47405
E-mail: krothen@indiana.edu

PALEOKARST AND KARSTIFICATION IN VARIOUS SETTINGS

Evolution of Karst: From Prekarst to Cessation, 405-406, Ljubljana-Postojna 2002

THE SCIENTIFIC STUDY OF POLYPHASE PALAEOKARST AS A CONTRIBUTION TO THE PALEOENVIRONMENTAL INTERPRETATION - CASE STUDIES IN PORTUGAL -

LUCIO CUNHA & LUCA ANTONIO DIMUCCIO

Abstract

Whenever carbonate platforms are subaerially exposed, karst development occurs, since karst features can develop very rapidly, even as deposition continues. Many carbonate sequences record not just one, but multiple phases of karstification (polyphase and polygenic palaeokarst), and their history can therefore be difficult to interpret. Moreover, some polyphase karst may result in discrete palaeokarst features, whereas others overprint earlier stages. The simplest case of polyphase karst results from multiple changes in sea-level, and produces stacked karst system. In some circumstances palaeokarst develops on an unconformity that may influence later subjacent karstification.

The situation can be even more complex in carbonate sequences exposed either to prolonged continuous exposure, or to complex burial and erosional histories in long-term polyphase karstification.

Successful identification of palaeokarst in outcrops has important implications for sequence stratigraphy, palaeoenvironmental interpretation.

In this paper we present a synthesis of the main palaeokarst features, their genetic interpretation and a palaeokarst system model of the Meso-cenozoic Lusitanian Basin (Portugal).

The methodology in this study basically involved the following aspects of the palaeokarst unconformities at the regional and local scales: (a) unconformity mapping; (b) analysis of exposure profiles; (c) interpretation of exposure environment; (d) analysis of underlying and overlying rocks to recognize immediately pre- and post-unconformity events. It is important to note that, mainly due to the strongly erosional nature of the analyzed unconformities, the exposure facies and profiles may be reworked or destroyed, which considerably complicates the reconstruction of palaeoenvironments.

The palaeokarst examples presented here are associated on the five important phases recognized in different parts of Meso-cenozoic Lusitanian Basin:

1. *a severe and complex phase of Karst development occurred in the Jurassic (Dogger, Malm);*
2. *during the Lower Cretaceous, the whole area was buried;*
3. *in the Upper Cretaceous and in the Tertiary, important erosive processes developed in tropical and sub-tropical climates, led to the exhumation of paleolandforms, to new Karst development and to the heaping of red sands in the Karst landforms;*
4. *in the Pliocene, a transgressive phase showing detrital deposits and another burial of the karst landscape appeared;*
5. *in the Quaternary, sea-level changes provoked new erosive processes and new karst development.*

Regionally, the importance of each karstification phase varies from area to area, but in general the first, third and fifth are the most noticeable.

It is important to note that not all the five phases recognized occur in every area and, in addition, the associated features are different according to the zone.

Address
Lucio Cunha
Institudo de Estudos Geograficos, Faculdade de Letras, Universidade de Coimbra, Portugal (luciogeo@ci.uc.pt).
Luca Antonio Dimuccio
Bolseiro da Fundação da Ciȩncias e Tecnologia, Departamento Ciȩncias da Terra, Universidade de Coimbra, Portugal (luca47@hotmail.com).

Evolution of Karst: From Prekarst to Cessation, 407-414, Ljubljana-Postojna 2002

SYNGENETIC AND EOGENETIC KARST: AN AUSTRALIAN VIEWPOINT

KEN G. GRIMES

Abstract
In syngenetic karst speleogenesis and lithogenesis are concurrent. Eogenetic karst and soft-rock karst are closely related terms. The distinctive features of syngenetic karst are: shallow horizontal cave systems; a general lack of directed conduits (low irregular chambers occur instead); clustering of caves at the margins of topographic highs or along the coast; paleosoil horizons; vertical solution pipes which locally form dense fields; extensive breakdown and subsidence to form collapse-dominated cave systems, a variety of surface and subsurface breccias and locally large collapse dolines & cenotes; and limited surface sculpturing (karren). These features are best developed in host sediments that have well developed primary porosity and limited secondary cementation (and hence limited mechanical strength). Certain hydrological environments also assist: invading swamp waters or mixing at a well developed watertable; or, near the coast, mixing above and below a freshwater lens floating on salt water. Where these factors are absent the karst forms tend to be more akin to those of classical hard-rock or telogenetic karst.
Keywords: *syngenetic karst, eogenetic diagenesis, soft-rock karst, calcarenite, solution pipes.*

INTRODUCTION AND TERMINOLOGY

Syngenetic karst is a term coined by Jennings (1968) for karst features, including caves, that form within a soft, porous, soluble sediment at the same time as it is being cemented into a rock. Speleogenesis and lithogenesis are concurrent. Jennings based his discussion partly on prior observations reported in Bastian (1964) for West Australia and Hill (1984) for South Australia (Hill's paper was written in 1957, but published posthumously).

Jennings was describing the active karst geomorphology of the Quaternary dune calcarenites of Australia. Concurrent studies by sedimentologists of paleokarst horizons at unconformities in the stratigraphic record used the related concept of eogenetic diagenesis: processes that affect a newly-formed carbonate or evaporite sediment when it is exposed to subaerial weathering and meteoric waters (Choquette & Pray, 1970). The resulting eogenetic karst (or "soft-rock karst") is distinguished from telogenetic ("hard-rock") karst that has developed on hard indurated limestones that have been re-exposed after a deep burial stage.

The terms syngenetic and eogenetic overlap but involve different viewpoints. The former is best used for geomorphological studies of modern soft-rock karsts; whereas the latter is best retained for diagenetic studies of paleokarst porosities, where the sequence of dissolution and cementation events is much more complex. Some, but not all, paleokarst is eogenetic: the separation of eogenetic, mesogenetic (burial), and telogenetic features requires a detailed study of cement morphology, mineralogy, chemistry, and related dissolutional and brecciation features; at both the microscopic and macroscopic scale (Moore, 1989). Recently some authors have applied the term "eogenetic karst" to modern syngenetic karst features (e.g. Mylroie et al, 2001).

FEATURES OF SYNGENETIC KARST

Syngenetic karst has several distinctive features as well as many that are shared with classical (telogenetic) karst. Quaternary dune calcarenites, or aeolianites, show the most distinctive features of syngenetic karst. Examples include those of Australia (Jennings, 1968, White, 2000), South Africa (Marker, 1995), Bermuda (Mylroie et al, 1995) and the Caribbean (e.g. Mylroie et al, 1995, Lyndberg & Taggart, 1995). However, other porous calcarenites, such as beach and shallow marine facies, can also develop distinctive syngenetic features; in particular solution pipes and calcreted caprocks. Examples include the Miocene Gambier and Nullarbor limestones in Australia (Grimes, 1994, Grimes et al 1999, Lowry & Jennings, 1974), as well as some of the limestones of the Yucatan and Florida. For less porous facies, such as micritic lagoonal limestones of oceanic islands, the syngenetic karst tends to show greater joint control and is more akin to the classical hard-rock karsts (Mylroie et al 2001, Grimes 2001). The Cretaceous chalk of Europe is a special case of a moderately consolidated limestone that has both a very fine-grained porosity and fractures–forming linear caves (Rodet, 1991; Gunn et al, 1998). Other soluble sediments (gypsum, halite) can also develop syngenetic karst when exposed to subaerial conditions (e.g. Sando, 1987) but these will not be discussed here. In the following discussion Australian dune calcarenites in a "Mediterranean" climate are used as an example (Figure 1).

In calcareous dunes, percolating rain water gradually converts the unconsolidated sand to limestone by dissolution and redeposition of calcium carbonate. Initial solution at the surface forms a terra rossa or similar soil depleted in carbonate but enriched in the insoluble grains (e.g. quartz). At the base of the soil precipitation of carbonate forms a cemented and locally brecciated calcrete layer or hard pan. Below this the downward

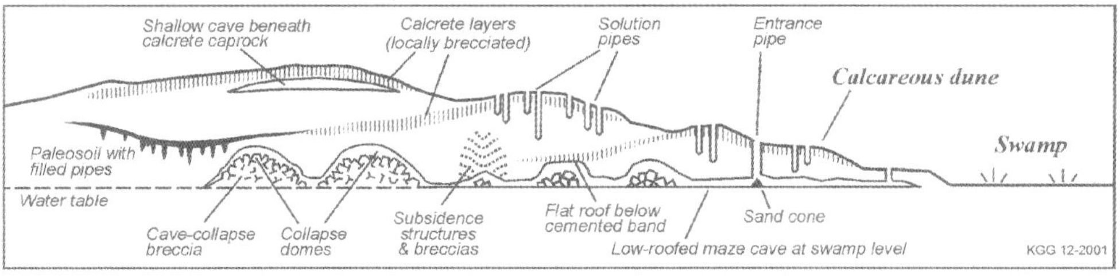

Fig. 1. Features of syngenetic karst developed on a calcareous dunefield.

percolating water becomes focussed to dissolve characteristic vertical “solution pipes” (Figure 2 & 3), and simultaneously cements the surrounding sand. Early cementation tends to be localized about roots to form distinctive rhizomorphs or rhizocretions. Cementation can progressively occlude the primary inter-granular porosity, but dissolution can generate localized secondary porosity of a moldic, vuggy or cavernous character.

Solution pipes (or, more strictly, dissolution pipes) are distinctive features of syngenetic karst on porous host rocks (Lyndberg & Taggart, 1995). They are vertical cylin-

Fig. 2. Solution pipes with cemented rims exposed by removal of less-cemented host sand (stereopair).

Fig. 3. Red paleosol with soil-filled solution pipes descending from it.

drical tubes with or without cemented walls, typically 0.3 to 0.6 m in diameter, which can penetrate down from the surface as far as 20 m into the soft limestone. The pipes may contain soil and calcified roots (and root growth may have occurred hand-in-hand with dissolution of the pipe). They occur as isolated features, or in clusters with spacings to less than a metre. In the Bahamas they have been referred to as Pit Caves, but that term also includes larger and more complex features (Mylroie & Carew, 2000).

Mixing corrosion occurs where percolation water meets the water table, which is frequently controlled by the level of a nearby swampy plain that also provides acidic water. In coastal areas, water levels fluctuate with changing sea levels and further complexity results from a fresh-water lens floating above sea water which results in two mixing zones, above and below the thin lens (Mylroie & Carew, 2000, Mylroie et al, 2001). Solution is strongest at the coast where the lens thins so that firstly the two zones overlap (within the fluctuating zone of the sea level) and secondly the thinning of the lens causes stronger flow rates which also promotes solution. The result is a "flank margin cave" (Mylroie et al, 2001) that has an irregular form of interconnected "mixing chambers" similar to those described below (Figure 4). At Yanchep, Western Australia, dune limestone overlies a quartz sand aquifer and aggressive water enters from below to dissolve caves (Bastian, 1991).

In the early stages of dissolution the loose sand subsides at once into any incipient cavities, possibly forming soft-sediment deformation structures. Subsidence dolines may form without caves (as described in South Africa by Marker, 1995). Once the rock is sufficiently hardened to support a roof, caves can develop. The uniform matrix porosity, slow moving groundwater, and lack of joint control means that directed linear conduits seldom form. Instead, horizontal cave systems of low, wide, irregular, interconnected chambers and passages (Figure 4) form either in the zone of maximum solution at the water table, or by subsidence of loose material from beneath stable calcrete layers. Flat cave ceilings are common: either marking the limit of solution at the top of the water

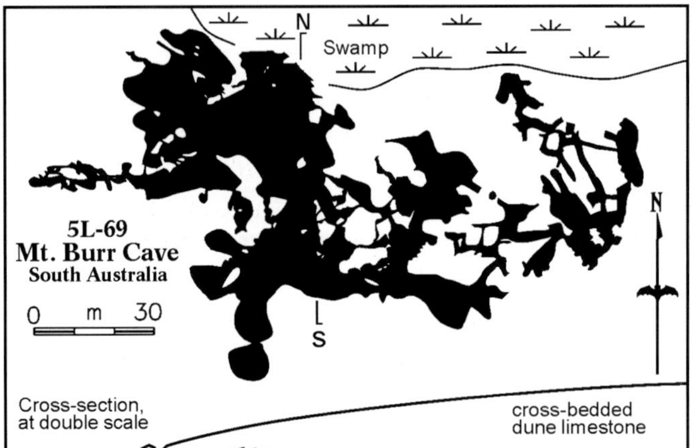

Fig. 4. A typical horizontal syngenetic maze cave in dune limestone adjacent to a swamp.

table, or where collapse has reached the base of an indurated (caprock) zone. Where a shallow impermeable basement occurs, its topography may concentrate water flow along buried valleys to form linear stream caves (Figure 5).

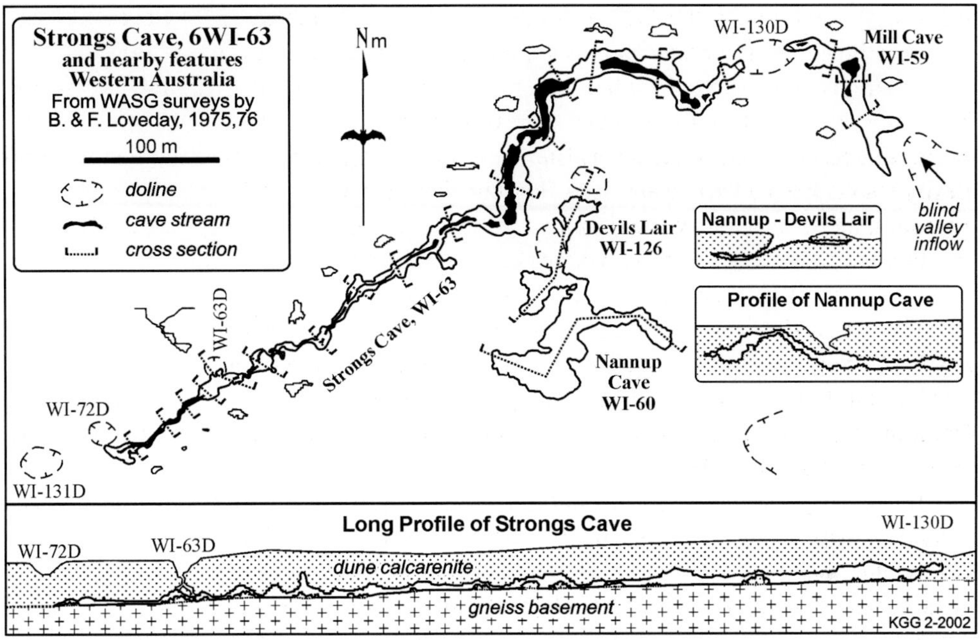

Fig. 5. Strongs Cave is a linear stream cave that follows the basal contact between the dune limestone and impermeable gneiss. By contrast the main, western, part of Nannup Cave is more typical of caves in dune limestone; being a series of large collapse domes with little of the original dissolutional cave remaining.

Sizable caves can form in less than 100 thousand years (Mylroie & Carew, 2000). Surface dissolutional sculpturing is rare, as there is little solid rock for it to act upon. However, some sculpturing can occur on exposed calcrete layers.

The subsidence of partly-consolidated material can form a variety of breccias and sag structures; these can be further cemented as diagenesis continues (Figure 6). Mantling breccias can occur as part of the surface soil (Figure 7). Within the caves breakdown of the soft rock is extensive. In many cases the original solutional cave system at the water table is largely replaced by rubble-filled collapse domes (e.g. Nannup cave in Figure 5). Subsidence may reach to the surface to form dolines; a special type referred to as a "banana hole" in the Bahamas results from the collapse of the near surface calcrete band above a shallow cave to form an overhanging doline. . In paleokarst exposures these collapse areas appear as both discordant and concordant (intrastratal) breccias. In extreme cases mass subsidence of broad areas can generate a chaotic surface of tumbled blocks and fissures (Bastian, 1995).

Variations can occur in different climates. For example, calcrete is supposedly best

Fig. 6.

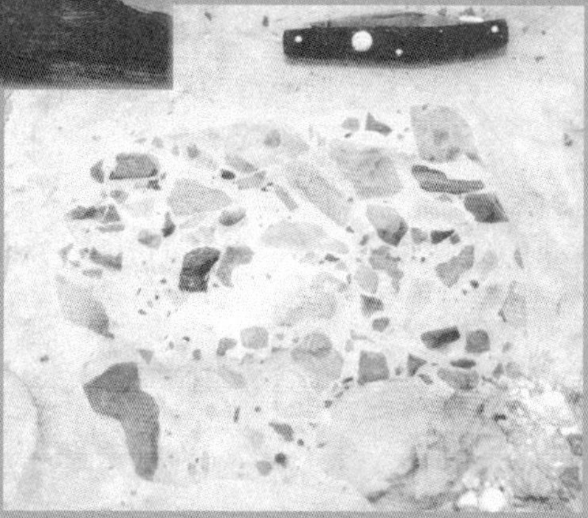

Fig. 7

Fig. 6. A subsidence structure in syngenetic karst. Thin horizontal beds of a beach calcarenite were partly cemented into individual plates that then subsided as dissolution undermined them. Continuing cementation stabilized the tilted beds before the present cave formed.
Fig. 7. A calcreted, multi-generation, mantling breccia in dune calcarenite. The large, 20 cm, clast contains at least two earlier generations of smaller clasts.

developed in semi-arid climates, whereas dissolution and brecciation are thought to be more abundant in wet climates.

SUMMARY

Syngenetic karst shows a number of distinctive forms as a consequence of its formation from soft sediments that are being consolidated and cemented at the same time as karst cavities are forming within them. It is quite different to classical "hard-rock", telogenetic karst. The related term "Eogenetic karst" is best kept for diagenetic studies of paleokarsts.

REFERENCES

Choquette, P.W., & Pray, L.C. 1970: Geologic Nomenclature and Classification of Porosity in Sedimentary Carbonates. *American Association of Petroleum Geologists Bulletin,* **54:** 207-250.

Bastian, L., 1964: Morphology and development of caves in the Southwest of Western Australia. *Helictite,* **2:** 105-119.

Bastian, L., 1991: The hydrogeology and speleogenesis of Yanchep. *in* Brooks, S., [ed] *Proceedings of the 18th Biennial Speleological Conference.* Australian Speleological Federation, Nedlands. pp. 19-24.

Bastian, L.V., 1995: Mass Subsidence at Yanchep. *in* Hamilton-Smith, E., [ed] *Abstracts of Papers, Karst Studies Seminar, Naracoorte.* Regolith Mapping, Hamilton Vic. p.29.

Grimes, K.G., 1994: The South-East Karst Province of South Australia. *Environmental Geology* **23:** 134-148.

Grimes, K.G., Mott, K., & White, S., 1999: The Gambier Karst Province. *in* Henderson, K., [ed] *Proceedings of the Thirteenth Australasian Conference on Cave and Karst Management, Mt. Gambier, South Australia.* Australasian Cave and Karst Management Association, Carlton South. pp. 1-7.

Grimes, K.G., 2001: Karst features of Christmas Island (Indian Ocean). *Helictite,* **37(2):** 41-58.

Gunn, J., Lowe, D., & Waltham, A., 1998: The Karst Geomorphology and Hydrogeology of Great Britain. *in* Yuan, D., & Liu, Z., [eds] *Global Karst Correlation.* Science Press, Beijing. pp. 109-135.

Hill, A.L., 1984: The origin of the Kelly Hill Caves, Kangaroo Island, S.A.. *Helictite,* 22: 6-10. [written 1957, published posthumously with a note by J.N. Jennings]

Jennings, J.N. 1968: Syngenetic Karst in Australia. *in* P.W. Williams and J.N. Jennings [eds] *Contributions to the Study of Karst,* Research School of Pacific Studies, Australian National University. Department of Geography Publication **G/5.**

Lowry, D.C., & Jennings, J.N., 1974: The Nullarbor karst, Australia. *Z. Geomorph.* **18(1):** 35-81.

Lyndberg, J., & Taggart, B.E. 1995: Dissolution pipes in northern Puerto Rico: an exhumed paleokarst. *Carbonates and Evaporites* 10(2): 171-183.

Marker, M.E., 1995: The Hydrology of the Southern Cape Karst Belt, South Africa. *Cave & Karst Science.* **21(2):** 61-65.

Moore, C.H. 1989: *Carbonate Diagenesis and Porosity,* Amsterdam, Elsevier.

Mylroie, J.E., Jenson, J.W., Taborosi, D., Jocson, J.M.U., Vann, D.T., & Wexel, C. 2001: Karst Features of Guam in Terms of a General Model of Carbonate Island Karst. *Journal of Cave and Karst Studies,* 63(1): 9-22

Mylroie, J.E., & Carew, J.L., 2000: Speleogenesis in Coastal and Oceanic Settings. *in* A.B. Klimchouk, D.C. Ford, A.N. Palmer and W. Dreybrodt [eds] *Speleogenesis: Evolution of Karst Aquifers,,* Huntsville, Alabama: National Speleological Society. pp. 226-233.

Mylroie, J.E., Carew, J.L. & Vacher, H.L.1995: Karst development in the Bahamas and Bermuda. *in* H.A. Curran and B. White [eds] *Terrestrial and Shallow Marine Geology of the Bahamas and Bermuda,* Geological Society of America Special Paper, **300**, 251-267.

Rodet, J., 1991: *La Craie et ses Karsts.* Centre de Géomorphologie du CNRS, Caen. 560 pp.

Sando, W.J., 1987: Madison Limestone (Mississippian) paleokarst: a geological synthesis. *in* James, N.P. & Choquette, P.W., [eds] *Paleokarst.* Springer-Verlag, NY. pp.256-277.

White, S. 2000: Syngenetic Karst in Coastal Dune Limestone: A Review. *in* A.B. Klimchouk, D.C. Ford, A.N. Palmer and W. Dreybrodt [eds] *Speleogenesis: Evolution of Karst Aquifers*,, Huntsville, Alabama: National Speleological Society. pp. 234-237.

Address
Regolith Mapping, PO Box 362, Hamilton, Vic. 3300, Australia
ken-grimes@h140.aone.net.au

Evolution of Karst: From Prekarst to Cessation, 415-424, Ljubljana-Postojna 2002

ARE THE PALAEOKARST SYSTEMS MARINE IN ORIGIN ?
CAYMANITES IN GEOLOGICAL PAST

LÁSZLÓ KORPÁS

According to Jones (1992) caymanites are „laminated, multicoloured...cavity-filling sediments with"...planar laminations, graded bedding, mound shape lamination, desiccation cracks, and geopetal fabrics...and with „depositional dips ranging from 0 to 60°". They are"...formed of mudstones, wackstones, packstones and grainstones..." consisting of „...foraminifera, red algae, gastropods, bivalves, and grains of microcrystalline dolostone". Their „...sedimentation was episodic and the sediment source changed with time..." and they have „...originated from sediments transported by storms onto a highly permeable karst terrain".

Caymanites and caymanite-like laminated cavity-filling sediments have been described in many parts of the world (Table 1, Figs. 1-15). Their common feature is that they appear both in platform margin and island reef complexes and in carbonate ramp sequences or isolated carbonate bank suites. Their occurences represent a wide stratigraphi range from Middle Cambrian to Quaternary. Caymanites are mainly marine in origin and represent signals of early palaeokarstification and fossil sea-level records.

Table 1: *Caymanites and caymanite-like laminated cavity-filling sediments reported from different parts of the world*

AGE	LOCATION	AUTHOR
Middle Cambrian	York County, Pennsylvania, USA	de Wet et al. 1999
Odovician	Ida Bay, Tasmania, Australia	Osborne and Cooper 2001
Ordovician-Silurian	Manitoulian Islands, Ontario, Canada	Kobluk 1984
	East Tennessee, USA	Leach and Sangster 1993
Upper Devonian	Transdanubian Range, Hungary	Korpás 1998
	Canning Basin, Australia	Word 1998
Lower Carboniferous	Carnic Alps, Austria and Italy	Schönlaub et al. 1991
Lower Carboniferous	Chipping Sodburry, England	Korpás 1998
Upper Permian	Guadalupe Mts., New Mexico, USA	Bebout and Kerans 1993
Middle Triassic	Silesian, Poland	Bogacz et al. 1973
	Silesian, Poland	Leach et al. 1996
	Mecsek Mts., Hungary	Korpás 1998

AGE	LOCATION	AUTHOR
Upper Triassic	Transdanubian Range, Hungary	Fülöp 1976
	Buda Hills, Bükk Mts., Hungary	Korpás 1998
	Krn Mts., Slovenia	Otonicar, pers. comm. 1996
Middle Triassic to Lower Jurassic	Silesian, Poland	Sass-Gustkiewicz 1996
Lower Jurassic	Transdanubian Range, Hungary	Fülöp 1976
	Northern Calcaerous Alps, Austria	Satterley et al. 1994
	Transdanubian Range, Hungary	Korpás 1998
	Betic Cordillera, Spain	Vera et al. 1988, Molina et al. 1999
	Krn Mts., Slovenia	Otonicar, pers. comm. 1996
Middle to Upper Jurassic	Betic Cordillera, Spain	Vera et al. 1988, Molina et al. 1999
Upper Cretaceous	Mte. Camposauro, Italy	D'Argenio and Mindszenty 1995
	Gorbea platform, Spain	Perez-Gomez et al. 1998
	Sierra de El Abra, Mexico	Minero 1988
	Kras Mts., Slovenia	Otonicar, pers. comm. 1996
Upper Eocene	Buda Hills, Hungary	Korpás et al. 1999
Lower to Upper Miocene	Grand Cayman, Cayman Bracq, Cayman Islands	Jones, 1992a,b
	Punta Maisi, Cuba	Korpás 1998
Middle Miocene	Érd-Diósd, Pest county, Hungary	Saint Martin et al. 2000
Upper Miocene/Lower Pliocene+A15	Mallorca, Spain	Pomar 1991
Quaternary	Grand Bahama, Bahama Islands	Smart et al. 1988

Frequent occurences of caymanites through geological past have prompted to present a proposed model for palaeokarstification:

1) Submarine-subaquatic stage

Depositional environment: carbonate shelf margin and upper slope (ramp-fringing reef)

Level of wave-base

Main controlling factors: Drop of water-level

Tectonism
Earth tidal pump
Mixing corrosion (dissolution)
Submarine bioerosion
Hydrothermal upwelling

Products: syngenetic and early diagenetic filling-sediments (caymanites, neptunian dikes), phreatic marine cement, phreatic and/or hydrothermal mineral association. No signs of subaerial exposure.

2) Peritidal stage

Depositional environment: reef–lagoon–tidal flat
Level of wave movement
Main controlling factors: Drop of water-level
Tectonism
Earth tidal pump
Mixing corrosion (dissolution)
Marine and continental bioerosion
Hydrothermal upwelling

Products: syngenetic and early diagenetic filling-sediments, palaeosols, alternation of vadose and phreatic (marine) cement, vadose and phreatic (±hydrothermal) mineral precipitations. Alternation of short term subaerial and subaquatic phases.

3) Continental stage

Permanent or long term subaerial exposure
Level of ground (karst) water table
Main controlling factors: Tectonism
Mixing corrosion (dissolution)
Continental bioerosion
Hydrothermal upwelling

Products: late, polyphase, mainly continental filling-sediments, palaeosols, vadose cement and vadose mineral (±hydrothermal) precipitations. Soleley signs of subaerial exposure.

Products of the palaeokarst phases above can be overprinted by hydrothermal events and undergone through multiplied burial and exhumation processes.

REFERENCES

Bebout, D. G., Kerans, Ch. 1993: Guide to Permian Reef Geology Trail, McKittrick Canyon, Guadalupe Mountains National Park, West Texas. Guidebook 26. Bureau of Economic Geology, Austin, TX.

Bogacz, K., Dzulinsky, S., Haranczik, C. 1973: Caves filled with clastic dolomite and galena mineralization in disaggregated dolomites. Annales de la Société Géologique de Pologne, 43 (1), 59-72.

D'Argenio, B., Mindszenty, A. 1995: Bauxites and related paleokarst: tectonic and climatic event markers at regional unconformities. Eclogae Geol. Helv. 88 (3), 453-499.

Fülöp, J. 1976: The Mesozoic basement horst blocks of Tata. Geol. Hung. Ser. Geol. vol. 16, 229 p.

Jones, B. 1992a: Caymanite, a cavity-filling deposit in the Oligocene-Miocene Bluff Formation of the Cayman Islands. Can. J. Earth. Sci. 29, 720-736.

Jones, B. 1992b: Void-filling deposits in karst terrains of isolated oceanic islands: a case study from Tertiary carbonates of the Cayman Islands, Sedimentology 39, 857-876.

Kobluk, D. R. 1984: Coastal paleokarst near the Ordovician-Silurian boundary, Manitoulian Island, Ontario. Bull. Can. Petr. Geol. 32 (4), 398-407.

Korpás, L. 1998: Palaeokarst studies in Hungary. Vol. 195, Occasional Papers of the Geological Institute of Hungary, Budapest, 139 p.

Korpás, L., Lantos, M., Nagymarosy, A. 1999: Timing and genesis of early marine caymanites in the hydrothermal palaeokarst system of Buda Hills, Hungary. Sed. Geol. 123 (1999), 9-29.

Leach, D. L., Sangster, D. F. 1993: Mississippi Valley-type lead-zinc deposits. In: Kirkham, R. V. et al. (Eds.), Mineral Deposit Modelling. Geol. Assoc. Can. Spec. Pap. 40, 289-314.

Leach, D. L., Viets, J. G., Kozlowski, A. Kibitlewski, S. 1996: Geology, geochemistry, and genesis of the Silezian-Cracow zinc-lead district, southern Poland. In: Sangster, D. F. (Ed.) Carbonate-Hosted Lead-Zinc Deposits. Soc. Econ. Geol. Spec. Publ. 4, 144-170

Minero, C., 1988: Sedimentation and diagenesis along an island sheltered platform margin, El Abra Formation, Cretaceous of Mexico. In: James, N. P., Choquette, P. V. (Eds.) Paleokarst. Springer, Heidelberg, pp. 385-405.

Molina, J. M., Ruiz-Ortiz, P. A., Vera, J. M. 1999: A review of polyphase karstification in extensional tectonic regimes: Jurassic and Cretaceous examples, Betic Cordillera, southern Spain. Sed. Geol. 129 (1999), 71-84.

Osborne, R. A .L., Cooper, I. B. 2001: Sulfide-bearing palaeokarst deposits at Lune River Quarry, Ida Bay, Tasmania. Australian Journal of Earth Sciences, 48, 409-416.

Perez-Gomez, I., Fernández-Mendiola, P., García-Mondejar, J. 1998: Platform margin paleokarst development from the Albian of Gorbea. Acta Geol. Hung. 41 (1), 3-22.

Pomar, L. 1991: Reef geometrie, erosion surfaces and high frequency sea-level changes, Upper Miocene reef complex, Mallorca, Spain. Sedimentology, 38, 243-269.

Saint Martin, J. P., Müller, P., Moissette, P., Dulai, A. 2000: Coral microbialite environment in a Middle Miocene reef of Hungary. Palaeogeography, Palaeoclimatolgy, Palaeoecology 160 (2000)179-191.

Sass-Gustkiewicz, M. 1996: Internal sediments as a key to understanding the hydrothermal karst origin of the Upper Silezian Zn-Pb ore deposits. Soc. Econ. Geol. Spec. Publ. 4, 171-181.

Satterley, A. K., Marshall, J. D., Fairchild, I. J. 1994: Diagenesis of an Upper Triassic reef complex, Wilde Kirche, Northern Calcareous Alps, Alps, Austria. Sediemntology 41, 935-950.

Schönlaub, H. P., Klein, P., Margaritz, M., Rantitsch, R. G., Scharbert, S.. 1991: Lower Carboniferous paleokarst in the Carnic Alps (Austria, Italy). Facies 25, 91-118.

Smart, P. L., Palmer, R. J., Whitaker, F., Wright, W. P. 1998: Neptunian Dikes and Fissure Fills: An overview and account of some modern examples. In: James, N. P., Choquette, P. W. (Eds.), Paleokarst, Springer, Heidelberg, pp. 148-163.

Vera, J. A., Ruiz-Ortiz, P. A., García-Hernandez, M., Molina, J. M. 1988: Paleokarst and realted pelagic sediments in the Jurassic of the subbetic zone, Southern Spain. In: James, N. P., Choquette, P. W. (Eds.), Paleokarst, Springer, Heidelberg, pp. 364-385.

de Wet, C. B., Dickson, J. A. D., Wood, R. A., Gaswirth, S. B., Frey, H. M. 1999: A new type of shelf margin deposit: rigid microbial sheets and unconsolidated grainstones riddled with meter-scale cavities. Sed. Geol. (1999), 13-21.

Wood, R. 1998: Novel reef fabrics from the Devonian Canning Basin, Western Australia. Sed. Geol. 121 (1998), 149-156.

Address
Geological Institute of Hungary
1143 Budapest, Stefánia út 14, Hungary
E-mail: korpasl@mafi.hu

Fig 1. Synsedimentary, laminated stromatolitic internal sediment (S) and fibrous cement with radiaxial calcite (C) in the cavity of the Middle Cambrian microbial Ledger Limestone, York County, Pennsylvania, USA (de Wet et al. 1999). Depositional environment: rimmed shelf margin or distally steepened ramp, submarine phreatic zone.

Fig. 2. Synsedimentary, laminated crinoidal limestone with graded bedding as fissure fill in the Ordovician Gordon limestone, Ida Bay, Tasmania, Australia (Osborne and Cooper 2001). Depositional environment: submarine phreatic zone with turbulent sea-water.

Fig. 3. Syndepositional laminated grainstone and mudstone with radiaxial calcite in the cavity of the Middle Devonian peritidal Polgárdi Limestone, Szabadbattyán, Kőszár-hegy, Hungary (Korpás 1998). Depositional environment: submarine phreatic zone.

Fig. 4. Syndepositional laminated mudstone and grainstone in the dissolutional pipe in the Lower Carboniferous Gully Oolite, Chipping Sodburry, Bristol, England (Korpás 1998). Depostional environment: marine phreatic zone

Fig. 5. Syndepositional laminated intraclastic dolomite-rudstone in the cavity of the Upper Triassic, Carnian-Norian Mátyáshegy Dolomite, Buda Hills, Hungary. Depositional environment: intraplatform anoxic basin. Upper slope facies of a submarine dolomite ramp.

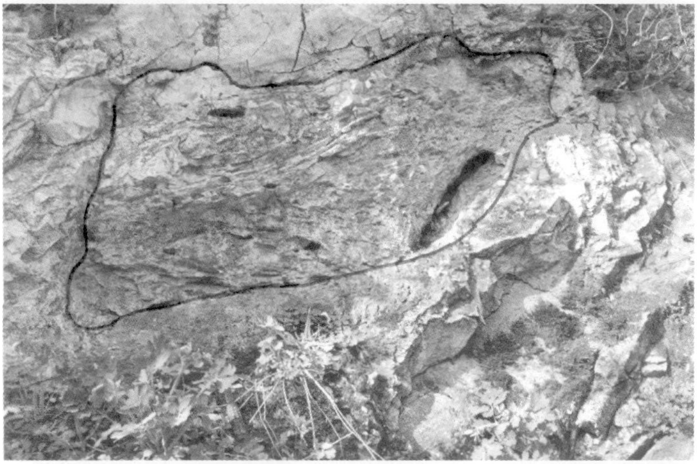

Fig. 6. Early marine laminated micritic-limestone with radiolarite extraclasts in the cavity of the Norian pelagic Felsőtárkány Limestone, Felsőtárkány, Bükk Mts., Hungary (Korpás 1998). Depositional environment: submarine phreatic zone.

Fig. 7. Alternance of early marine synsedimentary laminated micritic and crinoideal limestone with graded beddig in the cavity of the Upper Norian-Rhaetian „loferites", Dachstein Limestone, Kálvária Hill, Tata, Hungary (Fülöp 1976). Stratigraphic position: just below the Triassic/Jurassic boundary. Depositional environment: subtidal epiphreatic zone.

Fig. 8. Synsedimentary early marine laminated mudstone with fibrous radiaxial calcite in the cavity of the Upper Hettangian-Sinemurian Pisznice Limestone, Kálvária Hill, Tata, Hungary (Fülöp 1976). Stratigraphic position: just above the Triassic/Jurassic boundary. A) Microbioclastic Pisznice Limestone, B) Fibrous radiaxial calcite, C) Laminated mudstone as cavity fill. Depositional environment: subtidal, phreatic zone.

Fig. 9. Synsedimentary early marine laminated mudstone with intraclasts in the fissures of the Upper Hettangian-Sinemurian Pisznice Limestone, Kálvária Hill, Tata, Hungary (Fülöp 1976). Stratigraphic position: near to the Triassic/Jurassic boundary. Depositional environment: subtidal, phreatic zone.

Fig. 10. Marine laminated radiolarian siltstone-fill of the Toarcian Kisgerecse Marl in the cavity of the Sinemurian-Pliensbachian Hierlatz Limestone, Csárda-hegy, Úrkút, Hungary.

Fig. 11. Synsedimentary early marine laminated grainstone and mudstone-fill with radiaxial calcite in the cavity of the Maastrichtian rudist-reef, Lipica limestone, Kozina, Kras Mts., Slovenia.

Fig. 13. Early marine caymanite represented by laminated corallinacea-bryozoa-packstone and grainstone with Nummulites in the cavity of the Upper Eocene submarine limestone bank, Szépvölgy Limestone, Mátyás-hegy Buda Hills, Hungary (Korpás et al. 1999). Disconformable generation.

Fig. 12. Early marine caymanite represented by laminated corallinacea-bryozoa-packstone and grainstone with Nummulites in the cavity of the Upper Eocene submarine limestone bank, Szépvölgy Limestone, Mátyás-hegy, Buda Hills, Hungary (Korpás et al. 1999). Conformable generation.

Fig. 14. Early marine caymanite represented by laminated siltstone in the Moby Dick cave of the Upper Eocene submarine limestone bank of the Szépvölgy limestone, Mátyás-hegy, Buda Hills, Hungary (Korpás et al. 1999). Disconformable generation.

Brief genetic interpretation of caymanites of Figs. 12-14. These caymanites were generated by tides, wave turbulence and storms and deposited in the caves and cavities of a rocky shore at the sea-level. Their diagenetic and hydrothermal features are the recrystallised obliterated texture with slight dolomitization and slicification. Signs of subaerial exposure are missing. Their bright orange cathodoluminescence pattern and stable isotope compsition and the marine microfacies and cement indicate marine phreatic environment for deposition with later high temperature hydrothermal overprints. The Late Eocene age is based on biota, while the depositional record may be calculated for some thousand years as stated by magnetostratigraphy.

Fig. 15. Synsedimentary laminated „stromatolitic mound" in the cavity of a Middle Miocene coral patch reef, Rákos Limestone, Érd-Diósd, Pest County, Hungary (Saint Martin et al. 2000).

Fig. 16. Lower Pliocene marine laminated calcisiltites in the cave of the Upper Miocene barrier reef core, Cap Blanc, Mallorca, Spain (Korpás 1998).

Evolution of Karst: From Prekarst to Cessation, 425-432, Ljubljana-Postojna 2002

THE ROLE OF ENDOGENIC PROCESSES IN EVOLUTION OF KARST IN CENTRAL EUROPEAN MESOZOIC PLATFORM (EXAMPLE OF SOUTH POLISH UPLANDS)

MARIAN PULINA, ANDRZEJ TYC & JERZY ŻABA

Abstract

The paper deals with the geological conditions and karst of Cracow-Silesia homocline, the main part of the Central European Mesozoic platform, with reference to the Hamburg-Cracow fault zone, occurring in the Paleozoic base. In the discussed area the activity of Cracow-Lubliniec fault zone as segment of the Hamburg-Cracow transcontinental tectonic line, is manifesting by different phenomena till present-day times. Specific configuration of the base of the complex of Mesozoic carbonate rocks, multiple occurrence of magmatic and hydrothermal phenomena as well as intensified emanation of juvenile CO_2 are connected with this activity from Paleozoic to Cainozoic. Symptoms of its activity and influence on karst evolution can be seen in presence of large morphological depressions of karst origin, specific paleokarstic phenomena (with occurrence of Mississippi-Valley type of Zn-Pb deposits) and in contemporary hydro-geochemical environment. The theses presented in the paper, concerning the Cracow-Silesia Upland as well as cited examples related to the neighbouring regions put in new light the age of karst development and the contribution of endogenic processes in this development in relation to the role of climatic conditions.

***Key words**: tectonics, karst evolution, Cracow-Silesia homocline, hydrothermal karst, CO_2 activity, hydro-geochemistry*

INTRODUCTION

In Central Europe there are karst areas related with Paleozoic and Mesozoic geologic structures. These are, respectively, European Paleozoic platform and homoclinal rock setting of Mesozoic platform in the overburden. The main tectonic element of the Mesozoic rock cover is Cracow-Silesia homocline, forming at the same time the largest Central European carbonate karst area - the Cracow-Silesia Upland. In the base of this homocline there is one of the main European tectonic lines - Hamburg-Cracow fault zone, which forms, in the study area, Cracow-Lubliniec fault zone in a contact of the two tectonic blocks, Upper Silesia and Malopolska blocks, (i.a. Žaba, 1995, 1999). This extremely active tectonic zone exerted a significant influence on the style of Mesozoic top formation structure, on the specific way of Upper Jurassic limestone sedimentation as well as on activation and directions of karst processes development. Its activity, manifesting itself with configuration of the base of the complex of Mesozoic carbonate rocks, multiple occurrence of magmatic and hydrothermal phenomena as well as intensified emanation of juvenile CO_2, can be observed even at present times in the whole Cracow-Silesia region and its vicinity.

The paper presents the geologic conditions of Cracow-Silesia Upland with reference to the Hamburg-Cracow fault zone, occurring in the Paleozoic base, and symptoms of its activity and influence on karst evolution that can be seen in morphology, presence of paleokarstic phenomena, and in contemporary hydro-geochemical environment. The authors make a thesis that this multiphase tectonic activity is in large measure responsible for the present-day karst relief with remnants of large cave systems.

GEOLOGICAL SETTING AND TECTONIC ACTIVITY OF THE BORDER ZONE OF UPPER SILESIA AND MALOPOLSKA BLOCKS

In terms of geology, Cracow-Silesia Upland is part of a large tectonic unit - Cracow-Silesia homocline. It is composed mainly of flat-lying Triassic and Jurassic formations and fragmentarily preserved Cretaceous rocks (Fig. 1). These rocks form a Mesozoic cover, lying unconformably on various Paleozoic, and locally also Precambrian, successions. In the geologic profile two complexes of carbonate rocks - Middle Triassic limestones and dolomites and Upper Jurassic limestones, play an important role.

The complex geologic structure and multiphase tectonic evolution of the discussed part of Central Europe is the subject of numerous, often differing from one another, opinions (see i.a. Żaba, 1999). As investigations based on deep boreholes and observations in Mesozoic rock cover have been continued, more significant role in evolution of the discussed region is attributed to activity of the large fault zone Cracow-Lubliniec. This fault zone seems to be a segment of transcontinental tectonic line Hamburg-Cracow (Fig. 1). The Cracow-Lubliniec dislocation, striking NW-SE, makes up a direct border between the Upper Silesia and Malopolska blocks (terranes). These blocks are elements of the Central European part of the Paleozoic platform, and are located in the southwestern foreland of East European craton (Fig.1A). They make up components of a mosaic of crustal blocks, distinguished by different age and origin - the geologic setting has the form of a collage. The blocks were dislocated both in lower and upper Paleozoic, and the symptoms of displacement activity in the border zone of both blocks are noted till the present-day times. Upper Silesia and Moravian blocks form together the Bruno-Vistulian terrane. The Upper Silesia and Malopolska blocks are separated from the neighbouring areas with distinct structural deep seated discontinuities. Both blocks are located at the convergence point of three main European deformation fronts: Caledonian, Varsican and Alpine.

Rock formations that build up the Cracow-Silesia homocline are represented mainly by Mesozoic clastic and carbonate series. The average thickness of the Triassic formations is usually from 100 to 200 m (however maximum of 1400 m may be achieved), while the average thickness of Jurassic formations is from 150 to 200 m (maximum 400

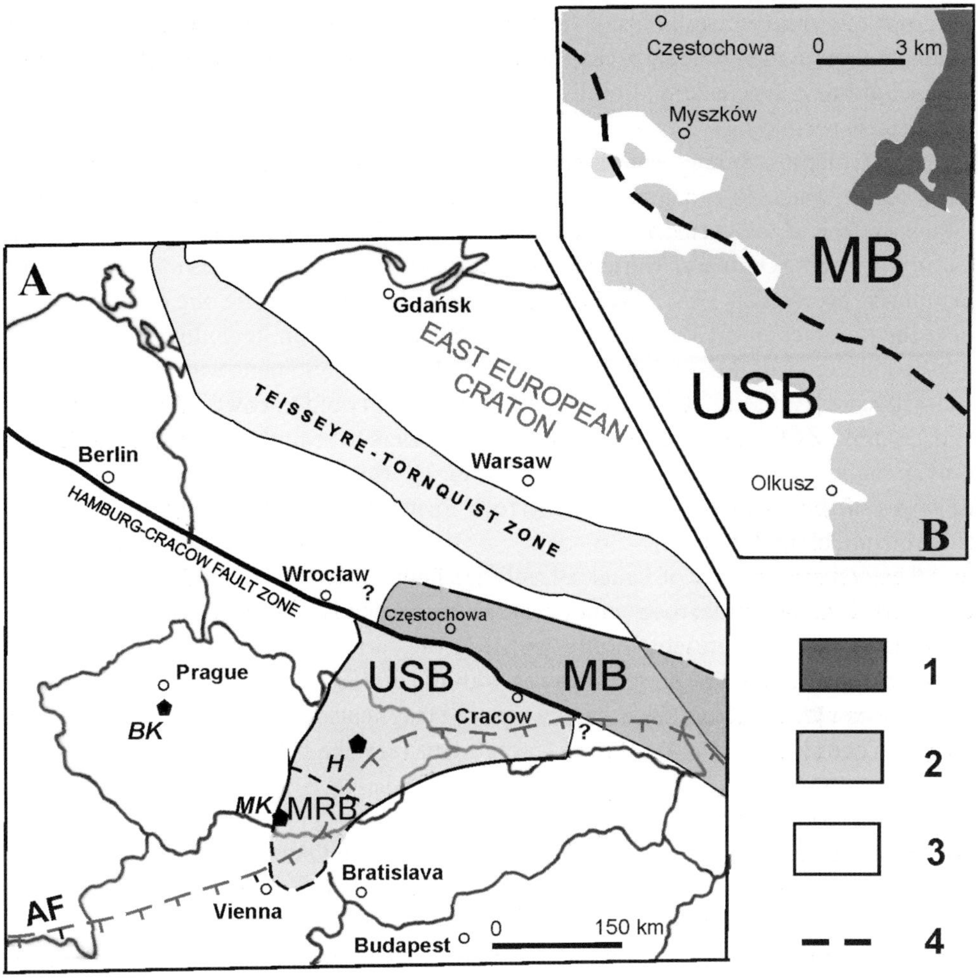

Fig. 1. Geological setting and structural position of study area with respect to the border zone of Upper Silesia and Malopolska blocks (based on J. Zaba, 1995, 1999 and M. Pulina et al., in print). ***A****- structural setting of Upper Silesia (USB) and Malopolska (MB) blocks. AF- Alpine Front, MRB - Moravian block (Brunnia), BK- Bohemian Karst, MK- Moravian Karst, H- Zbrashov Aragonite Caves and Hranice Abyss.* ***B****- structural sketch of Cracow-Silesian homocline in the area of boundary between Upper Silesia (USB) and Malopolska (MB) blocks. 1- Cretaceous, 2- Jurassic (mostly Upper Jurassic limestones), 3- Triassic (mostly Middle Triassic limestones and dolomites), 4- location of Cracow-Lubliniec fault zone (segment of Hamburg-Cracow fault zone) underneath the Mesozoic cover.*

m). The complex of Middle Triassic carbonate rocks (limestones and dolomites) is covered on a significant area with impermeable Keuper and Lower Jurassic formations. Within these formations karst of the south-western, Silesian part of the discussed region has developed (Fig. 1B). The complex of Upper Jurassic limestones makes up the main element of geologic structure of the north-eastern, Cracow part of the homocline. The outcrops of the carbonate rocks of this age extend in a wide range striking NW-SE and follow the above mentioned Cracow-Lubliniec fault zone (Fig. 1B). In the both carbonate complexes polygenetic and multiphase karst phenomena of Cracow-Silesia Upland are formed.

The Cracow-Lubliniec fault zone has Proterozoic assumptions and its tectonic activity covers the period spanning from the lowest Paleozoic to Cenozoic (Żaba, 1995). Along the line of this dislocation ranges the watershed between two important Central European rivers - Odra and Warta. This suggests that its activity covers also the present-day times (Morawska, 1997). With the deep range of the fault zone one could also connect the presence of ore deposits in the Cracow-Silesia region, including zinc and lead ores, connected with Mississipi Valey type paleokarstic phenomena within Middle Triassic carbonates. Close relations with location and activity of Cracow-Lubliniec zone also show symptoms of magmatism. This particularly refers to granitoid plutonism occurring only in marginal part of Malopolska block (Fig. 2), which played a significant role both in origin of the specific Upper Jurassic rock formation - rocky limestones, and their subsequent karstification.

The tectonic activity of Cracow-Lubliniec fault zone determined the formation of numerous block-type macrostructures within the Mesozoic cap-rock. Most of the joint complexes and faults present within the Mesozoic carbonate complexes in the area of Cracow-Silesia homocline show a relation with the discussed zone. In the southern part of the homocline the conditions become more complicated by the influences of Alpine tectonics coming from the vicinity of Carpathians (see Fig.1).

SPECIFIC KARST PHENOMENA OF CRACOW-SILESIA HOMOCLINE RELATED TO TECTONIC ACTIVITY OF PALEOZOIC BASE

Among other symptoms of carbonate karst of Silesia-Cracow Upland (geologically - Cracow-Silesia homocline) the ones that deserve special attention are large depressions very similar to poljes (Wilk et al. 1989; Pulina 2001; Pulina et al. in print) and, already mentioned, effects of hydrothermal activity in the caves (see i.a. Rudnicki 1978; Pulina et al. in print). The occurrence of basins and numerous large morphologic depressions with karst origin both in the top layer of Middle Triassic limestones and dolomites and of Upper Jurassic limestones testifies the presence of extraordinary geological conditions favouring the development of these forms. The basic factor was certainly the discontinuity lines (fracturing zones, faults, etc.) breaking the Mesozoic carbonate complex. Location and shape of large karst forms, referred to as fossil poljes (Wilk et al. 1989; Pulina 2001) is closely related to these zones and tectonic lines (Fig. 2). It should be emphasized that these forms occur in the area where karst relief has typical traits of residual ruined stage of development in the case of Upper Jurassic massif and intensively developed paleokarst in Triassic rocks (Pulina, Tyc 1987; Glazek 1989). Although the karst phenomena have been developed in much younger rocks than in karst regions of

Bohemia and Moravia in surrounding area, this relief is much more "ruined". The explanation for such an advanced karst development and exceptionality of the discussed zone compared to the neighbouring regions can be perceived in the presence of hydrothermal and gaseous intrusions connected with Cracow-Lubliniec tectonic line. Detailed investigations in the central, highest part of Cracow-Silesia Upland show that hydrothermal phenomena observed in remnants of large cave systems have developed thanks to upward migration of preheated waters and juvenile CO_2 connected with magmatic bodies encountered in the boreholes of the Mesozoic rocks base. Waters migrated through the discontinuity zones cross-cutting rock profile, to the floor of already mentioned rock formation - Oxfordian rocky limestones where the largest number of caves has developed. Smashing of rocky limestones and breaking of the cave systems into fragments occurred later than forms resulting from the circulation of warm waters (Pulina et al. in print). Also this process can be explained by occurence of the contact zone tectonic activity of the mentioned Upper Silesia and Malopolska blocks and Cracow-Lubliniec line.

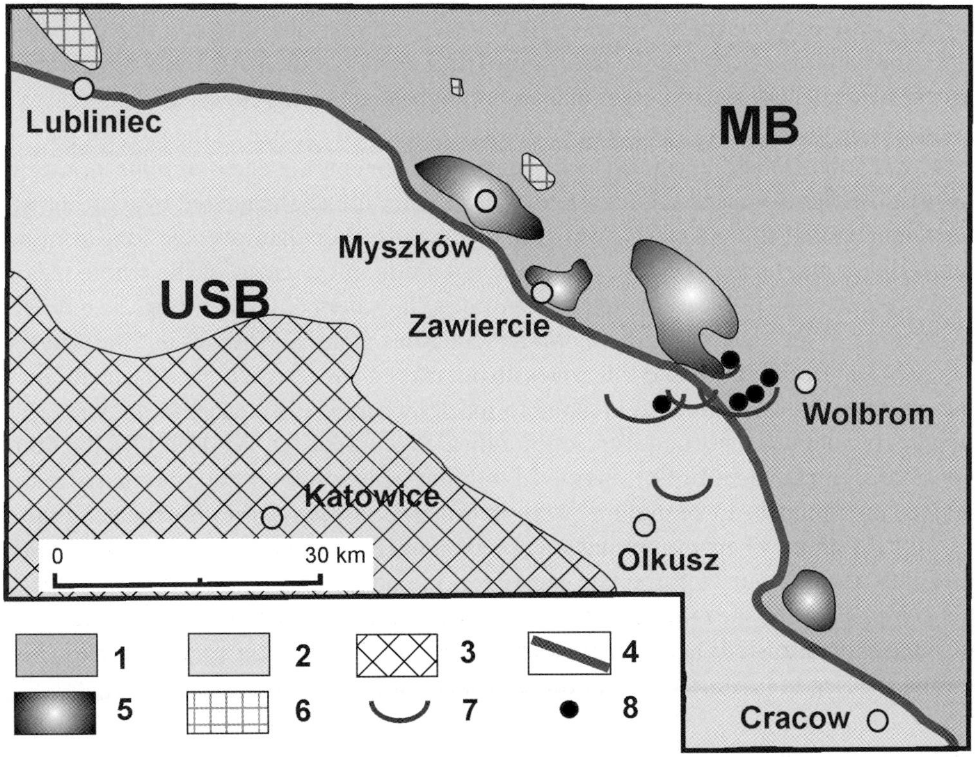

*Fig. 2. Structural setting of granitoid magmatism, large scale morphological depressions and selected springs at boundary zone of the Upper Silesia and Malopolska blocks. **1**- Malopolska Block (MB), **2**- Upper Silesia Block (USB), **3**- Upper Silesian Coal Basin, **4**- boundary of Cracow-Lubliniec Fault Zone, **5**- areas of granitoid intrusions and their contact interactions, confirmed by boreholes (after J. Zaba, 1995), **6**- supposed areas of granitoid magmatism, **7**- largest paleo-poljes within Middle Triassic and Upper Jurassic carbonates, **8**- location of springs with supposed effects of endogenic processes in water properties.*

PRESENT-DAY TECTONIC ACTIVITY MANIFESTING ITSELF IN GROUNDWATER PROPERTIES

The present day tectonic activity of the Upper Silesia and Malopolska blocks border zone and the whole Cracow-Lubliniec fault zone is registered through observation of tectonic movements in the area of Upper Silesia Coal Basin (Fig. 2). Due to the fact that most of the areas discussed are covered with Quaternary sediments, which suppress possible gaseous emanations, it is difficult to relate this activity to the development of present-day karst processes of Cracow-Silesia region.

The area of Cracow-Silesia Upland belongs to areas significantly transformed by human activity (i.a. Tyc 1997) which is an additional factor suppressing the effects of tectonic activity in karst waters of this region. Correct recognition of the problem of antropogenic influence on the course of present-day karst processes (Tyc 1997) combined with more than ten years observation of selected springs in the discussed area (Tyc, Opołka-Gądek 1999) allow to ascertain that there are some regularities. The effects of such activity manifest themselves in specific properties of waters flowing out of the karst aquifers of this region. These properties include principally water temperature as well as content of bicarbonates and carbon dioxide dissolved in water.

Among the examined population of a few dozens of springs of the eastern part of Cracow-Silesia Upland, complexes of springs occurring on the edges of polje-type large depressions deserve a special attention (Fig. 2). They are characterized by a higher water temperature (8,8 - 10,6^{0}C), which is distinctly higher than average long-term air temperature and higher than static zone temperature in the caves of the whole region (7,5^{0}C). The value of bicarbonates concentration in waters of these springs also differs from those of the springs in the region and amounts from 230 to 300 mg/dm^3 (in the remaining areas of the Upland the values do not exceed 90-160 mg/dm^3). The mentioned bicarbonates concentrations are related to springs where no influences of antropogenic impurities on the activity and dissolution rate are recorded (see Tyc 1997). In the same zones of springs, values of CO_2 dissolved in water higher than in the other parts of the region, amounting to 12-24 mg/dm^3, were recorded. Considering the climatic conditions of Central Europe, where the production of CO_2 in soil is relatively low, the values achieved in waters flowing out of carbonate massifs in the zones of occurrence of large karst depressions may be the effect or echo of tectonic activity of the base. These zones overlap magmatic intrusions occurring directly in the base of Mesozoic rocks complex (Fig. 2) and the largest fracture agglomeration of this complex.

FINAL REMARKS

When referring to the wide background of Cracow-Silesia region presented in the article, it should be emphasized that zones of past and present-day activity of similar tectonic zones occur and influence the karst evolution in the neighbouring areas of Czechia and Moravia (see Fig. 1A). A widespread tectonic zone striking S-N in the central part of Czechia played the key role in the transport of hydrothermal solutions towards the surface and in development of hydrothermal karst phenomena in Bohemian Karst (Zeman, Suchy 1999). Recently, more and more frequently, the question of contribution of similar processes to the origin of caves and surface forms of Moravian Karst is discussed. It is considered that hydrothermal karst of both mentioned regions occurred most likely in Tertiary or even in Quaternary, and therefore karstification in this region is much younger than it was previously considered. This testifies the great intensity of karst processes assisted or caused by the activity of heated waters migrating in the upward direction and gaseous emanations (mainly CO_2). The most interesting objects of present-day activity of the mentioned endogenic processes in the area of Central Europe are Zbrashov Aragonite Caves and Hranice Abyss in Teplice on Becva (Moravia), where karstification proceeds with the involvement of warm waters (40-50^{0}C) enriched with juvenile CO_2.

The theses presented in the paper, concerning the Cracow-Silesia Upland as well as cited examples related to the neighbouring regions put in new light the age of karst development and the contribution of endogenic processes in this development in relation to the role of climatic conditions. The latter have been considered, till the present-day times, a dominating factor, determining the karstification phases distinguished for the Cracow-Silesia region. They also cast a new light on the subject, discussed for many years, of the lack of ice cover and the functioning of negative nunatak in the eastern part of the discussed region during the Pleistocene glaciation.

REFERENCES

Glazek, J., 1989: Palaeokarst in Poland.- [in:] Bosak, P. et al. (ed.): Palaeokarst. A systematic and regional review. Elsevier and Academia, 77-105, Amsterdam - Prague.

Morawska, A., 1997: The Lubliniec fracture zone: boundary of the Upper Silesian and malopolska Massifs, southern Poland.- Ann.Soc. Geol. Pol. 67, 429-437, Cracow.

Pulina, M., 2001: Karst paleopolja from Cracow-Czestochowa Upland.- [in:] Karczewski, A., Zwolinski, Z., (ed.): Functioning of geosystems in different morphoclimatic conditions - Monitoring, Protection, Education. 439-442, Poznan (in Polish).

Pulina, M., Tyc, A., 1987: Gide de terrains karstiques choisis des Sudety et Haut-Plateau de Silesie-Cracovie. P. 101, Sosnowiec.

Pulina, M., Żaba, J., Polonius, A., (in press): Relations of karst forms development in the area of Smolen-Niegowonice Range and tectonic activity of the Cracow-Wielun Upland' background.- Kras i Speleologia, t. 11(XX), Katowice.

Tyc, A., 1997: Anthropogenic impact on karst processes in the Silesian-Cracow Upland (Olkusz-Zawiercie area as example).- Kras i Speleologia. Special issue no. 2/1997, p. 176, Katowice (in Polish).

Tyc, A., Opolka-Gadek, J., 1999: The tendency of hydrological changes in springs on the area of Jurassic Landscape Park (Silesian-Cracow Upland) in the period of 1986-1996.- [in:]

Biesiadka, E., Czachorowski, S., (ed.): Zrodla Polski - stan badan, monitoring i ochrona. 209-226, Olsztyn (in Polish).

Wilk, Z., Kawalec, T., Motyka, J., Zuber K., 1989: Influence of karst passages upon the piezometric surface of the surrounding aquifer.- Kras i Speleologia, t. 6(XV), 7-22, Katowice.

Zeman, A., Suchy, V., 1999: Fossil hydrothermal karst of Bohemia and Moravia: general features and its modern equivalents.- Geoscience Research Reprts for 1998. Cesky geologiccky ustav, 83-84, Prague (in Czech).

Žaba, J., 1995: Heave faults of the Upper Silesia and Malopolska block border zone.- Przeglad Geologiczny 43, 838-842, Warsaw (in Polish).

Žaba, J., 1999: Structural evolution of the lower Paleozoic formation in the border zone of Upper Silesia and Malopolska block.- Prace Panstw. Inst. Geol., 166, p. 162, Warsaw (in Polish).

Address
Marian Paulina
Department of Geomorphology, University of Silesia, ul. Bedzinska 60, 41-200 Sosnowiec, Poland
E-mail: pulina@us.edu.pl, atyc@us.edu.pl
Andrzej Tyc
Department of Geomorphology, University of Silesia, ul. Bedzinska 60, 41-200 Sosnowiec, Poland
E-mail: pulina@us.edu.pl, atyc@us.edu.pl
Jerzy Žaba
Department of General Geology, University of Silesia ul. Bedzinska 60, 41-200 Sosnowiec, Poland

DATING AND GEOPHYSICAL METHODS

KARST-CONTROLLED RESERVOIRS, IDENTIFICATION AND PREDICTION OF RESERVOIR CHARACTERISTICS DISTRIBUTION THROUGH SEISMIC, WELL DATA AND OUTCROPS

P. A. LAPOINTE, H-J. SOUDET, B. COURME

Abstract

Karst-controlled reservoirs can be economically interesting. Case histories show that production depends on the knowledge of the karst organization. Reservoir description remains difficult because of the anisotropy of the karst system which is at field scale, and not characterizable at well scale. Three examples of karst-controlled fields (Rospo Mare -Italy, Al Khaleej -Qatar, Kharyaga -CIS) and one example of karst-modified field (Yadana -Myanmar) are illustrated. As core data are only available after drilling, seismic and log techniques appear as the first step for a karst reservoir evaluation. Use of outcrop analogue is still mandatory, then, laboratory seismic modeling calibrated by paleokarst outcrop studies allows the identification karstic features. A natural "next step" is the mapping and modeling of the karst characteristics. The first approach is a 3-D sketch showing horizontally-driven and vertically-driven cave developments. The ultimate step would be a full 3-D reservoir model of the paleokarst. Mapping remains critical in the prediction of the best reservoir zone distribution, and the prognosis of future production well locations, particularly for horizontal or highly deviated wells.
Key words: *Karst, Paleokarst, Reservoir, Hydrocarbon, Identification, Seismic, Modeling*

INTRODUCTION

Subaerial exposure in terrestrial and coastal environments initiates a series of physical, chemical, and biological processes that modify carbonate rocks (Cvijic, 1925; Sweeting, 1972; Ford and Williams, 1989; Esteban and Klappa, 1983; Wright, 1991, amongst others). The related karstic process is of paramount importance for reservoir enhancement.

Karst-controlled reservoirs can be economically interesting such as notable examples including Precambrian - Cambrian dolomites of Renqiu (Guangming and Quanheng 1982, Renda, 1986, Horn, 1990), Yanglin (Guangming and Quanheng, 1982) fields, both in China, Ordovician Ellenburger (Kerans 1988, 1990), Arbuckle (Bliefnick, 1992; Al-Shaieb and Lynch, 1993), and Knox carbonates (USA), Devonian Kharyaga field (Petukhov, 1996a; Petukhov, 1996b; Lapointe, 1997) (CIS), Permian Yates field (Craig, 1988; Tinker *et al*, 1995), Mississippian Madison carbonates (Sando, 1988), Maden and Garland (Demiralin and Hurley, 1993) fields (USA), Jurassic Amposta (Seemann *et al*,

1990) and Casablanca (Watson 1982; Lomando *et al.*, 1993) fields (Spain), Cretaceous Rospo Mare field (Dussert *et al.*, 1988; Soudet *et al.*, 1990; Andre and Doulcet, 1991) (Italy). A number of other reservoirs have been improved or modified by karstification, some examples include the Carboniferous-Permian Tenghiz field (Harris *et al.*, 1998) (Kazakhstan), Cretaceous Al Khaleej field (Qatar) or Miocene Yadana (Lapointe *et al.*, 1996) (Myanmar).

Case histories of karst-controlled reservoir show that the production of the field depends on an understanding of the karst organization. The reservoir description remains difficult because of the anisotropy of the karst system. Three examples of karst-controlled fields and one example of a karst-modified field are illustrated.

KARST RESERVOIR EVALUATION

As core data are only available after drilling, seismic and log techniques appear as the first step for a karst reservoir evaluation. Use of outcrop analogue is still mandatory, as the origin and recognition of fractures, breccia, and sediments fills associated with paleocaves are determined through the study of modern karst systems. Later, laboratory seismic modeling calibrated by paleokarst outcrop studies allows the identification of karstic features (Handford, 1995; Courme 1999; Lapointe *et al.*, 2001). Based on outcrop description, an impedance model is prepared. A study of the Apache Canyon (West Texas, Courme, 2001), the impedance model was built from sonic velocity measurements performed on the outcrop with the help of a hand-held sonic probe. In this case, the comparison of the seismic response at 60 Hz and at 40 Hz showed that, at a 110-ft trace spacing, large collapse features may be better imaged at the lower frequency. Objects 40 m high and 90 m long can be identified on this kind of seismic data, at a frequency as low as 40 Hz. Examples of Rospo Mare (Italy) and Al Khaleej (Qatar) fields show the advantage of 3-D seismic in locating important karst features such as large caves, sinkholes and dolines or in defining the limits of karstified areas.

A natural "next step" for understanding the karst reservoir is the mapping of the karst characteristics (Lapointe, 1997). The map is based on a compilation and integration of all the available data: mud loss distribution, bit drop locations, core recovery, rubble zones, core data (geological and petrophysical), fracture analysis, fault distribution from seismic, karst seismic patterns, log analysis, well test analysis, and computed productivity index It is also based on outcrop analogues and other known karstic hydrocarbon fields used as guidelines for the mapping. The first derived model is a schematic 3D representation showing horizontally driven cave developments within some lithological units, with probable open conduits and vertically-driven cave developments allowing connection between successive units.

For the Kharyaga field, the fieldwork done in the Bolshoi Karatau of Kazakhstan provided analogue for a paleokarst network developed in Paleozoic rocks (Lapointe and Hurst, 1996; Lapointe *et al.*, 1997). Former caves 200 m long and 50 m high, occur.

Cave conduits collapsed and early-formed internal breccias were re-brecciated. Following this, differential compaction of strata around and over the paleocaves developed breccias that radiate out from the conduits and which may intersect other collapsed passages (Loucks, 1996, 1999).

The ultimate step would be a 3-D reservoir modeling of the paleokarst (Kharyaga, Al Khaleej).

KARST-CONTROLLED FIELDS

Rospo Mare (Italy), identification based on seismic and core

The Lower Cretaceous limestone of Rospo Mare field, in the Adriatic Sea offshore Italy, suffered subaerial exposure and karstification process before the deposition of the Oligo-Miocene cap rock. The Rospo Mare experience showed the capability of 3D seismic to define a karstic landform at the top of a limestone reservoir. This Oligocene Mediterranean karst is of tropical type, similar to the modern day Cuba or Vietnam karsts. Isobath mapping has confirmed the karstic interpretation of the reservoir, first proved by a core study. It shows, clearly, numerous roughly circular depressions with depths ranging from 10 to 100 m and diameters from 100 to 600 m, looking like a typical sinkhole or doline landscape. The cores were used to set up a succession of criteria for karst identification (Lapointe, 1981) and allowed a good characterization of the karst:

- A gravity driven karst, tabular, in the Ford classification, developed under hot & humid climate, mature, with extended karst related porosity and hierarchy of the system from upstream to downstream,
- A clear organization with the upper infiltration zone (epikarst, 15-20m), the lower infiltration zone (vertical transit zone, 35 to 80m), the upper flooded zone (20-30m), the lower flooded zone (up to 200m) with slow water movements.

Reservoir impact: oil is trapped in vugs and fractures enlarged by karstification, the karst total porosity is about 1.5%, but permeabilities vary from 8 to 50D. Thus, the risk of very early water breakthrough during production was high.

Horizontal drilling application: to avoid clay and terra rossa filling dolines or sinkholes, horizontal drilling, controlled by 3D seismic model was used to intersect the maximum number of open caves and fractures, as far as possible above the oil-water contact in order to reduce the risk of early water breakthrough.

Kharyaga Objet 2 (CIS). Reservoir, identification based mainly on core and drilling parameters

The Kharyaga field, located in the Komi Republic (CIS), is a multi-horizon oil-bearing field. The Upper Devonian carbonates of Object 2 are one of the most interesting reservoir targets. While drilling, several wells reported heavy, sometimes total mud losses, tool breaks, and falls of several meters. Cores cut in these wells were generally poorly recovered and contained large vugs and an abundance of fractures.

Detailed examination of these cores reveals the karstic nature of the reservoir (Lapointe, 1997) and includes the following: conduits passing to large cavities, caves with network distribution, fissures enlarged by leaching, morphologies with an erosional overprint, karstic breccia, local filling of the cavities with green shales, geodic sparite cement and true speleothems. All these karstic features are documented from thin-section study.

A reference well KH-1019 was cored (170m) and logged, providing valuable information for the karstified reservoir understanding. Unfortunately, in this well KH 1019, it was not possible to control fluid loss during the drilling of the Object 2. The set of open hole logs recorded does not allow formal identification of the secondary porosity type. The seismic lines do not clearly exhibit karstic morphologies, inasmuch as they consist of a set of old 2D lines lacking sufficient resolution. Newly acquired 3D seismic with a 60 feet trace spacing and higher frequency content will improve the karst identification. The main observations on cores are:

- Abundance of macroscopic secondary porosity, with well-developed cavities from a millimeter to several centimeters;
- Discontinuous and anisotropic cavity development having selectively affected the non-stromatolitic units;
- Relationship with the former sedimentary structures (e.g., enlargement of fenestrae);
- Leaching along the sediment heterogeneities, such as microfracture networks (partial leaching of the network previously sealed by sparitic cement) or stylolites;
- Occurrence of fracture-related breccia followed by solution of stromatolites;
- General association of large cavities with a set of microvugs (less than 1 mm);
- Cavity network displaying high connectivity (up to several centimeters width on core);
- Sparite geode cavity infilling.

Reservoir impact: the karstified zone exhibits a wide vertical and horizontal distribution. The karst appears polycyclic, and one of the latest phases remains widely open. Overall porosity is increased and permeability is drastically improved by karstification. The tested wells in this zone have a very good productivity index. The reservoir characteristics of the breccias related to paleokarst in some ârt of the field are also attractive when compared to the non-karstified zones. The mapping of the karstified reservoir is based on all the data collected (mud-logging, electrical-logging, cores and production data) with outcrop model control and is a critical factor for reservoir management and field development.

Al Khaleej Field, (Qatar), Epikarst, combined identification

The Mishrif reservoir of the Al Khaleej located offshore Qatar is characterized by a succession of agrading elementary sequences (each about 10 m thick), that suffered strong diagenesis at the top, leading to epikarst formation (3 to 5 meters).

This karst is polygenetic and all the epikarstic systems were reactivated during a long period of emergence (Turonian to Santonian, # 4.5 My) partly induced by the diapiric structure of Rostam (Iran). The main observations on cores are:

- Pedogenic facies,
- Abundance of secondary vuggy porosity developed in all facies (wackestone to grainstone) and spectacular in rudist facies,
- Sharp base to the dissolution following an horizontal level, cross-cutting lithological variations,
- Strong cementation of the very top (30cm) of each sequence by marine calcite.

Reservoir impact: the karstified zone is well delimitated and visible on 3D seismic. The high permeability of the epikarstic drains (100md to 8 darcies) is correlated with sequence stratigraphy: permeability increases in each successive sequence during the regressive trend.

The reservoir quality is also related to the sensitivity to dissolve the sedimentary facies. The best are rudistic/bioclastic facies and the best drain (good continuity) are tempest levels with abundant caprinid debris (aragonitic rudists).

Carbonates dissolved in the epikarst are recemented at the border of the karstic area inducing a lateral cemented zone and a sharp boundary for the reservoir.

KARST-MODIFIED FIELD

Combined karst recognition, Yadana Field, Offshore Myanmar

The main gas reservoir at Yadana field, offshore Myanmar, south of the Irrawaddy Delta, occurs in Early Miocene shallow marine limestones. Losses of drilling mud were recorded in the same intervals as karstic features (subaerial exposure surfaces, breccia and large solution cavities filled with drilling mud) which were observed in cores (Lapointe *et al.*, 1996). The main observations on cores are:

- Pseudo-breccia on top of cemented and cavernous limestone,
- Large scale vugs or en-larged fissures,
- Karstic surface with vertical solution pipes developed for 2-3 m, filled by overlaying bioclastic-dominated limestone,
- Sub vertical fissures and network connected caverns, filled by drilling mud.
- Large range for the size of the cavities,
- Discontinuous and anisotropic distribution of the cavities within the sediment,
- Macroscopic secondary porosity.

Thin section analysis confirms the multiple stages of karstic dissolution and cavity filling and it shows a complex network providing information for phases of karstification development. The filling of caves and vugs highlight a complex history summarized in 5 phases. The stable carbon and oxygen compositions ($\delta\ ^{14}C$ and $\delta\ ^{18}O$) of most bulk limestones are typical of normal marine carbonate, however neomorphosed corals in some of those intervals have isotopic compositions characteristics of fresh water diagenesis. Complementary micropaleontological analyses have been used to enhance the interpretation. Karst features are also recorded in wireline log responses. Intervals cemented during emergence appear dense on sonic log and correspond to strong seismic events. Caves appear clearly on the Dipole Shear Sonic log interpretation (Hlaing *et al.*, 1994). In addition, seismic amplitude maps reveal an anisotropic distribution of karst related events superimposed on an atoll-like deposition model.

At field scale, similar karstic features have been observed and described on three other ap-praisal wells, allowing correlations based on these karstic events. 2D and 3D seismic lines support these where doline-like and sinkhole features are suspected at the top of the formation.

Reservoir impact: the karstification provide fluid flows within a specific facies strongly ce-mented. The remaining "classic" pores are moldic, organic and intergranular types with very poor interconnections. The average porosity is 11% compared to the average 25 % of the good reservoir facies. This rock type is not a true permeability barrier since the karstification process had provided vertical "pipes" or channels allowing vertical fluid flows. The very last karstic phase related to the top limestone emersion left an unfilled network that provides connecting channels through dense zones. The early cementation of the carbonates is balanced by the creation of this network. The related interconnected vuggy porosity is developed vertically over 50 m and increase the gas flow.

CONCLUSIONS

The karst system dramatically improves the permeabilities and the drainage of the host rocks. This improvement also affects porosity, albeit with a smaller impact. Mapping remains critical in the forecasting of the best reservoir zone distribution, and the prognosis of future production well locations, particularly for horizontal or highly deviated wells, and is the first step in karst modeling as applied to production reservoir modeling.

Karst-controlled reservoirs have a spatial complexity. Understanding the distribution of the heterogeneous reservoir facies resulting from karst-processes is mandatory for the economic production of their hydrocarbons.

REFERENCES

Al-Shaieb, Z., and M. Lynch, 1993; Paleokarst features and thermal overprints observed in some of the Arbuckle cores in Oklahoma.- *in* Paleokarst related hydrocarbon reservoirs, SEPM Core Workshop n° 18, p. 11-60, New Orleans.

Andre, P., and A. Doulcet, 1991; Rospo Mare field – Italy; Apulian platform, Adriatic sea.- *in* Stratigraphic Traps II, Treatise of Petroleum Geology, Atlas of Oil and Gas Fields: AAPG, p. 29–54, Tulsa, Oklahoma.

Bliefnick, D. M., 1992; Karst-related diagenesis and reservoir development in the Arbuckle Group, Paschall#2 core.- *in* Candelaria M. P. and C. L. Reed, eds., Paleokarst, karst related diagenesis and reservoir development: examples from Ordovician-Devonian age strata of West Texas and the Mid-Continent, 1992 field trip guidebook Permian Basin section SEPM, Pub. N° 92-33, p. 137-152.

Courme, B., 1999; Forward seismic modeling of a shelf-to-slope carbonate depositional setting from outcrop data, the Abo Formation of Apache Canyon, West Texas, and comparison to its subsurface equivalent, Kingdom Abo Field, Midland Basin.- Master's degree thesis, The University of Texas at Austin 200p.

Courme, B., 2001; Outcrop seismic modeling of a carbonate shelf-to-slope depositional setting, Apache Canyon, West Texas.- Géologie Méditerranéenne, Tome XXVIII, n° 1-2, p. 53-56.

Craig, D. H., 1988; Caves and other features of Permian karst in San Andres Dolomite, Yates Field reservoir, West Texas.- *in* Choquette, P. W. and N. P. James, eds., Paleokarst: New York Springer-Verlag, p. 342-363.

Cvijic, J., 1925; Types morphologiques des terrains calcaires: le holokarst.- Comptes Rendus Académie des Sciences, Paris, V. 180, p. 592–594.

Demiralin, A. S., and N. F. Hurley, 1993; Karst breccias in the Madison Limestone (Mississippian), Garland Field, Wyoming.- *in* Paleokarst related hydrocarbon reservoirs, SEPM Core Workshop n° 18, p. 101-118, New Orleans.

Dussert, P., G. Santoro and H-J. Soudet, 1988; A decade of drilling developments pay off in offshore Italian oil field.- OGJ., V.86, n° 9, p. 33–39.

Esteban, M., and C. F. Klappa, 1983; Subaerial exposure environment.- *in* Sholle, P. A., Bebout, D. G., and Moore, C. H.: Carbonate Depositional Environments, AAPG Memoir 33, p. 1–54.

Ford, D., and P. Williams, 1989; Karst Geomorphology and Hydrology.- London, Chapman & Hall, 601 p.

Guangming Z. and Z. Quanheng, 1982; Buried-Hill Oil and Gas Pools in the North China Basin.- in AAPG Memoir n° 32, The Deliberate Search for the Subtle Trap, p.317-335.

Handford, R. C., 1995; Stratigraphic geometry of cavern collapse and seismic modeling - A predictive tool for exploration.- AAPG Bull. **Vol.** 79, p. 38.

Harris, P. M., and R. A. Garber, A. Tyshkanbaeva, S. Birrmanova, and M. E. Clark, 1998; Geologic framework for the Tengiz-8 well, Tengiz Field, Kazakstan - Unconformities and porosity development.- AAPG Annual Meeting, Salt Lake City, Utah, AAPG Bull., V. 82, n° 13.

Hlaing, K. K., C. Lemoy, J. P. Maret, Y. Kremer, W. H. Borland and Myint Maw, 1994; Low frequency Stoneley Energy for stratigraphic evaluation.- AAPG Conference, Kuala Lumpur, Malaysia. AAPG Bull. Vol.78, p. 1194.

Horn, M. K., 1990; Renqiu field.- *in* Structural Traps II, Traps associated with tectonic faulting, Treatise of Petroleum Geology, Atlas of oil and Gas Fields:, AAPG, p. 227–252, Tulsa, Oklahoma.

Kerans, C., 1988; Karst controlled reservoir heterogeneity in Ellenburger Group carbonates of West Texas.- AAPG Bull. V. 72, p. 1160–1183.

Kerans, C., 1990; Depositional system and karst geology of the Ellenburger Group (Lower Ordovician), subsurface West Texas.- University of Texas at Austin, Bureau of Economic Geology, Report of investigation no. 193, 63 p.

Lapointe, P. A., 1981; Critères de reconnaissance des paléokarsts. Application aux sondages carottés.- Thèse de doctorat 3ème cycle, Université Paris-Sud, France, 307 p.

Lapointe, P. A., 1997; Kharyaga, Komi Republic, Example of a Late Devonian karstified field, consequences for the reservoir characteristics.- AAPG Annual Meeting Dallas, Texas p. 67-68

Lapointe P. A., M-C Bernet-Rollande., V. G. Zhemchuzhnikov, H. E. Cook, W. G. Zempolich, P. J. Lehmann, 1997; Evaporite collapse breccia versus karst breccia: the Upper Devonian-Lower Carboniferous Balaturlan Unit, Bolshoi Karatau Mountains, Southern Kazakhstan.- AAPG International Conference and Exhibition Vienna, Austria, p.1393.

Lapointe P. A, B. Courme, D. Van Der Wel and B. Soulhol, 2001; Outcrop and seismic data as improvement tools for Kharyaga field geological and reservoir modeling.- AAPG and VNIGRI International and Regional Meeting,

Lapointe, P. A., and J. M. Hurst, 1996; Karst in Devonian and Carboniferous carbonates, Bolchoi Karatau, Southern Kazakhstan: controls and reservoirs implications.- AAPG Hedberg Conference, Carbonate Reservoirs of the World: Problems, Solutions and Strategies for the Future, September 22–26, Elf Aquitaine Technology Center, Pau, France.

Lapointe, P. A., J. M. Hurst, A. Saller, Kyaw Nyein, Nyunt, Myint Oo and Thet Tun, 1996; Karst recognition and reservoir impact, Yadana Field, Offshore Myanmar.- 11th Offshore South East Asia Conference and Exhibition, Conference Proceedings, p.225-236, Singapore.

Lomando, A. J., P. M. Harris and D. E. Orlopp, 1993; Casablanca field, Tarragona basin, offshore Spain: a karsted carbonate reservoir, *in* R. D. Fritz, J. L. Wilson, and D. A. Yurewicz, eds., Paleokarst related hydrocarbon reservoirs: SEPM Core Workshop 18, p. 201–225.

Loucks, R. G., 1996; Origin, scale and heterogeneities of paleocave reservoirs.- AAPG, Hedberg Conference, Carbonate Reservoirs of the World: Problems, Solutions and Strategies for the Future, September 22–26, Elf Aquitaine Technology Center, Pau, France.

Loucks, R. G., 1999; Paleocave carbonate reservoirs: origins, burial-depth modifications, spatial complexity, and reservoir implications.- AAPG Bull. V. 83, p. 1795–1834.

Petukhov, A. V., 1996a; A karstified oil-gas bearing reservoir of the Timan–Pechora Basin.- AAPG Hedberg Conference, Carbonate Reservoirs of the World: Problems, Solutions and Strategies for the Future, September 22–26, Elf Aquitaine Technology Center, Pau, France.

Petukhov, A. V., 1996b; Integrated exploitation of fracture-karst zones in carbonate oil-gas bearing reservoirs in the Timan–Pechora Basin.- AAPG Hedberg Conference, Carbonate Reservoirs of the World: Problems, Solutions and Strategies for the Future, September 22–26, Elf Aquitaine Technology Center, Pau, France.

Renda, L, 1986; The management of Renqiu oil field during its medium-late development stage.- International Meeting of Petroleum Engineering, Beijing, China, SPE paper n° 14836, p 79–85.

Sando, W. J., 1988; Madison limestone (Mississippian) paleokarst: a geologic synthesis.- *in* Choquette, P. W. and N. P. James, eds., Paleokarst: New York Springer-Verlag, p. 256-277.

Seemann, U., V. F., Pümpin and N. Casson, 1990; Amposta oil field.- *in* Stratigraphic Traps II, Traps Associated with Tectonic Faulting, Treatise of Petroleum Geology, Atlas of oil and Gas Fields: Tulsa, Oklahoma, The American Association of Petroleum Geologists, p. 1–20.

Soudet H-J., P. Sorriaux and F. Michaud, 1990; Rospo Mare (Adriatic Sea) - An oil-bearing paleokarst in the Mediterranean Region.- AAPG Bull. Vol.74, p.769.

Sweeting, M., 1972; Karst Landforms.- London, Macmillan Press Ltd, 362 p.

Tinker, S.W., J.R. Ehrets and M.D. Brondos, 1995; Multiple Karst events related to stratigraphic cyclicity: San Andres Formation, Yates Field, West Texas.- *in* D.A. Budd, A.H. Saller, P.M. Harris Unconformities and Porosity in Carbonate Strata, AAPG Memoir n° 63, p. 213-237.

Watson, H.J., 1982; Casablanca field, offshore Spain, a paleogeomorphic trap.- *in* M.T. Halbouty, ed., The deliberate search for the stratigraphic trap. AAPG Memoir n° 32, p. 237-250.

Wright, V.P., 1991; Paleokarst types, recognition, controls and associations, *in* Wright, V. P., Esteban, M., and Smart: Paleokarsts and Paleokarstic Reservoirs, University of Reading, England, p. 56–88.

Address
TOTALFINAELF , 2 Place de la Coupole, 92078 Paris la Defense, Cedex - France

SPELEOTHEM CHRONOLOGY OF GASSEL CAVE, NORTHERN CALCAREOUS ALPS, AUSTRIA (PRELIMINARY RESULTS)

KARL-HEINZ OFFENBECHER & CHRISTOPH SPÖTL

Abstract

Gassel cave is located in the central part of the Northern Calcareous Alps close to its northern margin. Cut in Triassic dolomite the cave's extends over a vertical difference of 105 m with its entrance located at 1225 m a.s.l. The interior air temperature is close to +5.4°C which corresponds to the average annual air temperature at this altitude. Annual precipitation is high due along the northern fringe of the Alps and a long-term average of 2400 mm was measured at the nearby meteorological station Feuerkogel (1587 m).

Gassel cave is among the most highly decorated dripstone caves in the entire Northern Calcareous Alps, which is unexpected given the rather high altitudinal setting, the dolomitic host rock and the thin soil cover. Inspection of the speleothem inventory shows that probably more than two thirds of the speleothems are currently inactive and potentially fossil. A simple stratigraphy of cave sediments can be recognized in most chambers. The oldest deposit are red clays which resembles terra rossa known from many high-altitude caves in the Northern Calcareous Alps and traditionally attributed to the result of subtropical weathering during Tertiary times. These loamy deposits, which rarely reach up more than a meter in thickness, are overlain by calcitic flowstones and stalagmites. U-series dates of stalagmites tops yielded Th-U equilibrium ages and hence corroborate the rather high age of the underlying clay. This generation of speleothems was subsequently affected by erosion due to turbulent waters which locally eroded the clay causing collapse and tilting of stalagmites. White and partially active flowstones and stalagmites up to about one meter in height form the last generation in these chambers.

Two active looking stalagmites were removed and are currently being investigated to obtain a paleoenvironmental record for the Holocene in this part of the Eastern Alps. Petrographically, these samples are composed of inclusion-poor, coarsely crystalline columnar calcite. One of the samples reveals a discontinuity suggesting that the drip source may have changed slightly. Other than that, thin sections show no evidence of post-depositional alteration.

We are currently establishing age models for these samples based on U-series measurements using multicollector ICP-MS methods. Preliminary results suggest that both stalagmites comprise most of the Holocene, but growth appears to have ceased some 1000 years before present.

•

Supported by grant START Y122-GEO of the Austrian Science Fund

Address

Institut für Geologie und Paläontologie, Universität Isbruck, Austria

Myndin af heiminum

PÉTUR GUNNARSSON

Ljóð
Splunkunýr dagur (1973)

Skáldsögur
Punktur punktur komma strik (1976)
Ég um mig frá mér til mín (1978)
Persónur og leikendur (1982)
Sagan öll (1985)
Hversdagshöllin (1990)
Stórbók (1991)
Efstu dagar (1994)
Heimkoma (1997)
Myndin af heiminum (2000)

Greinar
Sykur og brauð (1987)
Vasabók (1989)
Dýrðin á ásýnd hlutanna (1991)
Aldarför (1999)

Leikrit
Grænjaxlar (1977)
Krókmakarabærinn (1977)

Þýðingar
Barnasaga eftir Peter Handke (1987)
Brýrnar í Madisonsýslu eftir Robert J. Waller (1994)
Frú Bovary eftir Gustave Flaubert (1995)
Hlutirnir eftir Georges Perec (1996)
Listaverkið eftir Yasminu Reza (1997)
Í leit að glötuðum tíma I–II eftir Marcel Proust (1997, 1998)

Pétur Gunnarsson

Myndin af heiminum

Skáldsaga Íslands I

Mál og menning
Reykjavík 2000

Heimildanotkun verksins verður best lýst með hliðsjón af atferli ljónsins sem segir frá í Physiologus, forngrísku fræðiriti: „það máði spor sín jafnan út með halanum."

Þó er skylt að taka fram að Hvers vegna – vegna þess I–II var þýdd og staðfærð af Guðmundi Arnlaugssyni (útg. 1956). Tilvitnanir í Játningar Ágústínusar eru úr þýðingu Sigurbjarnar Einarssonar (Bókaútgáfa Menningarsjóðs, 1962).

Staðir úr Hrakfallasögu Abelard og bréfum hans og Heloísu eru í þýðingu Einars Más Jónssonar (Háskólaútgáfan, 1997).

Aðrar þýðingar eru höfundarins.

1. prentun: nóvember 2000
2. prentun: desember 2000

Málverk á kápu: Vilhelm Hammershøi: Interiør med ung læsende mand (1898). Með góðfúslegu leyfi Den Hirschsprungske samling, København.
Kápuhönnun: Næst
Prentun: Prentsmiðjan Oddi hf.

ISBN 9979-3-2121-0

„Því að mynd þessa heims líður undir lok.“
(Páll postuli, I. Kór. 7:31)

I

Flötur hafsins splundrast, loftið fyllist af eimyrju, eyja rís úr djúpinu.

Ekki ráðsett land eins og þessi sem standa í skólastofum eða upprúlluð í áhaldaherbergjum og halda áfram óbreytt árgang eftir árgang. Það hefði ært óstöðugan að kortleggja það: heilu fjöllin hófust og hnigu, jarðskorpan hrækti hraunkviku og spýtti gufu dögum og vikum og árum saman – sem samt voru bara eitt og sama augnablikið af því að það voru engin vitni, ekki einusinni atviksorðið „svo" til að tákna breytingu yfir í ísöld sem kom þrátt fyrir það og lagðist yfir veröldina.

Þá kom rigning í þúsund ár, jöklar bráðnuðu og eyjan átti fullt í fangi með að halda sér á floti, fræ bárust með vindum og hreiðruðu um sig á klöppum og grænt teppi skreið yfir dali og fjöll. Vindurinn sáði og plantaði skógum sem rugguðu sér í lendunum og fuglar settust í lim trjánna milli þess sem þeir kekkjuðu loftið á fluginu.

Einhver hefði sjálfsagt freistast til að segja „harla gott" hér, en það var engu líkara en höfundurinn væri aldrei ánægður, aftur tók að kólna, skógarnir breyttust í mýrar, firðirnir fylltust af ís, jöklar skriðu niður í dali og allt var autt og dautt nema vindurinn sem ýldi í hrönglinu.

Þúsund og aftur þúsund ár sem vissu ekki hvort þau voru að koma eða fara, úrhellið tók á nýjan leik að skúra og skrúbba og vindarnir að sá og gróðurinn að dúk- og teppaleggja. Birki og mýrar skiptust á að vera í sókn, ýmist höfðu fjöllin ekki við að strjúka framan úr sér hríslurnar eða mýrarnar gleyptu heilu héruðin, sem náðu sér aftur á strik í myrkviði svo þéttu að leiðin frá Hornafirði til Reykjavíkur var ófær vegna skóga.

Þetta var land og samt hét það ekki neitt, líkt og tjaldurinn hét ekki tjaldur heldur tjú-tjú og veiðibjallan hét ekki veiðibjalla heldur vaa-vaa. Þingvellir voru þarna án þess að vita af því, líka Lónsöræfi og Vatnajökull – leiktjöldin voru komin upp og biðu orðlaus eftir leikritinu.

* * *

Í upphafi er þögn. Ekki svo mikið sem skrjáf í karmellubréfi, enginn sem ræskir sig eða hóstar, ekkert nema óendanlega smár og heitur orkupunktur sem þéttist og hitnar uns – verði ljós! – efnið ryður sér til rúms í sprengingu sem enn í dag lætur öll lýsingarorð fölna. Líkt og milljónir sæðisfruma þeysir efnið í kekkjuðum gusum út í tómið í æðisgengnu kapphlaupi mót lífgefandi eggi.

Upphafið. Það sem eitt sinn var óendanlega smátt er orðið að öllu sem er. Þetta er svo ósennilegt, svipað og foreldrar okkar áður en þau kynntust, allar tilviljanirnar sem urðu til þess að þau hittust, hvað hefur mátt lítið út af bera í byrjun til að ekkert yrði úr neinu, kannski fárra mínútna seinkun á strætisvagninum og við hefðum aldrei orðið til – eða seinkunin, að það hafi verið hún?

Tilhugalífið er sveiflukennt með óvæntum uppákomum. Loftsteinar æða um himinhvolfið með tíðum árekstrum. Það er loftsteinn sem keyrir á jörðina með þeim afleiðingum að hún hallar um 23,5° sem aftur veldur því að árið hefur tíðir. Út um allan geim eru aðrir hnettir með öðrum höllum eftir aðra árekstra og Úranus sem hefur hreinlega oltið á hliðina.

Fyrsta kastið hefur himingeimurinn verið eins og Tívolísalur með bílum sem tomma vart áfram fyrir árekstrum. Sumir svo harðir að engu má muna að barnið hrökkvi útbyrðis. Loftsteinn hittir jörðina af afli sem sendir jarðslummu út í geiminn þar sem hún umbreytist í tungl sem síðan dansar stífdans við hnöttinn með þeim afleiðingum að við höfum flóð og fjöru en á tunglinu er enginn sjór og fyrir bragðið er yfirborð mánans teygt og togað með braki sem berst með hljóðnemum alla leið til jarðar.

Ef ekki væri jörðin myndi tunglið rjúka út í buskann, ef ekki væri tunglið væri jörðin reikul í rásinni. Tunglið virkar eins og fínstilling á jörðina, gangur hennar verður stöðugur og jafn sem aftur býr í haginn fyrir nýjan leikanda.

* * *

Það er eins með lífið og alheiminn – eina sem okkur stendur til boða er undrun. En þegar það er einusinni komið undir tekur eitt við af öðru eins og á tilraunastofu. Allar gerðir og stærðir eru prófaðar með tilheyrandi stökkbreytingum yfir í nýjar tegundir, ekkert liggur á, tíminn er utan enda, milljónir og aftur milljónir – hverju fengi maður ekki áorkað ef maður hefði allan þennan tíma til ráðstöfunar? Væri ekki líklegt að manni tækist á endanum að skapa æ flóknari efnakeðjur, jafnvel orm?

Það er í mörg horn að líta, jörðin þarf að kólna til að lífið vogi sér á land, það þarf að myndast skurn til að gróðurinn skjóti rótum, skriðdýrin skríði og fuglarnir fljúgi. Lífið hefur ekki við að máta ný og ný form: lífverur koma og prófa sig áfram í einhverjar milljónir ára og síðan exit. Þær eru búnar að segja það sem þeim var ætlað að segja. Það væri annað en gaman ef leikararnir héldu áfram á sviðinu eftir að hlutverki þeirra væri lokið. Af öllum þeim grúa sem litið hefur ljós sólar er aðeins eitt prósent með í núverandi uppfærslu. Sumir lognast út af af sjálfsdáðum, aðrir fá duglegt spark í afturendann, til að mynda risaeðlurnar, þær voru búnar að eiga sviðið í eitt hundrað sextíu og fimm þúsund aldir þegar loftsteinn kom utan úr geimnum og hæfði jörðina.

Tjaldið!

Rykmökkurinn sem þyrlaðist upp dró svo rækilega fyrir sólu að eðlur yfirborðsins liðu undir lok, en spendýrin sem fram að því höfðu verið lítilþæg neðanjarðarkvikindi, fikruðu sig upp í sviðsljósið.

* * *

Lífið í öllum sínum myndum, þetta ófyrirséða líf sem kviknar á einum hnetti í öllum stjörnusandkassanum, gróðurþekjan sem lifir á loftinu og lífverur sem lifa á gróðrinum og kjötætur sem lifa á grasætum – allt lifir á öllu og endurnýjar sig og líður undir lok. Þannig hefði leikritið getað haldið áfram jafn óbrigðult og þessi absúrd-leikrit eftir Ioneskó eða Beckett sem búið er að sýna í bráðum hálfa öld án afláts alltaf á sama sviði, nýir og nýir leikarar í sömu hlutverkum: að fæðast, fá sér í svanginn, fjölga sér og fjara út.

Sjálft leikhúsið tekur að vísu breytingum, undirniðri heldur eldvirknin áfram og leitast við að brjóta sér braut upp á yfirborðið, ristir það í sundur eins og saumspretta og hraunkvikan þrýstist upp í reglubundnum flogum. Möttull jarðar springur og gliðnar og meginlöndin verða til eins og púsluspil fyrir byrjendur. En líka himingnæf Himalajafjöll þegar jarðfleki ýtist inn í annan. Í Afríku brotnar sviðið hreinlega í tvennt, annar flekinn rís upp á rönd og þar sem áður var samfellt skógarflæmi og kjörlendi apa verður háslétta með breyttu veðurfari. Skógur ummyndast í gresju.

Hér gerist það. Skógarmegin halda aparnir áfram að vera apar. Gresjumegin þurfa þeir að æfa alveg nýtt hlutverk, einn af öðrum er látinn spreyta sig í einhverjar milljónir ára – sem fyrir leikstjóranum er „dagur ei meir“ – næsti!

* * *

Hvenær stígur maðurinn á fjöl? Þessi senuþjófur sem í dag fyllir út í sjóndeildarhring sköpunarverksins svo dýrin hafa ýmist hrakist út í útnára eða feta alfarið meltingarvegi mannsins. Einusinni var hann sjálfur lítið hrætt dýr sem önnur kræfari lögðu sér til munns. Það er ekki sjálfsöryggginu fyrir að fara þegar hann stígur sín fyrstu skref. Og það er áreiðanlega alveg rétt mat, þótt nú sé hann löngu flosnaður upp frá rótum sínum og hafi um aldir gert sér svo háar hugmyndir um sjálfan sig að þegar Darwin rétti honum spegil á 19. öld rauk hann út í fússi og vildi ekkert við ætt sína kannast.

Maðurinn kominn af dýrum! Svo ótrúlegt þegar maður lítur í spegil, dýr líta ekki einusinni í spegil og þótt þau líti í spegil þekkja þau sig ekki. Jú, sjimpansinn ber að vísu kennsl á sig, þessi nákomni ættingi mannsins, við erum að 98 hundraðshlutum samstofna.

Allt frá því að Darwin kom fram með þessa óheyrilegu tilgátu, að maðurinn ætti sér apa að forföður, tóku menn að svipast um eftir beinaleifum frummannsins. Og þetta fjarstæðukennda hefur á einni og hálfri öld orðið æ ljósara: steingerð brot púsla myndinni smátt og smátt saman allar götur suður til Afríku syðst. Þar stendur vaggan. Þar finnast elstu leifar mannvistar hingað til, tæplega fjögurra milljón ára gamlar. Þar er aldingarðurinn. Eden.

* * *

Afríka! Alveg vissi ég það, ekki einleikið hvað þessi heimsálfa átti kjörinn sess í undirvitundinni, einhver samhljómur í sálinni sem tók Tarzan svo tveimur höndum. Eitthvað innra með okkur sem fór að ymja um leið og við sáum apamanninn. Hvað við skildum piltinn sem komst í heimsfréttirnar þegar hann hugðist ræna flugvél á evrópskum flugvelli. Ekki flóttamaður frá einræðisríki sem þráði að komast í frelsið heldur réttur og sléttur Hollendingur sem vildi láta fljúga með sig til fundar við Tarzan.

Edgar Rice Burroughs kemur fram með goðsöguna sem sættir mann og apa. Í hópi tugþúsunda sölumanna æddi hann um götur bandarískra bæja og borga um aldamótin síðustu. Strokleður og yddarar var varningurinn sem hann falbauð. Hvarvetna þar sem hann kom lágu frammi myndasögublöð sem voru svo heimskuleg að honum ofbauð. Í framhaldi af því kvaðst hann geta framleitt að minnsta kosti jafn vitlaust efni án umhugsunar. Og stóð við það. Las aldrei yfir það sem hann hafði einusinni skrifað. Uns eina nóttina að Tarzan sveiflar sér inn í hugskot hans, einhver magnaðasta skáldsagnapersóna sem fundin hefur verið upp (þá gerum við ráð fyrir að Jesús hafi verið í alvörunni).

Tarzan apamaður.

* * *

En hinn raunverulegi mannapi, ósköp sem hann hefur verið lítill fyrir mann að sjá: einn og hálfur metri á hæð og höfuðkúpan rúmar varla heila til stórræðanna, 800 kúbik borið saman við 1360 homo sapiens. En af hverju er hann þá ekki api? Hvaða tilkall getur hann gert til þess að við segjum: *ecce homo.*

Ásamt górillunni, órangútunni og sjimpansanum líður hann um skóginn. Eins og þeir er hann full þungur til að hlaupa á greinum og leitast því við að hanga á framfótunum og lesa sig áfram. Þessi lafstelling mótar beinabygginguna, teygir á brjóstkassanum og býr hann undir næsta skref, já einmitt skref: gönguna miklu!

Maðurinn verður til á göngunni: andlitið réttist mót sólu,

framfæturnir dingla með síðum og breytast í hendur með gripi sem gera honum kleift að flytja farangur og tól sem auðvelda honum lífsbaráttuna.

Á göngunni þrengist mjaðmagrindin uns mæðurnar eiga í erfiðleikum með að fæða. Hér er komið nýtt úrlausnarefni fyrir náttúruna sem leysir það óaðfinnanlega eins og allt sem fyrir hana er lagt: afkvæmið fæðist áður en höfuðið hefur náð fullri stærð sem aftur þýðir að barnið tekur síðasta þroskasprettinn í örvandi umhverfi samskiptanna. Það er aukinn skilningur sem opnar manninum leiðina. Það sem hann hefur fram yfir önnur dýr eru nokkur umframgrömm af heila sem duga til að bæta upp veikleikana. Með graftólum nær hann jarðargróða, með bareflum brýtur hann hnetur, með eggbeittu grjóti ristir hann og sker. Hann kann að grafa gryfjur sem hann leggur yfir hríslur og getur fangað allt upp í fíl. Reiðiöskrin þegar stórgripirnir líta þessi slútandi enni á barmi gildrunnar. Öll eiga þau fyrir höndum hina auðmýkjandi göngu í gegnum meltingarveg mannsins og útkomu um endaþarm.

Mennin taka höndum saman og samvinnan fæðir af sér málið. Í fyrsta skipti hefur dýri merkurinnar tekist að skapa eitthvað nýtt. Fuglarnir syngja alltaf með sama nefi, ljónið og fíllinn öskra eins og fyrirrennarar þeirra um milljónir ára. Maðurinn einn bætir mennsku við náttúru. Á meðan önnur dýr endurtaka ævinlega það sama fitjar hann upp á nýju.

Málið er uppfinningin mesta. Meiri en eldurinn. Sem verður á vegi mannsins eins og annarra dýra sem eiga fótum fjör að launa þegar skógareldar geisa. Háskinn er svo mikill að ljónið og antílópan semja grið á meðan þau eru að koma sér undan. Maðurinn einn er áhorfandi og snýr aftur þegar eldurinn hefur lokið sér af. Skarar í öskuna, veiðir upp glóðina og framlengir eldinn með nýju fóðri. Endar með að framkalla hann á eigin spýtur.

Þar með gat hann búið sér skjól fyrir rándýrum, lýst upp náttmyrkrið, ornað sér við funann.

Horft til stjarnanna.

* * *

Hvergi opnast önnur eins himnasýn og í hinu þurra lofti afrísku hásléttunnar. Það bókstaflega skrjáfar í stjörnunum, þessu glimmeri sem ókunn hönd sáldrar yfir húmteppið. Vetrarbrautin hallar sér yfir jörðina sem er hafin upp til himna. Jafnvel hýenan lítur upp frá hræinu og tekur að spangóla. Og máninn, þessi færanlegi lampi, fylgist með svarta hlébarðanum með grænu augun og hvítu tennurnar sem bíða þess að sökkva í holdið rauða, mjúka.

Morgunsöngurinn þegar sólin kemur upp og heill frumskógur fer á fætur. Eða eldingin sem ristir í sundur lofttjaldið svo jörðin leikur á reiðiskjálfi, himnarnir opnast og yfir steypist úrhellið. Mennið hjúfrar sig upp að trjástofni sem skyndilega verður beinhvítur og þetta sem var hefur breyst í öskuhrúgu.

Hvað veröldin er voldug og augljóslega lifandi. Sólin hreinlega snertir mann og vindurinn kemur við mann og vatnið og eldurinn ætla að gleypa mann. Allt er lifandi, jafnvel hræið iðar af lífi sem étur holdið upp til agna uns kjúkurnar að síðustu bjóðast moldinni.

* * *

Draumarnir. Hvenær koma þeir til sögunnar? Það er í draumi sem maðurinn leysir landfestar, vitundin sýður upp úr þessari litlu kúpu og flennir sig yfir veröldina og undirdjúpin og uppheimana. Bregður sér í allra kvikinda líki og stofnar til fundahalda, fær vitneskju úr öðrum heimi. Maðurinn er ekki allur þar sem hann er séður, einmitt ekki þar sem hann er séður, maðurinn er annars staðar. Allt þetta ótrúlega, það er ættað úr draumi.

Og trúin? Þegar við segjum trú megum við ekki einskorða okkur við dottandi söfnuð andspænis klerki í stól og sálmanúmer uppi á vegg. Án trúar hefði maðurinn visnað og dáið eða farið aftur á fjóra fætur og bakkað inn í skógarþykknið.

Dans. Það verður að dansa. Þessi háttbundna hreyfing útheimtist til að verða móttækilegur fyrir yfirnáttúrunni. Það þarf að strekkja húðir yfir hola stofna og seiða fram þyt blóðsins og láta berar iljar berja bumbur jarðar uns göngin opnast á milli kviðar og heila með hvirfilsambandi við ómælisvíðáttur himnanna – í þannig ástandi stígur maðurinn inn í helgidóminn.

II

Veröldin er svið. Það er litla sviðið og stóra sviðið og smíðaverkstæðið og saumastofan og nemendaleikhúsið . . . Alls staðar er verið að færa upp og leika. Við erum öll þátttakendur í sýningum þar sem við leikum aðalhlutverkið í okkar eigin lífi og aukahlutverk í ótal uppfærslum annarra. Allt niður í vegfarendur í hópsenu. Meira að segja sólin sem er prímadonnan í þessari uppfærslu hér, hún er eins og hver annar statisti í sýningum sem fara fram annars staðar í geimnum og eru ekki lítið sjónarspil frá sínum bæjardyrum séð – og samt eins og móða á gleri öflugustu stjörnukíkja horft frá jörðu.

Fjarlægð jarðar frá sólu er 150 milljón kílómetrar. Jafnvel þótt við tækjum okkur far með hljóðfráustu þotu (1000 km á klukkustund) og lífið væri samfellt sumarleyfi tæki því ekki einusinni að leggja af stað. Við kæmum í áfangastað eftir 150 þúsund ár. Maðurinn verður að taka ljóshraðann í sína þjónustu ef honum á að skila eitthvað áfram, þrjú hundruð þúsund kílómetra á sekúndu.

Reykjavík-Peking tæki þá 1/2000 úr sekúndu, enginn morgunmatur, engin Saga-bútík og farþegarnir í laginu eins og spagettí á leiðarenda. Sama ljós er hundrað þúsund ár að sendast yfir vetrarbrautina endilanga og þá tekur við sjálft geimdjúpið þar sem vetrarbrautirnar mynda eins og eyjur og þrjár milljónir ljósára að meðaltali á milli þeirra. Ystu mörk hins sýnilega heims eru á að giska tíu þúsund milljón ljósár og innan þess „ramma" eru áætlaðar hundrað þúsund milljón vetrarbrautir.

Þetta er svo óheyrileg sviðsetning, líkt og stæði til að taka upp eitt andvarp í kjallaraholu í Vesturbænum og leiktjöldin væru öll Reykjavík, Hveragerði, Þorlákshöfn, Eyrarbakki, Stokkseyri, Hella, Hvolsvöllur og áfram allt landið hvert einasta krummaskuð, sveitabæirnir líka með kviku og dauðu, hver einasta hnífaparaskúffa fyllt með tilheyrandi dóti – og ekki nóg með það – Evrópa, Asía, Afríka, Ameríka, já Eyjaálfan einnig – með manni, mús og munum – fyrir eitt andvarp í Vesturbænum!

Heimsmyndin horfir ekki í kostnað.

* * *

En það er ekki laust við að maðurinn bregðist við þessu „örlæti" af nokkurri feimni. Er verið að hæðast að honum? Hvers vegna er verið að tjalda til öllum þessum sólkerfum og vetrarbrautum sem enginn mun nokkru sinni líta, hvað þá stíga fæti á? Er verið að gefa í skyn að leikritið snúist alls ekki um hann? Ónotatilfinning svipað og þegar maður mætir sólskinsbrosi í kokkteilboði og réttir út höndina, en brosandinn gengur framhjá og tekur í útrétta hönd á allt öðrum jafnbrosandi einstaklingi á bak við þig. Fyrir vikið stendurðu umkomulaus með höndina út í loftið, ekki vegur að stinga henni í vasann, langsótt að hagræða hárinu – ef þú ert heppinn kemur bjargvættur með bakka og þú getur notað ferðina til að seilast í kokkteilber á ostköggli.

* * *

Homo erectus er ekki nýjungagjarn maður og helst óbreyttur árþúsundum saman, verkfærataskan hans er svotil eins í milljón ár. Allan þennan tíma leikur hann sama leikritið: að framfleyta sér og fjölga. Einasta nær hann fyllri tökum á hlutverkinu: jurta- og hrææta þróast yfir í veiðimann og safnara.

Til skamms tíma var enn verið að leika þessa frumuppfærslu í bakhúsaportum sögunnar: í Kalaharí eyðimörkinni í Afríku, að fjallabaki á Nýju-Gíneu og í regnskógum Brasilíu. Einskonar tossabekkir í skólagöngu mannkyns, líkt og barnið sem tókst að láta svo lítið fyrir sér fara að það var aldrei tekið upp og stóð að endingu uppi ólæst og óskrifandi á fullnaðarprófi.

En á síðustu árum hefur einkunnaskalinn farið langt með að snúast við. Öndvert við að vera þrælar lífsnauðsynjanna, eins og fyrri mannfræðingar töldu, birtist samfélag veiðimanna og safnara nú sem hið eina allsnægtafélag sem mannkynið hefur þekkt. Færni þessa fólks og hraðlæsi á umhverfi þar sem við erum eins og ómálga börn.

Hreyfanleikinn bannar þeim eignasöfnun, aleigu sína þurfa þau stöðugt að bera með sér, tólf kíló er hæfilegur skammtur, álíka og venjulegur flugfarþegi tekur með sér í handfarangri. Menninguna bera þau í höfðinu: söngva, dansa og sögur. Þau kunna skil á yfir tvö hundruð plöntum og hafa sér til framfærslu. Þau safna engum forða til „mögru áranna". Þau eru eins og fiskar í vatni og treysta alfarið á færni sína til að afla nauðsynja úr umhverfinu.

Þau hafa litla tækni en mikla færni – öfugt við okkur sem ráðum yfir allri þessari tækni, en stöndum ráðþrota um leið og rafmagnið fer.

* * *

Skrefið sem maðurinn tók út úr Afríku var afdrifaríkt. Í stað næringarforða árið um kring færa árstíðirnar nú mismunandi feng: vor með nýgræðing, sumar með jarðargróða, haustið með gnægð af hnetum og ávöxtum – en veturinn skellir í lás.

Landnámið í Evrópu og Asíu táknar nýja getu mannsins. Veiðimenn og safnarar eru á stöðugri hreyfingu, ca. 20 kílómetra í kynslóð. Þannig hefur tekið manninn um 20 þúsund ár að ferðast þessa 14 þúsund kílómetra frá Nairóbí til Peking. Ekkert liggur á. Þúsund ár dagur ei meir.

Obbinn varð samt eftir í Afríku og þegar ísaldir ríktu hefur sú tala auðveldlega hækkað.

Ísinn þakti þá Skandinavíu og stærstan hluta Bretlands. Til suðurs var trjálaus túndra og endalaus steppa með hreindýrahjörðum, mammútum og hrossum. Hæðir og dalir Suður-Evrópu bjuggu í haginn fyrir dýragarð þar sem sumarhiti var að meðaltali 15° með frostköldum nóttum. Loðni nashyrningurinn og sauðnautið, mammúturinn og hreindýrið komin óralangt frá upprunanum. Fjallageit og gemsi reikuðu um ísi krýnd fjöll. Villisvín, hjartardýr og elgir leituðu skjóls í skógivöxnum hlíðum. Ljón, hlébarðar og úlfar ráfuðu um Rivieruna.

Og ekki má gleyma sjálfum safnverðinum: hinum vitiborna manni. Hann tjáir sig fyrst með ótvíræðum hætti í varanlegt efni djúpt í hellum við jaðar ísaldarjökulsins. Lokið fer skyndilega af málningardósinni og upp á bergveggina streyma hjarðir vísunda og hrossa. Síðar þegar ísöldinni lýkur og jökulinn tekur upp heldur mannkynið ferðinni áfram og skilur eftir þessi listasöfn í iðrum jarðar.

Sýningin stendur í þrjátíu þúsund ár án þess að sála slæðist inn í salina. Uns tilviljunin grípur í taumana. Á Norður-Spáni þar sem heitir Altamira (Sjónarhæð) er hundur á harðahlaupum á eftir ref. Fyrirvaralaust fellur seppi niður um sprungu. Húsbóndi hans, veiðimaður að nafni Modesto (Hógvær) rennur á hljóðið og lætur sig síga niður hundi sínum til bjargar.

Árið er 1868.

Var það tilviljun eða úthugsuð ráðstöfun að eigandi jarðarinnar, de Sautuola greifi, var áhugamaður um fornleifafræði? Við skoðun á hellinum tekur hann eftir einhverju pírumpári á veggjum, en gerir ekkert með það. Fólk sér aðeins það sem það er að leita að og hann var á höttunum eftir forngripum á gólfi. Skömmu áður hafði franski fornleifafræðingurinn, Lartet, vakið heimsathygli með munum sem hann hafði grafið upp á hellisgólfi innan um bein horfinna eða útdauðra dýra. Þar með var forsagan komin á blað. Fram að því hafði sagan einfaldlega byrjað í Mósebók.

Árið 1876 fer greifinn á Heimssýninguna í París og hittir sjálfan Lartet sem hvetur hann til að kanna hellinn frekar.

Og það gerir hann. Í för með honum slæst dóttir hans ung, María. Á meðan pabbi hennar krafsaði í gólfið hljóp hún helli úr helli uns hún kom í skúta þar sem faðir hennar hafði skriðið um áður. Maríu verður nú litið upp í loft og hrópar: *Mira, Papa, bueyes!* (Sjáðu, pabbi, naut!).

Með þessum orðum opnaði hún áhrifamestu myndlistarsýningu allra tíma. Í flöktandi skini olíulampans litu feðginin nautahjörð á fleygiferð. Litirnir rauður, okkurgulur, svartur. Ferskleikinn eins og þeim hefði verið smurt á bergið nýverið. Bergnuminn meðtók de Sautuola undrið áður en hann ruddist upp í dagsljósið til að kunngera heiminum fundinn.

Eureka! Eureka! Eureka!

En nú höfðu ótrúlegar tilviljanir tekið enda í bili. Vísindaheimurinn sneri við honum baki. Myndirnar væru svo augljóslega nýmálaðar og nútímalegar. Var ekki einn af góðkunningjum greifans listmálari? Annaðhvort hlaut de Sautuola að vera loddari, eða einhver var að fíflast með hann.

Vonsvikinn lokaði greifinn hellinum, lagðist fyrir og dó.

Heil tuttugu ár liðu áður en fræðingarnir játuðu mistök sín. Þá höfðu fleiri tilviljanir opnað aðra hella og ný listasöfn bæst við Sjónarhæð.

* * *

Hvað er það sem hellamyndirnar birta okkur? Listin fyrir lystina? En dýrin sem koma fyrir (hestar og naut) eru ekki endilega þau sömu og finnast í maga málaranna (hreindýr og rjúpur).

Tjáning á heimsmynd? Mannfræðingar hafa þóst finna kerfi þar sem dýrin standa fyrir kynin tvö: hestarnir karlkynið, nautin kvenkynið. Hreindýrið og fjallageitin karlkyns, mammúturinn og uxinn kvenkyns. En svo hafa aðrir fræðingar komist að þveröfugum niðurstöðum: þar sem hinir sáu karl sáu þeir kven og öfugt.

Nú síðast hefur komið á daginn að mynda er helst að vænta þar sem hljómburður er góður. Sem bendir til einhvers konar helgihalds: að ísaldarfólkið hafi komið saman andspænis myndunum og framið söng og hljóðfæraslátt. Flautur eru vissulega í farangri steinaldarmanna.

En að sumu leyti halda myndirnar áfram að vera lokuð bók, eða hvað gætu geimverur framtíðarinnar ályktað út frá myndum af skeggjuðum manni með staf og heldur á lambi – ef allt annað skorti? Fræðimenn í þeirra hópi myndu sjálfsagt grísa á lambakjötsát, aðrir stinga upp á því að lambið stæði fyrir kvenkynið og þriðju uppgötva að myndinni væri grunsamlega oft fundinn staður þar sem hljómburður er góður.

Eftir stendur tjáningarþörf þessa safnaðar sem kom inn úr kuldanum. Listin fyrir listina. Sumsstaðar hefur fólkið atað lófana í lit og þrýst þeim á veggina líkt og börn gera í leikskólanum. Fyrir kemur að vantar framan á fingurna. Frostbitnar kjúkur manna, kvenna og barna.

Við fyrir 30 þúsund árum.

III

Í kennslubókum hefst Nútíminn með því að ísöld lýkur (lauk henni eða erum við stödd í hléi?). Þá eins og hleypt sé af rásbyssu byrjar mannfólkið kapphlaup yfir hnöttinn. Ísinn hafði brúað Beringssund, þúsundir Asíubúa sættu lagi og runnu yfir til Ameríku, engin landamæri, engin vegabréfsskoðun, í hæsta lagi barrskógar sem spruttu upp óðar og jökullinn hopaði.

Mannfólkið brýtur sér leið gegnum myrkviðið og nemur ekki einusinni staðar þar sem landið þrýtur heldur flotar sér út í eyjar og sker á trjábolum. Að hverju var það að leita? Alltaf þessu sama: landinu þar sem hvorki væri hungur né dauði.

Og nú verður stökkbreyting. Eins og venjulega vitum við ekki af hverju. Af hverju nú? Af hverju hér? Af hverju allsstaðar? Í stað þess að elta veiðibráðina og ávexti jarðar tekur mannkynið að rækta jörðina og temja kvikfénað sem má ganga að í haga. Landbúnaðarfólkið safnar í hlöður og búr og binst sama landsvæði til æviloka. Verkaskipting verður á milli úti og inni: konan verður húsdýr. Um leið er rutt úr vegi getnaðarvörn hirðingjanna, í stað þess að eiga fjórða hvert ár fæðir konan árlega. Mannfjöldasprengja sem leiðir til víxlverkunar útþenslu og árekstra. Rán og akuryrkja leikast á: að hrifsa það sem aðrir hafa safnað.

Er tilviljun að rán skuli merkja bæði haf og stuld? Handanfólkið og héðanfólkið stendur skyndilega augliti til auglitis. Hernaðurinn færir sigurvegurunum þræla og þrælahaldið útheimtir hervæðingu. Jafnvægi samfélagsins riðlast, reislan sporðreisist og lóðin renna öll út í annan endann þar sem fámennur hópur presta og valdstjórnarmanna ríkir yfir vinnudýrunum. Það stirnir á sveitta líkami sem strita við steinblokkirnar sem fórnarprestarnir vilja láta hlaða alla leið til himna. En nokkrum vængjatökum norðar er fólk að dansa í hátíðarskapi og fimleikamenn fara heljarstökk yfir æðandi tarfa og leika listir sínar á milli flugbeittra nautshorna. Mittismjóir menn og berbrjósta konur, hallir með rennandi vatni og háþróaðri lífsgæðatækni.

Og hringsvið sögunnar snýst, flæðandi sólarljós og guðir og menn sem deila sömu veröld. Hópur þúfutittlinga frá nafnlausu eyjunni í norðrinu lendir á torginu þar sem Sókrates efnir til kappræðna við gest og gangandi og hefur ekki hugmynd um að *Oxford University Press* á eftir að gefa það alltsaman út með neðanmálsgreinum og skýringum.

Hvernig geta fuglarnir þekkt muninn á mönnum og styttum? Jú, styttan stendur kyrr, jafnvel þær sem eiga að tákna hreyfingu, fuglinn getur treyst því að kringlukastarinn láti ekki kringluna vaða né stríðsmaðurinn höggið ríða.

Og sólin fæðir af sér nýja veröld á hverjum degi og þurrkar hana jafnharðan út að kvöldi. Undantekningarlítið er uppfærslan sem leysir þá fyrri af hólmi frumstæðari. Hið óheflaða sigrar hið fágaða. Síðan þurfa barbararnir að setjast á barnaskólabekk. Eftir formyrkvun kemur dagrenning, menning rís upp af arfabeðinu og ber blóm í siðfágun uns næsta holskefla traðkar niður reitinn.

* * *

Nú var svo komið að mannkynið hafði sendifulltrúa heims um ból – að undantekinni þessari nafnlausu eyju sem studdi við himininn í norðrinu og hafði ekki samband nema við fuglinn fljúgandi, fiskana syndandi og frjóin fjúkandi. Álfu vorrar yngsta land, aðeins tuttugu milljón ár síðan hnattiðrin höfðu kastað því upp.

Allsstaðar var komið fólk nema hér, bara hér sem fuglarnir svifu án þess að vera „fuglar", fiskarnir syntu án þess að vera „fiskar" – allt var fljótandi eins og óorðaðar hugsanir.

Uns.

Fuglarnir æptu og görguðu þegar skip braust inn í myndina. Vindurinn þrýsti því nær, það steytti á skeri og sjórinn varð andartak krökkur af alveg nýrri tegund, fullri með framandi hljóð. Sumir krömdust á klettum, aðrir náðu að svamla í öldurótinu sem lék sér að þeim eins og korktöppum og kastaði þeim að endingu upp í fjöruborðið þar sem þeir lágu hreyfingarlausir og rann úr vitum þeirra. Þegar veðrinu slotaði mátti sjá hvar skipbrotsmaður freistaði að safna saman sprekum og kveikja eld í hráblautu efninu – allt undir vökulu eftirliti fuglanna sem fengu engan botn í athæfi mannsins. Kösturinn stóð óbrunninn, engan reyk lagði til himins og loks var engin hreyfing utan veiðibjöllur og hrafnar sem hossuðust á hræjunum á meðan brakið liðaðist í sundur í fjörunni.

Á endanum var eins og ekkert hefði gerst.

Það hafði ekkert gerst.

* * *

Þegar reykjarsúlu bar við himin var bálkösturinn fjall. Mökkurinn náði marga kílómetra í loft upp og fuglarnir biðu átekta í hæfilegri fjarlægð. Kannski var það eldstólpinn sem kallaði á hafvillt skip sem þrælar reru í blankalogni upp að ströndinni. Lengi lónuðu þeir útifyrir áður en þeir fundu lendingu. Hlekkjamenn báru vistir upp í flæðarmálið, slegið var upp tjöldum, eldar kveiktir og farnar könnunarferðir um nágrennið.

Landið ósnert eins og íbúð með yfirbreiddum húsgögnum.

Þegar þeir héldu á brott voru engin verksummerki utan

eldstæðið samlitt hrafninum sem hoppaði um og goggaði í leifar af matseld. Og þarna var eitthvað sem glampaði á. Svolítil pyngja hafði slitnað frá belti og sjóðurinn vall út um opið.

Skipið þokast úr sjónmáli, skýin hnappast að fjallinu eins og sáraumbúðir.

Terra nupis, muldraði leiðangursstjórinn með sjálfum sér og síðan hærra um leið og hann benti til landsins: TERRA NUPIS!

Skýjaland – vindurinn tætti orðin í sundur og svo var það ekki meira. Allt bjó sig undir að verða eins og ekkert hefði í skorist – nema hrafninn sem hóf sig á loft með silfurmynt í gogginum.

* * *

Í laupi hrafnsins glittir í pening. Öðrumegin er mannsandlit, hinumegin ögn stílfærðari mynd, en við berum strax kennsl á Rómulus og Remus, hvert skólabarn hefur lært um upphaf Rómar og sveinana tvo sem úlfynjan tók í fóstur. Á sínum stað hefði þessi peningur getað séð einum manni farborða í heila viku, í hrafnslaupi á bak við heiminn er hann tómt glingur.

Hvernig stóð á honum hér? Rómaveldi, þessi mikli heimsstjóri hefur slitnað upp og setur allt nágrenni sitt á hreyfingu. Nýjar og nýjar flóðbylgjur aðkomuþjóða steypast yfir landamærin, Germanir eru komnir inn í Gallíu og Rómverjar þurfa að flytja fastalið sitt frá Bretlandi til að hefta innrásina. Kannski var það angi af þessum liðsflutningum sem barst alla leið hingað norður í nafnleysið?

* * *

Hvernig hafa þjóðflutningarnir litið út í auga fuglsins? Var það eins og fólkið í neðanjarðarlestinni sem æðir með störu eftir ótal göngum og fjarlægt mið í kollinum? Iðandi hersing úr einu landi í annað. Einkennilegt að fólk skyldi ekki vera kyrrt á sínum stað. En það á engan stað, löndin eru ekki komin á blað, það er enginn alþjóðaréttur með dómstól í Haag. Hnefarétturinn allsráðandi þeim sterka í hag.

Þótt talið sé að gervallt mannkyn hafi ekki numið nema um 350 milljónum þá (á móti sex milljörðum nú) er eins og mennirnir hafi átt í mestu brösum með að koma sér fyrir. Hinir stöðugu flutningar og útrásir ættbálka benda til að tekið hafi að sneiðast um lífsbjörgina heimafyrir. Hvernig haldið þið að hnötturinn liti út ef sex þúsund milljónir reikuðu um í leit að æti? Ef hver og einn gæti ekki farið út í sína búð og bakarí? Að sá ætti sem réði yfir mætti?

Hestamannafélagið Mongólar sem í árhundruð hefur þeyst um slétturnar fer í óvenju langan reiðtúr og leggur undir sig nærliggjandi sveitir með þeim afleiðingum að fólkið flosnar upp og ryðst inn í næsta land og hreyfing kemst á fólkið þar og þannig öldu af öldu uns brimskaflinn brotnar á sjálfu Rómaveldi sem er orðið svo innantómt að það fellur saman eins og hol skurn.

Það er alltaf sama sagan: aðkomumennirnir fá lánaðan hugbúnað fyrirfólksins og semja sig að siðum þess og háttum. Smátt og smátt líða hræringarnar hjá með lítilsháttar eftirskjálftum. Á endanum breytist aðkomufólkið í fyrirfólk.

Allt hrynur og rís í tortímandi dansi gyðjunnar Sívu, já Indverjar eru þarna líka og Kínverjar og Astekar – alls staðar hefur menningin verið gangsett eins og úrverk, hver mælir sinn tíma eins og klukkurnar sem við sjáum á brautarstöðvum, flughöfnum og kauphöllum, allar eins utan misvísandi vísar: 1215 París, 2015 Tokyo, 2115 Mexíkó . . .

* * *

Lengi höfðu myndir hugarins liðið um loftið, álíka varanlegar og söngur fuglanna eða skrjáf skógarins. En frá því að maðurinn fann upp aðferð til að festa hug sinn með táknum tóku þær að hrannast upp og lifa sjálfstæðu lífi. Maðurinn mátti hafa sig allan við til að halda í við þær.

Til marks um altæki hugmyndanna var skoðun sem sagði að jarðlífið reiknaðist ekki með, raunverulega lífið væri eftir dauðann. Leitinni að landinu góða var beint til himna. Fararstjórinn er farinn að búa okkur stað: gefið eigur yðar, hafið ekki áhyggjur af morgundeginum, lítið til fugla himins . . .

Til að mæta þessari kröfu leggjast menn út, ýmist einsetumenn eða margir saman. Það verður til nýtt lífsform: klaustrið. Þar geta menn óskiptir gefið sig að samtalinu við Guð. Sólarhringnum er vandlega deilt upp í messugjörð og bænastundir og iðju sem þarf til að fullnægja brýnustu nauðsynjum. Líkamanum hefur verið settur stóllinn fyrir dyrnar, hann er einvörðungu hús sálarinnar. Sálin þarf ekki meira pláss. Sálin þarf ekki mikinn mat og alls ekki kynlíf, ekki frekar en fóstrið í móðurkviði. Jarðlífið er meðganga í myrkri. Dauðinn er fæðing inn í ljós.

Fyrir utan er veröldin: fólk sem lifir og stríðir. Að lifa jafngildir að syndga. Það er ekki hægt að hreyfa sig án þess að syndga, ekki frekar en maður gengur í nýföllnum snjó án þess að spora.

Klaustrið er leið til að halda kyrru fyrir, komast þurrum fótum til himna. Bjarga til eilífðar sál á kostnað einnota líkama sem brennur upp, flækir sig í snörum girndarinnar, festist og verður eilífum dauða að bráð.

Klaustrið rís eins og landgangur til Eilífðar. Munkarnir leggja inn gott orð fyrir þá sem standa fyrir utan. Biðja fyrir sálum syndaranna, þessara sem neyðast til að taka þátt í lífinu eins og það kemur fyrir af skepnunni. Og þeir sem standa fyrir utan stinga lítilræði að klaustrinu til að munkarnir biðji um gott veður fyrir þá. Furstinn gefur þeim landið, framlög berast til kirkjubyggingar, fjármunir renna í sjóði vegna fyrirbæna. Utan um fáeina bræður hleðst vinnulið með skylduliði, klaustrið er orðið að litlu þorpi sem getur talið mörg hundruð manns. Sjóðirnir gildna, skrautið og munaðurinn heldur innreið sína, yfirdrottnun og fylgifiskurinn nauðsynlegi: spilling.

Þá er þess ekki langt að bíða að kjarninn klofni og brott gangi þeir sem þrá að endurheimta hið upphaflega mið: eininguna við Guð, með Guði, í Guði . . . Nýtt klaustur verður til úti í auðninni sem að sínu leyti vex og dafnar uns . . .

* * *

Munkar ýta frá landi í húðkeipum og láta öldur og strauma bera sig á afskekkta staði þar sem ekkert mannlíf er til að glepja fyrir, bara Guð og handarverkin hans.

Því miður varði það sjaldnast lengi, það var hlaupinn einhver hormón í mannlífið: segl birtast við sjónarrönd og munkarnir skríða á nýjan leik út í húðfötin og fela Guði fararstjórn.

Þannig hlaut fundum þeirra og eyjunnar nafnlausu að bera saman.

Þeir koma á skinnbátum eins og munnbitar sem hafið hefur jórtrað og læðir nú út úr sér á ströndina. Og hefur ekki fyrr sleppt af þeim tungunni en það reynir að innbyrða þá aftur – en of seint – bitarnir eru komnir með hendur og fætur sem krafla sig upp í flæðarmálið.

Þeir hafa ekki fyrr brýnt bátunum en þeir láta fallast á ásjónur sínar. Einn hefur reitt á loft krosstré og nú rísa þeir upp á hnén og hefja söng.

Domini gloriae in excelsis.

Undir vökulu eftirliti fuglanna sem halda sig einni hæð ofar.

* * *

Landið allt er eitt risavaxið klaustur. Framferði fuglanna er mælskara en orð: það var hægt að ganga að þeim og velja sér í soðið. Hér voru ákjósanleg skilyrði til að tala við Guð og sköpunarverkið. Þeir formuðu ekki einusinni að nefna það. Guð hafði ekki séð ástæðu til að klína á það heiti. Aðeins látið nægja að staðhæfa að það væri harla gott.

Var þetta fyrirheitna landið? Þurfti ekki að deyja fyrst? Var hægt að láta vind og segl bera sig til Paradísar?

Allt sem fyrir augu ber er sköpun Guðs. Þetta er bein útsending. Þetta er Guð. Loftið fyllist af lofgjörð og latínan blandast gargi sjófuglanna. Hreiðurkörfurnar fullar af eggjum standa svo þétt að það er vandkvæðum bundið að stíga til jarðar. Þeir leggja netstubba í ár og læki og uppskera eins og í Biblíunni eftir að Kristur hafði um vélt: þeir ætluðu aldrei að ná að bisa því á land.

Og fjaran er krökk af kópum og urtum sem mæna á kuflmennina og trúa ekki sínum eigin augum þegar þeir reiða á loft klumbu. Mátti það? Hafði ekki Guð opinberast Pétri í þrígang þegar hann var nagaður af óvissu um hvað honum væri heimilt að eta.

„Rís upp, Pétur, slátra og et!"

Og hverirnir bjóða soðið vatn á nóttu sem degi. Þeir þurfa ekki einusinni að kveikja eld, hverirnir sjóða allt sem fyrir þá er lagt, landið er samfellt allsnægtaborð.

Og tíminn stendur kyrr í tilbeiðslukenndu algleymi, það er eilífur dagur, á hverju andartaki eiga þeir von á því að rödd Guðs hljómi til þeirra úr skýi og lýsi því yfir að tíminn sé hafinn upp og eilífðin tekin við.

En það er tíminn sem tekur á rás, skegg þeirra vex, hárið síkkar, dagarnir styttast og nóttin færist í aukana. Einn morguninn hefur snjórinn kastað blæju yfir sviðið, for-smekk að teppinu þunga sem vindurinn veltir yfir öll kenni-leiti. Frostið dregur ísþil yfir vötn og ár. Veturinn læsir matarkistum. Sorgir búksins sækja á.

„Lítið til fugla himins . . ." En þeir eru flognir burt. Er það vísbending um að þeir eigi að leggja á djúpið á ný?

Hafið hefur breyst í rymjandi ófreskju og loftið er ósýni-legt fyrir snjóflyksum. Dögum saman kyngir niður snjó sem vindurinn tekur til við að sópa í dyngjur. Kofarnir eru orðn-ir að neðanjarðarbyrgjum, þeir þurfa að moka sig upp á við margar tröppur til að líta þetta litla tór.

Kristnihald undir jökli.

* * *

Útifyrir ströndinni getur að líta úthafsselina, þessa voldugu skrokka á þyngd við naut. Kollarnir standa upp úr eins og svört mannshöfuð sem horfa inn til strandarinnar. Hreifarn-ir líkastir höndum í fingravettlingum. Verur djúpsins.

Svo fyrirvaralaust er friðsældin rofin, hafið sýður og kraumar í átökum. Brimlar heyja grimmilega baráttu um urturnar. Sá öflugasti ætlar sér allt upp í marga tugi kven-dýra og á fullt í fangi með að verjast ágangi vonbiðlanna.

Hljóðin berast skerandi inn yfir landið. Sjórinn litast rauður.

Á öðrum víkum búa aðrir brimlar og þurfa að nægjast við færri urtur, tvær og jafnvel eina. Aleinir lóna útifyrir landi öldungar og unglingar sem láta eins og þeir sjái ekki svarta skrokkana veltast um í öldurótinu. Karldýrið sem læsir kjaftinum í hnakka urtunnar og hefur sitt fram með blindu afli.

Áhorfandinn stendur í síladri fjörunni. Kuldinn hefur gert hann dofinn og til þess er leikurinn gerður. Holdið þarf að temja svo að það verði húsdýr í fjósi Guðs. Að þreyta holdið með þrautum, berja það til hlýðni, frysta það úti. Að beina allri ást sinni til Guðs og uppskera að launum eilífðina.

* * *

En gaddurinn megnar ekki að loka hverunum, þeir halda áfram að púa sínum reyk út í hvíta auðnina. Og kuflmennirnir afklæðast og skríða naktir ofan í heita volgruna. Það er engu líkara en öll lögmál hafi verið numin úr gildi: hægur vandi að striplast í frostinu. Þeir tipla naktir um hjarnið, skríkja eins og börn og henda snjóboltum hver í annan. Eins og Guð skapaði þá. Hinir eldri og ráðsettari halda kyrru fyrir í heitapottinum og horfa kímnir á ungu mennina. Þangað til snjókastið tekur að beinast að þeim. „Ekki þetta!" hljómar á latínu fyrst, gelísku svo. En lögmál klaustursins hafa gufað upp, þagnarheitið, hlýðnin við yfirboðarana. Snjóboltarnir þjóta allt í kring og splundrast á krúnurökuðum kollunum. Öldungarnir taka fyrir nefið og láta sig síga undir yfirborðið. Boltarnir synda snöggvast í vatnsskorpunni og leysast svo hratt upp.

Þannig líður veturinn.

* * *

Hvað voru liðin mörg ár? Dagatal er óaðskiljanlegur hluti af kristninni. Tíðir verða að eiga sér stað á föstum tímum sólarhrings, hvíldardagurinn má ekki fara á milli mála og hátíðirnar – kirkjan hefur þegar klofnað út af ágreiningi við að reikna út páska.

Það eru komnir þrír krossar í reitinn undir brekkunni þar sem þeir munu á endanum allir hljóta leg. Klaustrið lognast út af ef ekki berst liðsauki – og það er gott: jarðlífið er eins og að neyða sig til að vaka á meðan himnasængin bíður mjúk og hrein. Hafði ekki Frelsarinn boðað að Endirinn myndi koma þegar fagnaðarerindið hefði náð til endimarka jarðar?

Sumum verður tíðlitið til sjóndeildarhringsins þar sem hann mynnist við himininn. (Manstu í sveitinni hvað við gátum horft fast til þjóðvegarins og bíla sem liðu eftir beinni línu í firrðinni, eða voru það ský? Eftirvæntingin þegar bíll sást beygja inn á afleggjarann og nálgast. Glórulaus von um að það væri verið að sækja þig).

Dag einn birtist segl á sjónhimnunni. Ópið sem bróðirinn rekur upp bindur enda á bænir munkanna. Hver og einn lítur upp þar sem hann er staddur og tekur til fótanna í átt til hljóðsins.

Hægri hönd munksins stendur lárétt út í loftið, langatöng æðir til móts við fjarskann á meðan sú vinstri gefur vokandi bræðrunum mokandi bendingu um að koma. Einn af öðrum tínast þeir frá bænum sínum og mynda krans á kögunarhólnum þar sem þeir gera skyggni með lófum.

Þetta er ský.

Nei, það er segl! Ertu sjónlaus! Sérðu ekki að það er segl?

Snöggvast getur það farið á milli mála, síðan er ekki um að villast: skip vex út úr skýi.

Ekki skinntuðra eins og munkarnir notuðust við. Víkingaskip!

Sumir ætla að flýja til fjalla, neyta forskotsins. Aðrir vilja bíða átekta og reyna til þrautar hvern mann aðkomufólkið hefur að geyma. Hér er hvort eð er engu að ræna. Nokkrir taka til fótanna, aðrir láta fallast á knén. Einn laumast til að veifa.

Á meðan þokast skipið nær. Þeir sem fránasta hafa sjónina lýsa því sem fyrir ber. Í bland við mannshöfuð eru kýrhorn, hrosshaus, hrútshorn . . . þetta er örkin hans Nóa!

Snöggvast kviknar von um friðsamlegan fund.

Munkarnir halda til móts við aðkomufólkið. Maður

grípur um meðalkafla sverðs. Annar mundar spjót. Bræðurnir halda á loft róðukrossi. Strax og komið er í kallfæri hrópa þeir blessunarorð. En aðkomumennirnir skilja ekki einusinni *pax vobiscum* og senda í staðinn spurningar á máli sem bræðrunum er lokuð bók.

Hinir aðkomnu hafa séð kross áður og vita hvað hann táknar, en það bætir ekki úr skák, þvert á móti eykur það líkurnar á úthellingu blóðs: þeir eru aðrir en við.

Áður en alþjóðamál stálsins tekur völdin upphefst kona sem hefur staðið aftarlega í röðinni og tekur að hrópa um örlög sín. Hún er samtyngd hinum kristnu og hefur lent í höndum ræningja. Hættir ekki fyrr en hún hefur verið löðrunguð.

Á meðan hefur öðru skipi skotið upp á sjónarröndina og þokast nær, tekur land í kjölfar hins.

Munkarnir hefja söng á meðan menn og skepnur halda áfram að stíga ölduna löngu eftir að þau eru komin á land. Hnusa, nasa, svipast um.

Allt er nýtt.

IV

Fréttir berast af mannlausri matarkistu úti í hafsauga. Þangað sækja ekki stríðsmenn í von um skjótfenginn gróða, heldur fjölskyldufólk í leit að landi. Hér þurfa að rúmast í einu fari mannfólk, vistir og búfénaður. Að minnsta kosti tvö eintök af hverri tegund: kind, hestur, kýr, hundur, köttur, sýr . . . Siglingin getur varað frá tíu dögum upp í þriggja mánaða volk. Fyrir utan þá sem halda alla leið til himna via hafsbotn.

Hvenær komum við? spyrja börnin, nákvæmlega með þessum orðum (þótt framburðurinn kunni að hafa breyst). Ýmist við skeggjaða vanga feðranna eða í pilsfaldi mæðranna. Og andlit foreldranna snúa mót vestrinu, augun sjónhenda öldur utan enda alveg þangað til haf og loft renna saman í eitt. Vindur blæs í segl, leiðarsteinn vísar veginn, hvalir senda stróka til himins. Kýr baular, kind jarmar, hestur frýsar, hundur geltir, köttur mjálmar, gylta rymur – en laumufarþeginn lætur lítið fyrir sér fara: mús! Svo lítið ber á læðist hún í forðann sem var naumur fyrir. Nagar hraun af hrossi.

En er ekki annar laumufarþegi um borð? Sá vegur þyngst og er þó minnstur að fyrirferð: hugurinn! Þessi harði diskur sem enn hefur ekki tekist að ákvarða hvað er mörg megabæt. Og rúmast í einu litlu heilabúi. Aldrei hægt að gera nákvæmt afrit, ekkert „copy conform“.

Aftur á móti fóstrið í kviði, án þess að móðirin viti er lífsklukka byrjuð að tifa í legi, það fer ekki mikið fyrir því, tvö grömm, við þyrftum smásjá til að greina það, það líkist einna helst síli, við erum síli! Við vorum einusinni síli, við erum komin úr hafinu þaðan sem fóstrið fer í gegnum þróunarsöguna og hefur gert í milljónir ára áður en Darwin stamaði henni upp í *Þróun tegundanna*.

Á öðrum stað í skipinu er annar fósturvísir, þrælahaldarinn hefur ruðst framhjá bónda nýfenginnar ambáttar. Jóðið sem sú írska ber undir belti verður eign húsbónda síns eins og hvert annað amboð eða gripur. Víkingar hafa gengisfellt evrópska þrælamarkaðinn með offramboði. Það er varla til svo aumur bóndi að hann hafi ekki ráð á ambátt eða þræl í bland við önnur dráttardýr.

* * *

Brotlending. Það verður ekki aftur snúið. Öldurnar reyna að hrifsa til sín góssið í fjörunni. Vonandi hefur fólkinu tekist að bjarga eldinum til að helga landið. Sem reyndar hefur helgað sig sjálft með eisu úr iðrum jarðar, glóandi kviku sem vellur og bullar.

Það eru fleiri á leiðinni og einhverjir þegar komnir. Landnámsmenn mega engan tíma missa, arka af stað, hlaupa við fót, keppast upp á hóla, klífa fjöll til að henda landið með sjóninni.

Hvar viljum við eiga heima?

Þeir tala við sjálfa sig, en líka landið, því þótt það sé ónumið mönnum er það þéttsetið öndum. Gapandi trónan er skrúfuð af stafni skipsins til að styggja ekki vættirnar. Með sameiginlegu átaki er farkostinum breytt úr lagardýri í landdýr. Sem horfir á eftir fólkinu fjarlægjast. Hlutverki þess er lokið. Næst þegar mennirnir birtast er það til að hluta það í sundur og breyta því í sperrur og þil landnámsbæjarins.

* * *

Ellefu hundruð og eitthvað árum síðar þegar víkingaskip var loksins smíðað á Íslandi var það umsvifalaust bannað af Siglingamálastofnun og samgönguráðherra. Borið var við öryggissjónarmiðum. Siglingamálastjóri benti ennfremur á að skipið væri skráningarskylt „líkt og allir bátar sem eru meira en 6 metrar að lengd.“ Auk þess ótækt að sigla án vatnssalernis.

Víkingaskipið passaði ekki inn í reglugerðir nútímans.

„Hvar væri Ísland án víkingaskipa?“ spyr Ragnar Torseth, helsti sérfræðingur Norðmanna í byggingu víkingaskipa. Og svarar sér sjálfur: „Það væri ekki til einn einasti Íslendingur!“

Gunnar Marel skipasmiður: „Ef þessir menn hefðu fengið að ráða hefði Ísland aldrei byggst.“ (*Morgunblaðið* 12. júlí 1994).

* * *

Menn fara eldi um löndin og konurnar kvígu. Og bæði kynin tungunni. Nefna það. Færa það í búning orðanna.

Örnefnin verða til við hvert fótmál, bókstaflega fót*mál*. Faxi stýrimaður hefur orð á því að flói sé stór: *Faxaflói*. Öxi fellur í á: *Öxará*. Menn leggja frá sér silunga í brekku: *Reyðarmúli.* Hvalur finnst rekinn á nes: *Hvalsnes.* Kona í landaleit etur dögurð á nesi: *Dögurðarnes.* Á öðru nesi tapar hún kambi: *Kambsnes.*

Ef hún hefði misst tönn stæði þar Tannarnes, ef hún hefði snúið á sér ökklann, Ökklanes, ef hún hefði steypt sér kollhnís, Kollhnísunes. Landið er eins og vaxhugur barns eða kalkipappír undir þunnu yfirborði endurómi hverja hreyfingu.

Hrútar koma hlaupandi ofan úr fjalli niður í Hrútafjörð. Trjádrumbur finnst rekinn á eyri. Trjádrumbseyri? Rekaviðareyri? Trjáeyri? Drumbseyri? Viðareyri? Maður skynjar hvernig þeir prófa nöfnin í munni sér eins og skáld í leit að nafni á ljóðabókina sína. Á endanum er það borið fram: *Borðeyri.*

Þeir koma í víði vaxinn dal: Víðidalur. Sauðir hverfa og finnast í Sauðadal. Svín hleypur út í Svínavatn.

Mann fram af manni býr sama ætt á staðnum og örnefnin ná að rótfestast þúsundum saman. Öndvert við það sem gerist á Grænlandi þar sem byggðin flosnar upp eftir 300 ár, tíu kynslóðir hrökkva skammt ef enginn fylgir á eftir. Hvalseyjarfjörður heitir nú Kakortok.

Og heitið sem Rómverjinn gaf eyjunni forðum – *Skýjaland* – það stóð við nákvæmlega jafn lengi og það entist í loftinu.

* * *

Hornstrandir, Skrúður, Ægisdyr, Alviðra, Bláskógar, Unaðsdalur, Hengifoss, Kaldakvísl, Kaldbakur, Helgrindur . . . Nöfn sem virðast koma að innan líkt og þau byggju í landinu og biðu þess eins að vera borin fram. Höggmyndir með yfirbreiðslu sem gyðja dregur af á vígsludegi.

Hvernig gátu þau tollað? spyrjum við í dag í eilífum vandræðum með að festa tilbúin örnefni á fyrirbæri nútímans. Og höfum við þó ritmál og vegaskilti. En allt kemur fyrir ekki, nöfnin vilja ekki loða við fyrirbærin: Reykjanesbær, Snæfellsbær, Vesturbyggð, Árborg – þau hrökkva af eins og vatn af gæs.

Og nú þegar landnámið hefur snúist upp í afnám þarf að framleiða allan þennan fjölda af götuheitum. Sveitirnar flosna upp og flykkjast í Grafarvoginn og kontóristar mega ekki vera að því að bíða eftir að nöfnin gefi sig fram af sjálfsdáðum: Apalhella, Arkarholt, Arnarsmári, Askalind, Askhella, Álalind, Álftröð, Ánaland, Árkvörn, Ásasel, Baggahella, Bikhella, Boðahlein . . .

* * *

Að hvaða leyti voru þeir frábrugðnir okkur? Hvað eigum við sameiginlegt með þeim? Jörðina náttúrlega, tunglið og stjörnurnar, að ógleymdri sólinni.

En hvað voru þeir að hugsa? Hvað erum við að hugsa?

Eitt sinn í barnaskólanum spurði kennarinn hvort Ingólfur Arnarson hefði verið trúaður. Allir réttu upp hönd, en það kom í þinn hlut að svara. Kannski af því kennarinn var í KFUK og þú vissir að Ingólfur var ekki sama sinnis svaraðir þú neitandi. En hún kunni ekki að meta það, ströng eins og hún var, og tók óstinnt upp ef menn stóðu á gati. Þér þótti það ekki síður leiðinlegt og misstir út úr þér: „andskotinn!“. Þar með var mælirinn fullur og þér var vísað fram á gang í kælingu.

Þarna upplifðir þú útskúfunina. Hvergi sála á ferli á endalausum gangi með óteljandi lokuðum dyrum. Svo heyrðist fótatak. Það var að sjálfsögðu skólastjórinn sem spurði þykkjuþungur af hverju þú værir ekki í tíma.

Ég blótaði.

Hverju?

Þú fórst að skýra út af hverju.

Ingólfur Arnarson blótaði, sagði skólastjórinn. Þú ert uppi á vitlausum tíma, væni minn, fyrir þúsund árum hefði þér ekki verið vísað fram á gang fyrir að blóta.

Fjarlægðist svo eftir ganginum framhjá heiðursverði yfirhafnanna.

* * *

Settu alla sem þér þykir vænt um í skip og láttu þá leggja á djúpið. Láttu þá vinda upp segl og vindana blása þeim á vit hins ónumda. Hver með sína áhöfn í kollinum. Ég ætla ekki að gefa upp farþegalistann minn – utan ömmu – hún er úrkonan mín. Ég var þrettán ára þegar hún dó, samt treysti ég mér ekki til að tilfæra eina setningu úr hennar munni, en andlit hennar birtist mér hvenær sem ég loka augunum.

Einusinni í hita leiks var ég búinn að krota með rauðkrít nafnið mitt á hvítan vegg vinstramegin við hjarta og síðan stóð til að setja stelpu sem ég var skotinn í hægramegin. En fyrr en til þess kæmi greip mig spéhræðslan, mér þótti óvarlegt að gefa mig þannig upp á almannafæri. Nú voru góð ráð dýr, því skrifað stóð:

nafnið mitt/hjarta

Sem út af fyrir sig var enn áhættusamara, það gat táknað að ég elskaði bara sjálfan mig, að ég væri að auglýsa eftir kærustu, að hver sem væri gæti sett hvað sem var í auða rúmið. Þetta var óútfyllt ávísun á mannorðsmissi.

Til öryggis setti ég ömmu í tómarúmið.

V

Hver og einn á sína heimsmynd, sína mynd af heiminum. Hún er kannski ekki kórrétt, en hún er staðreynd. Fyrr á öldum meðan heimurinn var einfaldur og jörðin flöt og kirkjan eini fjölmiðillinn hefur ein og sama myndin hugsanlega búið í flestum kollum. Bara einhverjir Keplerar og Kópernikusar og Galileóar sem hugsuðu sitt. Síðan fór sem fór og hin rétttrúaða heimsmynd sem eitt sinn breiddi sig svo stoltaraleg yfir gervallan heiminn – í dag er ekki eftir af henni nema tætlurnar af sprunginni blöðru.

Síðan hafa margar heimsmyndir blásið út og sprungið. Og nú þegar hugurinn fær að leika lausum hala – í hæsta lagi markaðurinn sem pantar niðurstöðuna – hefur leiðir fyrir löngu skilið á milli vísinda og hinnar hversdagslegu skynjunar. Aðeins örfáir sérhæfðir hafa möguleika á að gera sér heiminn í hugarlund nokkurn veginn í námunda við vitneskju samtímans.

En það er ekki þar með sagt að Jón og Gunna, ég og þú, höfum ekki heimsmynd. Hinn sauðalitaði heimur almúgans skiptir milljörðum. Hver maður er með sína mynd eins og tuggu sem blásið er út í kúlu, en missir fljótt þanþolið, á endanum er henni hrækt og verður að hvítri skellu á gangstétt hugmyndahússins.

Sú heimsmynd sem vísindin vinna með í dag kallast „Strengjakenning“ og er svo víðsfjarri daglegum reynsluheimi að það tekur venjulegan mann ekki nema örfáar sekúndur að láta hana lönd og leið og fara að hugsa um annað.[1]

---

1 „Þar er náttúrunni ekki lýst með hugmyndum um öreindir sem agnir heldur sem strengir, smáger einvíð rof á samfelldni tímarúms. Strengirnir eiga um að velja endalausa fjölbreytni í sveiflum, en hver sveifluháttur birtist okkur sem ný tegund öreindar. Þyngdaraflið kemur ekki aðeins fram eðlilega heldur óhjákvæmilega í strengjafræði, skammtur þyngdargeislunar er ein tegund sveiflu í lokuðum streng.“ (Einar H. Guðmundsson, 1998)

Sjálfur ferðu ósjálfrátt að hugsa um girðingar. Það er fyrsta sumarið þitt í sveit. Þarna tókst þér áreiðanlega í fyrsta skipti að ljá hugtakinu „óendanleiki“ innihald. En það voru ekki stærðfræðijöfnur sem hjálpuðu þér til þess heldur rigningin og leiðindin. Og girðingin. Bóndinn var nýbúinn að eignast þessa jörð og nú reið á að staðfesta eignina með gaddavír.

Þetta var Rigningarsumarið Mikla, þú heyrir enn rigninguna bylja á vaxgallanum, þá tíðkuðust þessir stífu regngallar úr vaxbornum segldúk. Þú veigraðir þér við að hreyfa þig til að finna ekki fyrir vætunni. Eiginlega varstu ekki þú, þú stóðst í sporum bróður þíns sem hafði verið ráðinn hingað í kaupavinnu, en hafði ekki afplánað nema þrjár vikur þegar hann var svo heppinn að fá botnlangakast. Þið fenguð lánaðan bíl til að sækja hann og í einhverju stundarbrjálæði fékkstu að vera eftir til að „leysa hann af hólmi“. Síðan tók hann auðvitað ekki í mál að koma aftur og ropaði nú sæll af öllu appelsíninu sem honum hafði verið fært á sængina.

Sængin þín aftur á móti kom með rútubílnum, ásamt tannbursta og áttavita.

„Ertu að leika myndastyttu?“ kallaði bóndinn þegar rigningin hafði læst þig í fjötra, þér hafði láðst að stilla upp næsta staur. Þegar þú hafðir tekið þér stöðu hóf hann á loft járnflikki (hlekk úr gröfubelti frá stríðsárunum) og þú skáblíndir grettur á afmyndað andlit bóndans þegar hann rak staurinn fet fyrir fet ofan í svörðinn.

Og stattu svo þarna til dómadags!

Ha, ég?

Bóndinn horfði á þig úr fjarska og formaði ekki að svara. Hundurinn Vaskur gelti til áréttingar, annars hafði hann ekkert hlutverk hér og ofvaxið þínum skilningi að hann skyldi nenna að hanga yfir ykkur. Öðru hverju settist hann upp og starði út í grámann eins og hann sæi eitthvað lengst inni í fjarskanum. Eða skaust eftir fugli þá sjaldan slíkur gaf sig fram. Fuglar hafa vit á að halda sig til hlés í rigningu. Kannski hafa þeir haldið að þið væruð að girða í þeirra þágu og botnuðu ekki í því af hverju þið höfðuð strengina fimm úr því að þeir þurftu bara einn til að tylla sér á.

Loks var Arinbjörn, eldri bróðir bóndans, hann sat á þúfu næst hundinum og hafði náð fullkomnu hreyfingarleysi, næstum eins og stytturnar manngerðu sem við sjáum á götuhornum stórborga og þiggja skotsilfur frá vegfarendum fyrir að láta ekki á sér kræla. Uns hann reis óvænt á fætur og tók strikið beint af augum.

Abbi! kallaði bóndinn með munninn fullan af lykkjum. En Arinbjörn jók bara hraðann, í stígvélum við vöxt og virtist detta fram fyrir sig í hverju spori. Það kom í þinn hlut að sendast á eftir honum og leiða hann mótspyrnulaust til baka þar sem hann hóf hreyfingarlausa setu á þúfu hjá hundinum.

Næst var járnkalli stungið í gegnum gaddavírsrúllu sem þið ferðuðust með á milli ykkar. Bóndinn þurfti að ganga töluvert hokinn til að rúllan færi ekki öll yfir á þinn helming. Öðru hverju varð honum litið til þín og hristi hausinn. Þú vissir hvað hann var að hugsa: bróðir þinn var helmingi stærri en þú.

Að því búnu tók við neglingin, galvaníseraðar lykkjur voru reknar á kaf í staurinn eftir að bóndinn hafði strekkt vírinn með kúbeininu.

Þannig dag eftir dag: staurar, gaddavír, lykkjur, járnkall, Vaskur, Arinbjörn, rigningin – lengi vel voru girðingar mestu mannvirki sem Ísland hafði upp á að bjóða. Tímunum saman gat maður ferðast framhjá þessum víðáttulöngu strengjum og ótölulega fjölda af staurum sem afmörkuðu löndin.

* * *

Þetta sumar dó Einstein frá ólokinni heimsmynd. Skrifborðið þakið blöðum með útreikningum sem nálgast örvæntingu. Sú heimsmynd sem þá hafði smátt og smátt þokast í sviðsljós heimsfræðanna, kenningin um Miklahvell, orkaði á hann eins og óráð („Guð kastar ekki teningum"). Hvað þá ef einhver hefði borið hana á borð fyrir ykkur þar sem þið sátuð inni í eldhúsi og slöfruðuð í ykkur grautinn. Skeiðarnar hefðu staðnæmst miðja vegu á milli munns og disks, grautarsletturnar hefðu fallið eftir lögmáli Newtons niður á diskinn og risið á ný eftir alveg stærðfræðilegum líkönum. Að gervallur heimurinn hefði í eina tíð verið pressaður saman í óendanlega þétta og óendanlega heita og óendanlega smáa agnarögn – sandkorn virkaði risavaxið í samanburði – og síðan sprenging sem ryður úr sér úníversinu eins og það leggur sig . . .

Þið hefðuð haldið að um misheyrn væri að ræða eða brjálaður maður hefði brotist inn í Útvarpið og náð valdi á míkrafóninum – þulurinn keflaður með vasaklútinn uppi í sér.

En auðvitað var ekki orð um „Miklahvell", það var „síðasta lag fyrir fréttir" – þetta kvalaóp sem Ríkisútvarpið rekur upp áður en það fer að segja fiskifréttir og tíunda uppákomur í Kúalalúmpúr.

* * *

Var það þá? Loki hafði bæst í hópinn, þunglyndislegur dráttarklár spenntur fyrir kerru. Þið voruð staddir í mýrarfláka að grafa fyrir hornastaur, komnir tvær pálstungur niður þegar sást glitta í eitthvað. Þú hrópaðir, skóflan nam staðar í loftinu og þú flýttir þér að veiða upp ryðgað járnskæni. Rigningin skolaði burt mold og bóndinn ætlaði að úrskurða að þetta væri gamall ljár, en hætti við og hagræddi því á alla kanta eins og hann væri að bíða eftir að sólin skini á það.

Það var spjótsoddur.

Varlega fjarlægði hann mold úr falnum og rigningin hóf að mynda tauma niður eftir fjöðrinni.

Í kaffinu hringdi bóndinn suður á Þjóðminjasafn og þar með var þetta náttúrlega komið út um alla sveit. Það var engu líkara en tilbreytingarleysið hefði þjappast saman og sprungið út í þessum atburði. Gestir tóku að streyma að undir alls konar yfirskyni, já sjálfur Þjóðminjavörður kom akandi í hlaðið á Willysjeppa. Fór æfðum höndum um oddinn og fékk fylgd á fundarstaðinn þar sem hann framkvæmdi vettvangskönnun. Í kaffinu varð þér starsýnt á kúlupennann sem stóð upp úr brjóstvasa fræðimannsins. Þú horfðir á hann handleika gripinn, fyrst klikkaði hann á toppstykkið og fram skaust kúla þegar hann hóf að rissa afstöðumynd á blað.

Síðan bjó hann um oddinn í hálmfylltum stokki og hafði á brott með sér. En jafnvel þótt oddurinn væri á brott átti hversdagurinn ekki afturkvæmt. Blaðamenn frá *Alþýðublaðinu* og *Tímanum* komu á vettvang og tóku ýmist mynd af þér eða bóndanum eða þér, bóndanum og Arinbirni, stundum hópmynd með Loka, Vaski og hestvagninum. Gamla og unga húsfreyjan höfðu ekki við að reiða fram bakkelsi og kaffi. Gamli bóndinn reis upp úr kör sinni og settist inn í eldhúskrók. Þessi þegjandalegi maður talaði nú hæst, lék á als oddi, hló og sagði sögur, efndi til eldhúsumræðna. Þetta var ekki sami bær.

Seinna um sumarið birtust útsendarar Þjóðminjasafnsins á nýjan leik, bogruðu í mýrinni í þrjá heila daga með skóflu og spaða, en ekki bólaði frekar á vopnum fornmanna. Aftur á móti fundu þeir leifar af skeifu sem var aldursgreind aftur til Sturlungaaldar – síðast þegar ég vissi sátu þau saman á hillu í glerskáp á Þjóðminjasafninu, oddurinn og skeifan.

Í kveðjuskyni stakk Þjóðminjavörður upp á skýringu sem hann sótti víst beinustu leið í Sturlungu, kaflann þar sem Sturla Sighvatsson stefnir Gissuri Þorvaldssyni til fundar við sig að Apavatni og neytir liðsmunar til að ná honum á sitt vald. „. . . menn brugðu við hart og brotnuðu spjótsköft þeirra sum . . .“ segir sagan.

Einhver liðsmanna Gissurar hafði hugsanlega misst spjótsoddinn úr pjönkum sínum á heimleið. Mýri II er miðja vegu milli Apavatns og Álftavatns þangað sem förinni var heitið.

Hann hefði betur tekið af honum hnappinn, sagði gamli bóndinn.

Það er alltaf þessi spurning: hvenær á maður að drepa mann og hvenær á maður ekki að drepa mann, sagði Þjóðminjavörður.

Gamli bóndinn: Að fara alla þessa leið með fjögur hundruð manna her fyrir ekki neitt . . .

Og allir væntanlega með tvo þrjá til reiðar, það gerir á annað þúsund hross minnst. Það þætti dágott Landsmót hestamanna, sagði Þjóðminjavörður og taldi sig þar með kominn með kveðjureplikkuna.

Og svo drap Gissur náttúrlega hann, sagði gamli bóndinn.

Ha? sagði Þjóðminjavörður út um opinn gluggann á jeppanum, búinn að setja í gang.

Hjó af honum hausinn.

Þjóðminjavörður rétti upp hönd í kveðjuskyni og ók úr hlaði.

Við stóðum í hnapp og horfðum á eftir honum og síðan leystist hópurinn í sundur, gamli maðurinn gekk í átt að smiðjunni. Skyndilega lyftist hann á sléttu hlaðinu, gersamlega óskiljanleg hreyfing áður en hann hvarf inn í smiðjuna.

* * *

Í andvökunni sástu í anda þúsund hesta ösla mýrina og glampaði á spjót og skildi. Vitundin um að Atburðarásin hefði farið hér hjá garði í árdagsins ljóma.

Og kúlupenninn.

* * *

Var ekki eins og allt breyttist við spjótsfundinn? Það stytti upp! Ég segi ekki að sólin hafi tekið að skína, en það kom þerrir. Tíkin gaut, einn morguninn var sex litlum loðputtum raðað snyrtilega upp við belginn á henni, staurblindir að sjúga. Það var farið í útreiðartúra. Það var farin baðferð í sundlaugina að Laugarvatni, unga fólkið í sveitinni stóð aftan á boddýbíl og söng:

Fyrr var oft í koti kátt . . .

Og þú áttir afmæli. Mjólkurbílstjórinn, þessi sem hafði ekki virt þig viðlits allt sumarið frekar en þú værir mjólkurbrúsi, nú las hann nafn þitt af pakka og rétti þér ásamt Tímanum og öðrum pósti.

Í pakkanum var *Hvers vegna – vegna þess.*

Hvílík undrabók. Hún virtist eiga svör við bókstaflega öllu: Hvað er loft? Hvers vegna falla hlutir? Hvað er rafmagn? Að ógleymdum kúlupennanum:

„Kúlupenninn var fundinn upp árið 1943. Hann er stundum kenndur við höfund sinn, Ungverjann Biro. Þegar skrifað er snýst kúlan og dregur með sér blek fram úr geyminum."

Upp frá því er þér borgið, það er sama hvernig viðrar í veröldinni, þessari stóru, þú átt þinn hulduheim sem lýkst upp í hvert skipti sem þú opnar bókina. Eini vandinn er næði. Enginn amast við manni sem stendur með hendur í vösum. En sá sem situr og les í bók um hábjartan dag, það þarf að ráðstafa honum.

Að sjá andskotans barnið! segir bóndinn þegar þér tekst að reka kýrnar með bókina fyrir andlitinu.

* * *

Þetta var á gullöld framræstingar mýranna. Doddi nefndist pilturinn sem þetta sumar fór hamförum á heimalöndum

Mýrarinnar. Þú varst látinn færa honum kaffi, hann var að vonum glaður yfir að sjá þig, drap á ferlíkinu og stökk til jarðar. Hvernig gat hann verið svona sólbrúnn á miðju rigningarsumri? Það lýsti af hárhjálminum við leirbrúnt hörundið. Hann hafði þá verið norður í landi að grafa allan fyrripart sumars, sól upp á hvern dag.

Það eru nefnilega tvö Íslönd, sagði hann. Þegar það er rigning fyrir sunnan er þurrkur fyrir norðan og þegar hann kemur á fyrir norðan hangir hann þurr hér syðra.

Spjótsoddurinn barst í tal. Doddi taldi sig hafa fundið annað eins, þótt enginn hefði að vísu séð ástæðu til að kalla á „Þá fyrir Sunnan".

Hvað átti hann við?

Hann gekk fram á skurðbakkann og hoppaði fram af. Þú horfðir í glóbjartan hvirfilinn á meðan krumlurnar hrifsuðu hér og hvar í jarðvegsþilið.

Sérðu, sagði hann og lagði fyrir fætur þér mauksoðnar hríslur. Og fyrir norðan eru sko lurkar. Þar voru eitt sinn frumskógar.

Um kvöldið hittist þið aftur í súðarherbergi sem er eins og byggt yfir tvö lítil rúmstæði og mjó renna á milli. Hnjákollarnir snertast þegar þið setjist fram á. Þið skiptist á að lesa valda kafla úr *Hvers vegna – vegna þess* og vefið inn í samræðurnar. Fyrr en varir er Doddi farinn að gera tilraunir. Rífur bút úr dagblaði í lítil snifsi, greiðir sér nokkrar rennur og leggur síðan greiðuna í grennd við agnirnar sem flykkjast að henni.

Rafmagn, segir hann stoltur.

Margar af spurningum bókarinnar vildi hann sannreyna strax, t.d. „Hvers vegna er manni kaldara í þröngum fötum en víðum?" og fór að troða sér í garmana þína. Þú aftur á móti hafðir meira gaman af textanum sem slíkum:

„Þú situr inni í herberginu þínu kyrrlátt vetrarkvöld og

lest í bók. Allt er kyrrt og hljótt umhverfis þig, þögnin umlykur allt, kyrrðin hvílir á öllu, engin óró, engin hreyfing. Kyrrlátt ljós lampans lýsir upp blað bókarinnar, loftið er notalega hlýtt og kyrrt. En eru kyrrðin og hreyfingarleysið jafn alger og þér virðist? Er óhætt að treysta því að hlutirnir séu í raun og veru eins og þeir koma okkur fyrir sjónir án frekari athugunar? Hvað er ljós og hvað er loft?“

* * *

Um nóttina vaknarðu við að Doddi stendur við rúmið þitt og sýnist halda á einum hvolpinum sem lágu nýfæddir á strigapoka í fordyrinu. Alveg eins hárlaus og blindur og teygir fram álkuna í leit að spena. Hann vill að þú strjúkir honum og þú hefur ekki fyrr komið við hann en hann tekur að æla mjólkinni í stríðum gusum, þú máttir hafa þig allan við til að verða ekki fyrir þeim. Dodda finnst þetta greinilega leiðinlegt, það líða frá honum andvörp – svo lyppast hann niður í rúmið sitt og hverfur undir sængina.

* * *

Bróðir þinn var kominn í sveitina án þess að léð væri máls á því að þér yrði skilað aftur í bæinn. Vélarvana heyskapurinn hafði ríka þörf fyrir hendur og fætur. Á meðan bóndinn fór með öllu sínu hyski út á tún að moka á vagninn voruð þið hafðir til að róta úr hlassinu og jafna til í hlöðunni.

Þið kepptust við að stinga kvíslunum í stabbann, réðust að honum með offorsi eins og ófreskju sem riði á að leggja að velli. Ef þið náðuð að vera á undan næstu sendingu kom sá tími allur í ykkar hlut og þið gátuð lagst í ilmandi heyið og hlustað á blóðið streyma.

Þú varst að tyggja strá þegar Ingi lét þessi orð falla: „Ég

held að pabbi og mamma ætli að skilja." Þú hélst áfram að tyggja. (Síðan eru það staðalviðbrögð þegar þú verður fyrir sjokki: þú heldur áfram að gera það sem þú varst að gera, eins og með því getirðu ógilt hina nýju atburðarás).

Á meðan sleit Ingi út úr sér framhaldssetningar um pabba sem svaf á dívan frammi í stofu. Kveinstafi um miðja nótt. Og hinn bráða bug sem var undinn að því að koma honum aftur í sveitina.

Þú skynjar enn áhrifin sem þessi frásögn hafði á þig. Áhrif sem engin frásögn hefur megnað að hafa og verður vonandi „*till the last syllable of recorded time*". Tilfinning sem fór frá heila samhliða niður eftir mænunni og andlitinu, tveir taumar sem kveiktust að endingu saman fremst í tippinu. Tilfinning sem þú hafðir aldrei fundið fyrr og fylgdi henni unaður samfara máttleysi og ávæningur af vætu.

Tilfinningin sem skilaði sér aftur upp í heilann var leiksoppsleg. Atburðarás var í gangi sem þú megnaðir ekki að hafa áhrif á, en varðaði samt grundvöll þinn. Jörðin skelfur undir fótum þér, sprungur koma í veggi og skorsteinninn fellur um koll – þú ert leiksoppur.

Svo birtist Loki með hlassið á herðum sér.

VI

Í huganum ferðu yfir þessa daga sem hljóta að hafa komið á undan, en þú finnur ekki neitt. Það var enginn aðdragandi, engin hemlavein eða tími til að setja sig í stellingar. Sagt er að dýr finni á sér jarðskjálfta löngu áður en hann kemur fram á mælum. Þið aftur á móti, fyrirvaralaust sátuð þið í heimilisbrakinu – það er að segja í óeiginlegri merkingu – það haggaðist ekki svo mikið sem postulínshundur í glugga.

Ég efa að öllu hnuggnari kúasmali hafi gengið á eftir kúm þetta sumar. Sumarið sem Ellý Vilhjálms söng smellinn: „Ég vil fara/upp í sveit . . .“ Þar kemur fyrir þessi lína sem er svo eftirminnileg af því hún fer eiginlega alveg út úr laginu og yfir í eitthvert annað lag: „og mig dreymir um það sem gerist þegar sólin sígur bak við fjöllin . . .“

Þú horfðir til fjallanna sem skyggðu á Reykjavík og reyndir að ráða í hvað þar færi fram. Þegar þú fluttir mjólkina á morgnana mændirðu á mjólkurbílstjórann eins og hann væri með svarið. Loks kom bréf að heiman sem minntist ekki á neitt, en staðfesti samt aðskilnaðinn – þau voru ekki lengur saman í umslagi.

* * *

Hér þyrfti að tímasetja frásögnina ögn nánar. Það var ekki eins og núna þegar börn einstæðra og fráskilinna eru jafnvel í meirihluta í hverjum bekk. Ykkur vitanlega voruð þið þeir einu í öllum skólanum. Hvítir hrafnar. Hálfir skósólar þessvegna líka.

Heimsóknin á „nýja heimilið", þú veigrar þér við að nota klisjuna „í fersku minni". Líkara að það hafi verið steypt yfir hana rotvarnarefnum eins og þessi vaxbornu lík kommúnismans sem halda áfram löngu eftir að hann er orðinn eitt af öskulögum sögunnar.

Mamma ykkar var óörugg, næstum feimin. Það fór ekki á milli mála að hún gekk með barni. Þú fannst það um leið og hún faðmaði þig. Hún hlýddi ykkur vandlega yfir sveitadvölina, líkt og hún væri að leita að einhverju sem hún vonaði að gæti varpað ljósi á allt.

Þið lituðust um í stofunni og báruð að sjálfsögðu kennsl á klukkuna. Næstum sviksamlegt að hún skyldi tifa eins og ekkert væri við þessar annarlegu kringumstæður.

Þið voruð í miðju kökuáti þegar hann kom heim. Hann hélt á stórri svartri öskju sem með einni saman lögun sinni ljóstraði upp um innihaldið. Þú tókst eftir stríðum lubbanum og flagaralegum hálsklút með skákmunstri. Frakkinn flakandi frá og yfir manninum öllum eitthvert kæruleysi sem þið funduð að kom illa við mömmu ykkar: hann var íðí (hvað þessir þrír stafir draga vel upp ástandið, reikult „eð" á milli skjögrandi sérhljóða). Og eins og jafnan var um menn sem voru íðí, gerði hann allt vitlaust. Hann hefði átt að draga sig í hlé, en fór þess í stað að hafa sig í frammi.

Langar ykkur til að kynnast Saxa? spurði hann. Þið Ingi sátuð eins og steyptir í eir, en Bjössi litli kinkaði kolli. Hann tók upp hljóðfærið, *væddist* því og hóf að leika. Fyrst var það temprað og hófstillt, eins og hver annar matmálsundirleikur. Þið hélduð áfram að gera bakkelsinu skil og kakóinu á meðan mamma ykkar fléttaði fingur.

En smátt og smátt færðist maðurinn í aukana, músíkin hækkaði, varð hásari, sundurlausari. Þið voruð hættir að tyggja. Þú hefðir ekki loftað svo mikið sem gyðingaköku. Mamma ykkar var hætt að flétta fingur og nefndi nú í fyrsta skipti nafn mannsins: Jakob . . . (síðan heyrirðu aldrei þetta nafn eða sérð að það taki ekki að engjast og tútna og standa á blístri). Uns hún gaf ykkur bendingu um að rísa á fætur og allan tímann sem þið voruð að klæða ykkur í yfirhafnir og skótau hélt hann áfram að safna glóðum elds að höfði ykkar.

Þið róluðuð svolitla stund um hverfið. Komuð á róluvöll og stóðuð í höm við skýlið. Aldrei hvorki fyrr né síðar hefurðu komið á þennan leikvöll, en sérð honum stundum bregða fyrir í gegnum bílrúðu og allt lifnar samstundis fyrir hugskotssjónum.

Mamma ykkar byrjaði orðavef sem átti að leiða til rökréttrar niðurstöðu en útsogið dró allt í öfuga átt. Loks lagði hún árar í bát og studdi sig við rólurnar: „Mér þykir svo vænt um ykkur." „Pabbi ykkar er góður maður", „Jakob er líka góður maður . . ."

Við verðum að fara núna, sagði Ingi.

Þér verður litið á hann. Allt í einu er hann orðinn fullorðinn. Holdgervingur skynseminnar í þessu sjóvolki foreldranna.

Það var stoppistöð og vagn og mamma ykkar sem vinkaði líkt og þið væruð að fara yfir í aðra veröld. Annað leikrit. Gömlu leiktjöldin voru þarna ennþá, en það var eins og hver annar slóðaskapur: að því drægi að einnig þau yrðu fjarlægð. Hús og munir eru svo undarlega ónæm, andinn getur verið á brott og samt halda þau áfram að standa eins og strandaglópar. Þannig verður ugglaust í heimsendi, fjöllin munu standa löngu eftir að mannlífið hefur liðið undir lok.

Svo hverfa þau líka.

* * *

Þið sátuð í þögn. Það ríkti fimbulþögn við eldhúsborðið. Það gerði útvarpið. Það var ekkert útvarp. Ekki að mamma ykkar hefði tekið útvarpið, þvert á móti: útvarpið var hjá ykkur, stærðarinnar hlunkur með tauklút framan á sér eins og smekk.

Ástæðan fyrir því að það var ekkert útvarp var Jakob. Hann var í útvarpinu. Hann var útvarpið. Það var hann sem las fréttirnar. Fyrir vikið hefur útvarp í þínum huga einhverja allt aðra merkingu en fyrir flestu fólki. Þú hefur aldrei getað skilið fólk sem lætur útvarpið bara mala. Þegar fyrir kom að „óvitinn" á heimilinu kveikti á útvarpinu rákuð þið upp öskur eins og hann hefði opnað fyrir blásýru. Samt, þegar frá leið, með tímanum, smátt og smátt . . . fyrst lágt og síðan hækka ef það var ekki hann. En ef það var „Fréttirnar les Jakob K. Storð . . ." voruð þið höndum fljótari að slokkva.

Aftur á móti hugur manns sjálfs, þar er ekkert *on/off*. Fyrirvaralaust um miðja nótt getur hafist útsending. Í strætó. Á klósettinu. Hvar sem er. Öll orkan sem fer í að bægja því frá. Trufla útsendinguna. En stöðin er of voldug: jafnvel með augun lokuð tekst þér að bera kennsl á rödd hennar. Mamma þín söng í Dómkórnum. Það er jarðarför og kórinn beljar „Allt eins og blómstrið eina". Barítónn sem þú reynir að útiloka þrengir sér nær og nær.

Að athöfn lokinni standa þau á stéttinni fyrir utan. Anda að sér ísætu haustlofti og finna næstum til sektarkenndar andspænis hinum syrgjandi sem rogast með hvítan stokk til fundar við sitt hinsta leg. Þau ganga saman út á Austurvöll. Hann býðst til að sýna henni Útvarpið sem er beint á móti. Hann sýnir henni Útvarpið.

Þessi rödd sem á allsstaðar heima, sem hljómar á hverju einasta heimili í landinu, svo dáleiðandi að „sjá" hana koma út um þessar varir.

* * *

Pabbi þinn var útvarpsvirki. Ég sé hann fyrir mér þar sem hann situr umleikinn viðtækjum í hreint ótrúlegu magni. Fólk virðist setja tæki í viðgerð sem það trassar síðan að sækja, kannski flutt í annan fjórðung, annað tilverustig jafnvel.

Yfirleitt var hann með lærlinga, einn eða tvo, þeir eru þarna líka. Og Áslákur meðeigandi sem var andatrúar. Umhverfis hann var ævinlega krökkt af fólki þótt enginn væri til staðar. Eitt sinn afhenti hann tæki sem hélt áfram að standa á afgreiðsluborðinu. „Veist þú hvernig stendur á þessu viðtæki?“ var spurt. „Ha, er það þarna ennþá? Ég get svo guðsvarið að maðurinn tók við því!“

Þegar farið var að grafast fyrir um það kom í ljós að eigandinn hafði látist fyrr í vikunni.

Útvörp voru heillandi, póleraður viðurinn og tausmekkur og innvolsið þegar bakhliðin hafði verið opnuð: lampar, víravirki og ótölulegur grúi smáhluta. (Sjónvörp í samanburði svo heimsk, þessi sljói skermur).

Og viðtækin ganga fyrir rafmagni. En maðurinn, fyrir hverju gengur hann? Að sjálfsögðu ástinni. Ástin er golfstraumur sem gerir ystu útsker byggileg. Þessi hitabylgja sem streymir alla leið frá Suður-Ameríku og dansar við strendur landsins. Hitaveitan úr hafinu. Ef skrúfað væri fyrir golfstrauminn yrði Ísland óðara statt á ísöld.

Ísak var staddur á ísöld. Svört skeggrótin gerði augntóttirnar enn holari, hvítt litaraftið skildi sig frá svörtu hárinu og flíkurnar flöksuðust um hopandi holdið.

Reiðin hélt honum gangandi. Reiðin er rafmagn. Hann nefndi Kolbrúnu aldrei á nafn. Ef hana bar á góma kom það út eins og truflun í útsendingu. Þar sem áður hafði verið skærasta stjarnan á himninum var svarthol. Samfallið stjörnukerfi þar sem massinn heldur áfram að draga allt til sín með heljargreip sem sleppir ekki einusinni ljósi.

Ísak situr inni í eldhúsi og hugur hans hringsólar í kringum svart hol. Samt er hann fullur af innantómri gleði sem er einhvern veginn fyrir utan hann sjálfan. Hann nefnir nafn þitt og þegar þú svarar bætir hann engu við, kreistir bara hönd þína.

Einn morguninn þegar þú ert að fara í skólann er honum ekið heim í lögreglubíl með hægri höndina vafða í sárabindi og handlegginn í fatla.

Hvað kom fyrir?

Hann bandar þér burt með heilu hendinni. En atburðarásin eltir hann uppi: hann hafði farið inn í Goðheima til Jakobs og Kolbrúnar um miðja nótt og legið á dyrabjöllunni. Endað með að kýla í gegnum sandblásið gler í hurðinni.

Mamma ykkar er áhyggjufull og reynir að fylgjast með úr fjarska. Öfugt við Ísak er hún stöðugt að grennslast fyrir.

Næst vaknarðu um miðja nótt og íbúðin fyllist af fólki. Það er draumi líkast nema þetta fólk dettur um húsgögn og röflar og upphefur söng sem er svo misheppnaður að lögreglan sér sig knúna til að skakka leikinn.

Ef ekki hefði verið fyrir Áslák er hætt við að Útvarpsvirkinn hefði lognast út af. Það var ennfremur Láki sem kynnti Ísak fyrir Ingunni. Hún var hárgreiðslukona að mennt en andalæknir að iðn. Nú er læknisfræðin hvað, sex ára strangt nám og síðan fjögur í sérnámi. Það tekur minnst áratug að verða læknir. Ingunn aftur á móti tók ekki eftir því, hún bara læknaði. Það er að segja: hún var verkfæri í höndum framliðinna lækna, þeir læknuðu í gegnum hana. Og hróður hennar barst víða.

Smátt og smátt varð hún heimilisföst hjá ykkur á Bjargarstígnum. Það byrjaði með heimsóknum sem drógust á langinn. Hún var gift manni sem ofsótti hana. Hún gat ekki farið heim. Og nú tók maðurinn að ofsækja ykkur. Síminn hringir um miðja nótt og þegar svefndrukkin rödd segir halló, berst ekkert svar utan andardráttur. Lögreglan stóð uppi ráðalaus. Eina sem hún gat gert var að taka skýrslu. Safn til sögu heimilanna.

* * *

Með tilkomu Ingunnar var eins og síminn hefði öðlast sjálfstæða tilveru. Þessi svarti hlunkur sem fram að því hafði setið prúður á hekluðum platta, nú hrein hann og veinaði í tíma og ótíma. Ingunn þjáðist af dularfullri gigt og gat ekki hreyft sig úr stað nema á hækjum þegar verst lét. Það tók hana tímakorn að bera sig að símanum (aðrir heimilismeðlimir svöruðu ekki frekar en þeir færu að ganga í prestverk).

Símtölin voru sjaldnast löng, hún hlustaði á sjúkdómslýsingu, nótaði niður nafn og heimilisfang og gekk afsíðis.

En hvernig stóð á því að hún gat ekki læknað sjálfa sig? Það var spurning um kraft. Hún var stöðugt að gefa frá sér kraft. Það er svo auðvelt að gera grín að þessu. En ég ætla ekki að gera það. Hæfileikar hennar voru áreiðanlega tvímælalausir. Auk þess að vera andalæknir tók hún fólk í einkaviðtöl. Á milli hennar og viðmælandans var sófaborð. Hún horfði andartak á mótaðilann og hóf síðan að lýsa persónuhögum hans í ótrúlegum smáatriðum.

Afgreiðslustúlka í bakaríi tekur í einu svipleiftri við urmli skilaboða úr andliti kúnnans. Því skyldi snillingur ekki geta lesið viðmælandann eins og bók? Hvað hann starfar, hverjar áhyggjur hans eru, hverja hann umgengst, hvað hann óttast, þráir . . . hverjar þráhyggjur hans eru.

Heimilið fylltist af fólki sem var komið til að láta lesa sig. Aðallega konur, þær virtust ófeimnari að forvitnast um framtíðina. Kannski af því að kvenfólk var síður gerendur í eigin lífum, þær þurftu að bíða eftir örlagavaldinum á meðan karlmaður neyddist til að smíða sína gæfu sjálfur. Spákona eða miðill gátu litlu þar um breytt.

Þetta andrúmsloft var ekki beint heimilisvænt. Það virkar ekki vel þegar barn truflar transinn með því að spyrja um leikfimidótið.

Ingi var orðinn unglingur og kominn á heimavistarskólann að Núpi í Dýrafirði. Þú fluttir til ömmu þinnar á Miklubrautinni og Bjössi í Goðheimana.

Það varð ekki aftur snúið.

* * *

Úr andliti barnsins mátti lesa harm heillar mannsævi. Frændur og frænkur sem sáu þig á götu hringdu í mömmu þína og boðuðu að það hlyti að vera eitthvað mikið að. Þú sem fyrir skömmu hafðir látið þig dreyma um framgang innan skátahreyfingarinnar og lifað og hrærst í nýjustu tækni og vísindum – nú varstu á stöðugu eirðarlausu rápi um miðbæinn. Búðargluggarnir voru farnir að kannast við andlitið á þér. Allt sem þig langaði að vita hafði vikið fyrir öllu sem þig dreymdi um að eignast. En skorti fjármuni til að öðlast.

Um kvöldið settistu úrvinda við litla eldhúsborðið á Miklubrautinni þar sem amma þín reiddi fram þúsund ára gamlan mat.

* * *

Amma þín var saumakona. Tegund sem leið undir lok með EFTA, en var á öðru hverju götuhorni þá. Vertíðin var á haustin þegar þurfti að sauma á skólaæskuna sem streymdi eins og safn af fjalli og hafði tekið þeim stakkaskiptum um sumarið að flíkur sem smellpössuðu um vorið voru orðnar eins og rytjur af reifi.

Fastir kúnnar voru bjargarlausir karlmenn sem af einhverjum ástæðum bjuggu við kvenmannsleysi og voru í vandræðum með að festa tölu. Að ekki sé talað um ef þurfti að stytta eða þrengja, víkka eða síkka. Allt þetta annaðist Jórunn saumakona. Með málband um hálsinn og saumavél sem sjaldan þagði.

En menn áttu líka við hana önnur erindi. Oft voru það piltar sem hún hafði saumað á í bernsku en voru nú lentir í einhverju bölvuðu klandri. Iðulega stóðu heimsóknir þeirra í sambandi við heitstrengingar um að hætta að drekka eða leggja af reykingar og vildu til sannindamerkis koma flösku eða hálfreyktum pakka fyrir í vörslu hjá gömlu konunni. Aldrei samt þýfi.

Þessi smávaxna kona sem ævinlega horfði beint í augun á þeim sem hún talaði við og þurfti þess vegna oft að halla sér aftur á bak, hvaða kraftar bjuggu með henni sem létu heljarmennin linast upp og gráta? Menn sem hefðu getað rústað íbúðinni með fáum vel völdum hreyfingum börðu máttlausum hnefum í hnéskeljarnar og hrinu eins og börn.

* * *

Í endurminningunni ertu alltaf staddur niðri í bæ. Samt veistu eins vel og stundataflan að þú hefur verið í skólanum lungann úr deginum. Af einhverjum ástæðum sér minnið ekki ástæðu til að halda því til haga. Þú ert á stöðugu rápi og Jakob er ævinlega nærri í snakahvítum Lincoln – húddlöngum, rasssíðum dreka.

Á rauðu ljósi í Lækjargötunni skrúfar hann niður framrúðuna og býður þér far. Það er ung kona með slæðu í framsætinu. Það hvarflar að þér að hann sé kominn með nýja konu, en þetta er þá systir hans, Saga Storð, líka kölluð Françoise Sagan eftir að hún skrifaði skáldsögu (Gengin er glaðværð).

Úr aftursætinu sérðu hana ýta á takka í mælaborðinu sem skreppur aftur út og hún ber glóandi járn upp að löngum hvítum sívalningi. Þau systkinin sitja hvort í sínum reykjarbólstri og halda áfram samræðum. Það sígur á þig værð og þú sofnar. Vaknar við tvö hlæjandi andlit milli framsætanna. Þér hefur verið skilað heim á Miklubrautina.

* * *

Smátt og smátt varð Bjargarstígurinn að einskonar útibúi frá Sálarrannsóknarfélaginu. Einhverju sinni sitja Ísak og Ingunn á tali við enska miðilinn Agnesi Banks og þá segir hún upp úr eins manns hljóði: „Þú átt að lækna!“ (það er eiginlega flottara á enskunni: „*You shall heal!*“, svo Nýjatestamentislegt).

Nei, flýtti Ísak sér að leiðrétta, það er hún og hallaði höfðinu í átt að Ingunni.

En hinn nafnkunni breski miðill var ekki af baki dottinn og tjáði þeim að það væru læknar að handan sem væru á tánum að gera hann að farvegi kunnáttu sinnar. Einskonar viðtæki (kemur það enn). „Allt sem þú þarft að gera er að taka við upplýsingum frá viðkomandi sjúklingi og biðja síðan fyrir honum. Þeir sjá um afganginn.“

Skömmu síðar er hringt. Það er móðir barns sem var með hvítblæði. Hvað gat hann gert? Hann kom erindinu til skila.

Þannig hófst ferill hans. Fyrr en varði var Ingunn orðin eins og hver annar læknaritari (það létti af henni gigtinni óðar og Ísak tók af henni álagið).

* * *

Eftir því sem Ísak verður andlegri þéttist veröldin kringum Jakob. Hann er búinn að kaupa spíttbát og býður ykkur Bjössa í vígsluför til Þingvalla. Það er snemma vors og ísvélarnar byrjaðar að rymja og stynja í Reykjavík. Jakob kemur við í Nesti og splæsir ís.

Þrjá ísa í brauðformi með súkkulaðidýfu og mylsnu. Mikilli mylsnu. Fröken.

Eins og alltaf þegar Jakob segir eitthvað starir fólk á hann. Þetta er röddin úr útvarpinu. Hún lítur svona út!

Framan af gengur allt eins og í sögu, en fljótlega á Mosfellsheiðinni byrjar báturinn að taka niðri á drullumjúkum veginum. Jakob bölvar og fer öðru hverju út til að aðgæta. Það er vont og það versnar: báturinn er tekinn að kljúfa brúna brimskaflana, bíllinn festist. Þið farið út að ýta. Á endanum er Bjössi litli sestur undir stýri svo Jakob geti ýtt líka. Það er orðið framorðið þegar þið náið yfir heiðina og vatnið blasir við eins og gólf í skautahöll.

Vatnið er á ís!

Þið leysið bátinn aftan úr hjá sumarbústaðnum og brennið í bæinn. Svanhvítur Lincolninn er eins og ís með súkkulaðidýfu. Og mikilli mylsnu.

* * *

Indriði tollari býr í sama stigagangi og þið. Eitt kvöldið kemur hann óvænt með bláan peningaseðil og leggur á borðið. Konan hans hafði farið í læknisrannsókn og þau heitið á þig hundrað krónum ef útkoman yrði jákvæð. Bláókunnugt fólk.

Hvað gerðir þú? Þú hljópst sem leið lá niður í Frímerkjahöll og keyptir tindáta. Segir ekki Biblían að Frelsarinn hafi leikið sér að útskornum fuglum sem hann í utanviðsigheitum gæddi lífi? Hjá þér voru það kábojar og indjánar á hvítum og brúnum hestum og yndið mesta að stilla fylkingunum upp andspænis hvor annarri og berjast fyrir þeirra hönd með teygju og pappírsskotum.

Það var kominn svolítill her á báða bóga, en mikill vill meira. Þegar velgjörðarféð var upp urið greipstu til þinna ráða. Neðst í svefnherbergisskáp ömmu þinnar var veski. Fingurnir opnuðu budduna og þú virtir fyrir þér vöndul af tíu- og fimmkrónuseðlum. Þú losaðir um einn fimmkrónuseðilinn og leiðst eins og í draumi niður í Frímerkjahöll og bentir á einn indjánann í borðinu þar sem hann sat vígreifur á hestbaki með hátt reidda öxi.

Hvernig myndi nú Guð díla við þetta? Þú baðst hann fyrirgefningar, en samt hélstu áfram að leika þér að indjánanum og lést alveg undir höfuð leggjast að orða glæpinn við sjálfan tjónþolann: ömmu þína.

Og það var ekki allt búið enn: í einni af daglegum heimsóknum þínum í Frímerkjahöllina mætti þér ótrúleg sjón: indjáni í leðurfötum eins og Davy Crockett og aðdáunarvert hvernig skaparinn hafði náð að kalla kögrið fram í plastið. Þó bar höfuðfatið mest frá: fjaðrahöttur sem náði niður á miðja lend á brúnskjóttum færleik. Andlitið var með stríðsmálningu og laust í greipinni fjaðurskreytt spjót.

Hann kostaði helmingi meira en óbreyttur liðsmaður.

Þessi sýn var svo voldug að þú hljópst orðalaust heim, leiddur eins og svefngengill rakleiðis að skápnum þar sem veskið lá á botninum og fiskaðir upp rauðan ókrumpaðan tíukrónuseðil.

Héðan í frá þurftu tindátarnir að fara huldu höfði, þú geymdir þá vandlega falda í poka á milli þess sem þú stilltir þeim upp. Þú varst hættur að ræða málið við Guð, enda ærið verk að fylkja mannskapnum til orrustu.

Í andvökum varð þér hugsað til pokans undir rúminu og strengdir þess heit að fara í guðfræði í fyllingu tímans.

VII

Hvernig verða trúarbrögð til? Gul eyðimörk, sól í yfirstærð sem á einum degi fer úr blíðulátum yfir í bruna og svo aftur kvöldgælur áður en hún hverfur í kuli og svörtu húmteppi er skutlað yfir heiminn með herskara af stjörnum og gljáfægðu tungli. Iðandi maurildasýning uns sárið opnast í austrinu og sólin fæðir af sér nýjan dag.

Það er eyðimörkin sem elur af sér þrístirnið Móse Krist Múhameð. Og alla minni spámennina. Líkt og undirvitundin hefði opnast og ausið úr allsnægtarbrunni á báðar hendur. Það er engill sem hvíslar Kóraninum í eyrað á Múhameð – að sögn innvígðra – dásamlegur texti sem ein saman fegurðin gerir guðlegan uppruna hans trúverðugan.

Hvers vegna lýkur því? „Hvers vegna kemur enginn að draga okkur á tálar?" spyr skáldið og bíður þess með blýant og blað að engillinn komi og hvísli orðum sem muni endurfæða alla veröldina.

„En það er harðlæst hvert hlið/og hljóður sá andi sem býr þar."

Undirvitundinni liggur æ minna á hjarta. Það er eitthvað í tímanum sem er henni óhallkvæmt: „flúinn er dvergur, dáið hamratröll/ dauft er í sveitum . . ."

* * *

Aldrei hefur neitt yfirnáttúrulegt borið fyrir mig. Og samt hef ég þráð það. Því þótt maður sé ekki beint trúaður, myndi maður ekki fúlsa við engli. Maður væri kannski að lesa, einn í myrku herbergi og bara skinið frá Lúxorlampanum sem endurkastast frá hvítri bókaropnunni. Skyndilega er eins og ljósmagnið aukist, maður lítur upp og það stendur engill á milli lofts og gólfs og ávarpar þig: „*Yður er í dag . . .*“

Maður yrði aldrei samur maður.

Mér kemur Hreggviður í hug. Einhver ólíklegasti maður til að upplifa kraftaverk. Stalínisti og guðleysingi fram í fingurgóma.

Einhverju sinni eru þeir á siglingu til Íslands og áttu 150 sjómílur ófarnar til Eyja. Það var björt sumarnótt og Hreggviður stóð vaktina. Stýrimaðurinn var eitthvað að bjástra í kortakompunni en námsmaður á leið heim frá Þýskalandi sat Hreggviði til samlætis í stýrishúsinu.

Þá sér hann hvar risavaxið loftfar kemur siglandi og nemur staðar í um hundrað metra fjarlægð. Þetta var líkast gríðarstórum diski og yfir honum kúpull, efnið gat verið málmur og gler og ekki að sjá nein samskeyti og ekki kom hann auga á neina hreyfingu innan í farinu fyrir utan þrjá bláa loga líkt og frá gasi.

Hann kallaði á stýrimanninn en stýrimaðurinn svaraði um hæl að hann væri upptekinn. Farþeginn aftur á móti starði eins og fjötraður af þessari sýn og hreyfði hvorki legg né lið fyrr en Hreggviður ætlaði út á brúarpallinn, þá kallaði hann: „Varðig maður! Þetta gæti verið geislavirkt!“

Skömmu síðar keyrði farið upp ljós sem voru svo skær að hafflöturinn lýstist upp og stýrimaðurinn sem fór ekki varhluta af birtunni kallaði: „Hvern andskotann eruð þið að fikta í ljósunum!“

„Kondu og sjáðu, maður!“ hrópaði Hreggviður og þá fyrst gaf stýrimaðurinn sér tíma til að líta upp í tæka tíð til að sjá farið sviptast á brott og hverfa eins og kusk.

Lengi gátu þeir ekki um annað hugsað né talað en alls staðar voru undirtektirnar þær sömu: menn hristu hausinn og skelltu í góm. Uns þeir hættu að minnast á það og ákváðu að halda því fyrir sig.

Hreggviður hafði að vísu sett sig í samband við Háskólann, einhvern stjörnufræðing, en sá bar meiri áhuga fyrir að segja Hreggviði hvað þetta hefði verið en hlýða á frásögn hans. „Það hefur komið ljósglampi yfir skipið . . ." og fleira í líkum dúr uns Hreggviður nennti þessu ekki lengur og kvaddi.

Nú var stýrimaðurinn látinn og verkfræðistúdentinn orðinn framkvæmdastjóri hjá Danfoss og þeir Hreggviður einir um hituna. En jafnvel þegar þeir hittust í fiskbúðinni minntust þeir ekki á það. Létu sér nægja að horfast í augu.

Enginn frelsari, enginn fagnaðarboðskapur, engir lærisveinar.

* * *

Fátt er jafn áhrifaríkt og köllun. Maður með köllun veður í gegnum heilt. En hvernig getur maður verið viss? Sérstaklega þegar allt gengur á afturfótunum. Hvernig stóð á því að einmitt Gyðingar virtust vera lestarstrákar mannkyns? Hlutverk spámannanna var að útlista það fyrir þjóðinni og sætta hana við hlutskipti sitt. Hún átti ekki betra skilið þar sem hún hafði ítrekað óhlýðnast Guði og brotið boðorðin eitt til tíu. En hvað um þjóðirnar sem Guð hafði ekki einusinni virt viðlits, sem höfðu yfirhöfuð engin boðorð, hvernig stóð á því að þeim vegnaði betur en sjálfri hinni útvöldu þjóð?

Hlutverk spámannanna var að sýna fram á að einmitt það væri kærleiksvottur: að vera tyftaður. Þannig ferst foreldri við barn. Það er kallað á það inn á meðan þeir sem enginn skeytir um fá að leika áfram úti. Það eitt er skammað á meðan hinir eru látnir afskiptalausir. Einmitt það sannar væntumþykjuna. Umhyggjuna.

Óvinaþjóðum er opnuð leið inn í landið fyrirheitna, musterið rústað og þjóðin útvalda herleidd. Það sannar bara að Guð var ekki alveg búinn að gefa þá upp á bátinn úr því honum þótti taka því að hirta þá.

* * *

Kristur kemur fram á Sturlungaöld í Palestínu (öndvert við lognið sem ríkti á Biblíumyndum sunnudagaskólans). Rómverskt hernám og uppreisnir með vaxandi þjóðerniskennd. Endurvakin von um að Guð grípi í taumana og setji hina útvöldu þjóð aftur á spor gullaldar.

Og nú verður bylting: landið fyrirheitna sem Gyðingar töldu sig öðlast í Ísrael – Kristur finnur því stað á himnum. Maðurinn er í útlegð á jörðinni, þegar hann deyr fer hann heim.

Kristur stígur út úr flækju Gamlatestamentisins og orðar meginreglur sem eru svo einfaldar að þær rúmast í aðeins tveimur setningum (elska skaltu Guð af öllu hjarta . . . og náungann eins og sjálfan þig).

Þá koma nokkrar sígrænar dæmisögur sem útleggja inntakið fyrir hverju mannsbarni og lærisveinar hafa skrifað niður (sjálfur skrifaði hann aldrei staf, það eru bara lærisveinar sem skrifa). Nýja testamentið eru frásagnir fjögurra samtíðarmanna af hinum stutta ferli (eitt ár) þegar hann gekk á meðal manna í Palestínu og kenndi. Hann virðist ekki gefa mikið fyrir lærdóm, þvert á móti: „Sælir eru einfaldir í anda því að þeirra er guðsríki.“ Hann þakkar jafnvel Guði fyrir að boðskapurinn skuli vera hulinn gáfumönnunum. Hann talar mikið um ríkið á himnum þangað sem við eigum í vændum að fara. Hann líkir því við mustarðskorn sem er allra fræja smæst en þenur sig út í laufþykkni (sbr. alheiminn sem byrjar í örsmáum punkti og flæmist út í víðáttur ómælisins). Jarðvistin er eins og bíslag inn í sjálfa dýrðina, svo fáránlegt að hreiðra um sig innan um skótauið og útigallana þegar sjálfur veislusalurinn bíður fyrir innan. Hann tekur börn sem vísbendingu um inntökuskilyrði. Hann umgengst konur eins og jafningja. Hann gengur þvert á viðteknar hugmyndir og reglur samfélagsins. Á endanum er hann handsamaður, dæmdur og festur upp.

* * *

Leiðtoginn sem þeir trúðu að myndi bjarga þeim yfir til eilífðar hangir lífvana á krossi milli tveggja misyndismanna. Yfir þeim vofa ofsóknir, limlestingar, líflát. Þeir hnipra sig saman hver í sínu horni og hengja haus.

Þá berast tíðindin: líkið er horfið. Konurnar óðamála láta ekki segjast þótt sussað sé á þær. En síðan rís áreiðanleiki frásagnarinnar á því að það voru konur sem áttu í hlut. Ef samtímahöfundur hefði viljað búa til trúverðuga frásögn hefði hann kjörið einhvern skilríkan karl, nærtækast einn af lærisveinunum. Að trúa konu til verksins var ámóta og ef í dag ætti að segja frá stórmælum og velja sýruhaus til sannindamerkis.

Frá því að vera samfallnir, sundurknosaðir, sinnulausir, huglausir, öllum lokið – öðlast lærisveinarnir fíton sem hríslast um hverja taug og streymir frá ásjónu þeirra, stendur fram úr fingurgómunum.

* * *

Lærisveinarnir eru fótgangandi fjölmiðlar. Eins og maurar sem velta á undan sér moldarköggli sem hleður utan á sig og endar með að verða hnötturinn allur. Páll fer um hin grískumælandi lönd að boða fagnaðarerindið. Postulinn er kominn alla leið til Aþenu, á heimavöll heimspekinnar. Hann stillir sér upp á torginu og hefur upp raust. Vegfarendur nema staðar, svolítill hópur hefur hnappast um ræðumanninn. Auðvitað eru allir óvitandi um að þetta er söguleg stund, þetta er bara karl um fimmtugt, sólbrúnn eins og róni, bersýnilegt að hann hefur sofið í fötunum. Skórnir eru útvaðnir og vætlar úr sári á stórutá. En röddin er voldug og það er í henni einhver knýjandi sem lætur þá staldra við og leggja við hlustir.

Páll reynir að setja sig í spor Grikkjanna með sína annáluðu heimspekihefð og mörgu guði. Er ekki að bera í bakkafullan lækinn að bjóða þeim guð í viðbót? En Páll hefur veitt athygli fráteknu sæti þar sem Grikkir hafa gert ráð fyrir „ókunnum guði“. Erindi Páls er að boða trú á hann. Staður hans er ekki eitthvert tiltekið hof heldur jörðin öll og upphiminn. Og samt er hann ósýnilegur. Af honum skal ekkert líkneski gera.

Hvaða erindi á hann við okkur?

Og Páll hermir þeim frá eingetnum syni Guðs sem hann sendi til að bjarga heiminum frá glötun.

Hvernig getur heimurinn glatast?

Páll upphefur ræðu um syndina og dæmigert að þegar hann hefur lokið máli sínu er fyrsta spurningin: Hvað er synd?

Og fleiri spurningar fylgja í kjölfarið: menn vilja fá skilgreiningu á efni annars vegar og anda hins vegar . . .

En í stað þess að svara fer hann að tala um krossfestinguna, Kristur krossfestur á að koma í staðinn fyrir allar spurningar og þar af leiðandi öll svör. Málið er ekki að skilgreina og skilja, málið er að tilbiðja og trúa. Fyrir krossdauða Krists býðst okkur að iðrast og öðlast fyrirgefningu og deyja síðan inn í Himnaríki.

Menn taka að tínast burtu. Krossfestur Guð? Það misbauð fegurðarskyni þeirra. Líkt og að tilbiðja hræ. Guðir áttu að vera spruðlandi af lífi, fullir af fýsnum og endalausum uppátækjum við að finna þeim svölun.

Páll brýnir raustina og tekur að hrópa um yfirvofandi endalok heimsins: Stundin er runnin upp, hinn efsti dagur færist óðum nær. Iðrist og öðlist fyrirgefningu áður en það er um seinan!

En Grikkir höfðu lítinn áhuga á endalokum, upphafið var þeirra hjartans mál. Hvernig hlutirnir verða til, hvernig þeir voru í árdagsins ljóma.

Að líða undir lok, hvernig gat það verið tilhlökkunarefni?

* * *

Páll stendur eftir með harðasta kjarna þrasara. Þá fýsir að fá einhvern botn í syndina. Páll veit ekki einusinni hvar hann á að byrja, honum er kunnugt um kynvillu Grikkja og saurlífi. En sagnarandinn segir honum að láta það kyrrt liggja. Þess í stað fer hann að tala um erfðasyndina. Höggorminn, eplið, Evu, skilningstréð. Grikkir vita að sjálfsögðu hvað höggormur er (tákn læknaguðsins). Epli eru þeim hversdagsfæða. Hvað þá skilningur. En hvernig það getur verið glæpur að bíta í epli til að öðlast skilning – það er slíkt óráðshjal að von bráðar stendur Páll eftir einn.

Einmana haltrar hann af sviðinu og fer að huga að stórutánni.

* * *

Ef Biblían væri skáldsaga myndu gagnrýnendur fljótlega reka hornin í alvarlega veilu. Allt er látið hanga á einu epli. Já, já, ég veit, symbólskt og allt það. En það er samt furðu veikt. Einmitt þetta sem Grikkirnir bentu á: hvað er athugavert við að öðlast skilning? Og viðbrögð himnaföður hlægilega barnaleg: hann virðist upplifa þau skötuhjú sem hættulega keppinauta, þau ætli að verða jafn klár og hann. Rekur þau fyrir vikið úr sæluvistinni.

Kannski ekki fyrr en á okkar dögum sem svarið er komið við spurningunni. Nú þegar maðurinn hefur með skilningnum tortímt og eytt og safnað glóðum elds að höfði gervalls sköpunarverksins. Maðurinn treður æ ófeimnari upp í hlutverki Guðs. Nú vill hann líka fara að skapa. Búa til dýrin hvert á fætur öðru og loks sjálfan manninn. Brydda upp á nýmælum: blanda saman geit og kind, hundi og ketti, hrossi og antílópu . . . Læknistæknin er komin á það stig að það er hægt að græða hjarta úr svíni í mann (og væntanlega gagnkvæmt). Ennfremur hefur opnast sá möguleiki að fjölfalda hreinlega eintök af mönnum og halda þeim á lífi til afnota í varahluti.

Sköpun í gróðaskyni, valdaskyni, drottnunarskyni. Og þetta skyn hefur gert manninn skynlausan. Hann klúðrar öllu sem hann kemur nálægt.

Það er þetta sem blasir við nú en kann að virðast smátt þarna á torginu hjá Páli.

Hann er svangur. Hann er þreyttur. Hann er örmagna. Hann lygnir aftur augunum, við það að lognast út af. Þá er hann ávarpaður. Hann opnar augun. Andspænis honum stendur kvenmaður. Hún býður honum næturgistingu og beina. Daginn eftir gefur hann sig alfarið að þessari konu og hún lætur frelsast. Einnig nágranni hennar, maður að nafni Díonýsíus.

Kona, maður, það var allur afraksturinn af Aþenuferð Páls postula.

* * *

Þannig smáferðast fagnaðarerindið fótgangandi frá Palestínu og sáir fræjum alla leið til Rómar. Þangað eru þeir komnir á endanum postularnir, Pétur og Páll. Í höfuðstað veldis sem spannar gervallan heiminn.

Krossfesting var ekkert nýtt fyrir Rómverjum, krossfesting var einfaldlega ríkjandi aðferð til að refsa glæpamönnum. Árið sem Kristur er talinn hafa fæðst (4 fyrir Krist) leiddi Júdas frá Galíleu uppreisn gegn Heródusi leppkóngi. Uppreisnin var kæfð í blóði og 2000 uppreisnarmenn festir upp. (Ekki er getið um að neinir Passíusálmar hafi verið ortir af því tilefni).

Og Rómverjarnir eru enn betur settir en Grikkir með fjölda guða, þá munar ekki um einn kepp í sláturtíðinni. Athygli vekur að þeir postular skuli ætla sínum guði að koma í staðinn fyrir alla hina. Einskonar *pax romana* á himnum.

Og gríska heimspekin er komin löngu á undan þeim félögum til Rómar. Hér mæta þeim sömu spurningar og í Aþenu, sami orðhengilsháttur og orðasukk. Rómverjar eru ræðumenn. Það skiptir höfuðmáli hvernig maðurinn ber sig, hvernig röddin hljómar, glæsileiki framsetningarinnar. Innihaldið er aukaatriði.

* * *

Hvað er það sem kristnin getur fært rómverskum þegn með alla sína guði?

Fyrirgefningu. Að syndir mínar skuli vera fyrirgefnar. Fyrst að frétta að maður hafi syndgað, að manns eigin smáskítlegu gerðir og hugsanir skuli skipta máli. Því næst að einhver skuli láta sig þær varða, sjálfur Guð almáttugur.

Ég sem er þræll, sem næ því ekki einusinni að teljast maður, ég er til fyrir augliti Guðs. Á bak við himnu himnanna er hann að fylgjast með mér, vakir yfir hverju fótmáli, telur hvert höfuðhár. Og ég sem er kona, æðsta húsdýr bónda míns, sem hann ríður í bland við ambáttir og þræla – ég er hrein fyrir augliti skapara míns. Og ég sem er hermaður, sem hef tekið þátt í viðbjóðslegum ódæðisverkum – einnig mér stendur til boða að skírast og verða nýr.

Fagnaðarboðskapur.

Fólk sem hittist á laun og staðfestir undrið og birtist að því búnu forklárað og endurhlaðið. Fólk sem styður hvert annað og liðsinnir. Þrælum er hjálpað úr ánauð, stutt er við ekkjur og alin önn fyrir munaðarlausum.

Forvitni vaknar um leynilegan söfnuð, kvittur um óhófslíf (vínlykt eftir altarisgöngu), orðrómur um sifjaspell (kærleikur til allra), jafnvel mannát (hold og blóð Krists). Yfirvöldin þóttu sýna þessu liði full mikið umburðarlyndi. Fyrir kemur að þau hrista af sér slyðruorðið, Neró sópar þeim hópum saman til heljar, þar á meðal postulunum Pétri og Páli. Og það sem er svo skrítið, Markús Árelíus, heimspekikeisarinn góði sem í *Hugunum* sínum er nánast staddur í túnfæti kristninnar – hann saumaði hvað grimmilegast að söfnuðunum kristnu.

Æðruleysi þeirra og fórnfýsi vekur aðdáun. Þeir óttast ekki einusinni dauðann. Síst af öllu dauðann!

Jarðlífið er öngstræti þangað sem mannkynið villtist í árdaga þegar Adam og Eva létu ginnast af djöflinum. Síðan hefur gangan verið samfellt villuráf frá allsnægtum til örbirgðar – þangað til Guð sá aumur á mönnunum og sendi þeim son sinn eingetinn til að vísa þeim leiðina til Paradísar á nýjan leik. Kristur er farinn að búa okkur stað.

* * *

Útbreiðsla hinna kristnu vekur furðu. Nú er svo komið að þeir teygja anga sína inn í sjálfar valdamiðstöðvarnar. Sérstaklega er konum hætt, sjálfsvirðing er svo smitandi. Samblendið færist í aukana: í hverri fjölskyldu er einhver frelsaður, jafnvel ekki fátítt að kristnin komist upp á milli hjóna.

Hinir kristnu eru sjálfir undrandi á jómfrúrbyr kristninnar og fyllast sjálfsöryggi. Trú sem var runnin upp meðal fáeinna óbreyttra sjómanna hafði breiðst út með kraftaverkakenndum hætti allt til útnára ríkisins.

Þegar Konstantín keisari lögleiddi svo kristnina snemma á fjórðu öld, var engu líkara en draumur hefði ræst. Vonin og sagan virtust ætla að ríma.

VIII

Rómverjar, enn í dag búa þeir í hugskoti okkar, hermenn í pilsum með sverð og skjöld og háttrísandi hjálma. Patrisíar í hvítum kyrtlum, veröld sem var í versjónum í menntaskóla, niðurlút lásum við úr kjöltu okkar þýðingu á latínutexta dagsins, ýmist Júlíus Sesar í endalausum leiðöngrum í Gallíu eða Ciceró í Senatinu þrumandi formælingar yfir Catilínu: „Hve lengi ætlar þú að misbjóða þolinmæði okkar, Catilína?“ (okkur fannst þá að við hefðum eins getað lært fuglamál).

Nú myndi ég glaður þiggja tómstundir til að lesa latínu. Lykilinn að veröld sem stóð í 1230 ár (Íslendingar hafa verið til í 1130 ár). Sumt er alveg eins og hjá okkur: þeir eru tvífættir, tvíkynja, einhöfða . . . Svo allt í einu óvænt opnast gjá. Í *Játningum Ágústínusar* segir af Alybiusi, leitandi ungum manni sem hefur afráðið að gangast kristninni á hönd. Vinir hans kátir fara á „völlinn“ og vilja fá hann með, en hann hefur fyrirlitningu á skylmingaleikjum, grimmd þeirra og grodda. Einhverju sinni kemur hann í flasið á félögunum sem eru á leið í leikhúsið og þvinga hann til að slást með í för. Allt í kringum sig heyrir hann æstan múginn, upphrópanir og hvatningaróp. Hann ætlar að láta það yfir sig ganga með augun lokuð, en skerandi vein kemur honum til að glenna upp skjáina. Við honum blasir maður sem hefur verið rekinn í gegn, blóðboginn stendur upp úr honum – jafnvel þótt Alybius klemmi aftur augun fer lyktin ekki á milli mála. Athöfnin grípur hann þeim heljartökum að hann er farinn að hrópa og stappa og heimta meira. Upp frá því er hann „húkt“ og eltir uppi skylmingaleiki hvar sem þeir bjóðast.

Að sjá mann drepinn „í beinni“. Það hefur að vísu borið fyrir augu í stöku fréttatíma á okkar dögum, en yrði bannað sem afþreying í nútímanum.

Rómverjar aftur á móti, þetta eru þeirra ær og kýr: að upplifa menn og dýr, dýr og dýr, menn og menn eigast við „í alvöru“. Það er þeirra sinfónía og þjóðleikhús, evrópukeppni, heimsmeistarakeppni, wimbledon, formúla og túr de frans.

Við höfum netið. Klámrásin býður upp á lifandi fólk að eigast við „í alvöru“ sem er í þykjustunni. Veruleikastigi nær þegar húsdýrin blandast í leikinn (dýr kunna ekki að leika). Eins þegar fullorðinn riðlast á barni.

Líkt og Alybius festast unglingar á klámrásunum, foreldrar fórna höndum yfir himinháum símreikningum og senda unglinginn í meðferð.

Og kvikmyndahúsin keppa í óhugnaði, án þess samt að geta boðið upp á raunveruleg líflát. Né hafa þau ráð á hinni heitu lykt blóðsins.

* * *

Ágústínus af Hippó er leiðsögumaður okkar um síðustu daga Rómaveldis (sem engan óraði fyrir þá að væru taldir). Það eru eitt þúsund og sex hundruð ár síðan hann setti punktinn aftan við *Játningar* sínar og samt finnst manni eins og hann sé að tala þetta til okkar núna. Þetta er bara svona strákur, graður og metnaðargjarn. Hann á heima í smábænum Tagaste í Norður-Afríku (þá útkjálki úr Rómaveldi, nú einhvers staðar í Alsír). Karþagó er stærsta borgin, næst á eftir Róm í ríkinu öllu. Hann ætlar að verða lögfræðingur þegar hann er orðinn stór. Það er menntaskóli, bókabúðir, kaffihús og leikhús sem eru ígildi kvikmyndahúsanna á okkar dögum, allt snýst um leikhúsferðir og leikrit og leikara. Þessi óseðjandi lyst unglingsins sem er alæta á heiminn.

Móðir Ágústínusar hefur frelsast til kaþólskrar trúar en faðirinn heldur tryggð við guði forfeðranna. Ágústínus aftur á móti vill hafa frjálsar hendur, heimspekin á hug hans allan. Vitaskuld hafa hinir kristnu textar borið honum fyrir augu, en þeir eru svo frumstæðir og barnalegir að það er ekki hægt að taka þá alvarlega. Kaþólskan er púkó. Maníkisminn er miklu flottari. Maníkisminn hafnaði Gamlatestamentinu og lagði áherslu á að eima hinn vitræna, siðræna kjarna úr Biblíunni. Maníkear breiða út faðminn mót heimspekinni, eins þótt hún sé frá heiðingjum runnin.

Aðeins 17 ára hefur Ágústínus fengið sér fylgikonu og tveimur árum síðar eignast hann með henni soninn Adeodatus (Guðsgjöf). Honum býðst staða bókmenntakennara í Karþagó. Skólastofan er aðskilin frá skarkala torgsins með einu fortjaldi. Nemendur eru efnasynir hvaðanæva úr Norður-Afríku. Menntunin felst aðallega í Ciceró og Virgli: takmarkið er að komast óaðfinnanlega að orði.

Réttur og sléttur kennari reiddi ekki gullið í þverpokum, þegar best lét tókst honum að ná kaupi iðnverkamanns. Ágústínus lætur sig dreyma um trygga stöðu, að komast innundir hjá einhverjum valdhafanum, eignast í fyllingu tímans sveitasetur, garð með rennandi vatni og marmaragöng með sinni svölu viðkomu. Hann tekur stefnuna á Róm til að freista gæfunnar. „Ólmur vildi ég komast til metorða, græða fé, kvongast.“

Honum býðst vel launað starf í Mílanó sem er aðsetur keisarans og því ýmsir möguleikar í stöðunni. En fyrst þyrfti hann að ganga að eiga einhverja vel ættaða stúlku og opna sér þannig leið inn í valdaklíkurnar. Og það gerir hann. Fylgikonan er send aftur til Afríku eftir 15 ára sambúð, við vitum ekki einusinni hvað hún heitir, hann nefnir hana aldrei á nafn í *Játningum* sínum. Barnlaus og nafnlaus er hún send til föðurhúsanna. Jú, eitt að skilnaði: Ágústínus tekur af henni heit um að hún muni ekki hafa holdleg mök við annan mann það sem eftir lifir ævinnar. Sjálfur er hann í vanda þar eð stúlkan sem hann ætlar að ganga að eiga er ekki nema tólf ára og því tvö ár í að hún teljist mannbær.

Í millitíðinni fær hann sér fylgikonu númer tvö til að brúa bilið.

„Hjá mér vóg þyngst sú svölun óseðjandi fýsnar, sem var orðin mér vani og harðsnúinn, kveljandi fjötur . . . Ég þoldi ekki að bíða í tvö ár þeirrar konu, sem ég hafði fastnað mér. Mér lék ekki hugur á hjónabandi. Ég var þræll hvata minna. Því fékk ég mér aðra . . ."

Hann biður Guð að gefa sér skírlífi, „en ekki strax. Því ég óttaðist, að þú myndir þegar bænheyra mig og lækna mig af sjúkleik girndar minnar, sem ég vildi heldur fullnægja láta en slökkva."

Úrvinda af togstreitu verður honum gengið út í garð. Hann varpar sér til jarðar og tekur ákaft að gráta. Honum er öllum lokið. Og eins og jafnan þegar manni er öllum lokið, er eitthvað nýtt að byrja. Hann heyrir glaðlega barnsrödd syngja aftur og aftur: „*Tolle et lege!*" (Taktu og lestu!) . . . Undrandi sest hann upp, þerrar tárin og í hlýðni við röddina seilist hann í ritið sem er hendi næst:

„Ekki í ofáti né ofdrykkju, ekki í ólifnaði né saurlífi, ekki í þrætu né öfund, heldur íklæðist Drottni, Jesú Kristi, og alið ekki önn fyrir holdinu í girndum." (Róm.13,13–14)

Allt verður ljóst að bragði.

* * *

Hvernig þá? Af hverju þurfti kaþólskur maður að fara í kynlífsbindindi?

Það byrjar strax með Páli postula. Hann tekur til við að skrifa óheyrilega flókinn kynlífsbálk inn í fagnaðarerindið. Hinn smurði hafði verið næsta fáorður um kynlífið: hjón eiga ekki að halda framhjá, en að öðru leyti: „sá yðar sem syndlaus er . . ."

En Páli bráðliggur á að prjóna við þetta fyrirmælum um undirgefni konunnar, hvernig hún eigi að sitja og standa og gleymir ekki að hoppa á hommum og saurlífisseggjum, boða og banna og boða.

Afstaða Páls til hjónabandsins helgast í fyrstunni af yfirvofandi heimsendi. Stundin er runnin upp, hinn efsti dagur, Kristur er væntanlegur á ný, himinn og jörð munu líða undir lok og búferlaflutningar hefjast til föðurins á himnum . . . „Þið munuð ekki hafa farið í gegnum allar borgir Ísraels áður en Mannssonurinn birtist . . ."

Það tekur því ekki að ganga í hjónaband og geta börn, ekki frekar en við myndum kaupa heilsárskort í skíðalyfturnar í maí. Tímabilinu er að ljúka.

Svo dróst veturinn víst eitthvað á langinn. Jarðlífið var komið til að vera.

Þá fer á fæturna alveg ný hugmynd: að hafna því, gerast einsetumaður, ganga í klaustur. Og hefst nú glíman ógurlega við kynhvötina, að halda henni í skefjum, ganga af henni dauðri, þeir sem lengst gengu vönuðu sig.

En kynhvötin er eins og ólátabelgur sem vísað er úr kennslustofu. Fyrr en varir er friðarspillirinn kominn á gluggana og veldur enn meiri óspektum þar. Gleypir alla athygli þeirra sem inni sitja.

Ágústínusi er ekki nóg að fara í kynlífsbindindi, freistingarnar sækja að honum í huganum, hann getur varist þeim í vöku, en í svefni er hann varnarlaus:

„Í svefni freista þær mín, ekki aðeins til að njóta ánægjunnar, heldur líka játast undir þær og sækjast eftir þeim . . . Þessar tálsýnir hafa slíkt vald á sálu minni og líkama að það sem ég ímynda mér að ég sjái í svefninum, ginnir mig til verknaðar sem ekkert sem fyrir mig ber í vöku gæti fengið mig til . . .“

Kynlíf hugans. Hér var klárlega um nýsköpun kristninnar að ræða.

* * *

Með Grikkjum og Rómverjum var kynlíf ævinlega tengt viðleitni til að sigrast á dauðanum með því að eignast börn. En hinn nýi hugsunarháttur sem fæðist með kristninni breytir áherslunni. Kynhvötin er ekki lengur staðaruppbót fyrir dauðann heldur höfuðorsök dauðans. Kynlífið færist í fókus sem einkenni mannkyns í fjötrum. Það er snákurinn sem kemur Evu á kynlífssporið, viðskilnaður Adams við Guð var í gegnum konuna, afturhvarfið til Guðs er framhjá konunni. Sú hugmynd fæðist og ferðast með kristninni að manninum sé mögulegt að stíga aftur inn í Paradís með því að hafna kynlífinu. Skírnin var einskonar innganga í kynlausa veröld. Fullorðið fólk steig nakið ofan í skírnarlindina og afklæddist tötrum kynlífsins.

Við erum andfætlingar þeirra í heimi þar sem kynlífið hefur blásið út í áður óþekkt veldi. Þegar sá sem hér yddar blýant var að alast upp átti kynlífið heima á bak við hús í hvíslingum og klámblöðum. Það var ein sjoppa í allri Reykjavík sem hafði þessa vöru á boðstólum og eigandinn aldrei nefndur annað en Kiddi sódó. *Satt* hét blað sem hafði í frammi fyrirheit á forsíðu sem voru jafnharðan svikin á innsíðum. *Hjónalíf* var bók sem við lásum skjálfhent á bak við sófa (kennslubók í samförum).

Kynlíf var ekki á glámbekk. Heimilisblöð á borð við *Vikuna* og *Fálkann* töluðu vandlega undir rós. Hvað þá dagblöðin. Ég man þegar ég sá í fyrsta skipti minnst á samfarir í *Morgunblaðinu*. Það var viðtal við fráskilda konu sem viðurkenndi að eftir skilnaðinn hefðu hún og fyrrverandi maður hennar haft mök. Það var engu líkara en blaðið tæki að loga í höndunum á manni, svo sjaldgæft að lifandi manneskja gengist við kynlífi sínu.

Þetta var seint á sjöunda áratugnum.

Í dag hefur matar- og prjónauppskrift fjölskyldublaðanna vikið fyrir skyldugri uppskrift að kynlífi: stellingar, tíðni, hjálpartæki, hámörkun . . .

Og *Morgunblaðið* sem hafnaði berorðum kynlífslýsingum í líf og blóð hefur heldur en ekki söðlað um. Sjálfur forseti Bandaríkjanna reið á vaðið, blaðið birti orðrétt skýrsluna þar sem lýst var fyrir gervöllu mannkyni viðureign leiðtoga hins frjálsa heims við liðlétting sinn.

* * *

Hvernig hefðu Rómverjar litið á málið? Um það bil sem kristnin var leidd í lög ólst ungur maður úr heldristétt upp við heimssýn þar sem hann hafði tögl og hagldir. Konur, þrælar og barbarar voru sett skör lægra. Munurinn mesti var á milli yfirstéttarkarls og kvenmanns. Læknavísindin útlistuðu að karlmenn yrðu þau fóstur sem nutu kjöraðstæðna við getnað. Það hafði með hita sæðisins að gera: karlmaður með alla eiginleika karlmanns varð til úr heitu sæði. Konan var líkt og kaka sem nær ekki að bakast til fulls, ónógt hitastig gerir að verkum að hún er alla tíð hrá í miðjunni. Konur voru misheppnaðir karlar. Mánaðarlegar blæðingar sönnuðu að þær náðu ekki að brenna upp umframhita jafnóðum eins og karlmenn með sæðisspýtingunni.

En karlmennska var fjarri því að vera gefin í eitt skipti fyrir öll. Karlmaður gat ævinlega átt á hættu að verða argur. Það kostaði stöðugt átak að viðhalda karlmennsku sem gætti í fasi og rödd.

Æsingurinn sem fylgir ástarleiknum var Rómverjum

framandi. Að ríða var að koma blóðinu til að sjóða svo útkoman yrði sæði. Sæði var blóð á suðupunkti. Fullnæging var minniháttar flog, samanber froðuna í munni hins flogaveika.

Ekki var ráðlegt að hafa tíð mök, sæðislosunin minnkaði hita karlmannsins og gat gert hann kvenlegan. Hinn karlmannlegi maður þurfti allra sinna muna með.

Samfarir urðu að taka mið af því að maðurinn mátti ekki missa stjórn á sér. Samkynhneigð var ekki stórmál, nema í passífri stellingu. Það gildir að vera gerandinn. Konan á ekki að vera ofan á manninum, það er passíft. Munnmök eru í lagi af konunnar hálfu, en maðurinn hættir karlmennsku sinni ef hann geldur í sömu mynt. Kynnautnin sem slík var ekkert mál fyrir siðferðið, ógnin stafar af þiggjandalegri stellingu í sjálfum ástarleiknum eða taka niður fyrir sig með lægra settum.

* * *

Þegar Ágústínus segir skilið við kynlífið er hann 33 ára. Það er í Mílanó á páskum árið 387. Í eldingu upprisudagsins gengur hann ásamt hópi trúnema á öllum aldri og báðum kynjum til skírnarkapellu sem er í útbroti frá meginskipi basilíkunnar. Einn og einn er leiddur á bak við tjald þar sem þau stíga nakin niður í skírnarlaugina. Það er sjálfur Ambrósíus biskup sem framkvæmir athöfnina, víðkunnur kennimaður og upphafsmaður sálmasöngs sem dregur mannfjölda til hverrar messu. Þrisvar sinnum færir hann höfuð Ágústínusar undir yfirborðið. Og hefur yfir orðin dularfullu. Því næst er hinn skírði færður í hvítan kyrtil og leiddur inn í meginskipið þar sem honum mætir fagnaðarkliður safnaðarins í bland við ilm reykelsanna og skjannabirtu kertanna. Nýgræðingarnir taka sér stöðu á upphækkuðu gólfi við altarið. Þeir eiga í vændum fyrstu þátttöku í leyndardómi hins upprisna.

Síðan stígur Ambrósíus í stólinn.

Hann er skeleggur talsmaður algers skírlífis. Skírlífið er það sem skilur okkur frá dýrunum. Líkaminn er aðeins hjálpartæki sálarinnar og fellur úr gildi óðar og sálin hefur fundið Guð. Kirkjan er í hlutverki brúðarinnar, brúðguminn er Kristur. Og líkingamál Ambrósíusar er gegnsýrt af kossum og kyssingum:

„. . . sálin hefur nú öðlast lausn frá líkamanum, hún hefur snúið baki við nautnum og lystisemdum holdsins og varpað frá sér áhyggju þessa heims. Nú þráir hún það eitt að mega anda að sér hinni guðlegu nærveru og tjáir óþol sitt með þessum orðum: „Hann kyssi mig kossi munns síns . . ." Og það er ekki einn koss sem hún þráir heldur kossaflóð uns þrá hennar er fullnægt."

* * *

Að lokinni skírn í Mílanó heldur Ágústínus aftur til Afríku þar sem hann gerist prestur fyrst, biskup svo. Og úr penna hans tekur að flæða sæði hins nýja siðar.

Auk Játninganna hafa menn talið á þriðja hundrað bréf, á sjötta hundrað predikanir og 113 fræðirit, sum firna löng. Hvöss árásar- og deilurit í bland við hómilíur. Því kristnin er óslitinn vígvöllur þrátt fyrir kærleiksboðorð. Samkvæmt skrá sem samtímamaður Ágústínusar tekur saman eru trúvillurnar í heiminum eitt hundrað fimmtíu og sex.

Kristur var mátulega búinn að þakka Guði fyrir að hylja merkinguna fyrir „hyggindamönnunum". Á endanum voru það þeir sem klófestu boðskapinn. Og menntamennirnir spurðu spurninga. Þeir vildu fá að vita hvers eðlis sambandið á milli Föður og Sonar væri. Voru þeir jafnrétthár, jafnöflugir? Hafði Guð tapað einhverju af krafti sínum við að stofna til sonarins? Var Jesú guð sem hafði gerst maður eða maður sem hafði gerst guð? Og heilagur andi, hvaðan kom hann? Hvernig bar að skilgreina engla? Hvernig yrði lífinu háttað í eilífðinni? Maður sem dæi gamall, yrði hann aftur ungur og barn sem dæi nýfætt tæki það út þroska á himnum? Og hvað með hjónabandið, myndi það endurnýjast í eilífa lífinu? Maður sem hafði átt margar konur, sæti hann uppi með þær allar eftir dauðann? Og hvernig yrðu menn útlits? Plató hafði talið keiluna fullkomnasta formið, var ekki sennilegt að menn yrðu keilulaga hjá Guði?

Á öllu þessu reynir Ágústínus að henda reiður í höfuðverki sínu: *Borg Guðs*. Rótin til þess var málflutningur heiðingjanna sem vildu kenna kristninni um ófarir rómverska ríkisins. Barbararnir sem Rómverjar höfðu brotið undir sig með háþróuðu samgöngukerfi notuðu nú þessa sömu vegi til að ráðast inn í lönd herraþjóðarinnar. Fyrr en varði voru þeir búnir að leggja undir sig höfuðborg ríkisins.

„Þarna sjáiði!“ hrópa hinir heiðnu og blása til nýrrar sóknar. „Á meðan við héldum tryggð við okkar gömlu guði gat enginn boðið okkur byrginn. Nú fara óaldarflokkar rænandi og ruplandi um sjálfa Rómaborg! Eða hvernig á öðruvísi að fara þegar hinn nýi siður býður hægri vangann þeim sem greiðir högg á þann vinstri?“

Þá er það að Ágústínus mundar pennann og spyr: Hverju reiddust goðin . . .? og tínir síðan til alla skelli mannkyns fram að kristnitöku. Það er fyrsta bók. Síðan koma tuttugu og ein í kjölfarið þar sem hann fer um víðan völl heimspeki og hjátrúar, setur fram rétttrúnað, ræðst gegn rangtúlkunum og brýtur til mergjar kynhvötina. Hann er 58 ára á blaðsíðu eitt, 73 þegar hann setur punkt.

Öll olían sem skal hafa brunnið á lampanum hans. Eða pennarnir, blekið og pappírinn. Þrjú þúsund þéttprentaðar síður í nútímaútgáfu.

Hér mótar Ágústínus skiptinguna örlagaríku í ríki Guðs og ríki manna. Hið síðarnefnda er undirlagt af hinum venjulegu handaskolum mannanna. Það er dæmt til að farast. En það gerir ekkert til, Borg Guðs bíður hinna útvöldu þar sem frómir munu finnast á „feginsdegi fira", alheilir og orðnir nýir.

Rómaveldi má hrynja.

Og Rómaveldi hrynur. Gotar steypast yfir Ítalíuskagann en Vandalar streyma niður Spán og láta ekki staðar numið fyrr en á norðurströnd Afríku. Í banalegunni berst Ágústínusi gnýrinn frá ragnarökum veraldarinnar. Barbararnir eru komnir að borgarhliðum Hippó. Kirkjur eru brotnar, guðsmönnum slátrað, eldur lagður í húsin og íbúarnir herleiddir.

Ljósið slokknar.

* * *

En barbararnir, hvað taka þeir til bragðs? Nú er ránsfengurinn orðinn þeirra og þar af leiðandi ekki hægt að lifa á ránum lengur. Þeir þurfa að koma einhverju sköpulagi á eignina. Heima hjá sér eru þeir sveitamenn sem lifa á sauðfjárrækt. Borgir eru þeim gagnslausar. Þær falla í auðn og eyði, hin rómuðu mannvirki Rómverjanna verpast mold, vefjast gróðri, springa, molna, hrynja. Tíminn hefur svo græna fingur, það má aldrei sofna á verðinum, þá grær hann yfir spor okkar.

Kirkjan aftur á móti vakir. Í kringum hana er tekið til hendinni, guðshús rísa: basilíkur, kapellur, dómkirkjur, klaustur. Og guðsmennirnir eiga erindi við barbarana, þeir vilja boða þeim Guð, Krist og Anda helgan.

Í fyrstu umferð eru þeir náttúrlega drepnir, en þeir láta ekki deigan síga og koma aftur og aftur. Á endanum semja barbararnir sig að siðum fyrirfólksins, taka trú (sem iðulega ristir álíka djúpt og þegar mannfjöldi streymir í gegnum vegabréfsskoðun og fær stimpil í passann sinn).

Höfðingjarnir komast í álnir og komast fljótlega upp á lag með að meta lystisemdir forvera sinna. Skilja nauðsyn þess að halda aftur af undirsátunum. Mannlífið tekur smám saman á sig kunnuglega mynd.

* * *

Miðaldir hefjast þegar arfur Rómverja og hefðir Germana mætast. Kristnin er eldurinn sem bræðir þetta tvennt saman. Ættflokkar setjast um kyrrt innan landamæra og verða að mörgum smáum konungsríkjum.

Sá kristindómur sem almenningi í Vestur-Evrópu stóð til boða var kominn ærið langt frá uppruna sínum. Messur eru sungnar á latínu sem er almúganum lokuð bók. Ímynd Krists breytist, hinn mannlegi þáttur hverfur og Frelsarinn ummyndast í dómara sem situr í hásæti. Í augum Germana var hann konungur himnanna. Kirkjan verður bólvirki konungsríkjanna, frá henni fengu valdhafarnir trúarlegan grunn til að standa á. Og skriftlærða menn sem gátu annast daglega stjórnsýslu.

Þjóðrekur heitir konungur Gota sem verður einskonar keisaraígildi í vestrinu á mótum fimmtu og sjöttu aldar. Aðsetur hans var á Norður-Ítalíu. Áhrifamesti ráðgjafi Þjóðreks var rómverskur auðkýfingur, aðalsmaður og heimspekingur, Boethius að nafni. Forfeður hans höfðu verið í fremstu víglínu valdstjórnenda í gömlu Róm. Í holskeflu heimsslitanna hafði hann keppst við að þýða Plató og Aristóteles yfir á latínu. Samtíminn er óðum að verða ólæs á þessa dýrmætu texta. Ólæsið flennir sig yfir sífellt stærri svið menningarinnar. Eða til hvers þurfa Rómverjar menntir þegar stjórnartaumarnir liggja ekki lengur í þeirra höndum?

Gegn þessari uppgjöf vill Boethius sporna. Einn góðan

veðurdag hlýtur martröðinni að ljúka og endurfætt mannkyn kemur að vitja síns andlega heimanmundar.

Barbararnir aftur á móti álitu að lestur og skrift væru beinlínis hættuleg fyrir karlmennskuna. Hermennska var allt og sumt sem þurfti að innræta upprennandi vígvélum og hetjumóð sem stafar af afreksdáðum forfeðranna.

Gotarnir höfðu máttinn, Rómverjar dýrðina, það er að segja pólitíkina og mannasiðina.

En til hvers þarf mannasiði ef maður hefur herinn? Jú, í austrinu var hinn ósigraði helmingur Rómaveldis með höfuðborg í Konstantínópel. Við þá þurfti að etja kappi og semja. Til þess þurfti að kunna leikreglur og lagaflækjur. Boethius og hans nótar voru nauðsynlegir til þess.

En óhjákvæmilega upplifa barbararnir hina rómversku menntamenn sem fimmtu herdeild. Það blasir við að Býsans geri bandalag við þá. Þiðrik kallar Boethius á teppið og eys yfir hann svívirðingum. En Boethius heldur uppteknum hætti og dansar þennan tunguballett sem rómverskir kunna.

Bla-bla-bla! æpir Þiðrik, kanntu ekki mannamál – og lemur hann í hausinn.

Játaðu helvítis homminn þinn að þú lætur Býsans ríða þér í rassgatið!

Ég bið forláts . . . segir Boethius.

Þú biður lífláts!

Þeir setja á hann rósakrans (leðuról með hnútum reyrð um höfuðkúpuna og síðan hert að).

Og síðan herða þeir að þangað til glyrnurnar ætla út úr augntóttunum.

Ætlarðu að játa!

* * *

Hvað gerir Boethius mitt í þessum þrengingum? Hann fær vitrun: sjálf Heimspekin birtist honum í líki gyðju. Hún spyr hví hann gráti. Og þegar Boethius hefur rakið henni raunir sínar býður hún honum endurmenntunarnámskeið í heimspeki. En fyrst þarf hann að skilja við sig beiskju stjórnmálamannsins sem hefur verið hafnað, sárindi auðkýfingsins sem hefur verið sviptur eignum sínum og angist fangans sem hefur verið firrtur ástvinum og senn fjörinu.

Ekki ósvipað Ágústínusi í Borg Guðs kennir Heimspekin Boethiusi að við séum öll dauðadæmdir fangar lífsins. Þar sem Ágústínus bendir á útgönguleið í ríki himnanna boðar gyðjan lausn heimspekinnar. Hún býður honum að takast á hendur ferð upp í ljósið, til hins raunverulega föðurlands í ríki hugmyndanna. Lífið sem hann lifði var blekking, nú býðst honum lausn til sannleikans. Dauðinn mun verða honum fæðing.

Ofbeldismennirnir eru skuggaboxarar.

* * *

Í kapphlaupi við böðlana hraðritar Boethius samtal sitt og Heimspekinnar. Fangelsið er honum á vissan hátt frelsun frá hinu yfirþyrmandi bókasafni þar sem hann var stöðugt að slá upp í skræðum, útleggja og endurrita. Í fangelsinu er honum nauðugur einn kostur að reiða fram sjálfan réttinn: elda.

Honum tekst að smygla blöðunum út til ættingja sinna og þaðan berst *Hugfró heimspekinnar* til umheimsins, það er að segja klaustranna. Árhundruðum saman standa munkar við púltin sín og afrita *De Philosophiae Consolatione*.

* * *

Klaustrin voru ljósritunarstofur miðalda. Munkarnir hafa ekki endilega áhuga á innihaldi bókanna sem þeir endurrita, ekki frekar en starfsfólk á ljósritunarstofu. Það sem skiptir máli er sjálft erfiðið: að skrifa. Sú yfirbótarvinna mun draga þá langleiðina til himna. Þeir mæla árin sem þeir spara sér í hreinsunareldinum í blaðsíðum, línum og orðum. Eða þvert á móti lengingu dvalar þegar þeim skýst yfir staf eða gera villu.

Engin klaustur lýsa skærar en þau írsku. Rómaveldi náði aldrei til Írlands og kannski þess vegna sem Írar faðma svo hiklaust arfinn rómverska sem klaustrin í Suður-Evrópu fælast. Og það er eitthvert æðiber í rassinum á Írum, þeir eru stöðugt á faraldsfæti og skjóta upp kolli hvarvetna í Evrópu að boða innfæddum trú og bókmenntir.

Og meinlæti. Írsku reglurnar eru orðlagðar fyrir strangleika. Í klaustrinu heyr munkurinn heilagt stríð við sjálfan sig og hvatir sínar. Fordæmið er að finna í ævum dýrlinganna sem þylja Saltarann standandi í ísköldu vatni eða buldra bænir tímunum saman með útrétta arma og fuglar gera sér hreiður í lófum þeirra.

Munkarnir írsku gera svo víðreist að í frásögnum þeirra skjóta hvalir upp kolli, ísjakar sigla eins og fljótandi virki, jökulkrýnd fjöll taka að spúa eldi og sjóðheitar uppsprettur rjúka mitt í fannbreiðunum. En næturhimininn iðar og bylgjast í ókennilegum ljósagangi líkt og lýsi af fjársjóðum himnanna.

IX

Það er kominn tími til að tengja.

Með kristninni nær Evrópa í skottið á Íslandi. Ísland verður hluti af Evrópu. Ekki þessari sem við þekkjum í dag, sem við sækjum heim til að frossa í menningu eða fara á útsölur eða kaupa jólagjafir eða mennta okkur. Ekki fyrrverandi heimsveldið á brauðfótum, lífsþreytti menningarrisinn, EEC auðkýfingurinn.

Sú Evrópa sem Ísland tengist er fátæk, fáfróð, fámenn. Ef okkur gæfist að sjá hana úr lofti væri það ekki köflótta teppið sem blasir við okkur þegar við komum fljúgandi heldur samfelld breiða af trjám líkt og getur að líta í frumskógum hitabeltislandanna.

Árið 1000 eru íbúar aðeins um 10 milljónir (lítið færri en þegnar Noregs og Svíþjóðar í dag). Neðst eru þrælar, þá örsnauðir bændur, en efst trónir yfirstétt sem hrifsar til sín lífsmeðulin og henni til hliðar eru klerkar sem vinna á akri andans. Klaustrin eru það eina sem ber ávöxt, með yfirnáttúrulegum hætti komast þau á legg, sama þótt þau séu reist á berangri yfir hugsjón fátæktarinnar.

Kóngarnir gína yfir löndunum, kannski tekst þeim að færa veldi sitt út um stundarsakir, en aldrei að festa landamærin til frambúðar. Að kónginum gengnum fara erfingjarnir í hár saman og kakan er hlutuð í sundur á nýjan leik.

Upp að Evrópu liggur hið ókunna, í austri er Býsans sem hún skildi sig frá, Evrópa er fátæki ættinginn sem þarf að sanna sig andspænis gamla veldinu með ættarauðinn og andvaraleysið, koðnandi niður á hægindum þess sem var. Í augum Evrópu eru þeir trúvillingar og gagnkvæmt. Það er spurning um eitt „og“, þessi stórhættulega samtenging fokkaði upp hverju kirkjuþinginu á fætur öðru og hratt heilu ríkjunum út í langvarandi styrjaldir. Það þarf að lesa þykka doðranta til að fá einhvern botn í það. Spurningin hvort Andinn útgangi frá Föðurnum eins og Austurkirkjan hélt fram eða Föðurnum *og* Syninum eins og Vesturkirkjan áleit.

Sunnan við Evrópu eru lönd Islams, herskáar þjóðir sem eru Evrópu lokuð bók. Í þeirra uppfærslu er Kristur eins og hver annar statisti, Múhameð er í aðalhlutverki, kaupmaður á sjöttu öld sem sá sýnir og fékk vitrun (sólsting?). Þeir leggja undir sig eyjar Miðjarðarhafsins, flæða upp Spán og láta ekki stöðvast fyrr en inni í miðju Frakklandi.

Úr norðri eru það víkingarnir sem ýmist gera strandhögg eða hafa vetursetu. Þeir skera væna flís af Frakklandi og kalla Normandí. Og Ermarsund er *piece of cake*: þeir breyta Englandi í Danalög. Njeva færir í sundur lærin og opnar þeim leiðina inn í Rússland sem verður að Garðaríki. Allt fram streymir alveg niður í Miklagarð sem er eins og hvert annað kaupfélag Skandinavíu og nágrennis.

Hvað getur stöðvað þá? Tíminn. Með tímanum mengast þeir af menningu innbyggjaranna. Tvær kynslóðir og þeir eru farnir að tala framandi tungu, komnir með nýjan hugbúnað. Eins og limur sem ryðst inn í skaut enda þeir með að linast og sprauta sínu sæði mót frjósömu eggi innbyggjaranna. Vakna svo nýir menn, flosnaðir upp frá sjálfum sér og farnir að heiman fyrir fullt og fast.

* * *

Á níundu öld er kristnin allt umhverfis Ísland. Sumir landnámsmanna eru kristnir og eiga erfitt uppdráttar innan um heiðingjana. Auður djúpúðga tekur ekki í mál að liggja í jörð sem er helguð hinum heiðnu goðum og lætur grafa sig í flæðarmálinu (hafið nýtur góðs af skírn Frelsarans í ánni Jórdan sem á endanum rennur til sjávar og helgar þar með höf jarðar).

En kynslóðirnar sem koma á eftir halda ekki út tómarúmið og taka aftur upp hinn forna sið. Ísland landnámsins er endurnýjun lífdaga. Íbúarnir koma úr aðstæðum sem eru á fallanda fæti andspænis miðstýrðu konungsveldi og kristni. Í ónumdu landi endurskapa þeir skilyrðin þar sem ættir mega sín aftur mikils og æsir. (Svipað og ef við gætum framkallað ástand þar sem Gufan væri allsráðandi, Þjóðviljinn kæmi út og Ellý Vilhjálms syngi: „Ég vil fara . . .")

En þetta eru bara stundargrið, konungsvald og kristni marséra hönd í hönd upp Evrópu. Kristnin er aðgöngueyrir að samneytinu við Evrópubúa. Ísland getur ekki verið aleitt í EFTA.

* * *

Það er fínt að vera kristinn, kóngarnir eru kristnir. Í Noregi brjóta þeir landsfólkið undir miðstýrt vald. Menn eru augnstungnir, tunguskornir, aflimaðir, innibrenndir og drekkt – í Jesú nafni.

Og nú er þessi hugsjón komin alla leið til Íslands.

Á Íslandi skríður Lögsögumaður undir feld þar sem hann liggur í sólarhring og kveður síðan upp úr með að landsmenn skuli vera kristnir. Í því felst að menn trúi á einn Guð almáttugan, skapara himins og jarðar, hætti dýrkun heiðinna guða, leggi af hrossakjötsát og útburð barna.

Bingó!

Síðan ríður hver heim til sín. Og hvað svo? Það eru engir prestar, engar bækur, engar kirkjur. Og fólki er heimilt að halda við siðinn forna ef það fer fínt í það.

Þetta er EES samningur sem þróast yfir í fulla aðild.

* * *

Að taka kristni, hvað táknar það? Að Þorgeir Ljósvetningagoði hafi undir feldinum pukrast með fjarstýringu, stillt af H yfir á K? Átökin í sálarlífinu virðast engu meiri en þegar sjónvarpið íslenska var stofnað og geislanum frá Kanastöðinni beint á haf út. Heiðninni er beint á haf út – og samt er hægt að blóta á laun – líkt og menn gátu með sérstökum útbúnaði haldið áfram að horfa á Kanasjónvarpið. Innan fárra ára var tekið fyrir það líka, þjóðin var orðin RÚV.

En hvernig er hægt að skipta um hugbúnað í þjóð sem er hvorki læs né skrifandi? (leikur einn í dag með sjónvarpi).

Ímyndum okkur fólkið sem kom ríðandi af þingi á miðju sumri árið þúsund. Inn í Hreppa, út í Dali, vestur á Firði, norður í Land, austur á Hérað . . . Við erum orðin kristin, það er kominn einn Guð fyrir hin heiðnu goð.

Og hvað gerir hann?

Hann ku hafa skapað himin og jörð.

Og hvað svo?

Við eigum að tilbiðja hann og son hans Kristus.

Hvað gerir hann?

Hann fórnaði sér á krossi til að við gætum öðlast eilíft líf.

En hvað með þetta líf? Hverjum eigum við að trúa fyrir uppskerunni?

Það fylgja engar leiðbeiningar.

Vill hann fórnir?

Þær eru bannaðar.

Hvað vill hann þá?

Það á að signa sig morgun og kvölds (svona).

Er það allt og sumt?

Það fylgir líka töfraþula á latínu:

Pater-noster-kí-es-in-kelis . . .

* * *

Það gegnir líku um Íslendinga og Rómverja, heiðnin hefur misst aðdráttarkraftinn. Hópur manna er orðinn munaðarlaus í trúarefnum og reiðubúinn fyrir næsta vers. Svo eru aðrir sem streitast á móti. Steinunn skáldkona býður Þangbrandi trúboða í guðajöfnuð: hvor sé sterkari Þór eða Kristur. Þau reyna að „heiðna" hvort annað og kristna á víxl. Hraunstraumur á Hellisheiði treður upp í hlutverki Barbaranna og sýnist stefna í átt að byggðinni. „Þarna sjáiði," segja hinir heiðnu og Snorri goði svarar með sömu spurningu og Ágústínus kirkjufaðir forðum: „Hverju reiddust goðin . . . ?" Hins vegar skortir hann hugbúnað til að fylgja athugasemdinni eftir með 3000 blaðsíðna doðranti.

* * *

Með kristninni berst þessi galdur: að fanga hugsunina og landa henni með hljóðtáknum. Allt sem hefur búið í huganum og hlaðist upp – eldsmaturinn sem nám og fundur nýrra landa hefur safnað – þessi himinhái skraufþurri köstur hittir nú í stafrófinu tundur og bálast í ritmál.

Nú léttir fargi af minninu sem skal hafa verið afrent að afli, vöðvastælt eins og skógarhöggsmaður.

Fólk án ritmáls sleppir ekki tökum af veruleikanum. Annað en við sem vitum að það er alltaf hægt að fletta upp í honum. Fólk án ritmáls býr við ósjálfrátt back-up. Lífið er samfellt talnaband þar sem þess er vandlega gætt að minnisfarmurinn flytjist á milli kynslóða, að fortíðin síist inn í börnin, þau taki hana inn með móðurmjólkinni, morgunskattinum, í dagsins önn og draumum. Heimur minnisins má ekki líða undir lok, harði diskurinn, heimur forfeðranna, áanna – einusinni varið.

Hver dagur í dag skilur eftir sig stafla af blöðum. Oblátuna sem stungið er inn um póstlúgu á hverri hurð í bænum, skolað niður með svartakaffi morgunskímunnar og endar um síðir í grænum gámi endurvinnslunnar. Rís svo upp skeiniblað áður en fleygiferð hefst til undirdjúpanna á vit fiskanna sem nettum munni innbyrða fæðuna áður en botnvarpa dregur þá upp í ljósið til fundar við neytandann sem tekur á móti þeim vöfðum í endurunninn pappír.

Og Netið er eins og þessar afturúrslitnu botnvörpur sem taka að lifa sjálfstæðu lífi í djúpinu, drauganet úr óslítandi næloni sem heldur áfram að góma endalausan upplýsingaafla.

Og ljósmyndirnar sem bíða á ofurnæmum filmum eftir framköllun, hvítar tennur tímans sem eiga í vændum að gulna í albúmum.

Mörg eru dags ljósop.

Myndaalbúmin, myndböndin, filmurnar, dagbækurnar, bréfin, einkunnabækurnar, bólusetningarvottorðin – hver einstaklingur flytur með sér gám af fortíð.

Mærðir á afmælum, minnst í Morgunblöðum, ljósmyndaðir frá vöggu til grafar. Birtast í spurningu dagsins eða vegfarendur í fréttatímum sjónvarps.

Í dag eiga allir sinn sekúndublossa.

* * *

Skáldlistinni er teflt gegn gleymskunni. Til hvers að vera kóngur og brjótast til valda og breytast síðan í sama duft og dónarnir? Skáldin lögðu til rotvarnarefnið og þágu að launum gull og pell og dagpeninga.

Dróttkvæðin eru hoggin út í þetta ósýnilega efni: málið. Það er næstum hægt að þreifa á þeim með tungunni, þau brjótast um í munninum, það mótar fyrir þeim lengi eftir að þau hafa verið sögð fram.

Yrkisefnið er ævinlega það sama: orrustur sem kóngur hefur háð og haft sigur. Þótt hér sé ekki beinlínis hversdagslegt athæfi býður það ekki upp á endalausa möguleika og fljótlega er efnið komið í svo þröngan farveg að það er erfitt um vik að búa til eitthvað minnilegt. Það eru vopnin, það eru hermennirnir, það eru líkin, það eru hræfuglarnir . . .

En útgönguleið skáldanna felst í að nefna fyrirbærin aldrei sínum réttu nöfnum, ummynda þau í eitthvað annað, búa til myndgátu. Öfugt við okkur sem erum alltaf að „tjá okkur", gera okkur skiljanleg, leituðust þeir við að dyljast, gera sig torskiljanlega.

Hvernig stendur á því að skáldin íslensku gera að sínu sérsviði að mæra kónga? Voru þau svona óforbetranlegar höfðingjasleikjur? Var það umbunin sem talaði til þeirra: utanlandsferð + dagpeningar? Hvernig stendur á því að dróttkvæðin verða deild Íslands? Íslandsdeild ódauðleikans. Skáldin íslensku eru önnum kafin við að stinga út yrkisefni, brjóta til mergjar og æfa. Í landinu hleðst upp fróðleikur um sögu, það er að segja kónga.

* * *

En líka óbreytta bændur og amstur sem er hafið upp í goðsögulegt veldi. Upphafið.

Yrkisefnið: að koma sér fyrir í nýju landi. Við upplifum það í smáum stíl þegar við flytjum: yfirfljótandi dótið sem kemur út úr skápunum, gamlar myndir flæða upp úr kössum og kirnum, hlutir sem maður hafði ekki hugmynd um að væru til eða var búinn að gleyma.

Allt er nú sem orðið nýtt. Eins og að fæðast aftur, eignast á ný þessi ár upprunaleikans – og hafa ráð á vitsmunum og vitsmunnum til að ná því í hús. Færa það í búning orða.

Reynslan hefur ávaxtast í eina og hálfa öld þegar ritmálið kemur til sögu. Og önnur hundrað ár líða áður en túrbínan fer af stað sem breytir sögufljótinu í bókmenntir. Endalausa endurnýjanlega orku. Á meðan hugirnir hafa rænu á að virkja.

* * *

Hverjir skrifuðu? Hverjir voru skrifandi? Hinir klerklærðu náttúrlega og skrifstofumenn klaustranna. Kristnin kann að meta sögulegan fróðleik því allt um guðdóminn vitni ber. Það er góðverk að skrifa. En öfugt við dróttkvæðin eru engin ritlaun önnur en sáluhjálp. Fyrir bragðið er ekkert sem kallar á höfundinn að koma fram, Guð þekkir sína.

Söguefnið kallar á form. Sögur sem höfðu gengið og gengist í munni mann fram af manni uns þær voru færðar í letur af ritvélum sem endurrita og misrita og bæta og barna.

Íslendingasögurnar eru samfelld landnáma. Flest verkin segja frá fyrstu byggð og atvikum sem spruttu af hreyfingum fólksins þá. Til verður einskonar gullinsnið fyrir þjóðarsögu þar sem margar raddir herma frá sömu rás viðburða. Það rís ágreiningur, það takast ástir, það er úthellt sæði og blóði, það er sitt hvað gæfa og gjörvileiki.

Sögurnar skarast, persónum einnar skýtur upp í annarri. Landnámuhöfundar seilast í efnivið til að fylla með landnámur sínar og söguhöfundar grípa til Landnámu til að fá beinagrind í frásagnir.

Og meðöl þessara sagna eru svo sterk að enn í dag fara rútuhlöss til fundar við sögustaðina þar sem leiðsögumenn stika út og benda: hér var það. Allt má til sanns vegar færa: áin sem hefur breytt um farveg, holtið sem var skógur, uppblásturinn sem hefur strokað út kennileiti. Vatn og vindar eru blýantur og strokleður sem hvíldarlaust halda áfram sinni iðju – en hólminn þar sem Gunnar sneri aftur – honum hlífir hulinn fjaðurpenni sem færði söguna af sinni á skinn. Og síðan af skinni á skinn, handrit af handriti, öld af öld, allt þar til prentsmiðjurnar tóku við.

* * *

Kálfar, sortulyng, álftir – það er þrenningin sýkna sem við vitum að stendur á bak við sögurnar. Og lifandi hendur sem hafa dýft fjaðuroddinum í byttuna og fært stafina á skinnið. Þessi reglulega skrift, línur sem skrifarinn hefur jafnað með reglu, aldrei yfirkrotað orð, eins og allt hafi orðið til í fyrstu atrennu. Stokkið alskapað úr höfði þjóðarinnar. Algert eins og náttúrufyrirbæri: mosi eða hraun.

Og upp af mosanum stíga myndir, fólk sem hreyfir sig og talar og lætur stjórnast af lögmálum sem þeim eru hulin en við þykjumst sjá jafn skýrt og strengina sem hreyfa brúðuna.

Hverjir hafi búið þetta til? Það sem okkur stendur til boða eru afrit af afritum sem iðulega hafa glatast og þau aftur verið afrit alveg aftur í frumrit sem í engu tilviki hefur varðveist.

En hlýtur að hafa verið. Ekkert er án uppruna.

* * *

Við sjáum þau koma af hafi með fortíðina í farteskinu. Þótt fari kannski ekki mikið fyrir henni er hún eins og skugginn: til staðar um leið og maðurinn rís á fætur. Þegar sólin er hæst á lofti er hún nær ósýnileg, en þegar hausta tekur og dagarnir styttast getur hún orðið mörgum sinnum fyrirferðarmeiri en maðurinn sjálfur.

Og fólkið flytur með sér ójöfnuð og átök. Strax í blábyrjun sjáum við þá fóstbræður Ingólf og Hjörleif með hertekið fólk úr ránsferðum um Írland og eyjarnar.

Maður sem þú ætlar að kúga til að framfleyta sjálfum þér, hvers geturðu vænst af honum? Varla kurteisishjals um ástand og horfur. Aðeins ofbeldi getur haldið þeim við efnið. Við fyrsta tækifæri gera þeir uppreisn. Drepa kúgara sína. Láta sig síðan hverfa.

„Sé ég svo hvernig fer þeim sem vill ekki blóta,“ segir

Ingólfur. Hann hefur aðra mynd af heiminum en sá sem er tekinn að rotna við fætur honum. Hugarheimur Ingólfs er á valdi afla sem þarf að viðurkenna og virða, ef ekki á að fara illa.

Hér hefur farið illa. Hópurinn hefur klofnað í tvær andstæðar fylkingar sem hljóta að berjast uns yfir lýkur. Leitin að öndvegissúlunum víkur fyrir nauðsyninni að hafa upp á uppreisnarmönnunum. Þrælar sem hafa komist upp með að drepa húsbændur sína – það verður að uppræta þá. Líkt og ljón sem hefur étið temjara sinn eða naut sem hefur banað nautabananum. Það verður ekki við þau tjónkað framar.

Ingólfur finnur hina herteknu í eyjum sem standa eins og kóróna í hafinu útifyrir landinu.

Og ganga aftur í örnefni klasans sem krýnir hafflötinn andspænis Íslandi.

* * *

Runnu aldrei á þig tvær grímur, maður, um veturinn þegar norðanbálið kom ofan af hinum nafnlausu jöklum með sinn kuldasviða?

Hvar leituðuð þið skjóls? Grjótið í fjallinu nú sem þá til að hrúga upp veggjum og skógurinn varla minni þá en nú að leggja ykkur til efni í sperrur og mæni. Ekki óraði ykkur fyrir sumarbústöðunum sem nú þekja svæðið, heilsárshús með miðstöðvarkyndingu, heimilistækjum, sjónvarpi og hljómflutningsgræjum og ísskáp með ölföngum – allt stendur þetta opið reikunarfólki nútímans. Og músinni sem fær inni yfir vetrartímann og dundar við að naga í sundur leiðslur og kapla.

Það er janúar, klukkan að ganga ellefu og sólin ekki komin upp fyrir sjónarrönd þótt langt sé síðan hún tók að lýsa upp himininn. Köld og brothætt birtan roðableik yfir í ljósgult minnir á baklýsingu á bar, ef ekki væri hátignarleg þögnin og þytur golu sem bærir hríslurnar sem standa upp úr fönninni.

Ekki gátuð þið vitað að landið væri með öllu óbyggt, máttuð eiga von á mönnum, það er að segja átökum. Líf ykkar hefur ekki verið stjórnarskrárbundið eins og okkar núna sem getum tekið upp gemsann og hringt í lögregluna á Selfossi ef einhver abbast upp á okkur.

Það blikar á sverðsegg, spjótsodd og þarna sést axarblað glotta og járnyddar pílur bíða þess að mynnast við bogastreng.

Þið gangið um hjarnið og lesið í snjóinn, mannheldur ís á vatninu, vitaskuld kunnið þið að dorga niður um vök og veitir ekki af nýmetinu: sami silungur og sportveiðimenn kaupa á veiðileyfi í sjoppunni við Þrastarlund.

Hvernig eruð þið klæddir, hvernig skæddir? Ég er í norskum vindgalla, Helly Hansen, made in China. 100% nælon yst, 100% polyester í fóðri. Vatnsheldur, vindheldur. Innanundir er ég í flíspeysu frá 66°N sem lauflétt jafnast á við svellþykka lopapeysu. En þingið mesta er norskur nærfatnaður, ermalangur bolur og síðar buxur og tekst með einhverri kraftefnablöndu að halda á manni hita með engum tilkostnaði. Gönguskórnir eru Meindl, sokkarnir þunnir en samt varmagefandi á við þykkustu ullarsokka. Á bakinu ber ég léttan bakpoka, húfan er úr ull og vettlingarnir Thinsulate, 85% Shetlandsull, 15% nælon.

Ég geng í fótspor ykkar, sé það sem þið sjáið: tvær endur fljúga upp frá einni víkinni, hrafn gjóar kolamolalegum augum úr lofti. Hvít örk landsins fyllist af táknum: þarna eru för eftir rjúpu, þarna ref, og þarna smátrítlandi mús. En engin slóð eftir bjarndýr, það á þetta land ekki til, en það gátuð þið ekki vitað. Ekki heldur fóstbróðir þinn Leifur sem kenndur var við hjör og átti fyrir höndum að verða fyrstur manna veginn á Íslandi þegar hinir herteknu bjuggu til sögu um bersa sem gengi laus í skóginum. Sættu síðan lagi að drepa kúgara sína þegar þeir dreifðu sér um svæðið í leit að hinu upplogna dýri.

Ég geng í spor ykkar, aðeins tvennt sem ég þarf að má út til að skekkja ekki tímann: fótspor minks niður við vatnið og för eftir jeppa á fjalli.

* * *

Sjónvarpsgreiður sumarbústaðanna hefðu vakið ykkur furðu, þessar hrífur sem standa upp af hverju þaki ætlaðar til að hrifsa hljóð og myndir úr loftinu. Útvarps- og sjónvarpsbylgjurnar eru til staðar, líka á ykkar tíma og hafa verið um ótilteknar milljónir ára, þótt enn séu þúsund ár í að þær verði uppgötvaðar og virkjaðar til þessa daglega brúks: að miðla hljóðum og myndum.

Hvernig hefðu flaggstangirnar komið ykkur fyrir sjónir? Þessi risavöxnu spjót með gullhnúð, óútskornar öndvegissúlur og lemst utan í þær slakur strengur eins og á boga.

Bjarminn frá eldinum í austrinu mætir loganum í kamínunni, notalegur ilmur frá brennandi birki úr skóginum. Um kvöldið þegar nóttin hefur hellt himininn fullan af stjörnum birtist tunglsigð. Rétt í þessu myndar hún eins og gullhorn við enni fjalls sem ber nafn þitt.

Við sitjum í griðum rafmagns sem er fengið spölkorn frá úr Ljósafossi. Og nú býðst hitaveita úr borholum í Öndverðarneslandi þar sem landnámsmaður Grímsnessins settist að eftir að þú hafðir flutt þig um set yfir heiðina í fylgispekt við öndvegissúlurnar sem voru komnar fram í Reykjavík.

Fannst þér tilkomumikið hvernig hnígandi sólin roðaði festinguna og nóttin með stjörnuskarann og tungldjásnið og iðandi hálsmen norðurljósanna?

Um kvöldið þegar þið voruð búin að gæða ykkur á

silungnum og lögst undir bjarndýrsfeld frá heimaslóð – hvarflaði þá að ykkur að þið væruð að gera allt fyrst?

* * *

Af Ingólfi er engin saga. Hann kemur til sögunnar og fer úr henni jafnharðan aftur. Hann er einn á öllu landinu og þar af leiðandi gerist ekkert „sögulegt“.

Ingó var einn á Íslandi.

Laugardalsvöllurinn er hans með áhorfendastúkum og flóðljósum, en engum mótleikara. Hann hleypur fram og til baka með boltann og skýtur á markið, en það er aldrei brotið á honum, aldrei hendi, aldrei fríspark, aldrei gult spjald, hvað þá rautt. Engin saga af því enginn er drepinn – allt er gleymt líkt og upphaf okkar sjálfra.

Við vöknum ævinlega í miðjum klíðum.

X

Tímatal var hinum kristnu ekki ofarlega í huga í fyrstunni. Þeir litu svo á að tíminn væri útrunninn, hinn efsti dagur yfirvofandi og senn yrði hringt út í heimsendi. Í millitíðinni gátu þeir alveg notast við tímatal Gyðinga eða Rómverja eða Grikkja, allt eftir því hvar þeir voru staddir þar og þá. Það er ekki fyrr en árið 525 að ábótinn Dionysos frá Sikiley leggur til að miðað verði við fæðingu Krists. En það gekk ekki í gildi nærri strax, það er svo nýtt þegar Ari fróði skrifar Íslendingabók að hann hælar niður fund Íslands með þremur viðmiðunum til öryggis.

„Ísland byggðist fyrst úr Norvegi á dögum Haralds ens hárfagra, Hálfdánarsonar hins svarta, í þann tíð . . . er Ívar Ragnarson loðbrókar lét drepa Eadmund hinn helga Englakonung; en það var sjö tigum hins níunda hundraðs eftir burð Krists . . .“

Nú segjum við bara 870 – umbúðalaust – hið kristna tímatal hefur rutt sér til rúms um öll Vesturlönd sem hafa sameinast um að setja árið eitt við fæðingu Krists – eins þótt fræðimenn telji almennt að hann hafi fæðst fjórum árum fyrir Krist!

Það er samkomulagsatriði á Vesturlöndum að upp sé að renna árið 2001. Hjá Gyðingum verður þá árið 5758, á dagatali Múslíma 1421 og Búddistar halda upp á árið 2545.

Gleðileg ár!

* * *

Ari fróði er talinn hafa skrifað Íslendingabók á árabilinu 1122 til 1133, það er 252 til 263 árum eftir að land byggðist. Sjálfur er hann fæddur árið 1068. Faðir hans drukknar þegar hann er á barnsaldri (mesti sagnaritarinn og mesta ljóðskáldið eiga þetta sameiginlegt). Fyrir bragðið elst hann upp hjá afa sínum, Gelli Þorkelssyni, á Helgafelli. Gellir er sonur Guðrúnar Ósvífursdóttur og Ari því langömmubarn þeirrar sem var þeim verst er hún unni mest.

Ósjálfrátt hrekkur maður við – langömmubarn Guðrúnar Ósvífursdóttur? Svipað og ef einhver væri langafabarn Hamlets Danaprins eða ömmusystir Tarzans apabróður eða bróðursonur Bjarts í Sumarhúsum. En af þessu má marka hvað það er í raun brúanlegt bil á milli ritmálsins og sögupersónanna.

Ari mótast af fólki sem á afa og ömmur sem hafa verið á dögum um 930, þegar þjóðveldið var stofnað. Þaðan eru ekki nema 60 ár til upphafsins.

Og jafnvel þótt við horfum til þeirra 250 ára sem skilja að ritunartíma Íslendingabókar og umfjöllunarefnið eru það ekki sömu ár og nú. Fólk sem býr á sama stað mann fram af manni við samskonar lifnaðarhætti og svipuð lífsskilyrði hefur samfleyttara minni en við sem hrærumst í síróti núsins. Amma var fædd árið 1876, alin upp í sveit, fluttist til smábæjar árið 1911 sem var orðinn að borg þegar hún lést árið 1961. Á ævi sinni eldaði hún með mó, kolum, gasi, rafmagni. Upplifði ritsíma, síma, útvarp, kvikmyndir. Hestvagn, bíl, flugvél. Torfbæ, timburhús, steinhús. Kamar, kopp, vatnssalerni . . .

Hlýtur ekki jafn samfellulaus ævi að bjóða upp á annars konar minni en ævin sem líður í sama nóa og ævirnar svo langt sem augað eygir þar á undan. Hvaða ástæðu hafði hún til að herma barnabarni sem lék sér á malbiki frá atvikum úr sveitalífi sem var horfið í aldanna skaut og ætti aldrei afturkvæmt?

* * *

Sjö ára gamall er Ari settur upp á hest og fluttur alla leið frá Helgafelli við Breiðafjörð að Haukadal í Biskupstungum. Þar er höfuðból Haukdælanna, helstu höfðingja á Íslandi sem meðal annars hafa lagt til efnið í fyrstu biskupana, Ísleif og Gissur. Í skjóli þeirra rís fyrsti skólinn sem sögur fara af á Íslandi („skóli í boði Haukdæla"). Þar dvelur Ari í 14 ár (skólaganga nútímamanns er einmitt frá 6 ára til tvítugs).

Eiginlega vitum við ekki meira um Ara fróða, hann leggur grundvöllinn að íslenskum fræðum með Íslendingabók, hneigir sig og hverfur síðan sjónum.

Exit Ari.

Hann tekur prestvígslu, en um prestakallið er ekki vitað með vissu, í vitund þjóðarinnar er hann prestur í sérverkefni: að rita Íslendingabók.

Hver hann var? Þessari spurningu um Ara er of erfitt að svara: við höfum ekkert í höndunum.

Mættum við ef til vill fá að láni einhvern annan 11. aldar mann sem meira er vitað um og efna þannig í bakgrunn Ara?

Ef okkur byðist geimvera myndum við ugglaust alhæfa út frá henni um ótölulegan grúa íbúa í ógrynnum annarra stjörnukerfa. En svo er eins víst að hún væri uppi á einhverri tiltekinni öld, frá afmörkuðu sólkerfi og ætti sér ævisögu (faðir hennar kannski drukknað).

Eða segjum beinagrindur í mannfræðinni, leifar af manni sem var uppi fyrir 2,4 milljónum ára eru flokkaðar með einstaklingi sem var uppi fyrir 3,6 milljónum. Skorinn skammtur upplýsinga sameinar. Upplýsingaflæðið flokkar í sundur.

Setjum okkur til að mynda í spor fræðimanna sem eftir níu aldir skortir allar upplýsingar um Stein Steinarr. Mættu þeir taka einhvern samtímamann Steins, til dæmis Jean-Paul

Sartre og fylla upp í myndina? Þeir eru nálega jafnaldrar og ýmislegt í aldarfarinu eiga þeir sameiginlega eins og gengur, til að mynda er Steinn Steinarr talinn fulltrúi existensíalismans í íslenskum bókmenntum, en Sartre var einmitt páfi þeirrar stefnu.

Um líkt leyti og Ari fróði lauk við Íslendingabók lagði franskur heimspekingur lokahönd á ævisögu sem jafnframt er talin fyrsta sjálfsævisaga Evrópubúa. Þetta er *Hrakfallasaga* Péturs Abelard („Harmsaga ævi minnar" hefði verið betri titill, en sá er frátekinn).

Þeir eru mjög jafnaldra, Abelard ellefu árum yngri, fæddur 1079. Báðir eru stórættaðir, Ari rekur föðurætt sína til konunga, Abelard er af aðalsmönnum kominn.

Abelard minnir á landa sinn Sartre í veraldargengi og baráttugleði, báðir skora heiminn á hólm í ritdeilum. En öfugt við Sartre var Abelard ákaflega fríður maður. Og semur ástarsöngva sem fara eins og inflúensa um allt Frakkland og koma út allskyns vökvum á kvenkyninu. Hann er eins og Jean-Paul Sartre og Paul McCartney í einum og sama einstaklingi. Eða með orðum ástkonu hans:

„Hvaða konungur eða heimspekingur gat jafnast að frægð á við þig? Hvaða hérað eða borg brann ekki af löngun til að sjá þig? Hver flýtti sér ekki að sjá þig, þegar þú komst á almannafæri, og hver teygði ekki hálsinn og elti þig ekki með augunum þegar þú gekkst á braut? Hvaða gift kona eða ung stúlka girntist þig ekki þegar þú varst fjarverandi og brann ekki af löngun þegar þú varst nærri?"

En Abelardæðið einskorðast ekki við konur, til hans þyrpast nemendur hvaðanæva úr álfunni, komnir til að hlýða á annálaða fyrirlestra hans. Samtímamaður Abelard skrifar:

„Engar vegalengdir, engir fjallgarðar, engin gljúfur, hvorki vegleysur né hætta af ræningjum, héldu aftur af námsmönnum að flykkjast til þín. Ólgandi hafið aftraði ekki fylkingum ungra manna frá Englandi. Þeir höfðu ekki fyrr heyrt nafn þitt en þeir flykktust til þín, fullir fyrirlitningar á hættum sem biðu þeirra: frá Bretagne, Angevin, Poitier, Gascon, Spáni. Frá Normandí og Flandri. Þjóðverjar og Slafar voru í skýjunum yfir snilld þinni, að ekki sé minnst á sjálfa íbúa Parísarborgar – alla þyrsti í kennslu frá þér."

Á elleftu öld kemur skólinn út úr skápnum, það er að segja klaustrinu, út í borgina sem var nýrisin kringum dómkirkjuna. Samband kemst á við handverksmenn, kaupmenn, kvenmenn: glauminn og gleðina. Einn af nemendum Abelard, Jón af Salisbury, skrifar Tómasi af Beckett:

„Ég kom við í París. Þegar ég leit allsnægtirnar sem þar er að finna, hve létt er yfir fólkinu, virðingarinnar sem menntamennirnir njóta, tign og dýrð kirkjunnar, margbrotna iðju heimspekinganna, þá fannst mér ég líta, fullur aðdáunar, Jakobsstigann sem efsti hlutinn snerti himininn og englar á ferð upp og niður. Upptendraður af þessari ánægjulegu pílagrímsför hlaut ég að játa: „drottinn er hér og ég vissi það ekki. Sæll er sá útlagi sem hefur þennan stað fyrir hæli!""

Námið lýtur sínum eigin lögmálum, það eru engin próf eða gráður, eingöngu sameiginleg leit að visku. Kennari og nemandi eru saman á báti og sigla í átt að fyrirheitnu landi skynseminnar. Fyrir kom að nemandi gerði uppreisn gegn meistara sínum, hrakti kenningar hans eða leitaði annað. Bil á milli kennara og nemanda var furðu stutt, nemandi gat fyrirvaralítið orðið kennari og gagnkvæmt. Allt og sumt sem þurfti var að kveða sér hljóðs og laða til sín áheyrendur. Kennslustofan oftar en ekki einhver af brúm Signu og aðnjótendur greiddu fyrir lesturinn (líkt og vegfarendur henda skildingi í hattinn hjá hljóðfæraleikara eða trúði nútildags).

Í skjóli vaxandi stéttar borgara sprettur upp hópur námsmanna, Golíardarnir (nafnið ýmist talið vera dregið af Golíat eða „gueule" sem merkir kjaftur). Golíardinn er borgarbarn og París er kjörstaður hans. Þeir fara um í háværum hópum og syngja *Carmina Burana*, kátar vísur með ádeilu á auðsöfnun kirkjunnar. Snúið er út úr guðspjöllunum og páfinn skopstældur sem peningapúki með skrælnað hjarta.

Kirkjan gat ekki lokað augum fyrir ógninni sem var í uppsiglingu: uppkomu nýrrar stéttar menntamanna sem hófu mannlega skynsemi til skýjanna, hæddust að yfirvöldum og blésu uppreisnaranda í skólaæskuna.

Afturkastið birtist í munkareglu kenndri við Citeux. Sálin í henni er Bernharður ábóti af Clairvaux sem snýst öndverður gegn rísandi borgum og skólunum þar:

„Forðið ykkur frá Babylone, forðið ykkur og bjargið sálum ykkar. Flýið hópum saman í griðastaðina (klaustrin) þar sem þið getið iðrast yfir hinu liðna, lifað heilbrigðir í núinu, og vænst vongóðir framtíðarinnar. Skógarnir munu gagnast ykkur betur en bækurnar. Trén og steinarnir munu færa ykkur meiri vísdóm en hvaða kennari sem vera skal.“

Abelard er holdtekja hinna nýju viðhorfa. Skólaspekingar af hans toga voru óhræddir við að véfengja og spyrja spurninga. Þeir voru sannfærðir um að Guð hefði skapað reglufastan og skynsamlegan heim og mannkyn í sinni mynd. Þar af leiddi að hinir gáfuðustu þeirra á meðal, menn á borð við Abelard, gátu komist að leyndardómum heimsins með því að spyrja kerfisbundið út í hann.

Abelard var sannfærður um að kristnin væri skynsamlegust allra trúarbragða. Um leið og sýnt hefði verið fram á hana með röklegum formúlum væri björninn unninn. Sem „heimspekingur Krists“ yrði Abelard nýr frelsari mannkyns. Aðdáendur hans voru honum samdóma, ábótinn í Cluny, Pétur virðulegi, kallar hann „okkar Aristóteles“.

En Bernharður hæðist að tilburðum Abelard til að gera „guðfræði“ að vísindum og kallar hana „fífla-fræði“:

„Segðu okkur, segðu okkur endilega hvað þér hefur birst sem öðrum er hulið . . . Ég hlýði á Spámennina og Postulana; ég hlýði Guðspjöllunum, en ekki guðspjöllunum samkvæmt Pétri Abelard. Ertu að semja nýtt guðspjall handa okkur? Kirkjan hefur ekkert pláss fyrir fimmta guðspjallamanninn.“

* * *

Í huga Bernharðs var óhugsandi að kirkjunnar menn gætu blandað geði við dónana á strætunum. Skírlífi var forsenda fyrir því að kennimaður væri tekinn alvarlega. Við skiljum þetta ekki. En í þeirra augum var kvæntur fræðimaður álíka óhugsandi og fyrir okkur ef súlu yrði komið fyrir á miðju altari Hallgrímskirkju og dansmey léki listir sínar undir altarisgöngunni.

Abelard er heimspekingur og kvennagull. Honum býður við vændiskonum, en vegna sleitulausra fræðastarfa hefur hann ekki haft tíma til að byggja upp sambönd við konur af betra standi. Hann er löngu kominn á það stig velgengninnar þar sem drambið myndar skíðastökkpall yfir í fallið. Þá fær hann upp í hendurnar tilboð sem hann getur ekki hafnað:

„Svo vildi til að í Parísarborg var unglingsstúlka ein að nafni Heloísa . . . Í útliti var hún ekki síðri en aðrar, en þekking hennar var svo umfangsmikil að á því sviði stóð hún öllum framar. Þar sem bóknám er ekki algengt meðal kvenna, jók þetta mjög á töfra hennar og hún var orðin víðfræg um allt konungsríkið . . .“

Hún er til heimilis hjá frænda sínum, kanúka við Notre Dame, Fúlbert að nafni. Sá tekur fegins hendi uppástungu hins heimsfræga Abelard um að deila með þeim fæði og húsnæði jafnframt því sem hann uppfræði frænkuna. Hún er 15 ára, Abelard tuttugu árum eldri.

Þarf að segja meira.

„Undir yfirskyni bóknámsins gáfum við okkur algerlega á vald ástinni, og lesturinn bauð okkur upp á þau fylgsni sem ástin sóttist eftir. Með bækurnar opnar fyrir framan okkur, töluðum við meira um ást en lesefnið, og kossarnir urðu fleiri en kennisetningarnar. Hendurnar leituðu tíðar á brjóstin en í bækurnar, og ástin sneri augunum oftar hvorum að öðrum en lesturinn að textanum. Til að vekja síður grunsemd gaf ég henni stöku sinnum högg, en það var af ást en ekki ofsa, af blíðu en ekki bræði og höggin voru sætari en nokkur smyrsli. Og hvað svo? Í ákefð okkar reyndum við öll stig ástarinnar, og ef ástin gat fundið upp eitthvað nýtt og óvenjulegt, bættum við því ofan á annað. Því óreyndari sem við vorum í þessum unaðssemdum, þeim mun ákafar gáfum við okkur að þeim og urðum aldrei uppgefin.“

(Af hverju vorum við ekki látin lesa Hrakfallasöguna í latínu menntaskólans? Í stað langdreginna Gallastríða Sesars og vaðalsins í Ciceró?)

Heloísa verður ófrísk og elur son. Fúlbert trompast yfir þeirri hneisu sem Abelard hefur gert honum. Abelard býðst til að giftast Heloísu til að bæta skaðann. En um leið var hann náttúrlega að stofna fræðimannsheiðri sínum í voða, Heloísa tekur það ekki í mál.

„. . . þótt heitið „eiginkona“ virðist helgara og traustara, hefur mér samt alltaf fundist orðið „ástkona“ fallegra, eða jafnvel, ef þú hneykslast ekki, orðin „frilla“ eða „hóra“ . . .“

En Abelard er svo barnalegur að halda að hann geti lægt opinbert hneyksli með leynilegri hjónavígslu. Fúlbert og frændur hans heimta að vera viðstaddir og kunngera síðan hverjum sem heyra vill að Abelard sé kvæntur maður. Abelard paníkerar og kemur ástkonu sinni fyrir í klaustri. Bæði þræta fyrir hjónavígsluna. Þá lætur Fúlbert til skarar skríða, æfur yfir þeirri smán sem Abelard hafði sýnt honum og:

„Nótt eina meðan ég lá sofandi í sérherbergi í íbúð minni, mútuðu þeir einum þjóna minna og hefndu sín á mér með svívirðilegri grimmd, eins og alþjóð frétti síðan furðu lost-in: Þeir sviptu mig þeim líkamshlutum sem það afbrot sem þeir kvörtuðu undan hafði verið framið með."

Abelard er tekinn og geltur. Hann og Heloísa ganga hvort í sitt klaustur.

* * *

Getum við notað eitthvað af þessu í útlínur á Ara? Menntun hans var alþjóðleg á evrópska vísu og því aldrei að vita nema þeir Abelard séu samferða einhvern spöl af leiðinni. Skyldi Ari fróði hafa orðið ástfanginn? Fyrir því eru engar heimildir, hann eignast að vísu pilt og stúlku, en konu er ekki getið. Við hljótum samt að gera ráð fyrir henni (ekki fyrr en á okkar dögum að kynlaus æxlun er gerleg).

En hvort hann bar til hennar ástarhug er annað mál. Hjónabönd á miðöldum eru fyrst og fremst ráðahagur. „Það vildi ég, bróðir, að þú bættir ráð þitt og bæðir þér konu," segir Höskuldur við bróður sinn Hrút í Njálu. Þetta er svona ámóta og ef Höskuldur hefði ráðlagt bróður sínum að kaupa hlutabréf. Þegar Hrútur spyr hvar þeir eigi að bera niður veit Höskuldur upp á hár hvar best sé að fjárfesta: „Hér eru nú höfðingjar margir á þingi, og er gott um að velja . . . Kona heitir Unnur og er dóttir Marðar gígju . . ." Þeir bera síðan upp bónorðið við Mörð og fyrstu viðbrögð Marðar eru: „Mikið munt þú verða fram að leggja með honum, því að hún á allan arf eftir mig." Og Höskuldur birtir Merði umsvifalaust efnahagsreikning ásamt greiðslustöðu: „Hann skal hafa Kambsnes og Hrútsstaði og upp til Þrándargils. Hann á og kaupskip í siglingum."

Mörður framkvæmir smá hugarreikning áður en hann kemur með gagntilboð: „Hún skal hafa sex tugi hundraða og skal aukast þriðjungi í þínum garði."

Þetta er arðsemisaukning upp á hvað mörg %?

Allan tímann er Unnur hvergi nærri, reyndar segir sagan

ekki af samfundi þeirra Hrúts fyrr en í sjálfu brúðkaupinu, „og var brúðurin döpur heldur."

Svona áttu hlutirnir að ganga fyrir sig, þetta var normalt. Svo var líka til í dæminu að menn létu girndina ráða för og gengju að eiga konu af því hún var falleg. Það var girndarráð. Þannig fer um Gunnar á Hlíðarenda og Hallgerði. Fundum þeirra ber saman á Þingvöllum. Hallgerður er kynhvöt klædd í rauðan kyrtil og ávarpar að fyrra bragði holdgerving karlmennskunnar sveipaðan konungsskikkju. Þau hafa ekki talað saman lengi í Almannagjá þegar Gunnar ber upp bónorðið utan við allt bókhald.

Allir vita hvernig fór.

* * *

Heloísa aftur á móti lítur öðrum og nútímalegri augum á hjónabandið:

„Sú kona sem vill heldur ganga að eiga auðugan mann en fátækan og sækist meir eftir sínum eigin hag í hjónabandinu en eiginmanninum sjálfum ætti ekki að líta á sig öðruvísi en sem markaðsvöru. Sú sem lætur leiðast í hjónaband af slíkri hvöt verðskuldar vissulega fremur kaupverð en lof. Augljóst er að hún sækist ekki eftir manni heldur eignum hans og hún myndi selja sig enn auðugri manni ef hún gæti."

Bréfaskipti Abelard og Heloísu, ásamt Hrakfallasögunni komu fram í dagsljósið og var snúið á frönsku um líkt leyti og Njála (1280), þótt sjálft samblendi líkamanna hefði átt sér stað einni og hálfri öld fyrr. Án efa hafa þau litið á sig sem nútímamenn (miðaldir voru ekki til á miðöldum, það er ekki fyrr en árið 1688 að hugtakið kemur fyrir í sagnfræðiriti eftir þýskan kurf).

* * *

Haukadalur stendur ennþá. Að nafninu til. Hin gríðarmiklu afréttarlönd sem tóku við þegar fjallsbrúninni sleppti eru orðin að sandkassa. Menn og skepnur hafa slitið upp gróðurteppinu og vindurinn þarf hvorki ámokstursvél né vörubifreiðar til að flytja jarðveginn á haf út. Uns svo var komið að dönskum manni blöskraði (íslenskum blöskrar aldrei) og keypti herlegheitin í byrjun heimsstyrjaldarinnar síðari. Gaf staðinn síðan Íslendingum til varnarbaráttu í styrjöldinni gegn landinu. Ekki fór blessaður maðurinn fram á að nafn hans yrði básúnað af þessu tilefni. Aftur á móti hafa aðrir komið nafnspjöldunum sínum fyrir á víð og dreif um svæðið: „Hér fer fram grisjun í boði Byko“, „Hér styrkir Skeljungur skógræktarverkefni . . .“

Hverirnir senda stróka með jöfnu bili í loft upp nú eins og þá. Geysir að vísu orðinn gamall og hrúðóttur, getulaus Casanova á meðan Strokkur strokkar á tíumínútna fresti.

Væntanlega hafa þeir blasað við Ara þar sem hann sat með hönd undir kinn mitt í allri latínunni. Innra með honum er í mótun háhitasvæði sem getur af sér hitt alþjóðaorðið sem íslenskan hefur lagt til tungumála heimsins.

Geysir og saga, þau eru ættuð af þessum skika hér (í boði Almættisins).

XI

Ég ætlaði að gerast rithöfundur, en mig vantaði svo sárlega lífsreynslu. Hvar var hana að fá? Á sjónum sagði almannarómur.

Þótt miðaldra menn myndu þá tíð að togarapláss væri í meiri metum en öruggt pláss í Himnaríki, höfðu um þessar mundir breyttar atvinnuhorfur í landi ásamt uppgripum á síld fellt svo gengi togaraplássins að skipin velktust um ó- og hálfmönnuð og uppistaðan í áhöfnum oftar en ekki eftirtekjan á nokkrum vínveitingahúsum bæjarins.

Ég hjólaði niður á höfn og sá leigubíl koma brunandi, hemla við bryggjusporðinn og út spratt maður í rosabullum. Samstundis var slegin um hann skjaldborg, menn sögðu útgerðina skulda kaupið fyrir síðasta túr, einn sagðist hafa fengið borgað í vinnuvettlingum . . . Maður í hvítum jakkafötum stakk sér ítrekað inn í leigubílinn en var dreginn út jafnharðan aftur.

Ég smeygði mér á milli Færeyinga og drukkinna Íslendinga og reyndi að komast að stígvélamanninum.

Er laust pláss?

Varst það þú sem hringdir?

Nei.

Láttu þá stýrimanninn fá nafnið.

Hvernig leit stýrimaður út? Ert þú stýrimaðurinn? spurði ég holdugan mann í brúnni sem stakk hausnum út um gluggann eins og ekkert hefði verið sagt. Ég bankaði í dyrastafinn og ítrekaði spurninguna. Hann tók niður nafnið mitt, hristi hausinn þegar ég sagðist vera óvanur og stakk honum svo aftur út um gluggann til merkis um að samtalinu væri lokið.

Hvenær fer skipið?

Ekkert svar (seinna skildi ég að það á aldrei að spyrja svona, heldur: „hvenær á að sleppa?“).

Ég hljóp í símaklefa og hringdi í systur mína og bað hana að sækja hjólið niður á bryggju, miðtakkarnir inn, síðasti út.

Ætlarðu að drekkja þér? spurði hún.

Ég ætla túr með Lýðveldinu, svaraði ég.

Lýðveldinu! hrópaði hún og reyndi að halda mér uppi á snakki eins og maður talar við mann sem ætlar að hoppa fram af þakskegginu. Það var byrjað uppþot á bryggjunni og ég flýtti mér að kveðja. Verið var að shanghaja síðasta hásetafarminn um borð og gefin skipun um að sleppa strax til að missa þá ekki aftur í land.

Ég hallaði mér fram á rekkverkið og horfði á undiröldu togarans taka litla bátsskel á innleið og gefa henni sitt undir hvorn. Lýðveldið var einn af togurunum sem lýðveldið hafði fengið í tannfé og þrátt fyrir allt viss sjarmi að vera staddur um borð. Íslendingur sem hafði ekki komið á sjó var álíka settur og hreinn sveinn í Sódómu.

Á göngum skipsins var rennirí af mönnum niðursokknum í að skemmta sér. Ekkert gaf til kynna að þeir væru hásetar, þeir voru klæddir í algengan danshúsaklæðnað og vantaði bara kvenfólk til að fullkomna stemmninguna.

Ég ákvað að leita mér að náttstað. Fór um undirheima skipsins uns ég rataði á lúkar með þremur daunillum kojum. Ég hreiðraði um mig í þeirri efstu, dró ofan á mig ábreiðu og sofnaði.

Um nóttina hrökk ég upp við að rifið var óþyrmilega í mig, öskrað og formælt og „mín koja“. Ég færði mig í næstu fyrir neðan og hélt áfram að sofa. Í aftureldingu vaknaði ég útsofinn og læddist fram úr til að kasta af mér vatni. Hvað þá! Við vorum staddir inni í miðri borg! Ég reyndi að leggja saman tvo og þrjá: ég hafði komið til Akureyrar og vissi að þetta gat ekki verið hún og engin borg af þessari stærðargráðu á Grænlandi. Með ískaldri röksemdafærslu fikraði ég mig aftur til þeirrar niðurstöðu að við værum staddir í Reykjavík. Því til staðfestingar stóð ÚTVARP á húsi Hafrannsóknarstofnunar. Reykjavík breiddi út faðminn eins og uppbúið rúm og allir í fasta svefni. Ekkert lífsmark um borð. Sjúkrabifreið stóð á hafnarbakkanum og í sömu andrá birtust hjúkrunarmenn á þilfarinu með mann í körfu, fetuðu sig niður landganginn, renndu körfunni inn í bílinn og hröðuðu sér eftir mannlausum bryggjum með hljóðlausu sírenuljósi. Maður gekk upp landganginn og tjáði mér að loftskeytamaðurinn hefði fallið ofan af stýrishúsinu á móts við Snæfellsnes og höfuðkúpubrotnað. Sjálfur væri hann nýi loftskeytamaðurinn og nú væri verið að bíða eftir borðbúnaði í stað þess sem hefði verið fleygt útbyrðis um nóttina. Snöggvast hvarflaði að mér að ég gæti sem hægast stokkið í land, en hvað myndi sú lífsreynsla draga langt?

Undir hádegi sat ég í matsalnum með kaffikrús og sporðrenndi smurðu brauði. Eitthvað óstand á kokkinum og nánast sjálfsafgreiðsla í eldhúsinu. Menn komu fremur lemstraðir undan nóttinni, einn bað um að sér yrði rétt brauðið og fékk allt fatið yfir sig.

Ég lét lítið fyrir mér fara. Kannski var ég hálft í hvoru að bíða eftir því að eldhressi bátsmaðurinn með stóra hjartað undir hrjúfa yfirborðinu, sem er fastur liður í öllum sjómannasögum, gæfi sig fram og byrjaði á því að skamma nýliðana: „Þið eruð ekki þorskvirði helvítis skítseiðin ykkar . . .“ – en tæki þá síðan að sér. En það var svo vart og skart að vottaði fyrir „sjómannastemmningu“. Þetta voru bara nokkrir timbraðir kallar og kunnugleg andlit úr Strætinu.

Ekki veit ég af hverju ég fór að rýna í töflu sem hékk uppi

á vegg. Það reyndist vera vaktatafla, hvernig áhöfnin skiptist á vaktir, verkaskiptingin. Og hver var ekki undrun mín þegar ég sá að ég átti alnafna um borð og hnýtt aftan við nafnið spil/stýri.

Sú hugsun læddist að mér að hér væri átt við undirritaðan. Ég hugðist grennslast fyrir um hið sanna og spurði um bátsmanninn en fékk þau svör að hann væri á fötunni. Hver spurning virtist leiða til nýrrar gátu. Ég ætlaði á klósettið sem var ólæst enda þótt það væri upptekið af hverjum nema bátsmanninum sem æpti á mig að pilla mig upp í hólinn.

Geturðu sagt mér hvar hóllinn er? spurði ég Færeyinginn sem benti mér upp í stýrishús.

Það var engu líkara en stýrimaðurinn hefði verið að bíða eftir mér: „Ég er búinn að setja kúrsinn, þú heldur þig á strikinu“ og þar með var hann rokinn.

Hvaða striki? Var þetta ef til vill orðtak til sjós, samanber „að halda sér á mottunni“? Varla var átt við strikin á gólfinu sem voru býsna mörg. Fram undan var hafið beinn og breiður vegur. Innan úr loftskeytaklefanum barst *Útvarp Reykjavík*: umferðarþáttur með sérstöku tilliti til hjólhýsa.

Þegar ég var byrjaður að finna mig í stýrimennskunni og jafnvel tekinn að undrast að til skyldi vera sérstakur Stýrimannaskóli, kom stýrimaðurinn öskrandi eins og Neptúnus.

Á að fara í Húsafell?

Er ekki bindindismót þar? spurði ég í trausti þess að maðurinn væri að grínast.

Spurðu kompásinn drengur, hann er við nefið á þér!

En varla var ég búinn að koma auga á kompásinn þegar stýrimaðurinn öskraði: „niður á spil með þig!“

Á dekkinu voru allir á þönum í ofvæni einhvers sem ég hafði ekki hugmynd um hvað var og ekki árennilegt að spyrja hvar spilið væri. En ég þurfti ekki lengi að bíða: um leið og bátsmaðurinn kom auga á mig, rak hann upp öskur og eftir bendingunni að dæma átti ég að taka mér stöðu undir hólnum framan við vírakeflið.

Nú var æpt „hífa!“

Ég svipaðist um en sá engan hífa. Köllin ágerðust en vantaði alveg framkvæmd. Loks fannst mér líkast því að áskoranirnar beindust að mér.

HÍFA!

Nú hrinti bátsmaðurinn mér til hliðar og tók að hreyfa stangirnar. Kallinn hrópandi og gargandi hálfur út um kýraugað.

Slá úr!

Hííífa!

Og viti menn: hafdjúpið opnaði annað augað og upp úr því sigldi risavaxinn poki og hrundu af honum fiskar eins og tár. Yfir miðju þilfari opnaðist hann og þjóðartekjurnar slipp-sloppuðust niður á dekkið, mest ýsa og karfi.

Nú kom ný hrina af óskiljanlegum fyrirmælum, en þegar menn tóku hnífa og byrjuðu að gera að aflanum var mér innanhandar að líkja eftir því. Skera á háls, rista á kvið, slóið í kassa, líkið í lest. En það var líkast því að bátsmaðurinn væri kominn með mig á heilann og öskraði í hvert skipti sem ég hreyfði mig. Þess á milli hljóp hann á fötuna. Öðru hverju réttu menn úr hryggnum og tóku til við að brýna. Mér var í lófa lagið að líkja eftir því og byrjaður að sættast við hlutskipti mitt þegar bátsmaðurinn tók að öskra:

Hvar er helvítis nálablókin?

Þessu virtist líka beint gegn mér, ég var greinilega ekkert smánúmer um borð. Nálablók? var verið að vísa til þess hvað ég var grannur? Ég var áreiðanlega orðinn í laginu eins og spurningamerki þegar Færeyingurinn benti mér á nálakörfuna, „tað er rifið“.

Ég sem hafði aldrei svo mikið sem fest tölu átti að fara að stoppa í net! Til allrar lukku bættust fleiri við saumaskapinn og gott ef verkið var ekki ögn tekið að skýrast þegar ný skipun barst úr barka bátsmannsins: ég átti að hafa til kaffi og ræsa.

Kaffið var hafragrautur eldaður í risastórum potti, smyrja síðan ókjör af brauði og hella upp á könnu sem náði mér í höku. Tvöfalt stímið hafði ekki enst til að afrétta kokkinn sem í þessum svifum kom aðvífandi eins og strengjabrúða, tók bakföll, hoppaði yfir þröskuldinn, bakkaði, sogaðist að eldavélinni, fiskaði kartöflu upp úr bullandi vatninu, stakk í hana rassmæli og bað mig vinsamlegast að fara með hann upp til Karlsins „með kveðju frá Gregory".

Ég ansaði því náttúrlega ekki, en byrjaði að hlaupa út um skipið til að hafa upp á vaktinni. Fann hana loks sofandi frammi í stafni. Reyndi fyrst að vekja hvern fyrir sig með því að koma létt við öxlina: vakna!

Þegar það bar ekki árangur kallaði ég: VAKNA! og meinti það.

Ekkert gerðist. Þá kom mér í hug jólabók frá því í fyrra sem hét RÆS! og viti menn, ekki hafði ég fyrr nefnt þennan titil en vaktin spriklaði eins og hún lagði sig á rúmstokknum.

Hvergi var vatn að fá til að vaska af sér slorið utan svolítil spræna úr kaldakrananum. Klósettið var setulaust og framreiðslan úr síðasta manni neitaði að kveðja. Sturtan hafði verið höfð í annað.

Þegar ég var skriðinn í koju gat ég ekki hugsað mér að fara að sofa til að byrja síðan allt upp á nýtt eftir fáeinar klukkustundir. Af hendingu var ég með Njálu í skeiniblaðsútgáfu Sigurðar Kristjánssonar og naut þess að sökkva mér niður í lesturinn, gleyma stund, en þó einkum stað. Ég gat meira að segja hugsað mér að lesa lagakaflann: „Nefni ég votta í það vætti . . ." ásamt upptalningu á sárum: heilundar, holundar og mergundar . . .

Bátsmaðurinn kom inn og byrjaði að hafa sig til fyrir svefninn og fólst í því að hann spreijaði á sig úr brúsa: andlit, holhönd og tær.

Hvernig heldurðu að sparifötin mín fari? sagði hann upp úr einsmanns hljóði um leið og hann reif upp mjóa skáphurð.

Ekkert nema saggi og mygla . . .

Ég taldi mig ekki eiga neitt vantalað við þennan mann eftir það sem á undan var gengið og með ólíkindum að hann skyldi voga sér að ávarpa mig. Hélt því áfram að lesa um handseldar sakir og löglýsingu og nefni ég í það vætti . . .

Uns hann segir upp úr einsmanns hljóði:

Alltaf hef ég haft samúð með Hallgerði.

Ég ætlaði ekki heldur að ansa því.

Mér hefur alltaf þótt Gunnar bölvað skítseiði. Þarna liggur hann í ferðalögum voða vinsæll gæ á meðan hún er bundin yfir heimilinu sem manni skilst að hafi verið hálfgert þrotabú undir fallegri áferð.

Öfugt við öskrin á þilfarinu voru þessar setningar mæltar fram fremur íhugandi og raunar ekki ógeðslega. Mér var ekki stætt á að þegja lengur og sagði frekar hlutlaust:

Þetta er nú víst bara skáldsaga.

Skáldsaga! hváði bátsmaðurinn í þilfarstón og hallaði sér út yfir kojuna svo öfugt andlitið gein við mér, ábyggilega ekki frýnilegra en Skarphéðins í brennunni.

Þá er ég líka skáldsaga, sagði hann um leið og hann rétti sig upp og ég heyrði hann bylta sér og bölva alltof stuttu teppi.

Sagði svo ekki neitt lengi.

Sagði svo:

Guð gefi þér góða nótt.

* * *

Gunnar og Hallgerður, glæsilegasti maðurinn, fallegasta konan. Hvað getur komið í veg fyrir að þau verði óhamingjusöm?

Njáll getur séð fyrir óorðna hluti af því að ævin er ákvörðuð fyrirfram. Áðuren fyrsti maðurinn er hreyfður er skákin tefld. Skamma hríð virðast einhverjir leikir í stöðunni: „ef þú heggur tvisvar í sama knérunn verður það þér að falli . . .“ Og auðvitað heggur Gunnar tvisvar.

Meira að segja Njáll sem býr yfir allri þessari visku og forvisku, einnig hann steypist í glötun og allt hans lið. Enginn er óhultur. Ef það eru ekki vígamenn með alvæpni, þá orðrómur. Það eru alltaf einhverjar nornir sem koma að hvoli upphafsins og herma frá því sem enginn átti að vita, sem búið var að leggja blátt bann við að yrði haft eftir.

Fornmenn án útvarps og sjónvarps, ekkert *DV*, *Fókus* eða *Séð og heyrt* og samt ferðast kjaftasögurnar eftir ósýnilegum bylgjum og hafna í hlustum þeirra sem síst skyldi.

Allir vita allt um alla – líka þá.

Ein einkennilegasta uppákoman í allri Njálu er þegar höfðingjarnir á Alþingi bera ekki kennsl á Skarphéðin. Einn af öðrum ber fram spurninguna: Hver er þessi maður? Skarphéðinn! Sem gervallt landið þekkti. Var það af því að hann er feigur? Af því að dagar hans eru taldir? Að hann er samasem dauður? Bara formsatriði að fullnægja dómi sem hann hefur fellt um sig sjálfur. Hann hefur framið ódæði sem er svo óheyrilegt að feigum verður ekki forðað.

„Þá skuld eiga allir að gjalda . . .“

* * *

Höskuldur Hvítanesgoði. Eins og heimaalningur elti hann þá um hlöðin hvert sem þeir fóru. Þeir báru hann á höndum sér, léku sér með hann, léku sér að honum. Hann blés nýju lífi í Bergþórshvol.

Börn gera allt nýtt. „Ég mun gera alla hluti nýja.“ Þannig hljóðar fyrirheitið.

Svo kemur haust og þá er jafnvel heimaalningnum slátrað. Það er Mörður sem kemur því í kring. Með tungunni einni. Slefberinn. Það er sagt að dropinn holi steininn. Slefan sýrir hann í gegn uns minnsti andvari breytir honum í rykský.

Mörður, sonur Valgarðs gráa, afsprengi heiðninnar sem ferst og vill taka heiminn með sér í fallinu.

Bergþórshvoll breytist í ösku. Kemst þá enginn undan? Jú, hefndin, að sjálfsögðu. Hefndin verður að hafa sinn gang. Kári klárar dæmið. Eltir brennumenn upp í kóng. Heldur nákvæmt bókhald yfir hefndina. Jafnvel þegar vöskustu mönnum þykir komið nóg á Kári enn ólokið mál. Hann getur fallist á að hefnt sé brennunnar, en sonur hans er eftir. Bókhald hefndarinnar liggur opið fyrir Kára. Með ermabönd og ennisskyggni bókhaldarans heldur hann áfram uns síðasta færslan er komin í dálk. Niðurstöðutalan er fundin þegar hann sníður höfuðið af Koli Þorsteinssyni þar sem hann er að telja silfrið úti á Englandi, „og nefndi tíu höfuðið er það fauk af bolnum“.

Þá fyrst er mál að tvístrika undir.

* * *

Hann heldur yfir hafið og heim. Skipið hjakkar ölduslóðina uns landið rís grásprengt úr sæ. Landið sem við gerðum að okkar. Landið sem gerði okkur að okkur.

Og samt er enginn mannlegur máttur sem getur hrært gleðistreng í brjósti hans. Hann er ryðgaður fastur. Fjölskylda hans, eiginkona og sonur. Það er allt farið. Ekkert eftir. Nema brotlenda.

Þeir ganga upp úr svartri fjörunni inn í iðandi náttmyrkrið. Úr dimmunni ýrir ótal ögnum sem þéttast og klessast í vit þeirra og hlaðast utan á föt þeirra og þyngja gang þeirra.

Er ekki tilvalið að enda hér?

Nei, ekki enn. Öndin blaktir enn í brjósti Flosa.

Á hlaðinu á Svínafelli standa tíu snjókarlar. Flosi ber strax kennsl á Kára. Faðmar hann að sér. Snjókarlinn bráðnar. Það lekur úr fötum hans og vitum.

Og Hildigunnur, ekkja Höskuldar, hún er enn á lífi. Þannig er sættin innsigluð. Þessir tveir fulltrúar andstæðra fylkinga ganga að eigast. Hatrinu er breytt í hjónaband. Er það ekkert mál? Hvernig voru atlotin við morðingja mannsins sem hún hafði elskað? Og hvernig var að elska einn af aðstandendum brennunnar sem hafði breytt augasteini hans í ösku?

Kristileg fyrirgefning loksins?

Við sjáum þau í anda færast hægt inn í faðmlagið, bylgjuhreyfing ástarleiksins tekur við af ölduhreyfingu hafsins. Allt umhverfis er sviðin jörð svo langt sem augað eygir.

Og ljúkum vér þar Brennunjálssögu.

XII

Þú manst upp á hár staðinn og stundina þegar þú ákvaðst að gerast menntamaður. Það var í sumarhúsinu á Þingvöllum, Ingi og strákur úr næsta bústað voru að skjóta á mark. Þú hafðir stigið á glerbrot og sast fótlama inni og last í bók: „Þá riðu hetjur um héruð“, valdir kaflar úr Íslendingasögum. Þú rakst augun í að Gunnar á Hlíðarenda var Hámundarson og hljópst með þessa vitneskju út á sparkvöllinn.

„Hvers son var Gunnar á Hlíðarenda?“

Þú skynjaðir að spurningin færði þér óljóst vald. Ingi hætti við að skjóta og markmaðurinn lét sig falla til jarðar. Hvorugur vissi svarið.[1]

* * *

Heiðnaberg hafði fallið Karli Storð í skaut þegar Alþingi Íslendinga samþykkti friðun Þingvalla í aðdraganda Alþingishátíðarinnar árið 1930. „Hið friðlýsta svæði skal vera undir vernd Alþingis og ævinlega eign íslensku þjóðarinnar“, segir þar. Fjárhald var bannað með lögum og bændum gert að axla sín skinn. Síðan skiptu áhrifamenn lýðveldisins „hinu friðlýsta svæði“ á milli sín til sumarhúsabyggðar.

Karl Storð hafði um skeið verið fjármálaráðherra í utanþingsstjórn. Nú bankastjóri og áhugamaður um fornsögurnar.

---

1 Nú rúmum fjörutíu árum síðar heldur Ingi því fram að þú hafir spurt: Hvers son var Gunnar Hámundarson? Ekki svaravert.

„Sárt ertu leikinn, Sámur fóstri", sagði hann þegar þú steigst á glerbrotið.

Hann gekk um vellina og benti með stafnum hvar hver og einn höfðingi hafði átt sína búð og samfallnar tóttir skutu óneitanlega skökku við húsakynnin á Heiðnabergi þar sem kristalhjálmur sveif yfir vötnum.

Þegar sólarlag keyrði um þverbak settist hann út á svalir með málaratrönur og freistaði að ná því á léreft. Kjarval var vinur hans og kollega: báðir reru á mið Þingvalla í leit að mótífum. En höfðu gert með sér einskonar heiðursmannasamkomulag: Karl átti við sólarlagið, Kjarval við mosann og hraunið.

* * *

Þingvellir. Séðir úr lofti (með augum guðanna) kemur leiksvið strax í hugann. Vatnasviðið baðað síbreytilegu ljósi með umgjörð fjalla og jökla. Hvílík ótrúleg heppni að mennirnir skyldu detta niður á þennan reit til að ráða sínum allsherjarráðum. Staðirnir sem komu til greina hljóta að hafa skipt tugum, þing voru haldin út um allt land, Elliðavatn hefði legið prýðilega við, staðurinn sem sjálfur landnámsmaðurinn hafði kjörið til þinghalds.

Ari fróði segir frá aðdragandanum: sendimönnum sem fóru um héruð til að kanna hugi manna og svipast um eftir hentugum aðstæðum. Og duttu niður á Bláskógaheiðina sem þó hafði ekki verið þingstaður áður. Jörðin var einfaldlega á lausu, eigandinn hafði gerst sekur um dráp á þræl (er verið að spauga?).

En aðdáunin hlýtur fyrst og síðast að beinast að skaparanum: það var hann sem bjó þetta til – mitt í eilífðinni – leikhús til reiðu fyrir fullan sal af áhorfendum. Og sala áskriftarkorta óðum að hefjast á harmleikinn sívinsæla: „Sitt er hvað gæfa og gjörvileiki".

* * *

Í augum Jakobs var sumarbústaður fáránleg uppfinning í sumarlausu landi. Hann kallaði Heiðnaberg aldrei annað en Veðravíti, jafnvel Víti. Ef hann fékkst austur var hann fljótlega kominn niður í Valhöll þar sem hann hitti fólk og datt í það. Á Heiðnabergi breyttist hann í óþægan krakka.

Saga Storð bætti það upp með sinni gangandi glaðværð. Aðdáun feðginanna var gagnkvæm. Þótt þessi íturvaxna yngismær væri iðulega í samfylgd ungra manna virkuðu þeir frekar eins og bílstjórar eða meðreiðarsveinar. Ofaukið líkt og ljósalampa í miklu sólskini.

Lovísa Storð var aftur á móti fjarlæg. Það var eins og hún hefði hrapað af annarri plánetu og fyrir misgáning lent á meðal þessa fólks, en ætti von á loftfari á hverri stundu sem kæmi að sækja hana.

Á milli hennar og eiginmannsins var ekkert sem minnti á hjónalíf. Það voru aðrar í því. Líkt og það voru aðrar sem sáu um hreingerningu á húsnæði, afþurrkun og bón. Þannig er það líka í sögunum. Höskuldur Dala-Kollsson kaupir ambátt úr gersku kvennabúri í Noregi og hefur sér til yndisauka uppi á Íslandi, þótt eiginkonan kunni ekki að meta það. Og Njáll sem sagan segir að hafi verið álitum eins og kona, einnig hann á sína frillu og við henni son. Hin geðríka Bergþóra lætur sér það lynda.

* * *

Hafiði séð Jakob?

Það er Kolbrún sem spyr. Þögn veit ekki á gott. En ef hann er á spíttbátnum má heyra hann og sjá hvar hann fleytir kerlingar á vatninu.

Jakob er holdtekja sjötta áratugarins. Tímabils sem var á vissan hátt sérkennilegt fyrir sakleysi sitt. Það var ekki búið að finna upp óhollustuna. Menn keyrðu um á bensínsvelgjandi drekum og önduðu að sér útblæstrinum með velþóknun í vissu þess að hann bæri með sér framfarir. Um þessar mundir var verið að virkja við Sogið og af því starfsmennirnir höfðu óþægindi af mývarginum var dúndrað DDT á árbakkana þar sem mýið klekst út. Og slegnar þrjár flugur í einu höggi: mý, fiskur og fugl.

Maðurinn var sjálfkjörinn ráðherra náttúrunnar.

Allur matur var hollur og reykingar voru sjálfsagður bónus fullorðinsáranna. Áfengi var að vísu varasamt, en áfengissjúklingar varla komnir til sögu. Rónar höfðu einkarétt á þeim sjúkdómi og aðsetur þeirra var Kardimommumiðbærinn.

* * *

Í hjarta bæjarins, á horni Austurstrætis og Pósthússtrætis, var tóbaksbúðin London. Það var mögnuð búð. Tóbak upp um alla veggi. Til viðbótar við sígarettuflóruna voru vindlar í pökkum, vindlar í hylkjum, vindlar í kössum – heilu plantekrunum frá Kúbu var rúllað upp og þær reiddar fram í ómótstæðilegum ilmi.

En pípurnar slógu allt út. Gljáandi brúnar og svartar, ýmist sléttar eða hrufóttar, beinar eða bognar, mjóar eða þykkar. Og píputóbakið ýmist í járndósum eða pungum. Sælan mesta hlaut að vera að eiga pípu og pung og geta handleikið þetta tvennt á almannafæri. Sérstaklega var ein feit og bogin sem þú hafðir augastað á og stalst til að máta þig við í speglinum frammi við dyr.

Við hliðina á London var Herradeild PÓ. Úti í glugga stóð gína í ljósbrúnum apaskinnsjakka. Klæddur þessum jakka með pípuna góðu og punginn yrðu þér allir vegir færir og ekkert að vanbúnaði að leika hlutverkið í leikritinu sem ósýnileg hönd hlaut að vera að skrifa. Og myndi leiða þig til fundar við mótleikarann eina.

Til viðbótar við hungrið og þorstann og syfjuna og tóbakslöngunina er komin ný tilfinning sem á skylt við þarfirnar að því leyti að henni verður aldrei svalað í eitt skipti fyrir öll. Þvert á móti endurnýjar hún sig stöðugt þrátt fyrir sífellda sjálfsafgreiðslu. Það er byrjuð glóð í líkamanum sem brennur án þess að eyðast.

* * *

Í fjórtándu bók *Borgar Guðs* fjallar Ágústínus um kynhvötina. Adam og Eva finna ekki til girndar. Fyrir bragðið eru þau nakin án blygðunar. Það er höggormurinn sem fyrir meðalgöngu konunnar innleiðir lostann í veröldina. Það er þá sem limur mannsins fer úr böndunum og tekur að bólgna og þrútna, maðurinn finnur til blygðunar og hylur sköp sín.

Syndafallið orsakar risið.

Eins og nærri má geta var *Borg Guðs* skyldulesning í klaustrum miðalda. Og um það bil sem Ísland er numið situr helsta menntaljós Evrópu, Johannes Scotius Erigenus (Jóhann Skoti Írasonur), og brýtur til mergjar hegðun limsins. Í verki sínu *De divisione naturae* útilokar hann ekki að Adam og Eva hafi getað haft mök í Paradís, en uppástendur að Adam hafi verið kleift að hreyfa liminn eins og aðra útlimi líkamans: með viljanum einum, vandræðalaust og án alls losta. „Af fullkomnu jafnvægi sálar bæði og líkama og án þess að meydómi væri spillt, gat maðurinn eða öllu heldur hefði getað, frjóvgað síðu eiginkonu sinnar.“ Þannig ímyndar munkurinn sér viðhald mannkynsins, að vísu ekki *sine coitu* (án samkomu kynfæranna), en *sine ardore* (án bruna). Við upprisuna verði kynlífið síðan afnumið, heimsendir muni upphefja kynjaskiptinguna, eða öllu heldur kvenkynið.

Hrösunin er fólgin í kynlífsvæðingu tegundarinnar, „þessum hlægilegu stellingum, þessu æðisgengna pati líkt og hjá hinum fordæmdu í víti.“

* * *

Miðaldamönnum verður starsýnt á liminn. Hann er tákn um fall mannsins. Það er sjálfsögð refsing á miðöldum að gelda menn. Þeir sem geltu Abelard voru sjálfir geltir. Og þótt Abelard horfi á eftir limnum með eftirsjá tekst honum jafnframt að réttlæta verknaðinn í bréfi til ástkonu sinnar:

„Þannig var þeim lim réttilega refsað sem hafði gert mér allt illt, með þjáningunni bætti hann fyrir það sem hann hafði brotið af sér í losta, og hann losaði mig úr þeirri for sem ég hafði verið sokkinn í, bæði í huga og líkama . . .“

Í Njálu er það limur Hrúts sem hrindir af stað örlagaskriðunni. Lýsingin á því hvernig það verður er einn af hápunktum verksins (og þá væntanlega heimsbókmenntanna). Höfundi tekst að orða hlutinn með svo margræðum hætti að hefur enst til umhugsunar allt fram á okkar daga. Við erum áheyrendur að samtalinu á Þingvöllum þegar Unnur segir föður sínum allt af létta um hjónalífsvanda þeirra Hrúts.

„Þá mælti Mörður til dóttur sinnar: „Seg þú mér nú allt það er á meðal ykkar er og lát þér ekki í augu vaxa.“

„Svo mun vera verða,“ segir hún. „Eg vildi segja skilið við Hrút og má eg segja þér hverja sök eg má helst gefa honum. Hann má ekki hjúskaparfar eiga við mig svo að eg megi njóta hans en hann er að allri náttúru sinni annarri sem hinir vöskustu menn.“

„Hversu má svo vera?“ segir Mörður, „og seg mér enn gerr.“

Hún svarar: „Þegar hann kemur við mig þá er hörund hans svo mikið að hann má ekki eftirlæti hafa við mig en þó höfum við bæði breytni til þess á alla vega að við mættum njótast en það verður ekki. En þó áður við skiljum sýnir hann það af sér að hann er í æði sínu rétt sem aðrir menn.""

Þegar við lásum þetta í skóla skildist okkur að hörund merkti hörund og gerðum okkur í hugarlund einhvers konar sóríasis, að Hrútur hlypi allur út í ofboðslegu exemi sem gerði konunni ókleift að koma við hann.

Þetta var gáta sem allir kennarar með sjálfsvirðingu hlupu yfir og nemendur gátu verið vissir um að kæmi aldrei til prófs.

En við nánari skoðun kemur í ljós að „hörund" hefur viðbótarmerkingu í fornu máli, nefnilega limur, hold.

Og þá verður setningin jafnvel enn furðulegri: er hægt að ímynda sér svo stóran lim að hann rúmist ekki í skauti konu? Undanfarið hafa öðru hverju blossað upp deilur um þetta atriði í blöðum og tímaritum landsmanna, sjö öldum eftir að blekið þornaði á skinninu. Umræðan hefur farið út um víðan völl eins og gengur þegar bréfritarar blanda sér í slaginn; allt frá því hvort Njáll og Gunnar hafi verið elskhugar yfir í það hvort ummæli Unnar bendi ekki eindregið til að höfundur Njálu hafi verið kona. „Aðeins sá sem aldrei hefur séð karlmannslim hefði getað skrifað setninguna", skrifar maður sem titlar sig hrossaræktarráðunaut. Og bætir við: „Því ekki nunna í klaustri. Allt í kringum sig sér hún til dýranna, hross með böll sem nemur nær því við jörðu og naut með lim sem nálgast sverðslengd. Og hún sem er hrein mey hugsar með ofboði til verknaðarins sem á sér stað á milli karls og konu."

Annar bréfritari (undirskriftin er kennitala) segir alveg eins hugsanlegt að höfundur Njálu hafi verið samkynhneigður karl og „þvert á móti haft mikil og sársaukafull kynni af limum karla".

Í kjölfarið sendi Kvenfélag Hvolhrepps frá sér ályktun þar sem þess var krafist „að Morgunblaðið hætti að ljá rúm fyrir svo svívirðilegan málflutning þar sem helgustu bókmenntir Íslendinga væru ataðar auri svo öllu heilskyggnu fólki væri fyrir löngu misboðið.“

Tekið hefur fyrir blaðaskrif í bili.

* * *

Sumarið eftir stúdentspróf ertu afleysingamaður á *Tímanum* (þökk sé Karli Storð). Pressan fór hópferð austur á Sólheimasand að gera frétt um leitina að hollenska gullskipinu sem átti að hafa strandað þar á sextándu öld.

Hvað það var gaman að vera með sólgleraugu og sígarettu í morgunljómanum þegar lagt var af stað. Eftirvæntingin þegar þið steðjuðuð út á sandinn. Og óvænt árás skúmsins sem kom pressufólkinu til að bera hönd fyrir höfuð og skakklappast í hlykkjum eins og í bíómyndaskotárás. Kvenfólkið í níðþröngu pilshafti, karlmennirnir í svörtum jakkafötum og hvítum skyrtum með lakkrísbindi á támjóum skóm.

Gullskipið – eitt sinn stóð það eins og hnífsblað upp úr svörtu sárinu og freyðandi hafið umleikis. Hvað gerist svo? Tímanum tekst að leggja yfir það svarta skikkju sandsins og hverfa það sjónum. Þrjúhundruð árum síðar koma leitarmenn með tól sín og tæki – 300 ár – fáein korn í stundaglasi. Og samt er komin átta hæða blokk af sandfargi ofan á flakið og það sem meira er: skipið hefur haldið áfram sinni siglingu eftir að það sökk. Ósýnilegir kraftar hreyfa það undir sandhlassinu. Sandbátur. Kafbátur.

Eldspýta kveikir í sígarettu og hverfur hálfbrunnin í öskubakka sandsins. Silfurlitar umbúðir fjúka um sandöldur en tyggjóplata vöðlast safarík í leik við tungu á meðan eftirvænting breytist í óþreyju.

Verkstjórinn hefur komið sér upp handhægu setti af einsatkvæðis orðum:

Nei (ekki vitað hvenær þeir koma niður á flakið).
Nei (ekki vitað hvort þetta er skipið).
Já (málmleitartækið gefur eitthvað til kynna).
Nei (þeir vita ekki hvað).
Nei (þeir vita ekki hvenær).
Já (ansans vesen).

Fréttin gufar upp eins og hverjar aðrar hillingar á sandinum. Þið hélduð til baka með einsatkvæðisorð og nokkrar fátæklegar myndir. Hvolfduð úr skónum þegar þið voruð komin að rútunni. Flaskan gekk, þið enduðuð í Naustinu innan um netakúlur og fleira dót úr liðinni sjómennsku.

Öðru hverju fóru menn annars hugar úr skónum og hvolfdu í öskubakka.

* * *

Saga Storð. Þegar þið voruð samtíða í sumarbústaðnum á Þingvöllum varst þú tíu ára drengur, hún tuttugu og fimm ára kona. Tvö sólkerfi sem ljósár skildu að. Nú ert þú tvítugur, þið eruð samstarfsmenn á *Tímanum*, ferðafélagar á sandinum, hlið við hlið á barnum.

Ha, hvað segirðu? segir hún opin.

Ég segi, við vorum eins og bastarðar.

Þið hverjir?

Ég, Ingi og Bjössi. Hildiríðarsynir.

Bíddu, heitir ekki mamma þín Kolbrún?

Skiptir ekki máli.

Af hverju segirðu að þið hafið verið eins og bastarðar?

Við vorum heimagangar, en aldrei heimamenn, skilurðu. Við vorum ekki blóð af ykkar blóði (þú roðnar þegar þú rifjar þetta upp). Við myndum aldrei eignast ættarauðinn . . .

Ertu að biðja mín, Máni?

Mamma þín, hún var alltaf svo hrædd um að við myndum ílendast, þú skilur. Að þið sætuð uppi með okkur.

Þetta er nú ekki sanngjarnt, Máni minn, ég hef aldrei heyrt hana mömmu segja misjafnt orð um ykkur.

Þú hefur aldrei heyrt hana segja aukatekið orð um okkur. Við vorum óhreinu börnin hennar Evu.

Hendi er lætt í lófann á þér og leiðir þig burt. Þið eruð stödd í húsi foreldra hennar sem í eru margar vistarverur. Hún brýtur egg og hrærir í skál og hellir yfir hvissandi pönnu. Þið eruð svöng. Hún bregður sér frá og kemur aftur í slopp úr silki og staðnæmist fyrir framan þig í laginu eins og knéfiðla.

* * *

Þú vaknar í mjólkurhvítri birtu við hliðina á kontrabassa. Þú klæðir þig hljóðlega. Það er sandur á gólfinu. Þú tiplar á sokkaleistunum með támjóa skó á milli fingra.

Í forstofunni mætirðu Lovísu gömlu. Hún hefur beygt sig niður til að taka upp Morgunblaðið og skynjar þig út undan sér. Henni gengur erfiðlega að rétta úr hryggnum, við sársaukann bætist skelfingin:

Hver ert þú? spyr hún í ofboði.

Frændi Raskolnikoffs, svarar þú.

Rass . . . ? endurtekur hún, ekki vitund rólegri og horfir á eftir þér niður tröppurnar.

Út.

XIII

Þér reið á að komast burt. Það var eins og í Nýjatestamentinu, þú leist ekki einusinni um öxl. Bara aðra leiðina burt.

Hafði Ísland gert þér eitthvað? Þú vildir ekki hugsa um það, ekki frekar en farfuglinn sem verður að taka á öllu sem hann á ef hann ætlar að hafa það yfir hafið.

Fyrsti viðkomustaður var Lúxemborg þar sem frænka þín var gift flugmanni. Þar hafði Ísland eins og steinrunnið: öskubakki úr hrauni, plattar með Gullfossi og Geysi, gæruskinn á gólfi, almanak Eimskipafélagsins . . .

Burt.

Hvert?

Á miðöldum liggja allar leiðir til Rómar. Þar er syndaaflausnin. Flosi fer til Rómar eftir Njálsbrennu, sömuleiðis Kári eftir að hann hefur afgreitt þá brennumenn. Fjörbaugsgarður er algeng refsing í sögunum, menn voru dæmdir til þriggja ára dvalar í útlöndum! Hver tæki ekki slíkri refsingu með þökkum nútildags?

En það eru fleiri sem fara til Rómar en manndrápsmenn. Frá og með kristni er Ísland í boði páfans í Róm. Páfabulla gat átt í vændum að ferðast alla leið til Íslands og hlutast til um málefni þar. Og bréfaskriftir niður til Rómar hvaðanæva úr Evrópu fylla hirslur Vatíkansins. Sendiboðar flykkjast á fund páfa til að hvísla í eyrað á honum og biðja um gott veður í álitamálum.

Og svo pílagrímar komnir til að njóta návistar við líkið. Í Róm hvíldi líkami Péturs postula og frá þessu líki streymdi kraftbirtingarvald guðdómsins.

Helgir dómar dýrlinga voru sambandsgjafar við hinn

ósýnilega heim. Það var ekki til sú kirkja eða klaustur að ætti ekki sinn helga dóm. Farið var með þá í skrúðgöngur á hátíðum, í fararbrjósti í styrjöldum. Þeir voru afl þeirra hluta sem gera þurfti og verslun með verndargripi var umtalsverð hagstærð í efnahag miðalda.

Hér stóð Róm með pálmann og óhætt að segja að píslarvottarnir sem teknir voru af lífi í fjöldaaftökum heiðninnar hafi ávaxtað sitt pund. Árið 817 lætur Pascal páfi grafa upp 2700 líkama dýrlinga úr kirkjugörðum utan við borgarmúrana og þeir síðan markaðssettir sem verndargripir.

Á elleftu öld tók eftirlit með helgum gripum að fara úr böndunum. Krossferðirnar komu á sambandi við sjálfa heimahaga Krists með framboði á barnatönnum Frelsarans (sem reyndust furðu margar) og efnismikil forhúðin sem fjarlægð hafði verið við umskurnina forðum. Mjólkin úr brjóstum Maríu var sömuleiðis enn á boðstólum.

Og Ísland fór ekki varhluta af þessum dásemdum, í Skálholti var varðveitt ein flísin úr krossi Krists, en það er talið að ef allar þær flísar kæmu saman í einn bjálka, væri hann ásamt Kínamúrnum, það mannvirki sem greina mætti með berum augum frá tunglinu.

Ætli sé eitthvað sambærilegt í nútímanum? Það væru þá helst munir úr eigu stjarna úr heimi kvikmynda og dægurlaga. Dögum oftar er verið að selja glæsivagn Presleys, kjól Marilyn Monroe, flygil Lennons . . . Þess er skemmst að minnast að yfirgefin gröf poppskáldsins Jim Morrison var um tíma mest sótta minnismerki Parísarborgar og nærliggjandi leiði í stórri hættu af ágangi safnara.

En á bak við eru engin frelsunartilboð. Bara steindauð lík.

* * *

Í Játningum sínum verður Ágústínusi kirkjuföður tíðrætt um einn glæp. Það var þegar hann hnuplaði perunum af perutré nágrannans. Aftur og aftur kemur hann að þessari misgjörð. Aftur á móti skopar hann furðu létt yfir önnur afbrot sem nútímalesanda virðast vega þyngra, til dæmis hvernig hann skildi við fylgikonu sína eftir 15 ára hjúskap og sendi hana slyppa til föðurhúsanna af því hann hugðist kvænast 12 ára stúlkubarni sem vegna ættgöfgi myndi opna honum leið til embættisframa.

Perustuldurinn yfirskyggir allt.

Eins er með þig, samviskubitið fitnar á fénu sem þú hnuplaðir úr veski ömmu þinnar forðum.

En það þarf ekki einusinni peru eða tindáta til, tilvera hins kristna er eitt samfellt samviskubit sem nærist á upphafsglæpnum stóra: misgjörðinni í Paradís. Og það er þessi sínagandi tilfinning um sekt sem er Ágústínusi rækust sönnun þess að maðurinn hafi í árdaga þekkt annars konar ástand; það er ekki hægt að sakna annars en þess sem maður hefur einhvern tímann átt. Sálina munar í samveruna við Guð í Paradís.

* * *

Samviskan er kristin afurð. Hún kemur til Íslands árið þúsund. En það skal hafa tekið hana tíma að nema land. Hér gildir ekki að slá eign sinni á, fara eldi um jörð eða leiða kvígu frá sólarupprás til sólarfalls.

Hvernig skyldi staðan vera núna, 365 þúsund dögum síðar?

Hrossakjöt fæst í kjötborði stórmarkaðarins. Fóstureyðingar eru áætlaðar á annað þúsund í ár. Og hvað skyldu landsmenn trúa á marga guði? Óðinn og Þór eru inni í myndinni enn (þótt Ásatrúarmenn hafi svipaða stöðu og Þjóðdansafélagið). „Hið góða í manninum“ er vinsælt goðmagn, trú á endurholdgun töluvert algeng, „ég-veit-að-þér-líður-vel-þar-sem-þú-ert-núna“ sannkölluð þjóðkirkja ef marka má minningagreinar, stjörnuspáin lífseig, búddismi, nýaldarfræði ýmis og allskonar, en fyrst og síðast trúarbragðleysið fullkomið.

Nú sem þá eru tvær þjóðir í landinu, tvær álíka stórar fylkingar. Annars vegar þeir sem hafa alist upp við hugsunarhátt landbúnaðar og fiskveiða, fólk sem vill hámarka afrakst-urinn með meðölum sem helgast af tilganginum.

Hin þjóðin er náttúrudýrkendur úr borgarumhverfi. Hinn nýi siður er trúin á umhverfið, hið græna tré. Hin græna trú. Nú þegar hinn vélsmíðaði næturgali hefur orðið uppvís að framleiðslu ófarnaðar hefst tignun og tilbeiðsla hinnar upprunalegu náttúru.

Hollusta = frómleiki.

Náttúrvernd = guðsótti.

Nú er svo komið að hin nýja trú er hvarvetna játuð með vörunum þótt alls staðar sé blótað á laun. Til eru afskekkt svæði þar sem gamla trúin er enn opinber, en hinn nýi siður er sigurstranglegur. Eins og kristnin áður ræður hann yfir hugbúnaðinum. Hagvöxturinn er kominn í óefniskennd samskipti (sbr. klaustrin forðum).

Tengdur = trúaður.

Í stað *pax vobiscum* er komið a með hring.

* * *

Kristur er kjarni. Orka. Kjarnorka. Sending frá kjarnorku-verinu mikla sem tungumálið táknar með þremur stöfum. Þessi kraftur birtist í mannsmynd í hvert skipti sem barn fæðist og fer síðan smádvínandi eftir því sem einstaklingur-inn „kemst til manns“.

En stöku sinnum gerist að manneskja kemst á legg sem fer langt með að holdgera þessa krafta og miðla þeim í mót-tækilegu formi. *Bókin um veginn* verður til og hvað þær heita allar þessar vegahandbækur mannssálarinnar. Og fram koma menn sem þekkjast af því að samtíminn setur upp sólgleraugu og reynir að losa sig við þá fljótt og vel, en eftirtíminn tekur þá í guðatölu.

Kristur er kjarnorkusamruni af óþekktri stærðargráðu. Við sjáum það af framgangsmáta hans og orðunum sem eftir honum eru höfð og síðast en ekki síst á því hvernig ríkjandi öfl bindast samtökum um að ráða hann af dögum.

Enn má nema uslann sem hann gerir, en nú eins og náttúruhamfarir í fjarlægu sólkerfi. Miklihvellur, sprengingin sem fæddi af sér alheim, einnig hún endar með að þynnast út í nánast ekki neitt. Samt sér hennar enn stað, 15 milljörðum ára síðar, í örbylgjukliðnum og útrauða ljósinu. Hún kemur enn fram á mælum einhvers staðar í námunda við alkul.

Og hnettir sem hún fæddi af sér eru að sjálfsögðu enn til staðar. Þessi orð eru skrifuð á einum þeirra og annar nýkominn upp á himinhvolfið baðar hverfi sitt ljósi.

Eins er með Krist, hans gætir enn í trúarbrögðum á mismunandi kulnunarstigum.

* * *

Kristur talar til okkar á íslensku sem þýdd er úr grísku og latínu sem aftur er frásögn af því sem fram fór á aramísku. Haft eftir sjónar- og heyrnarvottum hálfri öld eftir að allt er um garð gengið. Og jafnvel þótt við berum ekki skynbragð á samhengið sem hann birtist í, verður okkur starsýnt á róttækni boðskaparins:

„Hver sem ann föður eða móður meira en mér, er mín ekki verður. Og hver sem ekki tekur kross sinn og fylgir mér eftir, er mín ekki verður. Hver sem hefur fundið líf sitt, mun týna því, en hver sem hefur týnt lífi sínu mín vegna mun finna það.“ (Matt.10.34)

(Þetta er táknrænt, segja prestarnir feimnir).

Máli sínu beinir hann til nektardansmeyja, forstjóra Sölunefnda varnarliðseigna, íþróttafréttaritara, eyðnismitaðra, eituræta, þroskaheftra, geðveikra . . . Skilningurinn veitist hinum útskúfuðu og einföldu. Hinum gáfuðu er hann lokuð bók („Faðir, ég þakka þér að þú hefur hulið þetta hyggindamönnum“). Bersyndugum eru gefnar upp sakir. Hæðst að góðborgurum. Mark tekið á konum (róttæknin í því skilst ekki í dag). Börnum stillt upp sem fyrirmyndum.

Þannig talar Guð, loksins þegar hann tekur til máls.

Kraftur sem bærist enn á næfurþunnum síðum Nýjatestamentisins.

* * *

Er ekki makalaust hvað mannkynið nær jafnan góðum tökum í upphafi? Hvað Biblían og Búdda og Bókin um veginn og gríska heimspekin eru risavaxin stökk. Þeir leika sér að því að stökkva í hástökki yfir rá sem eftirtíminn kallast góður að ná með stöng.

„Verði ljós!“ Er hægt að orða betur upphaf alheims? Sem hin málheftu nútímavísindi nefna „Big bang“? Og þó hefur á fáar bækur verið híað meir en fyrstu Mósebók. Allt fram á okkar daga var hún ljósasti vottur þess að Biblían væri barnabrek, hugarburður mannkyns með bleiu. Því vitaskuld hafði heimurinn verið til um aldur og ævi og yrði um ókomnar aldir.

Þangað til vísbendingar taka að safnast upp sem ganga í berhögg við þessa mynd. Smátt og smátt fjölgar dráttum í sýn sem er svo ótrúleg að menn sem vilja láta taka sig alvarlega veigra sér við að stama henni upp: ekki nóg með að heimurinn hafi orðið til á einu ábendanlegu augnabliki, hann á einnig eftir að líða undir lok, alveg eins og í . . . Biblíunni.

Eða tökum ævintýrið fallega um Adam og Evu og aldingarðinn Eden. Er hægt að orða betur niðurstöður mannfræðinnar: mannkynið er ættað frá mjög svo afmörkuðum reit í Suður-Afríku.

Og það er einmitt aukinn skilningur sem opnar því leiðina þaðan.

Og bölvunin sem Guð leggur á þau skötuhjú til að koma þeim til manns: „með sársauka skaltu börn þín fæða . . .“ Breytingin sem verður á beinabyggingu frá hangandi apa til hins upprétta gangandi manns kemur fram í þrengri mjaðmagrind sem aftur gerir að verkum að konan, ein jarðardýra, fæðir afkvæmi sín með sársauka.

Eða þegar Guð skapar konuna með því að fjarlægja rif úr síðu mannsins. Þarna er lifandi komin lýsingin á því sem gerðist í árdaga þegar loftsteinn keyrði inn í síðu jarðarinnar með þvílíku afli að slumma þeyttist út í geiminn þar sem hún breyttist í tungl. Og síðan dansa þessi tvö stífdans hvort við annað. Án jarðarinnar ryki tunglið út í buskann, án tunglsins færi jörðin að rása.

Varla tilviljun að tunglið birtist ævinlega sem kona í goðsagnaheimi mannsins. Mánagyðjan.

* * *

Og þú ert aftur farinn að tuldra þessa bæn sem Jesús kenndi (einu bænina sem hann kenndi og mælti svo fyrir að hana skyldi fara með í hljóði).

Til vonar og vara. Ef ske kynni að einhver væri að hlusta. Ef það skyldi vera Guð. Vonar-og-varatrú.

Eftir því sem fleiri falla frá umhverfis einstaklinginn dvínar krafturinn sem heldur honum við jörðina, áður var það bara amma sem var komin til himna, nú er hálf hersingin komin yfrum. Að því kemur að hugur þinn er farinn að dvelja fullt eins mikið við þá sem eru liðnir fram, æ fleiri komnir á kaðalinn þeim megin. Loks liggurðu eins og barn í vöggu og yfir hana grúfa sig öldruð andlit barnanna þinna.

Má því ekki ljúka þar? Hvað viltu meira? Áður fyrr þegar fólk var kallað frá hálfkláruðum, hálfköruðum lífum var skiljanlegt að þyrfti uppbót. En nútímamenn sem fá að teyga lífið í botn, hvaða þörf hafa þeir fyrir ábót?

Stærsti tilgangurinn sem okkur stendur til boða er nautnin að finna hann út. Ef við leiddum þó ekki væri nema brot af hugarorku tegundarinnar að þessu viðfangsefni myndi enginn lengur hafa tíma til að standa í neinni vitleysu: agndofa myndi mannkynið hraðfletta síðunum í bók lífsins.

Er hægt að hugsa sér afruglara nægilega sterkan til að afrugla heiminn? Hvað gæti það verið? Loftsteinn? Líf frá öðrum hnöttum? Njála?

XIV

París. Eins og endranær undir þessum himni fer mig að klæja í vasabókina. Borgin er eins og risastórt leiksvið fyrir óendanlegan fjölda leikatriða, eina sem vantar er eilífð til að njóta.

Ég færi til bókar hvað fólk er með falleg augu, hvað það er flínkt á línuskautum, hvað það hefur fallega rödd og getur talað glaðbeitt í síma á leið yfir götu.

Í skjóli við styttuna af Montaigne á rue des Écoles stendur lögregluþjónn og er að stelast til að reykja með sígarettu fyrir aftan bak og reynir að anda út úr sér reyknum í áföngum.

Við brúarsporðinn á Signu þar sem Notre Dame blasir við er mættur krypplingsdvergur, næstum ekkert nema höfuð í hjólastól og teiknar og málar Vora frú horft af brúnni. Hann var hérna líka þegar ég kom hingað fyrst fyrir rúmum mannsaldri. Og kirkjan er búin að standa þarna í átta og hálfa öld, alltaf í nýju og nýju ljósi.

Notre Dame og Njála, þær eru jafn gamlar. Og ekkert lát á manniðunni sem streymir í gegnum þær; túristar um kirkjuna, námsfólk um Njálu. Og kröfuharkan í svipnum segir: „Úr því þú ert svona fræg stendur upp á þig að hrífa okkur!“

* * *

Notre Dame var heila öld í byggingu. En Njála, hvernig er hún til komin?

„Og lýk ek þar Brennu-Njáls sögu“ segir höfundurinn og lætur ekki nafns síns getið, neitar sér þar með um heimsfrægð í bókmenntunum. Eins og maður sem vitjar ekki um lottóvinninginn, sjöfaldur pottur, aldrei verið jafn stór. Og gengur út. En sá lukkulegi gefur sig ekki fram. Vissi hann ekki hver heiður hafði fallið honum í skaut?

Þessi heiði hugur sem hefur getað speglað gervalla veröldina, fúlmenni jafnt sem ljúfmenni og svo útsmoginn að láta ótal smálæki koma saman í voldugan straum sem skundar hratt að ósi.

Brandur Jónsson, að það hafi verið hann? Sjálfur ábótinn í Þykkvabæjarklaustri, biskup síðar á Hólum. Jú, að vísu, þýddi *Alexanderssögu* „af mikilli hind“ og *Gyðingasögu* svo vitað er, auk þess af höfðingjaætt með innborna þekkingu á leikfléttum og lagaflækjum og svikamyllum. En kynslóð of gamall ef rétt er að sagan hljóti að vera saman sett eftir 1270 (Brandur deyr 1265).

Það er erfitt að þreifa fyrir sér í svo algeru myrkri. Gerum okkur í hugarlund þegar gleymskan hefur sogað okkur út í algleymið og við liggjum samanpressuð undir sjö alda fargi. *Kristnihald undir Jökli* hefur orðið viðskila við höfund sinn og fræðimenn fimbulfamba um hugsanlegan höfund. Í ljós kemur Sigurbjörn Einarsson, biskup eins og Brandur, meira að segja úr Álftaveri, þýddi *Játningar Ágústínusar* og skrifaði í efri hæðum málsins – en heimilar ekki að gera hann að höfundi Kristnihaldsins.

* * *

Klaustrið í Þykkvabæ var stofnað af Þorláki Þórhallssyni árið 1168, fyrsta klaustur á Íslandi af reglu heilags Ágústínusar (Ágústínus eina ferðina enn!). Þorlákur er fyrsti Íslendingurinn sem vitað er með vissu að hafi numið í París. Það var árið 1153 og smíði Notre Dame rétt að hefjast. Við vitum ekki hvernig Þorláki var innanbrjósts, en við getum ímyndað okkur hvernig honum leið í iljunum. Áreiðanlega í fyrsta skipti sem hann steig á steinlögn. Kóngurinn hafði látið þau boð út ganga að borgararnir skyldu leggja stétt framan við húsin og sætti sig ekki lengur við fnykinn sem lagði frá jarðveginum þegar vagnarnir breyttu slóðinni í eðju.

Heloísa er enn í fullu fjöri, 53 ára abbadís í Paraklet-klaustri. Abelard er allur fyrir áratug og hvílir nú í klausturgarðinum þar sem Heloísa á leið um oft á dag. Enn er áratugur þar til hún verður lögð til hinstu hvílu honum við hlið og rúm öld þar til umheiminum gefst að lesa bréfin sem þeim fóru á milli í lifanda lífi:

„Sú sæla elskenda sem við nutum bæði í sameiningu var mér svo sæt, að ég get ekki haft neina vanþóknun á henni og hún getur varla horfið mér úr minni. Hvert sem ég sný mér er hún mér sífellt fyrir augum með löngunum sínum, og tálsýnir hennar hlífa mér ekki einu sinni þegar ég er sofandi. Í sjálfri messunni, þegar bænirnar ættu að vera hreinni, halda klúrar ímyndanirnar vesælli sálinni svo fanginni að ég er uppteknari af nautnunum en bæninni. Ég ætti að harma þær syndir sem ég hef drýgt, en ég sé heldur eftir því sem ég hef misst.

Ekki einungis það sem við gerðum, heldur líka staðirnir og stundirnar þegar við gerðum það, eru svo greypt í sálina, ásamt hugsuninni um þig, að ég geri þetta allt aftur með þér og finn ekki einu sinni frið í svefni . . .“

Þannig skrifar nunna á 12. öld.

* * *

Á ritunarskeiði Njálu lýtur klaustrið í Veri stjórn lærðustu manna á Íslandi, Brandur Jónsson hefur þegar verið nefndur, en við ábótatign af honum tekur Runólfur Sigmundsson (sem meðal annars þýddi ævisögu Ágústínusar úr latínu).

Klaustrið er víðfrægt fyrir bókmenntaverkin sem þaðan koma og athyglisverð er ábending Einars Ólafs Sveinssonar um „bleika akra“ í Njálu. Þetta orðalag kemur aðeins fyrir á einum stað öðrum í samanlögðum fornbókmenntunum og það er í *Alexanderssögu* – sem sannarlega var þýdd og höfð um hönd í Þykkvabæjarklaustri.

* * *

Íslensk handrit skera sig úr í hópi systkina sinna evrópskra. Þau síðarnefndu getur enn að líta fjölmörg á söfnum, skinnið ljóst og hreint enda vandlega verið haldið frá kámugum höndum almennings í gegnum aldirnar. Íslensku skinnin aftur á móti eru yfirleitt krímug og sótug og bera þess vott að hafa verið flett af allskonar höndum við algengustu kringumstæður. Talandi dæmi er elsta handrit Njálu, skrifað á kálfskinn og bundið í selskinn. Álitum er það eins og komið úr eldi: skorpið og undið og sótugt. Og enginn kostur að reisa um það stillansa og spúla af því fingraför tímans eins og reglulega er gert við Notre Dame.

Hin stöðuga notkun í hlálegum húsakynnum var ekki hallkvæm endingu íslenskra skinnbóka. Aðeins brotabrot hefur varðveist af því sem eitt sinn var til. Djúpt í endalausri eyðingunni sofa heilu Árnastofnanirnar og allt sem var gulls ígildi, ef við bara gætum endurheimt það. En við höfum ekkert í höndunum, engin málleitartæki eins og málmleitartækin sem mennirnir beita til að finna flökin í iðrum sandsins.

* * *

Við sjáum hann fyrir okkur standandi við púlt. Að baki er hálfhringur fjalla og jökla, fram undan autt svið til sjávar. Klaustur er samtök um þögn. Hann lítur upp og það er hunangsfluga að húsvitja hjá sóley og fífli úti í garði. Brakið í pennanum á eggsléttu leðrinu. Garnagaul.

Og árstíðirnar ganga fyrir gluggann í halarófu, á vetrarmorgni er blekið frosið í horninu, hann þarf að byrja á því að þýða það með núningi handanna uns fast verður fljótandi og sagan getur haldið áfram að renna.

„Nú er að segja frá Skarphéðni . . .“

Hvaða lykt hefur hann fundið? Angan af leðri, ilm af bleki, lykt frá soðkötlum, fnyk frá kamri. Aldrei er líkaminn brjóstumkennanlegri en í kæfandi lofti saurgeymslunnar. Né andinn upphafnari en í tíðasöngnum á eftir. Átta sinnum á degi sem nóttu, fyrirkomulag sem fundið er upp á Ítalíu þar sem sólin kemur upp um hálf-átta þegar dagur er skemmstur og sest um fimmleytið. Á Íslandi aftur á móti lætur vetrarsólin rétt sjást í hvirfilinn áður en hún sígur í kafið á ný.

Og samt fara munkarnir upp á nóttu sem degi til að syngja líf og yl í veröldina.

* * *

Honum verður litið upp, það er grýlukerti skriðið fyrir gluggann. Honum verður litið upp, það er iða af hvítum kornum. Honum verður litið upp, það er heiðblár himinn. Honum verður litið upp.

* * *

Í túni liggja kálfar og æfa sig að jórtra. Vita ekki að á morgun verður þeim slátrað, egghvasst stálið mun rista sundur slagæðina við barkann og lífið hríslast úr þeim í fat. Síðan verður húðin flegin af og kjötið fært kæmeistaranum. Þá tekur sútarinn við skinninu og verkar eftir kúnstarinnar reglum þar til það er orðið leturhæft. Tilbúið að þekjast leturtáknum sem endurskapa fortíðina og varðveita gleymskunni til háðungar.

Svanurinn leggur til fjöðurstaf úr væng.

Skrifarinn sníður fanirnar af með eggbeittu vopni, yddar því næst odd. Horn af nauti hvílir á púlti og miðlar blekinu sem blekbróðir hefur búið til úr sortulyngi, svart og gljáandi og albúið að endast í þúsund ár.

Og nú mundar höndin fjöðurstafinn og stingur honum í hornið og lætur drjúpa af honum blekið áður en fjöðrin mætir skinninu og orðin raðast á bókfellið:

„Mörðr hét maðr . . .“

Var honum kalt, var hann með nábít af hungri, bjó með honum girnd, var hann þvert á móti með gigt, var í miðjum klíðum hringt til tíða, þurfti hann að leggja frá sér fjöðrina og taka til við að syngja saltara eða setjast til borðs með bræðrum að máltíð og heyra lesið úr sögu heilags Ágústínusar:

„Allra þeirra manna iðnir, er margar bækur hafa diktað, sigrar hinn helgi Ágústínus með sínu mannviti og snilld, því að hann diktaði og ritaði svo marga og mikla hluti, að því síður fær nokkur maður ritað hans bækur allar á sínum aldri, að enginn vinnst til þær allar að lesa . . .“

Hann hlýðir á annars hugar um leið og hann horfir á mötunaut sinn stanga tægju úr tönn.

Síðdegis sækir að honum svefn og setningarnar vilja ekki lengur fæðast, hann tekur eftir því að hann er svangur, honum er kalt, hann er skítugur, hann klæjar, honum rís hold.

En um nóttina hefur kraftaverkið gerst á ný, lindin er full við rismál, hann getur ekki beðið eftir að komast í gegnum bænirnar að púltinu þar sem brennan verður ekki umflúin, tortíming í eldi sem jafnframt verður hreinsunareldur. Á meðan tekur hann ekki eftir því að hann er til frekar en himinninn veitir athygli að hann er himinn. Tekur ekki eftir því hvaða dagur er, hvaða árstími, ár . . . Svo fullkomlega á valdi frásagnarinnar að honum súrnar í augum.

„Hvort grætur þú nú Skarphéðinn?“

* * *

Hvað hafa verið gerð mörg uppköst að þessum senum? Hlýtur Njáluhöfundur ekki að hafa staðið í ökkla í skinnpjötlum eða prófandi sig áfram með stílnum á vaxtöflum?

Fagurlega samverka þau kálfurinn og svanurinn og lyngið. Og hugur sem megnar að búa til heim sem hýst hefur á þriðja tug kynslóða. Þótt allt hafi sópast á brott mörgum sinnum heldur Njála áfram að vaka yfir veröldinni. Öll túnin sem hafa verið sléttuð, bæir reistir, kýr mjólkaðar, fé smalað, hross troðist í rétt, köttur hringað sig á poka, hundur gelt að komumönnum, fluga suðað undir sólarvegg, skeifa slegin, hrífa tinduð, fjós mokað, vatn sótt, slökkt á kolu, fingur teiknað kross – öld af öld – og alltaf Njála.

* * *

Hann leggst í grasið og punturinn þyrpist að honum eins og hjálmprúðir hermenn. Sólin stráir geislum niður um síu skýjanna. Það heyrist í hrossagauki og spóa, þrestir þyrlast um loftin.

Hann gengur yfir svartan sandinn til móts við höfuðskepnuna sem rymur og froðufellir á ströndinni. Skuggalegur kjóinn varpar sínum skugga og fársfullur skúmur glennir klær yfir krúnurökuðum hvirfli, en í hvítbryddu flæðarmáli hleypur óðamála tjaldur.

Á hverju hausti fljúga fuglarnir í flokkum suður um höfin og skilja landið eftir sönglaust. Eftir sitja kolsvartir krummar og krunka við munkana á burstum húsanna.

Og landið dregur sig inn í skel íss og þagnar.

En jafn óbrigðult koma flokkarnir aftur í réttri röð á vorin og landið tekur gleði sína á ný, smokrar sér úr líkklæðunum, tínir af sér ísprjálið og breiðir út sumarlitan faðminn.

* * *

Fjórar aldir eru frá því að land byggðist. Fram til þessa hefur það aðeins verið krýnt jöklum. En nú er það komið með kóng.

Bæirnir hjúfra sig að landinu. Innan um búsáhöld og verkfæri hefur mannfólkið sleppt taki á vökunni og öndunarvélin sjálfvirk leiðir lífsandann um nasir og munn. Í koti sem stórbýli sem klaustri sem sjóbúð. Það eru senuskipti. Ósýnilegir sviðsmenn búa í haginn fyrir nýjan þátt.